A BOTANICAL PIONEER
IN SOUTH WEST CHINA

Heinrich Handel-Mazzetti in the Alps near Kals, 1938
(photo by courtesy of Professor K.H.Rechinger).

A BOTANICAL PIONEER
IN SOUTH WEST CHINA

Experiences and Impressions

of an Austrian Botanist

During the First World War

HEINRICH HANDEL-MAZZETTI

Keeper of the Botanical Department,

Natural History Museum, Vienna

With 48 photographs

taken by the author

and seven maps

First published as "*Naturbilder aus Südwest China*" by

ÖSTERREICHISCHER BUNDESVERLAG,

Vienna, 1927

English translation, complete and unabridged,

with biography of Handel-Mazzetti

by David Winstanley

Published by

David Winstanley

ETS
20 St Thomas Road
Brentwood
Essex, CM14 4DB
England

Printed by
Antony Rowe Ltd
Chippenham

in Roman T

ISBN 0 9529230 0 9

Front cover: In the Salween Valley. View from Alülaka (2850m) over the Tschamutong (Gongshan) basin (right) to the Gomba-la (about 5500m) in the Salween-Irrawaddy divide. Left: the Tjiontson-lumba.

From left to right: *Pinus insularis, Quercus dentata, Buddleia asiatica, Deutzia corymbosa, Leontopodium sinense, Bletilla yunnanensis, Pteridium aquilinum, Carex cruciata.*

Lao Li; a Tibetan from Londjre; Kru (behind); Li Tere (right).

From an oil painting by Eduard Handel-Mazzetti based upon several photographs by the author.

Reproduced by courtesy of Prof. Dr. Michael Hesse, Director of the Institute of Botany and Botanical Garden, University of Vienna.

CONTENTS

Part I 1914. The Plateau and Mountain Ranges of Yunnan and Southwest Sichuan

Part II 1915. To the Tibetan Border

Part III 1916 To the Frontier of Upper Burma

Part IV 1917. Through Guizhou to Hunan

Part V 1918. Work and Travels in Hunan

ILLUSTRATIONS

Frontispiece   Heinrich Handel-Mazzetti in the Alps near Kals, 1938.
Fig.1 In the temple of Tjiungju-se ("five hundred genies") near Kunming.
Fig.2 Stoneworts (*Chara*) mixed with mud for use as manure.
Fig.3 A fig (*Ficus ti-koua*) common near Huili.
Fig.4 The Jinsha Jiang near Lagachang north of Kunming.
Fig.5 A village street in Jianchang, southwest Sichuan.
Fig.6 The abbot of Yongning.
Fig.7 *Rhododendron decorum* in pine forest (*Pinus tabulaeformis*).
Fig.8 *Primula vialii* near Yongning, 23 July 1915.
Fig.9 The sinter basins of Bedi.
Fig.10 Tibetans from Djiatshrin.
Fig.11 The largest of all gentians (*Gentiana stylophora*, now *Megacodon stylophorus*).
Fig.12 *Oroxylon indicum* on the Anning He near Huili.
Fig.13 The main caravan route from Kunming to Burma, between Lüfeng and Shezi.
Fig.14 Christmas in Kunming, 1914
Fig.15 *Lithospermum hancockianum* (now *Lithodora hancockiana*) near Kunming.
Fig.16 Karst on the Xi Shan near Kunming.
Fig.17 *Arisaema wilsonii* (*A. elephas*) above Xiangshuihe.
Fig.18 Market day in Songgui. Minchia women; buildings in Chinese style.
Fig.19 *Tsuga yunnanensis* at 3300m below the Zuningkou pass.
Fig.20 The south face of Satseto, the main peak of the Yulong Shan, 5450m.
Fig.21 Glacier snout, moraine and talus bed at 3700m in the Luoqu gorge.
Fig.22 *Cypripedium ebracteatum* (now *C. margaritaceum*) above Nguluke, 3350m.
Fig.23 Camp above Tuguancun at 4175m, looking WNW over the Chongdian plateau.
Fig.24 The ridge between Tuguancun and Haba at 4450m, looking NW.
Fig.25 High alpines on the ridge between Tuguancun and Haba.
Fig.26 Lüdi (Moso) women at Yongning with children in Chinese dress.
Fig.27 Alpine sward (yak pasture) at 4300m on limestone soil at the tree-line.
Fig.28 Interior of a temple at Muli.
Fig.29 Grain drying racks on the huts in an unidentified village.
Fig.30 Rope bridge over the Lancang Jiang (Mekong) near Tseku.
Fig.31 The Lancang Jiang (Mekong) gorge above Lota.
Fig.32 *Pseudotsuga wilsoniana* on the Doker La.
Fig.33 Lisu people in their village above Xiao Weixi.
Fig.34 *Rhododendron rarosquameum* (*R. caeruleum)* on the Ji Shan crest NE of Dali.
Fig.35 The Lisu village of Aoalo.
Fig.36 *Berneuxia tibetica* beneath *Rhododendron sanguineum* at the tree-line (3900m).
Fig.37 *Cardiocrinum giganteum* in the forest below Doshiracho (3100m).
Fig.38 Crossing the Nu Jiang (Salween) at Tjionra in a dugout canoe.
Fig.39 Subalpine woodland in the Saoa-lumba (3450m).
Fig.40 *Primula calliantha* beneath *Rhododendron beesianum.*
Fig.41 *Primula agleniana* beneath cherry tanglewood (*Prunus mugus).*
Fig.42 Temperate zone rain forest with *Strobilanthes* understorey at 2700m.
Fig.43 *Pegaeophyton sinense* in alpine springwater flushes.
Fig.44 *Meconopsis speciosa* on mica-schist on the Xi La.
Fig.45 *Omphalogramma souliei* beneath *Salix* sp. at 3900m on the Xi La.
Fig.46 *Didymocarpus eburneus* near Anshun.
Fig.47 The Jinsha Jiang gorge below the Yulong Shan.
Fig.48 A cataract on the Jinsha Jiang in its gorge below the Yulong Shan.

INTRODUCTION

Handel-Mazzetti's name is well known to all botanists and horticulturists who have worked on the flora of China, though it is usually seen in abbreviated form appended to the name of one of the many plants that he determined — for example, *Taraxacum tibetanum* Hand.-Mazz. As his publications, apart from this book and a few newspaper articles, are austerely scientific, and as he never introduced plants into cultivation, he has remained a shadowy figure, hardly known outside the world of the herbarium. Yet he was one of the most distinguished of the pioneer plant collectors who travelled in western China in the early years of this century. He greatly expanded our knowledge of the wealth and diversity of the flora of that great region on the borderlands of Tibet where the three mighty rivers of western China, the Mekong, the Salween and the Yangtse, dissect the high mountains.

Foremost among the plant explorers of the region were collectors such as Frank Kingdon-Ward, George Forrest and Ernest Wilson, who not only collected dried herbarium specimens for scientific study but introduced many plants into our gardens, plants for which they will always be remembered. Then there were the French missionaries who devoted their leisure to plant collecting: Delavay, Ducloux, Monbeig, Soulié and others made major contributions to our understanding of the flora. Joseph Rock also based himself primarily in NW Yunnan and the Tibetan hinterlands, as did many of the others, for they realised that the region with its diverse climates, high mountains, wooded hills and extensive lowlands offered a rich and unique flora, and many species which would be likely to prove hardy in western gardens. Rock, like Kingdon-Ward, was more than just a plant collector, but a expert and knowledgeable geographer and ethnologist with a keen interest in both plants and animals.

Most of these collectors wrote little or nothing on their travels; we have only a fragmentary record, for instance, of the extensive travels of George Forrest. But there were exceptions: Joseph Rock wrote extensively about the region and its peoples and Ernest Henry Wilson wrote a classic book on his travels and collections in *A Naturalist in Western China* (1913). However, it was Frank Kingdon-Ward who, more than any other, brought the adventure of plant collecting to the horticultural public. In a series of books he outlined vividly the trials and tribulations of the professional plant collector. His early books such as *The Land of the Blue Poppy* (1913), *Mystery Rivers of Tibet* (1923) and *Plant Hunting on the Edge of the World* (1930) have become collectable classics, now much sought after.

But what of Heinrich Handel-Mazzetti? Though relatively little known, he collected extensively in western China at a time when the country was undergoing enormous upheavals, both social and political. He was an Austrian botanist who later became the Keeper of the Botanical Department of the Natural History Museum in Vienna. In 1913 Handel-Mazzetti was invited to join Camillo Schneider, the General Secretary of the Austro-Hungarian Dendrological Society, on an expedition to China, the aim being to extend the pioneering work already achieved in the region by Delavay and Forrest. So, at the beginning of 1914, aged 32, Handel-Mazzetti found himself in western China under the auspices of the Vienna Academy of Sciences. The outbreak of the First World War marooned him in China until 1919, but during that time he was able to travel and collect in Yunnan, southern Sichuan and Upper Burma, as well as in Guizhou and Hunan. He published an account of his travels and plant finds in a book entitled *Naturbilder aus Südwest China* (1927). This rare and little known work was of course written in German and as such is inaccessible to the majority of English-speaking gardeners and horticulturists. With the current vogue for new editions of books on plant hunters and plant collecting it is surprising that this almost forgotten work has not already been seized upon and translated. But this has now been rectified and we must be greatly indebted to David Winstanley for his painstaking translation and for his determination to see the new edition published, an undertaking that he has achieved mainly by his own endeavours, financing the cost of publication largely out of his own pocket. In addition, David Winstanley has compiled a full and useful index to plants and places and (with Stephen Haw) an indispensable glossary of Chinese place names with their modern Pinyin equivalents, which make this important work far more serviceable.

Handel-Mazzetti's is a fascinating and accurate account written by a man who was first and foremost a scientist wishing to record details of his work. This might sound dry and matter-of-fact, but with considerable skill he manages to inject a sense of adventure and humour into his narrative.

His tastes in plants were catholic, from the tallest trees and the rich and varied shrubs to the herbaceous, bulbous and alpine species. In addition, he collected what many ignore, the lower plants such as ferns, mosses and lichens. His specimens reside in the Natural History Museum in Vienna and elsewhere as a lasting testament to his endeavours. A special interest in the genus *Primula* led him to describing several new species including *P. genestieriana* Hand.-Mazz., *P. leucochnoa* Hand.-Mazz. and *P. valentiniana* Hand.-Mazz. Other plants that he described include *Leontopodium haplophylloides* Hand.-Mazz., *Prunus mugus* Hand.-Mazz., the Tibetan cherry, and *Sorbus poteriifolia* Hand.-Mazz. Plants named in his honour include the charming *Arisaema handelii* Stapf.

Although the period when this expedition was undertaken was the golden era of plant exploration in western China, it was brought to an end by the political turmoil in China between the two World Wars. So this book serves as a unique record of part of China at a transitional time in its history and is a valuable addition to the more familiar books on the region.

Present day readers will be impressed by the dedication of these early plant hunters, despite the difficulties of travel and the hardships that they had to endure. Western China was not always a friendly place earlier in the century, communications were difficult and the task of collecting, storing and recording the details of plant finds and localities on a day to day basis must have been extremely exacting. Add to this the ever present dangers of bandits and local revolts, the weather (very wet in summer and bitterly cold in winter) and the at times appalling food and difficulty of travel, and one can appreciate the achievements of these men. Hardships there undoubtedly were but the excitement of visiting and exploring the region, of seeing such a range of plants growing and flowering in the wild and the thrill of seeing something rare or even new to science was spur enough.

Today we are fortunate in being able to travel freely in China once more and to see the richness of the flora, the amazing and varied landscapes and the delightful medley of different ethnic peoples who are so conspicuous in the west of that great country. It is easy to gauge the excitement and trials of these early pioneers while suffering none of their hardships. Today, one can reach China quickly by jet plane and the internal transport is relatively good. Most towns boast modern hotels with colour television and bathrooms (not always with the best toilet arrangements!). There is safe bottled water and beer in plenty and the food is wholesome and often excellent. Yet when one gets out into the mountains away from civilisation it is just as wild as it ever was, the weather can be just as unpredictable and the terrain no less severe. It is then that one can appreciate more the daily lives of the earlier plant explorers. Today, despite shocking deforestation, especially close to the Tibetan frontier, there is just as much to see in the wild and the excitement of finding plants in their native habitats is just as thrilling and unforgettable. We are indeed greatly indebted to collectors like Handel-Mazzetti and privileged to be able to read this account of his journeys and explorations, as well as to find out something of the man behind the name that adjoins so many familiar plant names.

C. Grey-Wilson

Handel-Mazzetti's Foreword

It was in the eighteen eighties that the French missionary Delavay sent back to Europe the first collections of plants from Yunnan, one of the remotest and at that time least accessible provinces of China. Nearly half the species he collected proved new to science and it soon became clear that his work had opened up a unique floral region, richer perhaps than any area of comparable extent in then world. This profusion of species has several causes, among them the configuration of the land itself, of great interest to geographers as well as botanists; the deeply cut river valleys between the lofty mountain chains, which are a continuation of the Himalaya though bent round to lie north and south; its location in the middle of an area in which so many large genera have evolved; and the direction of the mountain chains, which allowed plants to migrate to warmer climes during the ice ages and hence escape extinction. The great beauty of many of the plants and the similarity of the mountain climate to that of Central Europe roused the interest of gardeners and encouraged patrons of horticulture to send their collectors to carry on Delavay's work. The successes achieved by George Forrest were no doubt among the reasons that persuaded the Austro-Hungarian Dendrological Society at the end of 1913 to send their general secretary Camillo Schneider to Yunnan for a year with similar objectives. To broaden the scope of the expedition the Academy of Sciences in Vienna gave financial support to enable me to participate and, my return being prevented by the outbreak of war, continued to finance me for a further four and a half years. Three of these years were devoted to Yunnan and south-west Sichuan and the last two to Guizhou and Hunan.

Although I travelled as a botanist and was fully occupied by my own work, in this book I have tried to outline my observations in other branches of knowledge. The geological structure and unique characteristics of south west China cannot fail to make an impression on the traveller, more especially as a botanist with an interest in plant geography must pay some regard to geology and will regard cartographical surveying as a routine duty. However, I have confined myself to Nature and her works, among which may be counted primitive man and his activities.

In the map[1] I have endeavoured to incorporate the latest topographical surveys and in particular to give a correct picture of the relief, which is not satisfactorily depicted in any of the current maps. My map is based on Davies' map[2] for the western parts and Stieler's Hand Atlas for the eastern. The course of the Yangzi Jiang[3] from Tsilidjiang (Qilijiang) to Suifu (Yibin) is taken from Audemard[4]. Further information was gleaned from Legendre's[5] and Bacot's[6] maps, while my own surveys showed the need for certain amendments near the Lijiang loop and for redrawing the map of the mountainous country of Zhongdian, also from Yongning to Yongshen, and from the upper Nu Jiang (Salween) to the Irrawaddy. In the east some revision is needed in the remoter areas through which I journeyed. From longitude 103° to 110°, however, I traversed the country only once and in a more or less straight line, and here I can give only a sketchy impression of the terrain outside my route[7]. All the Latin names of the plants mentioned in the book are based on scientific identification of the collected herbarium material, which has been deposited in the Botanical Institute of Vienna University.

Books on China usually contain information on art, shooting, sport and such matters. The reader will find little of that kind, and if ethnographers feel that their interests have been neglected let them remember that a botanist spends most of his time far from human habitations, and when he returns from the field he is fully occupied in pressing and preserving the plants he has gathered. Nevertheless, I have recorded all observations that might be of value, briefly, factually and without comment. I must apologise to those readers who feel that my account gives a somewhat jaundiced view of the Chinese people. The war and its aftermath have convinced many thinkers of the utter wickedness of the entire white race and have prompted them

---

[1] The first edition (1927) includes a coloured map at a scale of 1:2,500,000 covering all his travels in China.

[2] Davies, Major H.R., *Yün-nan - the Link Between India and the Yangtze*, Cambridge University Press, 1909.

[3] The Yangzi Jiang, commonly known in English as the Yangtze river, is normally called Chang Jiang in Chinese (S.G.H.).

[4] *La Géographie XXIV.*

[5] See footnote on page 3.

[6] *Le Tibet révolté* 1909.

[7] For details see: Handel-Mazzetti, H., *Neue Aufnahmen in NW-Yünnan und S-Setschuan.* Denkschriften der Akademie der Wissenschaften in Wien, Vol. 97, also Vol. 100 (Hunan) and Kartographische Zeitschrift, Vol. 101 (Guidschou).

to look elsewhere in the hope of finding something better — conceivably among the Indians. But I am not a historian and even if I were I could not allow myself to be deceived by the faded glories of such a land as China, where the seamy side of life nowadays predominates; in the Far East the boundary between history and fable is in any case extremely blurred and indistinct.

Looking back, one remembers the enjoyment and forgets the hardships such as the food, which was sometimes revolting, or the unending toil in the rainy season, which is the botanist's busiest time because most of the plants flower in those monsoon months. It was my great good fortune to be free — far freer than anyone at home in Austria during those unhappy years. I set my own tasks; to fulfil them in the tropical luxuriance of mist-wreathed forests, on the soft carpets of the world's most gorgeous floral meadows and on the flower-spangled pastures and ridges of snow-crowned mountains twice the size of our own was indeed the greatest imaginable delight. Never have I been more acutely aware of the joy of freedom than in those days, when mounted on a splendid horse high above the dusty ground and far from the wretched doings of mankind, I rode through unexplored country admiring and recording the splendours of Nature.

Successful work in a foreign country by one ignorant of the language is impracticable without the help of Europeans resident there, and such help was granted to me in abundant measure. I have expressed my heartfelt thanks in the pages of this book. But during the preparations and after my return there were many who showed their goodwill in the form of active assistance. To them I am deeply grateful, as I am to the numerous specialists who guided and advised me during the scientific work on the collections, though that falls outside the scope

of this book. Our Ambassador in Peking, Dr A. von Rosthorn[8], not only granted aid through diplomatic channels, but lent money and gave unstinting help in translating the notes made by my collector after I had left China, and in the transcription of Chinese names.[9] Camillo Schneider kindly provided two photographs (Figs. 20 & 43, not reproduced in this edition). My deepest thanks, however, are due to the Academy of Sciences in Vienna, who financed my travel, and to my teacher, Professor R. Wettstein, who sponsored my application. To his unremitting support throughout my absence I undoubtedly owe my life and health.

I submit this account of my travels to the public in the hope that a fellow-feeling for nature will persuade my readers to overlook the shortcomings in text and illustrations.

Vienna, May 1926

HEINRICH HANDEL-MAZZETTI

[8] In 1891, while serving in the Chinese Maritime Customs, Rosthorn travelled in Tibet from Kwanhsien via Mungkungtung, Fupien, Rumitschango, Maoniu, Gata, and Tatsienlu. He was the first European to explore this route. Potanin travelled it two years later, and Isabella Bishop in the reverse direction in 1896.

[9] Handel-Mazzetti's method for transcribing Chinese place names was based on the German phonetic system. In this edition all names have been transcribed into the Pinyin system by Mr Stephen G. Haw. A glossary of place names in Handel-Mazzetti's version and in Pinyin is provided.

Translator's Preface

One day in the seventies, fired by a new (and still enduring) enthusiasm for the genus *Primula*, the translator visited the Lindley Library of the Royal Horticultural Society to read the papers presented at the Fourth Primula Conference in 1928. Among them was one entitled *The Natural Habitats of Chinese Primulas,* by Dr H. Handel-Mazzetti from the Natural History Museum in Vienna. At first reading it was obvious that he had travelled widely in China. Had he published an account of his travels? A glance at the card index led to his book *Naturbilder aus Südwest China.* I sat there enthralled until closing time came and soon decided to translate it into English. So scarce is the book that many years passed before I was able to buy a copy for my own use.

Why is this almost forgotten book worth reissuing in English? In the short window in time during which Western China became open to visitors from the western world — from the later years of the nineteenth century to the twenties, when political restrictions made travelling more and more difficult — only a small number of botanists and plant hunters worked there and very few of them left satisfactory narratives of their journeys. E.H.Wilson concentrated on an area north of the Yangtse and hardly touched Yunnan. Joseph Rock's interests shifted to ethnology and he published nothing on botany. George Forrest intended to write a account of his travels after retiring, but death came unexpectedly and in any case he had never kept a diary. Frank Kingdon Ward wrote several fascinating books about his plant hunting travels in China, but his writings are somewhat unsystematic and sometimes seem to have been composed from the diaries of two journeys conflated into one narrative. Handel-Mazzetti's book is quite different. Written from his diaries, it gives a sober and well organised account of his journeys. Though it is not in journal form, the date and place are nearly always discoverable, the plants are listed and the people he meets are vividly portrayed. Yet it is also a thrilling tale of exploration and adventure told with literary skill as well as scientific accuracy and leavened by occasional passages of sly humour.

Though a few of the plant names have been brought up to date, no attempt has been made at any systematic revision, nor have I thought it necessary to write more than occasional notes on the plants — over two thousand — that Handel-Mazzetti mentions.

This edition could not have been completed without help from many friends in Austria and elsewhere. I am deeply grateful to Hofrat Professor K.H.Rechinger, who in 1986 granted me two interviews at which he recorded on tape his reminiscences of Handel-Mazzetti; Paul Handel-Mazzetti, the botanist's nephew, who shared his memories of his uncle and unearthed numerous long forgotten articles in journals and newspapers;

Dr Else Handel-Mazzetti, the botanist's niece, who lent me Handel-Mazzetti's mother's diary for the year 1912, a record which threw light on his relations with Archduke Franz Ferdinand; Dr Eva Schönbeck, formerly Curator of the Herbarium at the Botanical Institute, Vienna University, for lending me the collection of 1700 photographs taken by Handel-Mazzetti in China and for tracing the reference to his journey through the Dolomites as the Archduke's botanical guide; Dr Riedl-Dorn at the Naturhistorisches Museum for helping to trace Handel-Mazzetti's photographs; Franz Hadacek, for general help and guidance during and after my stay in Vienna in 1986; Dr John Richards for advice on botany; Katharina Tabbernor, the only one of my German friends who succeeded in deciphering Handel-Mazzetti's mother's handwriting; Dr Rüdiger Hoffmann for advice on Handel-Mazzetti's mountaineering exploits (Chapter 29); Stephen Haw, who transcribed all the place-names into Pinyin and gave me much useful advice about Chinese customs; Herr Kai Køhler for information on Edward Amundsen; Dr Edmund Launert for introducing me to Professor K.H. Rechinger; Ingrid Roderick of the Bible Society for a copy of the committee's minutes (4th November 1915) dealing with Amundsen's recall from Kunming; Valerie Wheat of the American Museum of Natural History for information on Roy Chapman Andrews; Österreichischer Bundesverlag, the firm that published the first edition in 1927, for generously waiving their claim to copyright (which in Austria lasts for 70 years after the author's death), and the librarians of the Natural History Museum, the Royal Geographical and the Royal Horticultural Societies.

David Winstanley 1996

Heinrich Handel-Mazzetti

This biographical memoir is based on the detailed obituary by Handel-Mazzetti's friend and contemporary Erwin Janchen[1] (Berichte der deutschen botanischen Gesellschaft, 57, 179-201 [1940], with portrait and bibliography). This information has been supplemented by reminiscences kindly provided by Hofrat Professor K.H. Rechinger[2], who worked in the same room as Handel-Mazzetti in the Vienna University Botanical Institute in the twenties and thirties, acted as an emissary between Handel-Mazzetti and Keissler, the Director of the Department of Botany in the Natural History Museum, after their quarrel, and got to know him as intimately as was possible for anyone outside his family circle. Further details have been gleaned from his own writings and those of his contemporaries.

Heinrich Freiherr (Baron) von Handel-Mazzetti was born in Vienna on 19th February 1882. His family, still well represented in Austria today, trace their origins to a Franz Handel in Dettingen near Frankfurt in 1556, his forebears having migrated from Handel in Brabant a century earlier. Handel-Mazzetti's grandfather, Heinrich Freiherr von Handel, was a senior officer in the Austrian Army. He married Caroline Freiin (Baroness) von Mazzetti, and as she was the last of her family they decided to perpetuate her family name by joining it to his. Their son Eduard, born in Pavia in 1838, was the botanist's father. Perhaps the most widely known member of the family is the novelist Enrica von Handel-Mazzetti (1871-1955), a daughter of one of Eduard's brothers, the author of *"Die Hochzeit von Quedlinburg"* and other historical romances.

In 1881 Eduard married Fredina Marchesa de Mauro, born in Florence in 1853. Her mother, the daughter of a German family originally from East Prussia, moved to Germany after her husband's death in 1854. Fredina's earliest memories were of the flowers and animals of Nonnenwerth, an island in the Rhine near Bonn. As Handel-Mazzetti's mother grew up she developed a deep love of nature, which she passed on to all her sons, notably to Heinrich, her first-born. Heinrich was devoted to his mother. He dedicated his monograph on *Taraxacum* (1907) to her and named one of the new species that he discovered in China in her honour (*Arenaria fridericae*). Touching evidence of his affection is to be found in his account of their reunion after his five years' absence in China (Chapter 42).

At the time of Heinrich's birth in 1882 his father was serving as an officer on the General Staff in Vienna. His twin brothers Hermann and Friedrich were born there in 1883, followed in 1885, after his father had been posted to Innsbruck to command 15th Infantry Brigade, by his youngest brother Eduard. The four brothers always thought of themselves as Tyroleans and remained on the best of terms all their lives. Hermann accompanied Heinrich on several of his botanical tours in Europe and himself published nearly seventy papers on the flora of Tyrol, where he lived until his death in 1963. His interests extended to zoology, folklore and local history. Eduard (1885-1950) became an artist of some distinction and painted the picture of Handel-Mazzetti on horseback in the Salween gorge (front cover); it hangs in the Vienna Botanical Institute and Handel-Mazzetti chose it as the frontispiece for *"Naturbilder aus Südwest China"*. A retrospective exhibition of his work was held in 1990 [Tiroler Impulse für Bildung und Kultur, 7, Nr.4, 1990].

The brothers had their first schooling from their mother at home and not until he was ten years old did Heinrich go to school in Innsbruck, where his teacher of natural history was Karl Wilhelm von Dalla Torre (1850-1928), a botanist and entomologist, and author of *Flora der gefürsteten Grafschaft Tirol*, in six volumes, 1900-1903. From 1893 to 1898 he continued his education at the Gymnasium (grammar school) at Döbling near Vienna, and after his father's death in 1898 at the Benedictine school at Seitenstetten, where the lichenologist and mycologist Pius Strasser (1843-1927), author of *Zur Flecht-*

---

[1] Erwin Janchen (1882-1970) Austrian botanist; pupil of Richard von Wettstein; Dr phil 1907; 1905-1920 at *Univ. Botanisches Institut*, Vienna; 1920-1923 at *Bundesanstalt für Pflanzenschutz*, from 1923 at *Botanisches Institut*. Editor of *Österr. bot. Zeitschrift* 1931-1944.

[2] Karl Heinz Rechinger junior, born 1906; Dr phil 1931; plant taxonomist and phytogeographer; Head of Dept. of Botany and later Director-General of the Natural History Museum, Vienna. Author of *Flora Aegaea* and *Flora Iranica*.

enflora Niederösterreichs, was among the teachers. There he passed the Reifeprüfung (matriculation) in July 1900 and that autumn began a year's military service — virtually obligatory for a man of his background — as a one-year volunteer in the Tiroler Kaiserjäger, a distinguished infantry regiment. Janchen comments that

> "his physical stamina, clear sense of direction, decisiveness, steady nerves and all the military qualities that he inherited ensured an impeccable record of service."

Nevertheless, he adhered to his early resolve to devote his life to science, despite his late father's wish that he should follow him in a military career.

In the autumn of 1901 he enrolled in the University of Vienna, bringing to his studies an unusually deep knowledge of the flowering plants, ferns and even mosses of his native land. In his first semester, before his twentieth birthday, he published his first scientific paper — "A contribution to the flora of North Tyrol", followed in the same year by the description of a newly discovered natural hybrid: *Gentiana tiroliensis* H.-M. (= *G. aspera* Hegetschw. et Heer X *G. campestris* L.) — now *Gentianella X tiroliensis*. In Professor Richard von Wettstein he found a teacher who was sympathetic towards his scientific aspirations and who encouraged the unforced development of his natural talents, and it was mainly Wettstein's influence that caused Handel-Mazzetti to adopt the evolutionary approach to botanical affinities.

In January 1903 Handel-Mazzetti became a demonstrator in the Vienna University Botanical Institute and in September 1905 he was promoted to assistant. He had now completed the required eight semesters but had not yet been awarded his doctorate, partly because his duties were so time-consuming and partly because the subject of his thesis had proved unusually difficult and laborious. His chosen theme was a monograph on the genus *Taraxacum*, but the material expanded to such enormous bulk that he submitted only a portion as his written dissertation and postponed publication of the complete monograph until 1907. He was awarded the degree of doctor of philosophy on 8th February 1907, his departmental head von Wettstein being his sponsor. Dr John Richards, reader in the Department of Agricultural and Environmental Science, University of Newcastle upon Tyne, comments that

> "The *Monographie der Gattung Taraxacum* was the first major taxonomic account of the genus, but unfortunately, even by the standards of its time, it was extremely poor. It names some 60 species in the genus (which now has some 2200), and many of these are confused, heterogeneous and meaningless. .... He was perhaps

unlucky to bring out his work at a time when the Scandinavians Dahlstedt and Lindberg were starting to publish the 'microspecies' and the sections which are used today (from 1900, but mostly 1905-07), and he effectively ignores their important work. His figures are poor and difficult to interpret and his photographs are almost useless. .... Yet it would be unfair to judge his ability or his later work on the basis of the monograph. This complex genus was certainly not one for a beginner to tackle so early in his professional life, when he was under pressure to publish to help his career. .... His poor grasp of relationships must be seen as the result of inexperience and of panic under pressure of time. Nevertheless, the monograph is thoroughly documented and painstakingly prepared, even if the conclusions are narrow-minded and lacking in flair."

As assistant in the Botanical Institute his main duties were the management and reorganisation of the herbarium; from time to time he had to hold classes in microscopy for beginners, but as he thought of himself as first and foremost a research worker this was a task for which he felt little inclination.

From his early youth Handel-Mazzetti was a keen and skilful mountaineer. Besides the mountains of Tyrol, he walked and climbed in the Tauern, the Dolomites and elsewhere in the central and southern Alps. In 1902 he visited Pula and Split on the coast of Yugoslavia and learnt something of the Mediterranean flora. In July 1904, accompanied by a few young colleagues, he led a botanical trip to west Bosnia, travelling through territory previously almost unvisited by botanists. As the most experienced and knowledgeable of the party, he was put in charge of the expedition and was responsible for describing the plants they collected. In 1905, in conjunction with his friend Friedrich Vierhapper, he led some of the participants in the International Botanical Congress on a tour through North Tyrol and the Dolomites to Upper Carinthia, and it was he who wrote the relevant section of the Congress tour guide. It was at this conference that he met Carl Schröter (1855-1940), author of the well known pocket Alpine Flora, still in print today. In 1906 he visited Switzerland (Engadine, St Gotthard, Jura), and in later life, except when he was abroad, hardly a year passed without a walking tour in the Alps. His favourite territory was Tyrol and the High Tauern, and he discovered several new plants there. Among other ranges he visited the Vosges, the Abruzzi (Majella 1924) and Mount Olympus in Thessaly (July 1927).

In 1907 Handel-Mazzetti was invited at the last minute to join a party travelling to Turkey to investigate some mines near Trabzon. Leaving Vienna on 27th June, he met his companions in Constantinople

— the leader K.R. von Blumencron, the geologist F. Kossmat and their dragoman Marc Bojovitch, "whose inextinguishable humour helped to entertain us even on the wettest days." After seeing the woods of maritime pine on the island of Prinkipo, they sailed through the Bosporus to Bender Eregli, a place never before visited by a botanist; there for the first time he saw the rhododendron stands of the Pontus. Next day he landed at Samsun and noted fine avenues of *Fraxinus oxycarpa*. At dawn on 5th July he saw the distant summit of Sis-dagh among the clouds. After reaching Trabzon he spent a few days on short trips, notably one to a village called Stephanos. There he had a new experience:

"It was the first time I had sat upon a horse, and I was very pleased that all went well. There can be no comparison between the natural style of riding on these splendid Turkish steeds and the methods used on our elaborately trained horses in our own country. One can rely on the steadiness and good sense of the animal, as I found when we ascended narrow paths, barely a foot wide, up steep loose screes or along deeply cut water runnels. Some distance before reaching a difficult stretch the horse would cross to the other side of the path, and at the edge of a bog it would pause and take soundings with its hoof to find a way through."

Handel-Mazzetti quickly realised the advantages of botanising on horseback, and on his later travels in China he rode whenever possible. To an Englishman it seems surprising that a man of his family origins and military background should not have learnt to ride as a child, but though they belonged to the Militäradel (military nobility) his family were not wealthy and riding lessons would have been dismissed as an unnecessary extravagance.

On 9th July he left Trabzon and travelled for two days southwest to the mountain village of Fol Koi, passing along the Kalanema Dere valley where he found "the only area of genuinely Mediterranean vegetation on the north coast of Turkey," including a wood of *Arbutus andrachne*. The vicinity of Fol Koi was more densely forested than any other part of the Pontic coast mountains that he visited, but wherever the trees had been felled the undergrowth of *Rhododendron ponticum* and *R. luteum* prevented the forest from regenerating. Except where they had been cut down, the rhododendrons extended from the coast up to the tree-line, forming almost impenetrable thickets in which he tripped over long shoots of Colchian ivy. In low-lying spots on the mountainsides the going was even harder, as the rhododendrons were enshrouded with *Clematis vitalba* and *Smilax excelsa*, the latter having spines two centimetres long. The villagers pointed out Ardutschly Kiran, a wooded peak 1700m in height; they said it

had never been climbed because the woods were so dense and impassable. The ground flora was sparse, *Campanula lactiflora* being the only conspicuous plant at that season. His stay was marred by rain and mist, but the nights were clear.

"One of the greatest pleasures of our trip was to sit under the starry sky, well wrapped up against the cold (11°C), surrounded by countless fireflies, busy pressing herbarium specimens by the light of a big petroleum lamp, ...while jackals howled in the woods across the valley."

In the forest gorges the rhododendrons were not so dense, and there were spruces, hornbeams, huge alders and gigantic crowns of oriental beech. Beneath them he found *Cirsium pseudopersonatum* and the ostrich-feather fern *Struthiopteris germanica*.

On 13th July he travelled inland again, this time on muleback, and saw *Rhododendron caucasicum*. On the alpine pastures of Ulugoba (2050 m) he found *Scilla sibirica*. On the way down he had a friendly reception from the peasants, "in oriental dress with pistol and dagger, but always amicable and without any sign of religious fanaticism."

On 15th July he left Fol Koi and went westwards over a ridge to the Greek village of Eseli. This was a clear day and he had a view of Sis Dagh, but it was merely "a misshapen hummock", not more than 2100 m high, clothed in spruce forest. However, he found *Acer trautvetteri*, previously known only from the Caucasus. On 18th July, with a "hopeful and louseridden" Greek youth as his guide, he set out to climb Tschemlikdji Deressi in the hope of reaching the subalpine zone. In those happy days "you could not go past a Turkish house without being invited to take coffee". They climbed a cliff with some difficulty but were then stopped by dense thickets of rhododendron. On his return journey to the coast he revisited the pinewood at Kalanema Dere. "As I now realised that the people were entirely amicable, I had no qualms about making these excursions unaccompanied ....but I had a loaded revolver in my pocket". On 31st July he left Trabzon and after a few days at Ordu returned to Vienna on 14th August.

This was his first botanical foray outside Europe and undoubtedly taught him a great deal. He discovered four new species: *Herniaria zervudachii* Hand.-Mzt., *Orchis pontica* Fleischm. et Hand.-Mzt., *Chrysanthemum trapezantinum* Hand.-Mzt., and *Geranium jubatum* Hand.-Mzt. He did not take photographs and had to rely on Dr Kossmat to provide illustrations for his article. Neither in his report on his travels nor in his botanical account does he make any mention of collecting seeds or living plants for introduction into cultivation.

In the following year, accompanied by his brother Hermann, he visited Bosnia and Herzegovina. They arrived at Sinj, the railhead 30 km inland from Split, on 3rd July and travelled into the mountains, making for Konj, at 1849 m the highest and most southerly peak of the limestone range. After spending a night in the open they found *Androsace villosa* at only 1200m, and as they went along the ridge the flora became richer and richer, *Ranunculus sartorianus* and *Draba longirostris* being among their finds. Next day they went over the karst to Imotski and on to Posusje where they found the rare *Centaurea tuberosa*. They were entertained by a friendly young priest with whom they conversed in Latin. Further on, up the wild Crvene Stiene gorge, they found *Primula kitaibeliana* on wet rocks beside a waterfall. Journeying on to the main peak of Cabulja, they encountered *Sibiraea (Spiraea) croatica*, but were separated from it by a chasm five metres wide. Heinrich tried to shoot some down with his revolver. He describes his attempts at photography: he used his iceaxe as a monopod, but on this occasion, unable to drive the point into the hard rock, he placed the camera on a rock above his head, aimed it at the shrub and gave a 12 second exposure, divided into two stages as the branches began to sway in the wind. The result was "not entirely unsuccessful". They returned along the Drezanka valley and on 12th July left Jablanica on horseback. However, they had to send back the horses and followed the track over Trinaca (2045m) to Grabovica. Along the ridge leading to Veliki Vilinac they found *Dianthus freynii*, *Viola zoysii*, *Papaver kerneri* and *Saxifraga moschata*. Hermann's leave was now running out and they hurried on to Sarajevo to catch the train. Heinrich went on to Rogatica and Han Semec where he explored some lush forest meadows and saw *Polemonium coeruleum*. He visited the ruins of Hrta in the Drina gorge and on 18th July returned to Klekovaca, where he had previously been in 1907.

His next major expedition took him to Iraq (then Mesopotamia) and Kurdistan in 1910. Accompanied by the zoologist Viktor Pietschmann, he sailed from Istanbul on 1st March, and after brief visits to Mytilene, Izmir (then Smyrna) and Rhodes, he reached Iskenderun (then Alexandretta) on 7th March. He then drove in a four-horse landau to Aleppo where he stayed until 23rd March before sailing down the Euphrates. After passing the golden domes and minarets of Karbala he visited the excavations at Babylon. On 3rd May he set out along the Tigris for Mosul, travelling through sand desert with sparse but interesting vegetation. On the journey he saw Halley's comet in its full glory, not far from the morning star. On 4th June he left Mosul to make a circuit through the mountains of Kurdistan. This took him to Urfa, Ak Dagh (2670m), Diarbekr (Diyarbakir), Djeziret and back to Mosul. The highest mountain was an unnamed peak in the Armenian Taurus (2980m). His journeying was not wholly enjoyable:

"I was not sorry to leave Mesopotamia .... The temperature in the tent rose to 48°C during the day and dropped to 15° at night. In the evenings the simoom would fill the tent with sand and drive dust into my eyes and mouth. It often arose so suddenly that while I was busy putting plants into the press I would have to pin the papers down with both arms to prevent them from being blown away .... For up to a week we were unable to find any good water. The people were dirty, untruthful and infected with dangerous diseases ....".

He made another journey through Kurdistan, climbing Nimrud Dagh (2320m) on 12th July and seeing the tumulus of King Antiochus I. Later that month he went to Göldshik Lake and climbed Hasarbaba Dagh, the highest peak in the vicinity (2500m). On 11th August he climbed Meleto Dagh, at 3190m the highest point he reached. His photograph shows a gently sloping double summit. He returned to Vienna in November with a large collection of herbarium specimens among which were over twenty new species including *Salix eriopolia*, *Dianthus coloratus*, *Euphorbia sanasunitensis*, *Herniaria arabica* and *Sedum inconspicuum*.

In 1912, when Handel-Mazzetti was thirty years old, his mother was making him an allowance of three hundred crowns a year out of her income of 9800 crowns. These figures are taken from her diary for 1912, the only year for which the diary has survived. In that year the Austrian crown (containing 0.338 gram of gold) was worth £0.0416 or 10d (10 old pence), or 20 US cents; its present-day value would be about £2 or US $3.20.

By 1912 Handel-Mazzetti had come to the end of his time as an assistant in the University Botanical Institute in Vienna and was looking for another post. His mother's diary for that year records the unsuccessful approaches to various influential persons that he made in the hope that a post might be created for him in the Natural History Museum. In July 1912 he was invited to accompany Archduke Franz Ferdinand, the heir to the Austrian throne, on a motor tour through the Dolomites and to serve as his botanical guide. The details are recounted by Carl von Bardolff. (Bardolff, Carl Frh. von, *Soldat im alten Österreich; Erinnerungen aus meinem Leben*. Jena, 1938 [p.126-127]).

The party set out from Toblach (now Dobbiaco) on a sunny morning at the beginning of July and drove up to the Falzarego pass.

"The car had to stop again and again. Handel-Mazzetti brought handfuls of rare and beautiful plants to the Archduke in the car, and the two vied with one another in naming them as swiftly as they could. I was amazed at the depth of their knowledge ... Then the booty was sorted, labelled and stowed away in tin boxes ... And so the two of them continued their botanizing, ranging far from the road, on the mountainsides above Andraz, Pieve and Arabba, and up to the Pordoi pass, which we reached long after midday ... The evening was spent in identifying the plants which they had previously been unable to name... Next day we drove over the Rolle pass ... through Fiera di Primiero, over the Brocon pass and via Trient to Riva ..."

On 8th July Heinrich wrote to his mother saying that all had gone well and that he hoped for good news before long. It seems reasonable to surmise that Heinrich seized the opportunity of speaking directly to the Archduke and of requesting him to create a post for him. However, Franz Ferdinand was a stern disciplinarian and would probably have regarded any such approach as impertinent. Even if he did not brusquely reject the young Handel-Mazzetti's petition he certainly did not create the desired post. That is probably the reason why Handel-Mazzetti wrote in such derogatory terms of the Archduke in his book (Chapter 7), published thirteen years after the assassination at Sarajevo. Franz Ferdinand was noted for his abrasiveness towards his inferiors. A recent commentator (Kann, Robert A., *Erzherzog Franz Ferdinand Studien*, Vienna 1976) remarks on his "inconsiderate harshness" and adds that "there were many who found him unacceptable, and some who hated and feared him".

In 1913 the Austro-Hungarian Dendrological Society, prompted by George Forrest's achievements in introducing shrubs and trees from Western China for cultivation in European gardens, decided to send Camillo Schneider, their General Secretary, to Yunnan on a similar mission. To broaden the scope of the expedition the Academy of Sciences in Vienna suggested that Handel-Mazzetti should go with him, and offered financial support. Handel-Mazzetti, then 31 years old, had reached an impasse in his career as a taxonomic botanist at the Botanical Institute, and though he had previously shown no special interest in the Chinese flora he accepted the offer.

After landing at Haiphong, Handel-Mazzetti and Schneider travelled on the new railway to Yunnanfu (now Kunming) where they arrived in February 1914. Their first major journey took them northwards over the uplands and across the Yangtze (Jinsha Jiang) to Huili. After climbing Mount Lungju-shan (Longzhu Shan) they went up the valley of the Anning He to Ningyuen (Xichang), and visited the "black Lolo" (Yi) in the Daliang Shan range where they found *Rhododendron intricatum* and *R. denudatum.* At the beginning of the rainy season in May they moved to Yenyuen (Yanyuan),

from which they visited the Lolo village of Kwapi (Guabi). They then travelled westwards via Yongning to Lijiang, where they met George Forrest. Handel-Mazzetti spent only a short time on the Yulong Shan, the mountain range north of Lijiang, as he felt that its flora had been sufficiently explored. Nevertheless, he recognized its quality: *"Our own alpine flora cannot match the splendours of this mountain, and my later travels in Yunnan convinced me that the Yulong Shan is ....unrivalled in its glory, both scenic and botanic. The work of Delavay, Forrest and Schneider ...has already yielded some 5000 species of flowering plants, ...almost as many as ...the entire Balkan peninsula".*

Leaving Lijiang on 29th July he travelled northwest to the Chungtien (Zhongdian) range, visiting the sinter terraces at Bede on the way. On his journey he received news of the declaration of war. As it was now impossible for him to return to Europe the German consul advised him to carry on with his work in China, and thanks to the efforts of Richard von Wettstein, his chief and sponsor in Vienna, he continued to receive financial support until the end of his stay[3]. He sent regular reports to the Academy of Sciences and kept a diary (see pages 53 and 172) which he used when writing *Naturbilder aus Süd-West China.* Unfortunately it is now no longer to be found. After spending the autumn in the mountains around Yanyuan, he returned to Kunming for the winter.

Early in 1915 Schneider left to take up a post in the USA. In February Handel-Mazzetti made a short trip to study the tropical flora near Manhao on the Red River south of Mengzi. At the end of April he set off on a major expedition. After passing through the territory explored by Delavay he spent a fortnight at Nguluke, Forrest's base at the foot of the Yulong-shan. He then crossed the Yangzi and visited the Chata Shan, though he did not reach its summit. His next journey took him to Yongning and Muli, where he photographed a Buddhist temple. Travelling westwards towards Zhongdian, he climbed Gonshiga (4750m), the highest peak he ever

---

[3]Handel-Mazzetti was financed by the Academy of Sciences in Vienna and the following payments are publicly recorded in the Anzeiger der Akademie der Wissenschaften in Wien:

2nd June 1913	Crowns	14000
10th July 1914		3000
19th March 1915		6000
24th February 1916		6000
29th March 1917		4000
31st January 1918		6000
11th July 1919		12000

"to cover the costs of bringing home his botanical collections"
| 11th July 1919 | | 3500 |

"to print his map of the Chinese river system"
| Total | Crowns | 54500 |

In 1914 100 Austrian crowns were worth about £4.20 sterling or $21 US, but the value dropped with inflation towards the end of the war.

attained, finally reaching the Mekong (Langcang Jiang) valley. It was now September, but he continued up the valley, where he found woods of arbor vitae (*Thuja orientalis*). After crossing the river by a rope bridge he arrived at the Tibetan village of Tsedjrong (Cizhong), where there was a Jesuit mission. From there he followed the pilgrim's route up to the Doker-la on the Tibetan frontier, and after a short rest at Londjre crossed the next divide to Bahan in the Salween (Nu Jiang) valley. At the end of September he returned over the Si-la (Xi-la) pass to the Mekong, and via Weihsi (Weixi) and Lidiping to Dali and Kunming.

The flora of the Salween valley had proved so rich that Handel-Mazzetti resolved to revisit it in 1916. At the end of April he set off to Dali, where he climbed the Cang Shan range to the west of the town. Civil war had broken out and he had to keep his plans secret, but he was able to travel up the Yangzi valley and cross the divide to the Mekong. Continuing over the Xi-la, he was again made welcome by the Jesuits at Bahan. From there he travelled over the Chiangshel pass to the upper Irrawaddy, which was much wetter than the Salween valley. After a period of rest and convalescence at Bahan, he travelled northwards to the Shenzu-la, climbed a limestone peak (Maya, 4574m) and made a high level circuit round the heads of the valleys draining into the Salween. On the return journey he resurveyed part of the Mekong valley and took a new route from Weixi over the hills to Jianchuan. Back at Nguluke in October, he met the American zoologist Roy Andrews and attempted one of Yulong Shan's lesser peaks, but was forced to turn back at 4750m. After a further visit to the Yangxi gorge he returned via Yungbei (Yongsheng) to spend the winter in Kunming.

By 1917 Handel-Mazzetti had seen enough of the Yunnan highlands and decided to travel eastwards through Guizhou and Hunan, concentrating on subtropical areas at lower altitudes. He departed from Kunming on 5th June, leaving behind all his botanical collections packed in 51 tin-lined crates in the German consulate. Journeying across limestone karst terrain, he soon entered a part of Yunnan unsurveyed by any Westerner. The climate was warmer and wetter, and many of the plants were new to him, notably *Bletilla yunnanensis* and *Lilium delavayi*. The strange cone hills of the karst landscape near Luoping made a deep impression on him. Crossing the Huangni He, he entered the province of Guizhou and on 27th June reached the city of Guiyang. Among the plants which he found in its vicinity were *Hosta coerulea* and *Macleaya cordata*. Travelling onwards in intense heat he reached Sandu and botanized in a boat along the Du Jiang river. Before long he entered Hunan province, where he was destined to spend the remainder of his stay in China. Near Xinning the aquatic flora was at its

finest; he recorded lotus (*Nelumbo nucifera*) and several water lilies. China had now declared war on Germany, and Handel-Mazzetti decided to stay in Changsha, where there was a German community over twenty strong.

Despite the civil war he was able to continue collecting; the results were of considerable value because hardly any botanists had previously worked in Hunan. In 1918 he visited the antimony mines at Xikungshan; nearby he saw *Pseudolarix kaempferi* and three species of rose. He spent part of the summer in the hill forests of Mount Yun Shan. After the armistice had been signed he spent the winter in Changsha and was finally repatriated in 1919, though his herbarium specimens did not reach Vienna until 1922.

After his return from China in 1919 Handel-Mazzetti resumed his duties as an assistant in the University Botanical Institute. At that time there was a rule that no one might hold an assistant post for more than ten years without undergoing the process of "Habilitation", which entailed submitting a substantial dissertation and passing further examinations. Handel-Mazzetti had been an assistant since 1905, but did not wish to take this step because it would have involved him in teaching commitments towards which he felt no inclination. The nineteen-twenties were years of penury in Austria; academic posts were being axed or left unfilled, and it was not easy to find a position for Handel-Mazzetti where he could carry on his work as a taxonomist.

In Vienna there were, and still are, two centres of botanical study: the University Botanical Institute in the Rennweg, adjacent to the Botanical Garden, and the Department of Botany in the Natural History Museum, an imposing building on the Burgring. In 1922 the Director of the Department of Botany in the Natural History Museum was pensioned off and Karl von Keissler [4] was appointed in his stead. The second in the hierarchy, the Keeper (Kustos) — Dr K.H.Rechinger [5] senior, then only fifty-five years old — was compelled to take early retirement so as to create a vacancy. In April 1923 Handel-Mazzetti was transferred from the Botanical Institute to the Natural History Museum, still as a scientific assistant, and in June 1925 he was promoted to the vacant post of Keeper. Once again his first concern was the herbarium, but he also set about the task of reorganising

---

[4] Karl von Keissler 1872-1965, lichenologist. Dr. phil. 1895. Botanical Garden, Vienna 1895-1899. Department of Botany, Natural History Museum, Vienna 1899-1938.

[5] Karl H. Rechinger senior (1867-1952). Austrian botanist; studied under Wettstein; Dr phil 1893; demonstrator and later assistant at the University Botanic Garden, Vienna, 1893-1902; in various posts in the Natural History Museum 1902-1922, from 1919 as *Kustos* of the Department of Botany. Father of Professor K.H. Rechinger.

the entire Department of Botany, which had once been an outstanding centre of scientific excellence, though in the unhappy postwar years it had slipped into a sad state of decline. He took up the cudgels — perhaps too openly and uncompromisingly — against certain serious organisational shortcomings which had grown worse year by year with the demise of more and more of the genuine taxonomists, among them A. von Hayek, who accompanied Handel-Mazzetti on a visit to the Thessalian Olympus in 1927. Unfortunately his ideas failed to find sympathy and support among those who controlled the destinies of the department. His suggestions, though well-founded and reasonable, were considered inexpedient, his indiscreetly voiced opinions made enemies, and finally he came into open conflict with Keissler.

Although Handel-Mazzetti was averse to teaching — he regarded it as a waste of time that could better be devoted to taxonomic work — he was by no means devoid of ambition. He coveted academic honours and distinctions, and dreamed of stepping into Keissler's place as director. Keissler was a modest and unassuming man, perhaps somewhat afraid of Handel-Mazzetti, and some of his botanical research was not above criticism. Handel-Mazzetti seems to have naively supposed that by exposing Keissler's shortcomings he could curry favour with the authorities, induce them to dismiss Keissler and make him director. With this object in mind he published a review of a collection of plants brought back from Tibet by Zugmayer. These specimens had originally been studied and identified by Keissler in 1907. Handel-Mazzetti made no attempt to hide his disdain for Keissler's work:

"While working up the botanical material which I brought back from China I had occasion to inspect some of the plants collected by Zugmayer in North East Tibet, and it immediately struck me that they had not been correctly determined. .... I resolved to undertake a revision of the entire collection. This revealed that out of the species determined by the author himself [Keissler] ...32 were wrongly named ..."

He goes on to review the species one by one and seems to revel in pillorying Keissler's mistakes:

"The author described the flowers [of *Braya uniflora*] as still unknown, but they had already been described and illustrated in Hooker's Icones (1894)."

A few pages later he reclassifies an aster which Keissler had regarded as no more than a new variety and gives it specific rank as *Aster glandulosus* (Keissl.) Hand.-Mzt., discarding Keissler's epithet,

relegating Keissler's name to parentheses and appending his own.

The quarrel came to a head in 1929, before Handel-Mazzetti's review had appeared. His obituarist maintains a discreet silence, but Professor K.H.Rechinger junior takes up the story in a letter to his parents written on 29th September 1929:

"Yesterday Schaffer [F.X.Schaffer, 1876-1953, Director of the Department of Geology and Palaeontology in the Natural History Museum] told me how he had encountered Handel-Mazzetti on the day after his return from America. According to Schaffer, Handel-Mazzetti is completely crazy. His arrogance, self-importance and quarrelsomeness have become notorious, in America as well as here. By his behaviour towards Keissler Handel-Mazzetti has made himself intolerable, and he no longer sets foot in the Museum.
Today, as I was sitting in a restaurant peacefully enjoying my luncheon, my gaze, drawn by some magic force, lighted upon a table in the window. There sat Handel-Mazzetti himself, as large as life, seemingly eating his meal with a good appetite despite everything. We nodded to one another, and during a break in the meal I went over to his table. His greeting was friendly and he was less taciturn than usual. Speaking so fast that his words tumbled over each other, he at once began to pour out the story of the affair from his point of view. I did not understand everything, but his main complaints were that Keissler's faults stank to high heaven and that he was furious at having to put up with him as his superior for another five years although he, Handel-Mazzetti, had been promised the Directorship of the Department of Botany as long ago as 1924."

The affair was handled with great discretion and the details never became public. However, there were rumours that Handel-Mazzetti had threatened Keissler with violence and had actually attempted to strike him. He was immediately suspended from his duties and forbidden to enter the Natural History Museum. In due course he was obliged to submit to examination by a psychiatrist. After considering the medical report the authorities compelled Handel-Mazzetti to take early retirement and he relinquished his post on 1st July 1931. Under the regulations in force at the time his pension would have been 80 per cent of his salary. However, his salary would have been meagre, first because he would have been below the ceiling that he could have reached in the later stages of a successful career and secondly because academics were in any case poorly paid. Even as late as 1963 the salary of a *Kustos* in the *Naturhistorisches Museum* was only one third of that of a Keeper in the British Museum (Natural History) in London.

Handel-Mazzetti, still less than fifty years old, now found himself free from all official duties and able to devote all his time to research. A place was found for him in the Botanical Institute in the Rennweg, where he was given a corner in the herbarium. After a time he began to find the accommodation too cramped and the ban on entering the Natural History Museum became increasingly irksome. The library at the Rennweg did not take all the journals he required and above all he needed access to the Natural History Museum so as to compare his plants from China with the type specimens in the herbarium. After a few years a compromise was negotiated: the ban on entering the Natural History Museum was lifted, and a timetable was devised to avoid any contact between the adversaries. Keissler used to leave the Museum punctually at 2 pm and Handel-Mazzetti, having spent the morning at the Botanical Institute, arrived a few minutes later[6].

For the rest of the thirties Handel-Mazzetti was free to concentrate his vast energies on the mass of botanical material which he had collected in China and which had been shipped back, soldered up in airtight tin-boxes, after the war. He published the results under the title "Symbolae Sinicae" (1929-1937). The first five parts deal with algae, fungi, lichens, mosses and liverworts, and were written by specialists, but Parts VI (ferns) and VII (flowering plants; 1450 pages) were mainly his own work. His own herbarium material from China comprised over thirteen thousand specimens, and he included in his studies a number of plants collected by others. Many of the plants listed in Symbolae Sinicae had not previously been found in China. Out of the 8015 species dealt with, no fewer than 1307 were new, and there were 35 new genera. He had already published many of these new discoveries as *"Plantae novae Sinenses"* in the Anzeiger of the Academy of Sciences in Vienna from 1920 to 1926.

He used Symbolae Sinicae as a vehicle for critical comments and revisions of various genera; his account of Chinese oaks, for example, runs to twenty pages, and his researches extended to the collections in Berlin, Edinburgh, Kew and Paris. Yet Symbolae Sinicae is a disappointingly uninformative work: for most species, apart from new discoveries, the entry gives only the name, the reference to the original description and a list of the places in China where specimens had been collected.

Some of his investigations of Chinese plants led him to undertake separate revisions of certain genera

(*Androsace, Lysimachia, Ligularia*), culminating in a monograph on his old favourite *Leontopodium* (1927 — 172 pages). As a leading expert on the Chinese flora he received several invitations to study collections made by other travellers. These labours are recorded in *Plantae Mellianae, Plantae Chingianae, Plantae Tsiangianae,* in his contributions to *Plantae Sinenses a Dre. H. Smith lectae* and numerous lesser works. In the late thirties he embarked on a large-scale flora of China and had completed much of the preliminary work, but after his death there was no one with the necessary experience to bring it to fruition.

Handel-Mazzetti's scientific achievements found due recognition in his own country and abroad. In 1928 he was invited by the Royal Horticultural Society to read a paper at the Fourth Primula Conference in London (*The Natural Habitats of Chinese Primulas.* J. Roy. Hort. Soc. **54,** 51-62, 1929) and became an honorary member of the Society. He was also an honorary member of the Botanical Society of Edinburgh (1934) and a corresponding member of the Société Botanique de Genève, and he was awarded the Silver Nightingale Medal of the Geographical Society in Berlin. In 1939 he was elected a corresponding member of the Academy of Sciences in Vienna, but he died before the appointment had been confirmed by the Ministry in Berlin.

Since the scientific tasks that Handel-Mazzetti set himself vastly exceeded the powers of a single individual, prodigious as was his capacity for work, he enlisted a succession of scientific helpers to carry out special investigations under his direction and constant supervision. Unmarried and without family responsibilities — he lived as a subtenant in a simply furnished room — his pension, supplemented by the sale of duplicates from his personal collection of herbarium material, was sufficient to allow him to pay a reasonable salary to his private assistant and also to meet the expense of a walking tour in the Alps every summer. Despite his personal reserve and aloofness from social life — his brothers were practically the only persons to whom he displayed any warmth — all his personal assistants were devoted to him. Among them were Dr Wilhelm Mack, Dr Theodor Just (subsequently Professor at Notre Dame University, Indiana, USA), Dr Lotte Kretschmer, Dr Georg Kufodontis and Dr Elfriede Peter, née Stibal, who worked with him for several years and was perhaps more closely acquainted with him than any of the others.

During these years he sponsored several students from China. Among his family's photographs is one of a bespectacled young man in European dress, inscribed in German *"to my most respected teacher Dr Handel-Mazzetti, with friendly memories from Yin Yuan Pai 1936-1939."*

Because hardly any of his letters or personal papers have survived, it is not easy to assess his

---

[6]In his obituary Janchen states that Handel-Mazzetti spent the mornings in the Museum and the afternoons in the Botanical Institute, but Professor K.H.Rechinger, who worked there in the thirties, says that Janchen was mistaken.

contacts with other botanists and plant hunters who worked in China in the same era. He describes his meetings with George Forrest at Nguluke (Chapters 7 and 13). There is no record of any meeting with Frank Kingdon Ward. He was serving in India while Handel-Mazzetti was in China and when Handel-Mazzetti came to London for the Primula Conference in May 1928 Kingdon Ward was in Burma (see his book *"Plant Hunting on the Edge of the World"*, p.65). However, Kingdon Ward refers to correspondence with him. In his article *"The Snow Mountains of Yunnan"* (Geog. Journ. 1924, **64**, 222-231) he writes...." (Handel-Mazzetti's) height of 5900m (later 5815m) for Satseto was obtained by photogrammetric construction over Lidjiang 3340m". In May 1921 Handel-Mazzetti received a visit from the Swedish botanist Karl August Harald (Harry) Smith. The latter was on his way to Peking to start the first of his three expeditions, and wanted to meet Handel-Mazzetti and see his collections, though he must have been disappointed to find that most of the material was still held up by the Chinese. In 1922 Harry Smith travelled the route from Kunming via Ningyuan that Handel-Mazzetti and Schneider had followed on their first journey in 1914, but he was less fortunate: on the way to Chengtu he was attacked and robbed, losing 1000 herbarium sheets. He never went back to Yunnan or traversed any other of Handel-Mazzetti's routes [7]. Handel-Mazzetti met Joseph Rock when the latter made a short visit to Vienna in the winter of 1933-34. In her biography of Rock, Stephanne Sutton [8] describes how *"they sat together in the dining room at the Hotel Sacher over Naturschnitzel and conversed amiably"*.

From time to time there was talk of another visit to China, but in the twenties no funds were available. In the thirties Hermann Sleumer invited Handel-Mazzetti to join him on a trip to China but their plans were wrecked by the war.

The end came unexpectedly. At dusk on 30th January 1940, as he was crossing the Rennweg after leaving the Botanical Institute, he was knocked down in the blackout by a German military vehicle. He was taken to hospital with multiple rib fractures and severe lung injuries, and died of an embolus at 6pm on 1st February. Only two hours earlier, fully expecting to recover, he had given Janchen, his obituarist, a detailed account of the accident.

****

Janchen concludes the obituary with a sketch of Handel-Mazzetti's personality:

Handel-Mazzetti was tall and powerfully built. His features were distinguished, his bearing erect and military, and his address confident and direct, though never assertive. His intellectual talents would have fitted him for a career in any walk of life, but his interests were so narrowly focused on plant taxonomics and phytogeography that there was little room in his life for anything else. Nevertheless, it was this concentration on a single field of research, coupled with his tireless industry, that made possible his huge output of scientific writing. Everything that he produced was thorough and reliable, totally free from carelessness or superficiality. However, when he found neglectful errors in other botanists' work he castigated them severely. In his personal dealings he was irreproachably honest and straightforward, and never let himself be influenced by considerations of personal advantage. He had a strong sense of justice and was a shrewd judge of character. His assessments of his fellows were sometimes severe, but usually accurate, and he had no patience with weakness or idle compromises. His was a fighter's nature and he never shirked conflict or danger. In his relations with his colleagues he maintained a dignified reserve. Closer social contact was reserved for his family, and even here it was kept within narrow limits, for his working hours were sacrosanct. Yet withal he was not unduly earnest; he had a cheerful temperament and was not without a sense of humour.

****

Handel-Mazzetti certainly felt at his best out of doors, high in the mountains, especially in his beloved Tyrol. For a large part of his childhood and youth he lived in Innsbruck and spent many summer holidays at the family farmhouse at Völs, a few kilometres west of the city. Later he never failed to pay an annual visit to his mother in her home in Tyrol, and to the end of his life he enjoyed walking tours in the Austrian Alps with rucksack and iceaxe. Because of his wide experience of botanical work under field conditions he was invited to write the chapter entitled *"Der Ökologe auf Reisen"* [The Ecologist on an Expedition] (1928) for *Abderhaldens Handbuch der biologischen Arbeitsmethoden.* A contemporary photograph shows him on a mountain path near Kals in 1938 [frontispiece]. His love for these mountains and their flowers led him to champion the cause of nature conservation, most notably when the Gamsgrube on the Pasterzenflanke (Upper Carinthia), famous for its unique flora, was threat-

---

[7] Herner, G. *Taxon*, 1988, **37**, 299-308.

[8] Stephanne B. Sutton *In China's Border Provinces — The Turbulent Career of Joseph Rock, Botanist — Explorer.* 1974, Hastings House, New York.

ened by commercial exploitation [9]. Yet he was far from fanatical; in a note published when he was only twenty-six [*Mitteilungen des Dtsch. u. Öst. Alpenvereins, 1908, p.35-36*] he rebuts the protests levelled against a colleague who dug up 20-30 plants of *Wulfenia carinthiaca* for cultivation in a botanic garden. "As anyone familiar with *Wulfenia* in its habitat will realise, there is no danger of its extermination." He remarked that it was important not to make conservation seem ridiculous or to provoke hostility. He adds an amusing story. One day he was walking through the woods on the limestone hills near Perchtoldsdorf south of Vienna. On the ridge of the Föhrenberg he came across a boulder on which were growing: *Erinus alpinus* from the Western Alps and the Jura, *Erigeron alpinus* from the Central and Western limestone Alps, *Dianthus alpinus* and *Veronica fruticans*, both found on the Schneeberg.

> "This community would deceive nobody;" he writes, "one would at most smile at the 'eccentric fellow' that planted them there. But suppose they died out, as they sooner or later will, leaving only *D. alpinus*. It might then be mistaken for a preglacial relict."

His command of languages comprised Italian, learnt from his mother, French (sufficient to converse with missionaries in China), English (he delivered a lecture to the Royal Horticultural Society) and Latin, spoken as well as botanical. By 1916 he claimed to speak Chinese well enough for the everyday needs of travel.

He was a competent draughtsman, as the drawings in his monograph on *Taraxacum* attest, but the only sketch in *Naturbilder aus Südwest China* [Chapter 25] is somewhat uninspiring. He devoted much effort to photography, but his pictures, both those reproduced in the book and those in the archives of the Botanical Institute (nearly 2000), are disappointing. At that time the standards of photography in black and white were scarcely inferior to those achieved today, though emulsions were not as fast. Some of the plant photographs taken by his contemporary in China (reproduced in J. Macqueen Cowan, *The Journeys and Plant Introductions of George Forrest*, Oxford, 1952) could hardly be bettered today. Yet Handel-Mazzetti's pictures of plant life are spoilt by lack of skill in composition. Instead of trying to portray a single plant, he aimed his camera at a mass of vegetation and captioned the plate with a list of species; the result is a confused and jumbled image. Most of his landscape photographs are equally unsatisfactory, and even after

making due allowance for the difficulty of obtaining photographic plates in good condition in wartime China and for the problems caused by mist and rain, it has to be said that Handel-Mazzetti was not a talented photographer.

He was a botanist pure and simple and had no interest in horticulture. He never had a garden of his own, nor did he ever have any duties in the Botanic Garden in Vienna. When giving his paper on *"The Natural Habitats of Chinese Primulas"* at the Royal Horticultural Society's Fourth Primula Conference in 1928, he began with the words *"... as a systematic botanist I know about as much of gardening as a zoologist as such knows of horsemanship."* Though he says in his foreword that he had tried to outline his observations in other fields of knowledge, and he certainly did valuable work in geography and geology, he has practically nothing to say about birds or mammals, and when he met the American scientists from the American Museum of Natural History he was naïvely surprised at their success in trapping small nocturnal mammals on Mount Yulong Shan.

Several passages in *"Naturbilder aus Südwest China"* seem to betray an intolerant and censorious personality. He makes gratuitously unkind remarks about some of the people he met in China — for instance, the British consul in Kunming who *"was alleged to have gone there because of an excessive fondness for alcohol."* On hearing of the assassination of the Archduke Franz Ferdinand at Sarajevo — a man he had known personally and who, had his chauffeur not taken a wrong turning and thus enabled Gavrilo Princip to take steady aim at the Crown Prince, would have become Handel-Mazzetti's sovereign — all he could find to say was that *"it was fortunate that he never came to the throne"* — an uncalled for comment that leaves a bitter taste even today (Chapter 7). He also reveals that he was a convinced pacifist, though he did not try to evade call up for military service, and a rabid nonsmoker.

He lived a celibate life and seems never to have been in love. As Professor K.H. Rechinger remarked to me, had he ever had a liaison with a woman it would not have remained a secret for long, Vienna being the city it is!

His obituarist, writing in 1940 when Austria had just been swallowed up into 'Greater Germany' and Vienna was virtually under occupation by the Wehrmacht, tells us that Handel-Mazzetti regarded himself as entirely German and that he showed no external signs of his Italian blood. That is not to say that he had any sympathy with the Nazis; on the contrary, so Professor Rechinger assured me, he wanted nothing to do with them. Janchen goes on to say that Handel-Mazzetti was free from any aristocratic pride or snobbery: his attitudes and sentiments were socially conscious and democratic. He adds that his helpfulness was known to all who had dealings

---

[9] Gams, Helmut — *Carl Schröter und Heinrich von Handel-Mazzetti* — Jahrb. d. Vereins z. Schutze d. Alp.-pfl. u. Tiere, 1940, **12**, 63-70.

with him. As one of his juniors, Professor Rechinger formed a somewhat different impression:

"I would have liked nothing better than to have learnt from him, but Handel-Mazzetti, without saying much, had a way of repelling any friendly overtures."

This biographical memoir may fittingly be concluded by a character sketch written by Professor Rechinger in 1944, when he was living in the country outside Vienna in circumstances of some hardship. Having time on his hands, he sat down with pencil and paper and drafted short vignettes of some of the leading botanists of the day. Forty-two years later he looked out the exercise book in which he had written it, and with his permission I reproduce it below:

HEINRICH HANDEL-MAZZETTI

His appearance, his gait and his movements were, like his handwriting, stiffly erect, angular and ungainly. A long face framed by a prematurely grey beard, the skull brachycephalic, the eyes blue, their gaze somewhat shifting; his bearing autocratic and haughty; his address plain-spoken, often offensive, even aggressive. Though motivated by a genuine love of nature, he was also propelled by a no less powerful egoism. The latter was so overwhelming that in time it gradually undermined his entire personality, although his mind had originally been as vigorous and robust as his body. In his unconscious mind he must have felt that the recognition that he longed for and the influence that he sought to exercise were goals which he could attain only by single-minded concentration on his work. Yet even in his circumscribed field of research, which he pursued to the exclusion of amusements or diversions of any kind — forswearing even the most basic human relationships — his was not an effortless or enjoyable creativity but a burdensome and unremitting toil, made more laborious by stern self-criticism. The volume and importance of his published writings bear witness to his unceasing industry, his iron constitution and a degree of single-mindedness bordering on asceticism. His scientific papers are lucid and well set out; they display a clear sense of form and a proper feeling for natural affinities, but they are sometimes marred by forced attempts to draw artificial distinctions.
I can see him still, sailing along in his battered old hat, his loden cloak floating in the wind, maintaining his course and speed regardless of his surroundings, and I can well imagine how it came about that, driven on by his almost pathological self-

confidence, he strode on to his destruction — 'where I am, no other man can be' — unwilling to the very last to accept that Fate could lay her hand on his shoulder before he had brought his ambitious plans to fruition. A glance at the portrait of Keissler is enough to show that any compromise or understanding between two such contrasting personalities was out of the question, especially when the stronger was subordinated to the weaker.

The first edition and its reviews

NATURBILDER AUS SÜDWEST CHINA — ERLEBNISSE UND EINDRÜCKE EINES ÖSTERREICHISCHEN FORSCHERS WÄHREND DES WELTKRIEGES — by *Dr Heinrich Handel-Mazzetti*, Custos an der botanischen Abteilung des Naturhistorischen Museums in Wien. Pp. xiv+ 380+77 plates. With a map and 148 illustrations from the author's photographs, including 24 Autochromes. 1927, Österreichischer Bundesverlag für Unterricht, Wissenschaft und Kunst, Wien und Leipzig. Price 24 Reichsmarks.

The first edition was published in purple cloth with a handsome floral motif on the cover. It is now a very scarce book.

Most of the reviewers treated it kindly. Writing in *"Nature"*, Augustine Henry remarked on *"the wealth and beauty of the illustrations"*. Noting its *"strong appeal to horticulturists"*, he expressed the hope that a translation would soon be published. (*Nature*, May 7, 1927, **119**, 667-668). "L.D.S.", writing in the *Geographical Journal* (1927, **70**, 300), praised the colour plates, but commented that *"a generalised account of the vegetation of China from the ecological standpoint is still a desideratum."* The anonymous reviewer in *La Géographie* (1927, **47**, 475) was less gracious: *"On pourrait cependant regretter de trouver ... des appreciations peu courtoises à l'adresse de personnes des pays alliés avec lesquelles l'auteur fut en relation."* In *Petermanns Geographische Mitteilungen* (1928, **74**, 54), Tiefsen, while welcoming Handel-Mazzetti's descriptions of geological formations, noted that his geological experience could not be expected to equal his botanical knowledge. Another critic remarked that although Handel-Mazzetti had not formed a very favourable opinion of the Chinese, he nevertheless nearly always enjoyed protection and support from the authorities and lodging and hospitality from the people (*Mitt. Geog. Gesell. München*, 1927, **20**, 143).

Map 1

Handel-Mazzetti's Itinerary — 6th March to 16th October 1914

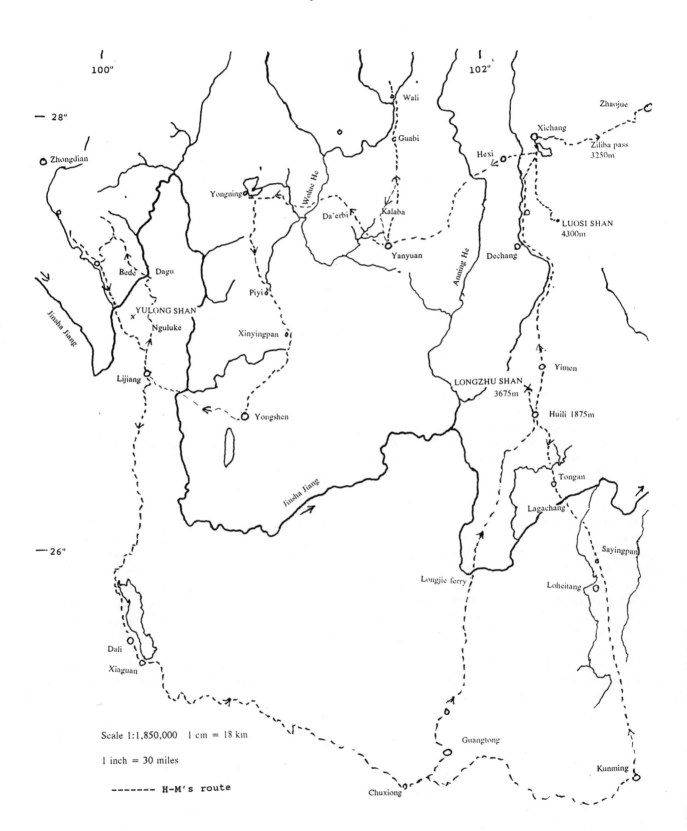

PART I 1914

The Plateau and Mountain Ranges of Yunnan and Southwest Sichuan

Chapter 1. The Journey to Kunming and Our First Expeditions

In tropical Tonkin — the Yunnan railway — the provincial capital — Europeans — Government of the province — recruiting our caravan — wild and cultivated plants — how manure is collected

Departing from Trieste on 21st December 1913, Camillo Schneider and I sailed via Alexandria, Port Said, Singapore and Saigon to Haiphong where we landed on 28th January 1914. After a railway journey broken at Hanoi, the capital of Tonkin, we reached the frontier of what was to be our area of operations, the Chinese province of Yunnan, on 1st February 1914. The twin towns of Laokay and Hekou lay on the Red River separated by its tributary the Nanxi and as they were only 90m above sea level the surrounding landscape was wholly tropical. To learn something of its flora we spent a day in Laokay, then under French control. We enjoyed the hospitality of government officials, and the next day the forest officer took us to Ngoi-ko-den, a little valley near Phomoi where the vegetation was still completely intact. The side channels running into the broad river valley were largely filled with wild bananas which extended some way up the slopes; then came a jungle of huge light green bamboos, while the ridge tops were covered with broad-leaved tropical forest made up of trees of varying height including palms (*Caryota mitis*) interspersed with bamboos. A narrow footpath climbed up our little valley, here and there blocked by fallen bamboos or swamped by the stream. To go more than a few steps from the path was impossible, so thick was the vegetation. Bananas and other broad-leaved trees were sparser here, but there were many large ferns and interesting shrubs. Two herbaceous plants were new to science: the narrow-leaved *Elatostema longistipulum (Urticaceae)*, rooting among the pebbles and growing in large clumps which shaded the brook, and the stemless *Begonia handelii*, the largest of all Asiatic species, with pink flowers up to 11cm in diameter looking as if they had been moulded in wax. Considering that the French had recorded the area as already explored, this was a very good start to my collecting activities, though at the time I was of course unaware that the species were new.

Up to now we had formed favourable impressions from our brief stays in the clean and prosperous British and French settlements, but in Hekou our illusions were shattered. The place was nothing more than a dirty street lined by dilapidated bamboo huts, and the Customs Director, a Frenchman, had a miserable room as his office. Next morning the train carried us swiftly away from the Red River through a short tunnel to the Nanxi, which the railway, completed in 1910, follows almost to its source. It penetrates 465km into China to the provincial capital Kunming (formerly Yunnanfu) and is a major engineering feat. Driven through very difficult terrain, it cost a thousand human lives and 160 million French francs. Though Laokay is only 90m above sea level the terminus is at 1900m and the highest level is at 2025m. At another point, 650m above the West Canton River, the railway reaches 1709m. Trains ran on the narrow gauge (1m) line in daylight only, and the journey from Laokay to Kunming took two days. The Nanxi valley runs for some distance parallel to the Red River, gradually narrowing though the gradient is still slight. It is bordered by steep bare slopes with a few patches of tropical forest or bush. The Chinese are the forest's worst enemy; they burn everything, even the steppe grass which replaces the trees. We saw fires everywhere on the mountainsides; the reason for them was not clear, for there was no attempt to cultivate the areas cleared by fire and they were seldom if ever used for pasture. *Mucuna bracteata (Leguminosae)* with racemes of almost black flowers twined up the bushes and tall grasses and filled the air with its heavy, nauseating scent. The bare landscape with its uniform steep hillsides was quite monotonous; not until we reached Wantang, where the line starts to ascend, did it become more varied.

Here the valley merged into an almost inaccessible gorge, its depths filled with virgin tropical savannah forest. The line climbed over bridges and through tunnels up on to a hillside consisting of sedimentary slate capped with limestone, and through a landscape which, in its winter garb at least, reminded us of the terrain above the treeline on the Brenner pass. A detour into the side valley of the Bai He gained some 300m in height. The Bai He itself was crossed by a 90m high iron bridge between two curving tunnels. With its tunnels, galleries and viaducts the line was reminiscent of the Semmering, but despite its far larger scale the barren landscape was not nearly comparable in beauty. The builders realised too late that they had chosen the wrong side of the valley, where the line cuts the steeply inclined strata which form the actual slope, and therefore had to contend with continual landslips, which cover the track with rubble for several months in the rainy season. Malicious tongues assert that they alternate — this year in the stretch constructed by one contractor, next year in that built by the other. After a short gorge, in which the line ran close to the stream in a cutting blasted out of the rock, the train steamed out on to the karst landscape of the Yunnan plateau, the lower slopes covered with terraced paddy fields and the heights crowned by steep jagged crests. Below Luoshuitang the line made a loop to ascend another valley, down which a waterfall tumbled, and then ran through a tunnel into the Mengzi basin.

Rice fields shimmered in the valley, and in the distance the lake came into view. The town of Mengzi, over 6km from the railway, lay in a depression of red earth divided into fields. The horizon was marked by the mountain range of Dahei Shan, none of its numerous peaks rising much above the rest. Hewn out of the rock, the line ran across fissured limestone pavement, passing small hollows (polje) planted with vegetables, beans, bananas and castor oil. Elsewhere the ground was covered by tall sedges, mainly acid-loving. Ami-zhou (now Kaiyuan), on a branch of the Baida He (now Nanpan Jiang) which drains into the West Canton River, was the station where travellers spent the night. From there the track went a little further down to the river itself and then straight northwards, rising gently along the well filled river. For long stretches it ran through deep gorges, their steeply sloping sides covered with a dense growth of mainly evergreen shrubs and low trees, except where the dark limestone outcropped in vertical faces. Between the gorges the valley broadened into sparsely cultivated areas with pinewoods and Yi villages, the houses built of unbaked mudbricks with minute windows and tall thatched roofs. This marked a second mistake in the planning of the railway, namely that the engineers chose this unpopulated terrain, probably because of the easier gradients, instead of the more westerly route, where prosperous towns lie in the fertile basins round the lakes. The only town which we touched was Yiliang (1690m). At the north west border of its intensively cultivated basin the railway turned sharply to the west, leaving the Baida He, and climbed steeply through a gorge with low vertical rocky walls, passing through numerous tunnels and over viaducts. We passed Lake Yangzhong Hai and, high above its west bank, reached the summit level on the Qigongpo ridge with splendid views over the azure lake, which was surrounded partly by terraced cultivation and partly by bare soil, deep red in colour, while the foreground became more and more karst-like. From there on the line ran gently downhill. The soil turned into a yellowish brown marl. The edge of the plain was largely covered by graves and burial mounds, but elsewhere it was green with bean fields, kitchen

gardens and cypress alleys, which occupied the ground between the grey-brown villages and made it difficult to get a general view of the terrain. We had only an occasional glimpse of the lake, but our gaze was riveted by the vertical precipice on its far side. Then the line curved to the right and that evening (4 February) the train steamed into the capital city of Kunming.

In the southern suburbs outside the city walls there were several hotels near the station, run by Frenchmen, Greeks, or Italians. Like all the hotels on the railway line, they were far from luxurious. We stayed at first in the Hotel Haeffner, but soon we rented a house in the city from the French Mission where we could unpack our heavy baggage and get ready our caravan. Kunming had about 100,000 inhabitants, but spread over a far larger area than such a population needs, as the rectangular plan of the city walls enclosed large areas of unbuilt on land. Broad towers rose above the narrow city gates, and over them grew the American prickly pear (*Opuntia monacantha* ?), naturalized everywhere in low lying spots and even on arid rocks. Where the traffic converged on the narrow gates, noise and filth reached their worst, and hundreds of water-carriers on their way from the river with open buckets over their shoulders and horses carrying pails with illfitting lids spilled so much water that pedestrians often had to wade. The air in the narrow illpaved streets was polluted by evil-smelling open drains, refuse from cookshops, dyers' vats and fishmongers' stalls, and worst of all, the contents of the residents' cesspits, carried totally unconcealed in gigantic open buckets out to the kitchen gardens. Along the streets were low wooden houses with their shutters open all day long. Glass windows were quite exceptional. There were very few houses built of stone, and most of them were shut off from the street by high windowless walls. In striking contrast were the electric light standards, which overtopped them by more than twice their height. In the business quarter conditions were somewhat better, but trade was very slack, because Yunnan, in terms of agricultural produce, was the poorest province of China and its mineral resources were almost wholly unexploited. The business quarter dominated the southern part of the city and boasted a long wide street which was being levelled by a steamroller, and a park with a memorial to Sun Yatsen, the spiritual founder of the Chinese republic, wearing tail coat and top hat.

There were only a few Germans in Kunming. Living next door with his family was Herr Stiebritz, who gave us unstinted help. Not far away lived Herr Maiwald, an installation inspector with an electricity company; he rendered valuable service by recording aneroid readings as a baseline for altitude calculations during my travels. Although the salaries paid to Europeans in China may seem magnificent by comparison with incomes at home, they are soon depleted by the need to keep up appearances and to entertain guests, to say nothing of gambling, wine and women, and there is seldom much surplus. The French Catholic missionaries were unable to tell us much about the interior of the country, and Père Ducloux, whose botanical activities were directed more towards plants of economic interest, was the coolest of all in his attitude towards us. The French army medical officer Dr Legendre [1] gave us good advice based on experience gained during his two-year expedition and most generously presented me with a proof, just received from the printers, of the map of the country which he had surveyed. Edward Amundsen [2], an Evangelical missionary who had made a name for himself among geographers by his journey from Kangding to Muli, gave us much useful information and remained on friendly terms until he was recalled by the London Bible Society in the second year of the war.

Our introduction to the French general consulate brought us a friendly reception from the administrator, Monsieur Crépin. He soon referred us to the British general consul, Mr Goffe [3], who then represented Germany and Austria as well. He was alleged to have come here because of an excessive fondness for alcohol, but his compatriots would not say much about that. He did not know the interior of Yunnan, and all he could say was that travel was very difficult and that reliable servants were quite impossible to find. How were we going to convey our baggage? We were taking a caravan, we replied, and we were already looking for horses.

"I think you'd better take mules," was the only advice he could give us. However, he introduced us to the dujun (military governor), the 28 year old General Tang Rirao, and also to the civil governor of the province. The yamen (government building) was situated on the most elevated point in the city, designed in the European style and looking like an elongated warehouse with large windows. Troops were quartered there, and it also housed the political prisons of the "free republic" behind a high wall,

vigilantly guarded from the other side. False notes from the buglers resounded over the city all day long. We arrived in sedan chairs; at each gate the sentry presented arms, and we were led through passages and courtyards to the reception chamber. Champagne and cakes were served, and our passports from Beijing were inspected with approval, although the special recommendation which we had been promised had not yet arrived from there. However, what they said to us was no more encouraging than the consul's words: "The men whom you engage will all run away at the end of a week."

Our first attempts to recruit servants, made while we were still in the hotel, were not very promising. One fellow, glistening with grease from top to toe and reeking of garlic even at a range of several yards, turned his back on us and spoke over his shoulder. He valued his services at no less than 30 dollars [4] a month. Soon afterwards we received a visit from a man called Li, of lean physique and short stature, whom we engaged. He was intelligent and self-confident, and spoke enough French for us to communicate with him. Servants working for Europeans in Yunnan speak a deformed and distorted language which may be termed pidgin French, by analogy with the pidgin English used in eastern China, the first language which every English resident has to learn. *"Moi pacler lui, lui pas complend,"* is a small sample. As my own servant, I engaged on probation another man called Luo, but he soon began to ape the manners of a gentleman, came to work in a sedan chair, showed himself incapable of asking the name of a village, and even attempted to hatch clumsy plots against Li. However, Herr Maiwald supplied us with eight reliable coolies.

Our house and garden were now hives of activity. Waterproof material was stitched into sacks for packing plants and paper, while walls of the same fabric were sewn on to the flysheet of the tent to provide sleeping quarters for the coolies. We bought giant bales of Chinese paper, which is well suited for pressing plants, and employed a horde of women to fold it into convenient sizes. Horses were tried, rejected or finally purchased, but always at a substantial premium, for in the first year the greenhorn has to pay dearly for his experience. One example will suffice to illustrate the crooked tricks practised on travellers not yet conversant with the language. Schneider once sent a man from Lijiang to Heqing, a day's journey away, to buy eight dollars' worth of paper. As he happened to be visiting the local official he asked for a soldier to accompany the

---

[1]From 1907 to 1912 Dr A.F. Legendre led a series of expeditions covering the country north of Kunming as far as Tatsienlou (now Kangding), their main purpose being to find mineral resources. In 1911 he and his party were attacked and robbed of all their possessions at Huangshuitang on the Jianchang river. *Mission A.F. Legendre (1907-1912) Massif Sino-Thibétain....Yunnan — étude geologique.* Paris, 1916, 249 pages, 5 maps.

[2]See biographical note, page 178.

[3] Herbert Goffe (1868-1937) joined the China Consular Service in 1888. While serving in Kunming (then Yunnanfu) in 1915 he referred to a missionary as *"an impertinent hound — an expression quite inadequate to describe him or my feelings."* [page 405]. *"Inside the service, in which he was remembered for bullying subordinates, Goffe was so little liked that when he died in retirement not one of its members attended the funeral."* **Coates, P.D.** The China Consuls — British Consular Officers 1843-1943. Oxford University Press, Hongkong 1988.

---

[4]The Mexican dollar, not the official tael (=$1.40), was the currency in general use. Before the 1914 war its value was one tenth of a pound sterling (two shillings), half a US dollar or roughly two German marks.

man. The official assented, but Li mistranslated his reply and told Schneider that the official regarded the purchase of paper as being no concern of his. Schneider was affronted, threatened to report the matter to Beijing and withdrew. The official, astonished at the effect of his words, must have realised that Li had not interpreted his reply correctly, and related the incident to the missionary, explaining that even if the foreigner required four soldiers he would be obliged to provide them. Meanwhile the man went by himself, came back with a minute parcel of paper and asserted that the rest had been confiscated by the lijin (inland customs). In reality he had split six dollars with Li.

It is a well known fact that, with few exceptions — and China is not among them — railway construction costs the same in all parts of the world, for wherever materials are dear labour is cheap. The railway from Changsha to Zhuzhou in Hunan, however, although built under the easiest possible conditions, was the most expensive in the world, for it was constructed by the Chinese themselves and they stole much of the materials. Yet when a German firm built an electricity station and kept matters in their own hands, even paying the coolies directly, they were astonished to find how little it cost.

A German working for the Chinese Post Office kindly agreed to recruit a caravan for us and despatched two of his Chinese officials to look for men and horses. At last the contract was presented to us: a large sheet of paper with the seals of several merchants acting as guarantors. Fifty cents per horse per day was the going price, but they had failed to set a lower charge for rest days as was customary. An advance payment of eight hundred dollars of the expected total of twelve hundred dollars would, they said, save us the trouble of carrying large sums with us, but it was a nasty pitfall for us — beginners as we were in Chinese business dealings. Our boy Li examined the contract — only because he saw no chance of making anything for himself out of it — and soon discovered that some of the seals lacked the signatures which should have accompanied them. Enquiries revealed that the merchants in question did not wish to repudiate their guarantees entirely, as the request had originated from the Post Office, but that they knew nothing of the mafu (the owner of the pack animals). Out of the advance payment two hundred dollars had allegedly disappeared into the pockets of the Chinese post officials, though it was generally believed that they had really been appropriated by our worthy fellow-countryman. For some time afterwards he told everyone whom he invited to dinner how much it had cost him, and on a later occasion, when reproached with dishonesty in organising the caravan, he replied: "I simply procured the caravan for the gentlemen; if they entered into the agreement, that's no fault of mine." The twenty five animals proved far too few for our

enormous pile of baggage, and Li engaged another caravan of ten animals for the same price as far as Ningyuan.

For the most part February was cool and dry, the temperature fluctuating between $4°$ and $20°$ C and the lowest humidity being 34%. We of course were keen to spend every available day in exploring the district and its flora. Despite the dry winters the grasslands which covered the mountainsides offered a few flowers, among them the little *Viola philippica*, the nodding white blooms of *Gerbera henryi*, the pinkish mauve *Erigeron praecox*, closely resembling our native *E. alpinus*, the small yellow *Crepis acaulis*, a low growing yellow green spurge (*Euphorbia prolifera*), a pink gentian (*Gentiana duclouxii*) and a bellflower with small blossoms on slender stalks (*Wahlenbergia gracilis*). Towards the end of February the dwarf shrubs of the grassland were already in full bloom. A small rhododendron with bristly hairs (*R. spiciferum*, now *R. scabrifolium* var. *spiciferum*) grew everywhere, as did the hairy *Vaccinium fragile* with reddish leaves, the white *Spiraea schochiana* with miniature umbels in rows along its twigs, a stiff thorny *Berberis* with tiny seagreen leaves (*B. wilsonae*) and various species of *Papilionaceae* including the delicate *Campylotropis polyantha* and the prostrate *Desmodium microphyllum*. A characteristic plant of the steppe grassland was the fern *Gleichenia linearis*. Our fellow countrymen usually chose the neighbouring temples as destinations for their outings, the main theme of which was plenty to eat and drink. We visited them in the hope of botanical novelties, for in their vicinity the woods were protected and hence well preserved. The nearest was the copper temple, Jindian Si, which lay to the north east only a little above the plain, here covered with numerous villages. Their houses were built of unbaked mudbricks and their high roofs were of a kind which I never saw again. Besides curving outwards at the bottom in the well known Chinese style, they swelled out into a rounded shape at the top near the ridge, so that viewed from the gable end they looked like a longitudinal section through a bell. The sparse woods consisted chiefly of three species, a pine, a fir and an oak. *Pinus yunnanensis* with its slender pale green needles up to 20 cm long and its long thick male catkins, now shedding their pollen, made a much more pleasing impression than our pines. *Keteleeria davidiana*, a stately tree with dry grey-green needles, resembles the firs, though spreading out more widely as it grows, and is actually related to them, as shown by the structure of its long cones. *Quercus variabilis* was in flower and was putting out narrow leaves with long slender teeth, while last year's withered leaves still hung on the branches. The undergrowth consisted of scrub together with the herbaceous plants and grasses of the steppe, while ferns, clubmosses and mosses flourished along the sides of the channels. Behind the temple were some springs, and the boggy ground around them looked as if it were covered by snow, so dense were the masses of small flower heads of *Eriocaulon schochianum* (a new species). Here and there was a primula (*P. pseudodenticulata*).

Before long we made a profitable three day trip to the electricity works at Shi Longba, setting out along the main road to Dali and Burma. This was one of the better maintained caravan routes, although the horses were continually slipping on the irregular stones, many of which were set at an angle, worn down or hollowed out. On the western mountain ridge we left the road and turned south west, marching over broad gently sloping hills through almost unpopulated country. Yet not much of the forest remained. After being chopped down and burnt, the pines yielded nothing more than a low tangle of scrub, while wide stretches were covered by sparse thorny bushes. As yet there was little in flower, through some of the evergreen shrubs such as *Thea speciosa* (*Camellia saluenensis*) and the magnolia-like *Michelia yunnanensis* bore large and magnificent blossoms. *Pieris japonica*[5] would be inconspicuous but for the clustering of its countless white bells into semi-erect panicles. Everywhere the red earth — either *terra rossa* from the weathering of the limestone or soil derived from the sandstone — imparted its colour to the landscape. We often encountered steep-sided channels with marshy bottoms, bordered by small bamboos and a jasmine with large yellow flowers (*J. mesnyi*). The outflow from the lake, the Pudu He, provided power for the hydroelectric station 30km from Kunming. A day's stay gave us an opportunity of making close investigations, but we did not find much new and on 21st February we returned.

The hill to the north, Changchong Shan, rises 500m above the city in irregular summit cliffs of serrated Devonian limestone strata and later became my favourite outing. A visit to the temple on the Xi Shan, the rock wall which rises from the western side of the lake, took a day. We went there on 1st March accompanied by a party of some size. From the west gate of the city we were towed in a houseboat along a narrow canal to the lake. Not until we entered the lagoon at the end of the lake was the sail hoisted. Chinese smells were everywhere as we squeezed between the closely packed boats, for some of them, filled to overflowing and totally uncovered, conveyed the contents of the city's latrines out to the fields, while others carried large piles of waterweeds. These stoneworts grew in great abundance in the lagoon and because of their richness in lime the Chinese valued them for use as manure. Mixed with mud, they were plastered into flat cakes and left to dry (Fig. 2). The manure-based economy is one

feature of Chinese life which constantly obtrudes upon the foreigner's eyes and nose. As only a few oxen are needed for draught, all the cultivated land is pervaded by the stench of latrines. Yet the Chinese know how to exploit horse dung, which they collect by laying straw along the caravan trails, usually where they run between earth banks or between baulks of timber laid on either side. We met boats laden with fruit and vegetables or with limestone for the city, some carrying whole families and holiday parties and others steered by a solitary woman with her baby slung on her back. When the wind was contrary the crossing took several hours. The view was obscured by islets of reeds, on which masses of primulas (*P. hypoleuca*) were in flower, together with *Eriocaulon schochianum* and later the tall blue *Iris phragmitetorum*, a new species. In the water there were various kinds of *Potamageton* together with *Xystrolobos yunnanensis* with yellow flowers in juicy floating sheaths with soft spines — a species discovered here — and other plants, not to mention the microscopic fauna and flora which were so abundant as to make the water quite turbid. We landed where a narrow spit projected from the left, demarcating the deeper part of the lake, and went up a steep path with stone steps, first through bushes intertwined with lianas, white grapevines and the yellow *Senecio scandens* and then through woodland. The temples were 360m above the lake and from the highest a passage hewn out of the rock led to the left through arched gates and a short tunnel on to the vertical rock face, from which we had a bird's-eye view of the lake and the plain. The main canals, bordered by avenues of sombre cypresses, ran from afar towards us across the wide expanses of land which their waters have irrigated for more than five centuries. Their construction was begun by the Mongolian emperor Kublai Khan and today they are still of great benefit to the Mohammedan people of Yunnan. *Primula duclouxii* grew in moist shady rock crevices. The tall Japanese *Cryptomeria*, evidently planted, grew round every temple, but *Cupressus duclouxiana* grew wild up to the crest.

On the plain the sweet scented beans (*Vicia faba*) had gone over, and with them the flowers of the common small *Primula androsacea* (*P. forbesii* var. *androsacea*), the clover-like *Parochetus communis* with solitary flowers of splendid skyblue and some other weeds familiar among our European flora. After the bean harvest, the peasants were beginning to flood the rice fields and to cultivate them with primitive light-weight ploughs drawn by water buffaloes. Each peasant sows his rice in a nursery plot. When the young plants are about one span (20 cm) tall he digs them up and plants them out in rows in the rest of his fields. The rice field landscape looked totally unnatural and with its patches of muddy water divided by narrow dykes and terraces was far from beautiful. It was, however, an eloquent token of human industry and yielded a

---

[5]Correctly *Pieris formosa* (*P. japonica* is not recorded from China). Symbolae Sinicae, VII, 790.

bountiful harvest. The water was raised from the channels into the terraced fields by water wheels which in these parts were operated solely by manual power. Small wooden plates threaded on to cords fitted closely into a wooden gutter which might be as much as two metres long; this chain of paddles was kept in motion by turning one or sometimes two axles and propelled the water along the gutter.

By the end of the first month, before setting off into the interior, we already had several crates of specimens and photographs ready to send home. The pictures included some striking Autochromes of temple interiors, their vivid colours being more pleasing than the grotesque images housed within them (Fig. 1).

Chapter 2. Over The Jinsha Jiang Gorge to Huili in Sichuan

Our caravan — landscape and plant life of the Yunnan plateau — trails and hostelries — an unsuccessful boarhunt — intrigues of our caravanmen — arid subtropical flora in the gorge

We had ordered our caravan for 6 am on 6th March. It arrived at 11 am and at 3 pm we were off at last. Many of the horses and mules were in such poor condition and some of the donkeys were so tiny that by no means all the animals were able to carry the customary load of 80kg or more. Yunnan ponies are small, shaggy and unimpressive in appearance, but very tough. Nearly all the pack and riding ponies are stallions; geldings are very uncommon and mares are used for breeding only. The mules are for the most part larger than the ponies, and both sexes are used; indeed mares are more sought after and command a much higher price: up to $200. The pack saddle rests on quilts padded with chaff or chopped palm leaves and is held in place chiefly by the breast plate and crupper, the latter being fitted with a crescent-shaped piece of wood and turned rollers to prevent rubbing. The leading animal carries bells on the breast plate, large red tassels on the head harness and a mirror on the forehead. The wooden piece on the crupper is inlaid with silver and a flag is often planted on the load. The saddle itself is of wood, and the load is not lashed on to it but to a wooden frame which fits loosely on its projecting ledges and is not secured in any way. This ensures that any accident will involve only the load and not the animal, that being the mafu's main consideration. Matters are made worse by the laziness of the Chinese when packing and unpacking; they do not care in the least if an ill-secured and jolting load causes agonizing pressure sores, and the suffering which the ponies endure from this far outweighs the advantage of not being driven on with a whip. Any traveller who wished to alter this state of affairs would first of all have to convert the Chinese into new and different men. In practice he has to submit to the inevitable. The animals' sufferings reminded me of the torments

which I used to endure from blistered feet during earlier mountain journeys and on military service.

Sichuan ponies make better riding horses and are used in Yunnan too. They are said to be thoroughbred and are somewhat larger, though still only 1.3m in height. Some of them are really splendid animals, with a powerful neck and chest, a small but relatively broad head, short ears and a smooth silky coat. With their broad upright manes trimmed to a curved crest apart from a tuft of hair on the withers, they give an impression of artificiality, which is heightened by the Chinese practice of "embellishing" them by cutting two or three rings in the hair of the tail near its root, carving steps in the mane and cropping the forelock. With the exception of walk and gallop their gait is abominable, but the explorer has no time to teach them better habits. He must be content to select a pony which is strong enough to carry him, not too old and not too young, and not, like so many of them, headstrong and intractable. The price is from $50 to $100 depending on the prevailing conditions. Our decision to travel on horseback and to have our own mounts proved absolutely right. Riding saves time and energy, and leaves one free to make minor detours and to catch up with the caravan afterwards, as I often did when I required to ascertain its speed for route surveys or if safety so demanded. From the saddle one sees far more, not merely because of the higher view point but simply because one does not have to pay constant attention to the path — which in some stretches is so bad as to defy description — but can safely leave that task to the horse. On wet days it is admittedly not the most agreeable mode of travel.

Li had hunted up another servant to replace the dismissed Luo. He was called Yang, was somewhat less stupid and could speak a little more French, albeit sadly mangled. He was mounted and carried my plane table and sextant hanging from his pack. Two coolies came on foot as plant collectors. Schneider had six of them, and they carried his big camera and other delicate equipment, and also a sack containing a cold luncheon, so that we were not tied to the places which they or the caravan mafu chose for the midday halt. My coolies were indeed capable of standing to attention on the word of command — there are some Germans who consider that this is the first lesson that they have to teach their servants — but in other respects they were exceedingly lazy and they pretended to be more stupid than they really were. All the same they were honest and useful enough and accordingly I did not bother to enforce discipline in mere externals; any such effort would have been too military for my liking and the inevitable clashes would have spoilt my good temper.

It was of course too late to complete a proper day's march, but we were glad to be out of the city at last. A miserably ill-paved path led north westwards through the ricefields of the plain to the little village of Buqi, which we reached in just over one and a half hours. In accordance with Chinese custom, the groom always walks in front of his master's horse, a practice which can infuriate a competent rider and is one of the reasons why the Chinese — cavalry officers not excepted — are the worst horsemen imaginable. Pointing an ironshod stick at the nose of the leading animal, the groom forces any oncoming caravan off the path and down into the ricefields. Though I strongly disapproved, it was not easy to cure one's men of such habits, puffed up as they were with conceit at serving such fine gentlemen as ourselves.

In keeping with the advice given to us we chose a hayloft for our lodgings in Buqi, so as to have some protection from vermin. At the edge of the Kunming basin the bare and eroded slopes rose to heights of 400 to 600 m. Our path led on to a low saddle, recognisable from afar by two magnificent trees. It looked down into another deep basin with numerous villages, into which we had to descend. The stream ran across the basin towards us and bent to the left into a cave which pierced a high limestone crest separating its valley from that of the Fumin Xian to the west. The path continued uphill towards an impressive double peak, the Laomei Shan, also visible from Kunming. Our caravan had already taken the straight route to the north, but guided by Legendre's map we followed the route via Suge. Although this proved to be a considerable detour, it ran over the Dalijing-Yakou saddle through uncultivated land and was more rewarding to us as botanists. Our guide, an object of mirth to our men, was a lean old man with tattered garments and a huge goitre. In the mountains round Kunming there were some villages where a third of the inhabitants were feeble-minded and goitrous. It was in that

district that I later had occasion to ask the way to the city, only to find that not one of the women in the village — they being the only people there — could give me an answer.

This was the flowering season of most of the trees and shrubs. The dense dark green foliage of the evergreen maquis was brightened by the large scented white flowers of *Michelia yunnanensis*, a relative of the magnolias, the pink or reddish flowers of *Camellia saluenensis*, the smaller pseudo-umbels of various white, pink and dark red azaleas, the broad corymbs of *Viburnum cylindricum*, the racemes of white bells of several species of *Vaccinium* and *Pieris*, the yellow flowers of thorny *Berberis* species and the dull red flowers — individually tiny but massed together in enormous numbers — of *Myrica nana* and *Myrsine africana*. Most of the deciduous shrubs such as the wild pears (*Pirus pashia*), *Pyracantha crenulata* var. *yunnanensis*, *Sophora franchetiana* and *Berberis* spp. were thorny, as were the green and brown flowered species of *Smilax* scrambling among them. The fruit trees around the farmyards were also in flower, and on their upper branches were dense clumps of *Loranthus balfourii*, a relative of our mistletoe, now carrying purple flowers. Higher up and on moister hillsides we saw fresh green alders and poplars and various species of *Litsea*, resembling in appearance our cornelian cherry, and finally the most luxuriant forest type of the Yunnan plateau made up of the evergreen oaks *Castanopsis* and *Lithocarpus*, though they and the species which accompany them do not display any special floral beauty. All these plant communities and those of the open rocky landscape are very similar to the corresponding vegetation of the Mediterranean coast, but up to the treeline in the mountains of Yunnan one must always subtract 2000m from the altitude before making comparisons with conditions in central and southern Europe. Lower altitudes are subtropical and have no equivalent in Europe. Just beyond the col at 2425m we found *Rhododendron delavayi*, a small tree with fissured whitish bark. Its round heads of large fleshy purple blooms had opened and had remained fresh under a layer of newly fallen snow.

From Suge we travelled eastwards over a low saddle into a valley which we followed downhill towards the north. Suge and this valley supplied most of the charcoal consumed in Kunming. Sometimes the charcoal burners dug into a steep slope and hollowed out a chamber with an air shaft at the top, but often they simply shovelled loose earth over a pile of wood and set fire to it; this produced excellent charcoal. The valley was at first broad and shallow, but below Santang (our second campsite) it narrowed into a limestone gorge, only to widen again at Xiao Majie, a larger village where we spent the third night at an altitude considerably below that of Kunming. Each day's march was not long — only 20 to 30 km — but plant collecting and detours to viewpoints for survey purposes took up the whole of the day. Here we visited a hot spring at Reshuitang where the shrub community was quite different. There were *Pistacia* and *Photinia* species (*Ph. loriformis*) with stiff leaves, *Osteomeles schwerinae* with pinnate grey leaves, and a small-leaved *Cotoneaster*, all very dry and encrusted with lichens of diverse colours which cried out to be collected. Bordering a stream, a helleborine with yellow-green flowers (*Epipactis handelii*) formed close carpets beneath a low growing narrow-leaved fig (*Ficus pyriformis*), while non-prickly hollies and pinnate-leaved *Mahonia* species with stiff thorns flourished in the ravines. In an exceptionally steep walled gorge we were ferried over the Pudu-ho, which drains the Kunyang-hai, and then went steeply uphill into a side valley. A little mule carrying the ammunition boxes was unable to get round a steep corner and tumbled back several times. The boxes fell down more than once, some of them landing in the water, and in the end the coolies had to carry them. Plant collecting caused us to lag far behind and when we finally caught up the caravan we found them on a cold windy shoulder of the hillside, far from water, the horses having dispersed to graze. Dusk was coming on and when the mafu was called to account he explained that he did not know how far it was to the village. It took the threat of a sound thrashing to induce him to load the horses and march on.

We therefore reached Xinlong after dark, but we stayed there next day as its situation between woods and gorges seemed just what we wanted. Jutting crags of red sandstone rose like vaulted bastions out of the soft green pine woods. Here and there were substantial bushes of *Rhododendron irroratum* with large pale sulphur-yellow flowers, while the pale pink *R. obscurum* (now *R. siderophyllum*) was nearly everywhere. *Lithocarpus dealbata*, an oak with hard grey leaves, was mainly confined to the ravines. A waterfall splashed down a rockface, dividing into numerous threads. Maidenhair fern and creeping mosses covered the wet rock, and in the crevices behind the waterfall was *Ophiorrhiza japonica* (*Rubiaceae*) with its limp tubular pink flowers. That evening, just after the "boy" had thrown out the ever-present onlookers and shut the door of the smoke-filled attic where we worked, the wall began to shake, a board fell out and then another, and there they were, back in the room again.

"What the devil are you doing here?" I asked.

"We only want to have a look," came the reply, just as I expected.

From Xinlong the track climbed up an undulating ridge, and suddenly from a clearing in the forest on its northern crest we came upon a splendid view, framed by well grown pine trees as if

composed by a painter of the picturesque. Far below us stretched the intensively cultivated Xiaozang valley with half-a-dozen villages, shut in between limestone peaks, some of them rising steeply from the valley floor. Looking further to the right, we saw the shapes of the steep mountains on either side of the gorge of the Pudu He, flowing to join the Yangzi, and above them the crest of the 4000m high Qiaoding Shan. The path went down in steep zigzags through the pine forest into the basin. Next day we continued north-north-west over a rounded saddle into a broad valley which ran down from the north and curved past on our left towards Luchuan. I wanted to photograph it and climbed steeply up an illmade path to a commanding summit, but the view was far from satisfactory and I had to set up the camera more than once in a circle several hundred metres across, have tall grass beaten flat and small trees bent aside before I got the picture I wanted — an annoying and time consuming labour. What made it even more infuriating was to come upon the very same view — under conditions much more favourable for photography — from a bend in the track on the descent. The entire valley — about 12 km across — seemed to be traversed by broad low ridges covered with pine forest and bushes. It was sparsely populated, rice terraces being confined to the narrow channels of the streams. The narrow-leaved evergreen *Lithocarpus spicata* var. *collettii* grew under the pines, together with *Quercus aliena*, a species much more like our oaks. Coloured marls — red, white, grey, yellow and violet — superimposed in very thin layers, as often found in Yunnan, outcropped in the valley, especially on its eastern side. The air was hot and dry, the ceaseless wind swept the dust across the sunlit earth and even the low stunted thorny lichen-encrusted bushes which grew on this soil had the same colour as the dust. As we neared the village of Luoheitang where we planned to spend the night we found yet another oak with leathery silver grey leaves (*Quercus franchetii*) forming woods. Now that the dry season had begun, the villages themselves with their fruit trees in blossom, dark green palms (*Trachycarpus*) and bright green bamboo clumps 15m tall (likewise planted) seemed almost like oases, but no peace was to be found within them.

Everything conspired to make our stay unbearable. A fair-sized hostelry might be described as follows. A broad gateway leads into a yard round which are the guest rooms, dark low-ceilinged holes with earth floors, cracked mud walls blackened with soot and small lattice windows made of wood covered with paper. Along the walls are the beds — a few boards laid across a pair of trestles and covered with a straw mat. No one ever airs these mats or sweeps under the beds. On a later occasion, in 1916, when my servant had swept the room and collected a fair-sized pile of rubbish, I ordered him

Fig.1 In the temple of Tjiungju-se
("five hundred genies")
near Kunming. Chapter 1.

Fig.2 Stoneworts (*Chara*) mixed with mud
for use as manure. Chapter 1.

Fig.3 A fig (*Ficus ti-koua*)
common near Huili. Chapter 2.

Fig.4 The Jinsha Jiang near Lagachang
north of Kunming. Chapter 2.

Fig.5 A village street in Jianchang,
southwest Sichuan. Chapter 6.

Fig.6 The abbot
of Yongning.
Chapter 6.

Fig.7 *Rhododendron decorum* in pine forest
(*Pinus tabulaeformis*). Chapter 6.

Fig.8 *Primula vialii* near Yongning, 23 July 1915.
This is the most robust form, and two of the spikes
have abnormal cockscomb expansions at the apex.
Chapter 7.

Fig.9 The sinter basins of Bedi.
Chapter 8.

Fig.10 Tibetans from Djiatshrin.
Chapter 8.

Fig.11 The largest
of all gentians
(*Gentiana stylophora*, now
Megacodon stylophorus)
in the Piepen mountains
at 3750m. Chapter 8.

Fig.12 *Oroxylon indicum*
on the Anning He near Huili. Chapter 9.

Fig.13 The main caravan route
from Kunming to Burma,
between Lüfeng and Shezi. Chapter 9.

Fig.14 Christmas in Kunming, 1914. Chapter 10.
Back row, from left:
Handel-Mazzetti, Hieber, Pawelka, Stiebritz, Schoch
Second row:
Maiwald, Fräulein Fense, Frau Stiebritz, Fr. Schoch
In front: Stutzke

Fig.15 *Lithospermum hancockianum* (now *Lithodora hancockiana*) on the Laojing Shan near Kunming, 2450m. Chapter 10.

Fig.16 Karst on the Xi Shan near Kunming. Chapter 10.

to sweep it out of the door. He replied: "I'll just sweep it there, under the bed!" The ceiling consists of a bamboo mat, stiff with dirt and hanging in tatters, and the rats scurry across it, squealing. Other vermin — besides the three usual genera, fleas, lice and bedbugs, there are centipedes and two kinds of large cockroaches — emerge from the ceiling, the straw mats and the cracks in the walls. A camp bed is therefore absolutely necessary. Any traveller who puts his nose through the door into such a room will involuntarily recoil at the stench, and will probably strike his head on the lintel, as the door is usually far too low. Above the entrance is the Da Lushan, a large attic with a board floor and walls black with soot, which also hangs in festoons from the ceiling. The cooking stove is usually beneath it, and as Chinese houses have no chimneys, for the greater part of the day the room is pervaded by acrid smoke from the fire, which is always fed with green wood. Though perhaps this is healthier, it makes the room almost uninhabitable. Besides this there is the smoke from a smouldering heap of rotting vegetation, which is supposed to keep midges away. At the back of the yard is the reception room with the domestic altar, a cleaner and usually somewhat larger room which is willingly offered to foreigners, but is often separated only by torn paper windows from the second yard. This contains a fair number of pigsties and another necessary place, a description of which — concise yet truthful — must not be shirked. Laid across an open pit, often as large as a fair-sized room, made waterproof by a coat of plaster, are two or three planks or beams. That is all; not even the smallest screen is provided; and let it be remembered that the Chinese diet consists of easily digestible rice. The stench from this pit spreads through the entire building. The children, however, never bother to go there; at best they go as far as the front door, where the dogs, allured by cries of "aa-au" from Mama, clean up the mess. Is the dog by nature a dung eater? In China the daintiest European lapdogs (dachshunds) can be seen to behave as such. Ancient sewage and drainwater from diverse sources, allowed to collect in the front yard alongside other garbage, contribute to the stink, and guttering oil lamps add a touch of diversity. It is indeed a blessing that all this is drowned by the reek from the stables, which usually occupy the remainder of the space around the second yard and are cleaned as seldom as the Augean stables. The animals are often so closely crowded together that not all of them can lie down, and they stand there behind the manger without any litter on the floor, in a bottomless morass. What they look like next morning is easily imagined; in many Alpine districts the cattle have crusts of dung on their hindquarters, but here in China only their backs are free from it. The Chinese never bother to groom their horses, and if one instructs a mafu to perform that task he will, unless he has been trained by Europeans, use a yard broom for the purpose. I always stabled my horse somewhere else and made sure that straw was provided, for I do not enjoy riding on a living dungheap. The amenities of such a hostelry are matched by the attractions of living in it. Though one realises that such ideas as dirt and stench are totally foreign to the Chinese, one also has to accept that noise comes into the same category. Work goes on late into the night and begins again before daybreak, and the mafus sometimes busy themselves with their horses all night long. Everything is done as noisily as possible, and no one gives a thought to the foreigner, yet having worked until midnight and starting again at 6 am, he must have an undisturbed night's rest. Whenever possible I would have my bed put up outside the room, and if a Chinese came and stood beside it at 2 am and shouted at the top of his voice to the neighbours I found that my rest was seriously disturbed. The traveller who does not carefully select the place for his camp bed will find that a cock of the magnificent Cochin China breed will be roosting somewhere above his head and while it is still pitch dark will commence his appalling din, which has little similarity to the clear crow of our cocks at home. One is well advised to avoid close contact with one's dogs even at night, for they generally spend long hours with dogs from the other end of the village. Hens and pigs run in and out of the rooms and the Chinese are surprised if one chucks them out without ceremony, for the pig often has his cosy sleeping place beside the stove, and more than once did I see Chinese kissing one of these hideous black bristly creatures. I have already mentioned the inquisitiveness of the inhabitants, and their unwillingness to be excluded from the room which we occupied. People crowded round our table, pushing each other aside, reeking of garlic, spitting, smoking and belching. When a "superior person" introduced himself, he would waste hours of our time with questions and would insist on inspecting and touching our "foreign things". Nevertheless it was pleasing to find that while we were in the country nothing was ever stolen, however dense the crowds were.

The track from Luoheitang continued over the saddle between two triangular peaks. Further on it passed deep dolines with sink holes, these being one of the commonest features of the karst landscape of the Yunnan plateau. As we had chosen the village of Sayingpan as our next destination, we left the main track and travelled along the east side of the curved course of the stream. We passed through a village inhabited by Yi who had been completely transformed into Chinese, and found accommodation towards evening in the temple at Sayingpan. The headman asked us whether we could use our rifles to shoot a boar, which had for several years been grubbing up the fields belonging to a nearby cottage, so that the occupiers had given up any attempt to cultivate them. We willingly agreed and that afternoon — the boar always emerged at dusk, so he said — we set out on our boarhunt accompanied as usual by a large troop of coolies. We arrived at a tiny hut situated in a field on a steeply sloping hillside. After searching the neighbourhood for plants, we took up positions behind two woodpiles with our rifles at the ready and waited. The sky became overcast; it began to rain and grew colder and colder. Before long we were wet through and half frozen, and perhaps the boar was too, for he did not put in an appearance although we waited until it was too dark to take aim. On parting we gave the poor devils in the hut a few cents, but they were unwilling to take them, as the only coins familiar to them were the old 'cash' with a hole — here, barely five days' journey from the provincial capital! Then we returned along the bumpy road. I chose the easy way and rode on horseback. Schneider's young, high-spirited horse ran off into the bushes and had to be caught before we could proceed. While trying to catch it the mafu fell into a deep ditch and lost his master's walking stick, which was only found after a laborious search. It was pitch dark before people from the village at last came to meet us, carrying pine torches to light the way. Next morning the rain changed to snow, and as the room was completely open the eddying flakes settled on our blankets and sleeping bags and melted into pools beside our beds. Whether because of the snow or because it was a holiday, people came crowding into the temple to place offertory candles in the basins. Their smouldering filled the whole room with fumes which might have smelt pleasant to some but not to us. In response to a gesture from ourselves one of the coolies swiftly gathered them up and put them outside in the yard, where they blazed up in the fresh air and soon burnt away. One can well imagine what would happen in a Christian country if some foreigners camped in front of the statues in a church, and threw out the candles or holy water stoups because they found their odour too strong. In matters of religion there really cannot be any people more tolerant and long-suffering than the Chinese.

As soon as the snow began to thaw a little I climbed Laoling Shan, a mountain to the north of the village clothed with fine *Lithocarpus* woodland. Many of the flowers, especially the larger and more delicate ones, had been frosted during the snowstorm, and I therefore turned my attention mainly to the numerous mosses on the tree trunks.

On the morning of our departure a "boy" suddenly turned up from Kunming, wearing a European khaki suit. He was one of those whose services we had earlier declined. He brought a letter from our worthy compatriot in the Post Office, the message being as follows. Before the journey began our caravan leader had sent him a letter, which he

enclosed, signed by all our coolies. In it they declared that Li, our head servant, was always reviling and beating them. They could no longer submit to this, and somewhere in the mountains they would fall upon him and slay him. He therefore begged us in our own interest to dismiss Li, and said that he had sent us this new servant to replace him. When we told this story to the coolies they burst out laughing and, together with the "head mafu" who had come with them, assured us that they were perfectly content with Li. The whole business was an impudent plot, concocted by the caravan leader who had disappeared when we were in Kunming, to discredit Li, who had discovered his frauds. He demanded an extra ten dollars travelling expenses for the man he had sent after us, but we of course refused to pay.

We travelled onwards, first west and then north, towards the Jinsha Jiang[6]. The route still trended gently uphill, finally reaching a low col at 2400m. Here there was an abrupt change in the landscape. Steep ravines led down to the river valley, the bottom of which was out of sight. Narrow ridges and rugged summits jutted out between them and plunged down in vertical rock precipices or steep, barren, constantly shifting screes. There was still some woodland, but only near the top; lower down everything was dried up and at first sight devoid of plant life. The Huili plateau in Sichuan, similar in shape, seemed almost close enough to touch, yet it was separated from us by the river. Our route led at first for some distance outwards along a crest, and then turned quickly downwards to the right into one of the steep side ravines. The subtropical xerophytic vegetation of the deeper parts of the gorge began at the little village of Zhenminde. Dried up steppe grasses, reddish brown in colour, clothed the soil, which here overlay igneous rock and assumed yellow and grey tones. Herbaceous plants, scarcely overtopping the half metre tall grasses, included a dock with brown flowers (*Rumex hastatus*) and several species of *Acanthaceae*, some of them thorny, with beautiful blue flowers (*Barleria mairei, Cystacanthus yunnanensis*); the taller shrubs and trees attained only modest heights and most them had an umbrella-like profile with branches spreading sideways from their tops. Their leaves were for the most part small and inconspicuous, thick and leathery or covered with silvery hairs. They formed a savannah woodland, conspicuous among which was *Nouelia insignis*, a composite with solitary white flower-heads the size of a hen's egg, and *Delavaya toxocarpa* laden with scented pink flowers, two genera of trees confined to Yunnan and south west Sichuan, whereas *Quercus dilatata* reappears in

---

[6]Throughout Yunnan this is the name for the Yangzi Jiang, a term which denotes only a short stretch in its lower reaches. Jinsha Jiang means "River of Golden Sand" or, more correctly, "Gold-dust River" (S.G.H.).

the north west Himalaya. A little further down we found two imposing trees with deep red flowers which open before the leaves unfold — *Bombax malabarica* and *Erythrina stricta*. The prickly pear, *Opuntia monocantha*, brought from America, formed large colonies together with a cactus-like *Euphorbia* which also occurs in the Himalaya (*E. royleana*); in conjunction with pomegranates they were used to make hedges. *Jatropha curcas*, turgid with juice, yields oil from its seeds, but whether it is truly native remains to be ascertained. Abundant on rock faces were the rosettes of *Selaginella involvens*, larger than a man's hand; during drought they roll into balls, spreading out again when the rain comes. Another species was *S. wightii*, with creeping stemlets covered with shaggy white hairs. Hanging down over it from the ledges were the large fluffy white tufts of a cotton grass (*Eriophorum comosum*). The winding path which led down the steep hillside was well laid out, though in some places extremely exposed. The caravan went past the village where we had decided to halt, because it did not suit the mafu to spend the night there. Darkness overtook us and we had to make our way cautiously along the narrow path which ran beside the river a little further upstream to the ferry building at Lagachang (Fig.4). It was a wretched mud hut with a hot and evil-smelling room under a low thatch, but its location — only 900m above sea level — was so important that we decided to stay for two days. The river was now at its lowest; windblown sand and boulders lined its banks, though in some stretches the rocks plunged vertically right down to the water, hemmed in the stream and created rapids. The southern wall of the gorge was topped by jagged peaks of diverse shapes which altered with every change of viewpoint, and the steep 1500m slope on the opposite side was scarcely less impressive. We searched the lateral ravines, which still contained remnants of forest, and we found other species of trees and numerous woody climbers scrambling up them. A little stream, flowing only in the rainy season, tumbled down over an overgrown rock and had over the years deposited so much tufa that the waterfall, as we saw it now in the dry season, appeared to have been turned into stone. Along its margins grew the creeping fig *Ficus ti-koua*. Though it was common in the steppe grassland, this was the only place in Yunnan where I saw it in fruit — small figs in the leaf axils lying close to the ground (Fig. 3). On 21st March we crossed the Jinsha Jiang in the little ferry boat. At first things did not go smoothly because too many horses had been taken on board. They crowded together and became restless, the boat started to ship water and nearly capsized, and some of them leapt into the water and swam back to the bank. The operation was then restarted less hastily and was safely concluded. Li paid on our behalf a few cents

for each man and each load, and rather more for each horse, with a tip as well. The ferryman probably received only the latter and I think Li pocketed all the rest, for as I later discovered this ferry like most others was public, in other words maintained by the government and free of charge. But we were greenhorns, and were happy to have completed another stage of our journey and reached Sichuan.

The route led at first between dreary screes in the bed of the Shazhuo He gorge straight up towards a row of dazzling yellow rock towers which glowered down from high above. Before long, however, it diverged to the left and climbed up a firm strip of older rock. Everything was dried up, a landscape in shades of brown. On either side we saw steep slopes laid bare by landslides with broad outflows of sand and mud beneath them. Only on the left, where the landslides terminated at the end of the plateau itself, did the rock display any variation in colour. The summits of the mountain range superimposed on the plateau were also totally barren, like those of Mount Dienshan in the north east; all the trees had presumably been cut down to fuel the copper mines. Such colour as the landscape displayed was given to it by the rock strata; up here, lying on top of the vivid red weathered limestone of the edge of the gorge, there was again multicoloured marl in a rich sequence of thin layers with a gentle northwesterly dip. The market of Tong'an, situated at 1900m on a diminutive tributary of the Shazhuo He, gave us lodging for the night. A Lisu prince was said to reside here, but we saw nothing of his tribesmen, who if they indeed lived there must have been far distant from the main body of their tribe. The track continued northwards through bleak barren country over a low ridge and then crossed the valley of the Yangzhu He which flowed towards us in broad meanders. Though shallow at this point, further to the left the valley was deeply incised. We went on over Mount Leidashu and spent the night at the village of Zhangguanzhong, where — for the first time on our travels — we were provided with guards for our baggage because of thieves. Beyond the village we crossed yet another mountain, one of many rising about 400m above the level of the plateau. Towering above their undistinguished contours we saw the triple peak of Mount Longzhu - (3978m) at the northeast end of another mountain chain, also completely bare of vegetation, but more varied and pleasing to the eye. Lying at its foot was Huili, a town of some size situated on the Yangzhu He, where we arrived on 23rd March after travelling through a refreshingly green little valley.

Chapter 3. The Jianchang Valley and its Mountains

Ascent of Longzhu Shan — Yi tribespeople — a Chinese banquet — the Anning He valley — Dechang and the Houziya — difficulties of surveying — Xichang and the mission — ascent of Luosi Shan (4300m)

Longzhu Shan[7] was the first real mountain which we had an opportunity of climbing. All the innkeeper could tell us was that unfriendly Yi (Lolo) lived in the mountains, from which they descended to plunder caravans. We wanted to arrange an escort of soldiers and called on the magistrate for that purpose. He was extremely friendly; smartly rigged out in a bowler hat, he showed how civilized he was by turning aside before spitting on the floor and blowing his nose on his hand. In order to facilitate our climb he entered into an arrangement with a Yi prince outside the town. The prince sent us two of his men, and with two soldiers, a servant, six of our own coolies, two muleteers and four pack animals we set out on 25th March. Our path soon left the caravan route, branched off into a valley on the left and climbed up its side. The bedrock was still red sandstone, but in the coarse shingle of the almost dried up stream we found the igneous rock, green diabase with or without actinolites, which forms the core of the mountain range. Remnants of evergreen oak forest (*Lithocarpus variolosa* and *Quercus schottkyana*, with *Thea speciosa*[8] among them) were still to be found above 2650m, but frost had destroyed the blooms. At the head of the valley the path climbed steeply to a saddle between the two nearest peaks. Attracted by the noise of our men, a number of Yi shepherds with ancient matchlocks had gathered there. Though our soldiers looked frightened, our two Yi escorts went forward and made friends with them. The group was so picturesque that I wanted to take a colour photograph, but they withdrew to one side, and when I set my camera to instantaneous and suddenly swung round they ran away as fast as they could round the corner.

From this point the crest continued in undulating curves to the main summit, branching off into lateral peaks and shoulders to the southwest and east. We proceeded towards the peak on the left, which was clothed with almost impenetrable thickets of yellowish brown holly-leaved oaks and rhododendrons. On the east side of the crest the former (*Quercus semecarpifolia*) formed low bushes, but on the west side it grew into trees about 5m high, and with its gnarled, much branched trunks this forest reminded me of the beech tanglewood[9] of the Bosnian mountains. Between the trees were bamboos

and all of them were festooned with mosses in long tufts and wisps, notably *Floribundaria setschwanica*, golden green in colour where it was lit up by the few sunbeams which penetrated the forest. Of much the same colour was another moss, *Actinothuidum hookeri*, resembling our bog mosses; swollen by moisture from lingering snow patches, its cushions covered large stretches of the forest floor. We followed the path downhill beyond the col. Growing on the hillside were splendid tree rhododendrons with stout trunks 8m high, circular crowns and leathery leaves 30 cm long hanging down from the branches. From a distance they seemed to be in flower, as the leaves were topped with snow-white balls, but these were merely the woolly buds of this year's growth. The tree was *Rhododendron rex*, a species widely distributed in southwest Sichuan though not common.

We spent the night at Jifangkou, a Yi village at 2875m, in a low-ceilinged thatched house, where we shared the only room with the owners and various other inmates, feathered and four-legged. Though we met with a perfectly friendly reception, my attempts at photography were as unsuccessful as those of the day before. On 26th March we climbed up the same path to the crest and then along the latter to the summit, a steep rocky dome at 3675m by my measurement. No flowers were open yet, so I was able to give my whole attention to the cryptogams, and indeed on a subsequent visit these were still the mountain's most interesting feature. There were some mosses which I found here for the first and only time, for example *Dicranum papillidens*, a new species which formed glistening golden cushions with large fruits. Together with a few other species it enveloped the densely branched bamboo stems, which were kept very low and almost leafless by the wind, and transformed them into dark cylindrical broomsticks. Coloured lichens spread over the dark green diabase, nearly all of them species new to science, and the large red berries of *Cotoneaster microphylla* gleamed among its tiny round evergreen leaves. The atmosphere was hazy, and because of the lack of good maps, because I had had no previous opportunity to get my bearings and because my photographs were failures, the view did not greatly enlarge my knowledge of the terrain, though under better conditions it would certainly have been valuable. To the northwest, beyond the Yalong, there was a large blank on the map, and in it I saw some fair-sized mountains, one of them still snow-capped, but to fix its position I needed a bearing from a second place.

Far away to the southeast beyond the Yangzi a high crest, carrying far more snow than our mountain, towered above the layer of mist; as we later discovered, it was the Qiaoding Shan (4000m according to Deprat and Mansuy). The Longzhu

---

[7]Height given as 13,050ft on ONC H-11 = 3978m.

[8] Now *Camellia saluenensis.*

[9]The German word *Krummholz* generally denotes the tangled and almost impenetrable thickets of *Pinus mugo* encountered in the Alps, but Handel-Mazzetti applies it to several other species, and the translator chose *tanglewood* as the nearest equivalent.

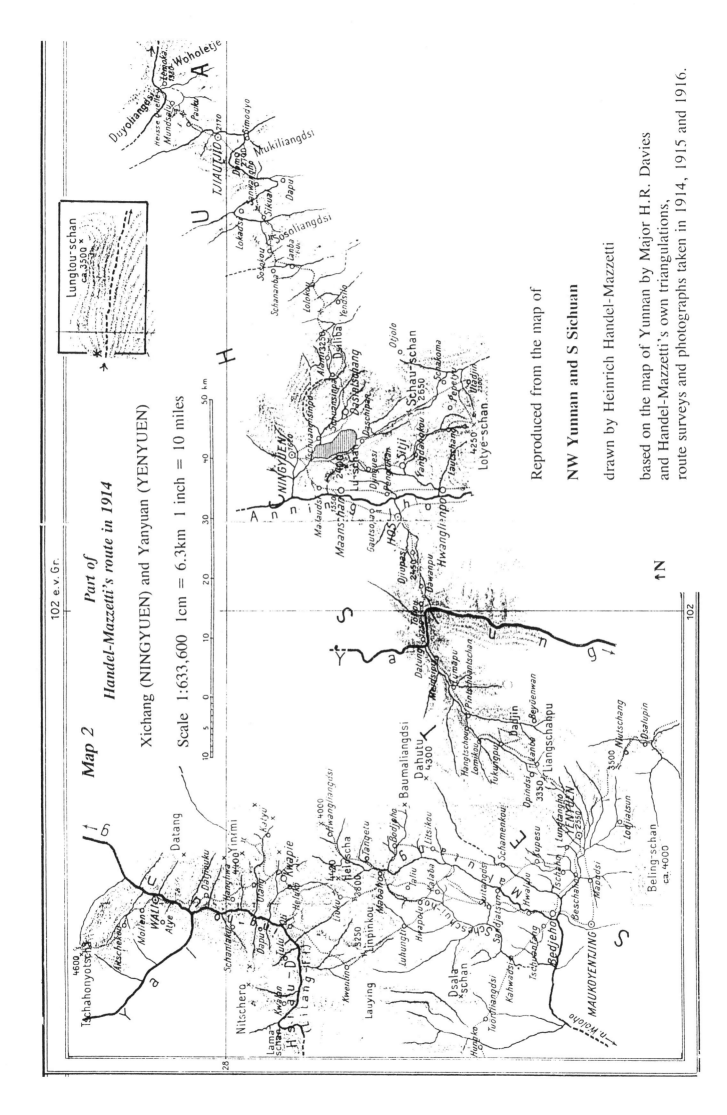

Map 2

Part of
Handel-Mazzetti's route in 1914

Xichang (NINGYUEN) and Yanyuan (YENYUEN)

Scale 1:633,600 1cm = 6.3km 1 inch = 10 miles

Reproduced from the map of

NW Yunnan and S Sichuan

drawn by Heinrich Handel-Mazzetti

based on the map of Yunnan by Major H.R. Davies
and Handel-Mazzetti's own triangulations,
route surveys and photographs taken in 1914, 1915 and 1916.

Shan itself appears to be a laccolith, a volcanic intrusion which did not at first reach the surface and was subsequently exposed by erosion. It was tempting to interpret the curved crest with its three summits as the margin of a volcanic crater torn open on its western side (towards Jifangkou). However, since the crest in its entire length of some 10 km towards the north consists of the same eruptive rock together with granite, and since I found no lava or tuff this seems unlikely. At our midday halt halfway down someone spotted wild boar and shouted for the rifles. I myself saw two disappearing across a clearing in the forest, but they were out of range.

Down at Huili the flora in the irrigation ditches and on the banks between the rice and bean fields was much further advanced than the equivalent at Kunming; a cut-leaved form of *Potentilla supina* and the white *Lysimachia prostrata* were in flower. Leading over the Yangzhu He was a low bridge, its pillars built of round boulders held together solely by interwoven bamboos. On the dry slopes beyond there were a few prizes worth collecting, such as the steppe lichens, *Diploschistes argillosus* and others, forming grey or yellowish crusts. Huili was a much cleaner town than Kunming, though not so animated. Blue and red were the prevailing colours of Chinese country towns; the swarms of people in the streets were clad in blue, and the door posts were decorated with strips of bright red paper inscribed with greetings. The same red predominated in the images of the gods at the gates, and outshone the reddish-brown of the woodwork. Plants of *Rumex hastatus* on the town walls provided a further contrast.

We were conducted to the missionary Père Dugast and he in turn took us to his friend the mayor. The latter paid us two return visits, first with a single friend and then with several, all of whom wanted to see "our pretty foreign things", and we had to turn out everything in our crates. Then he invited us all to a meal. First of all we sat down at small tables along the walls of the room and were served with tea and little cakes. The teacup is made in three parts. The ring-shaped saucer protects the varnished surface of the table, while the cover holds back the tealeaves, on to which hot water is repeatedly poured, while one savours the infusion. Meanwhile the dishes were set out upon a large round table in the middle of the room and we took our places. Seventeen courses, some most tempting delicacies but others more questionable, were set before us. The host urges his guests to eat first, and it is a signal mark of politeness on his part to pick out titbits from the dish with his chopsticks and present them to his guests on deep narrow porcelain spoons. Gravy may be spilt on the table and it may be littered with the husks of sunflower and melon seeds which the guests nibble between courses, but these are mere trifles, though they do nothing to make the dinner more appetising. Rice spirit, kept warm in little bowls immersed in hot water and continually refilled, helps one to digest the excessively fatty items which make up most of the menu, but I always found its flavour abominable. The last course consists of rice and finally, after about four hours at table, tea is served once more.

The host then goes round the table asking his guests "Chi baole? Chi baole?" ("Have you had enough to eat?") and indeed most of them have already given audible evidence to that effect. My stomach is like an ostrich's and endured those Chinese dinners without complaint, but my companion's was more fastidious and relieved itself of the unaccustomed burden next morning in a double-ended explosion. We felt rather surprised when Père Dugast offered a guide to take us to the place of execution; he told us that criminals were to be beheaded outside the gate today, but he himself was unable to come.

On 31st March we left Huili with a small escort of soldiers provided by the magistrate, as the route was allegedly unsafe. We travelled due north again, at first along the valley to the east of the Longzhu range, where the limestone bedrock is overlain by mica schist extending from the east, then over a low col into the Yimen basin, which is traversed by a broad bed of talus and filled with coloured marls exposed beneath limestone and sandstone. Yimen was a dismal little town but had some valuable coalmines in the limestone on the next ridge, which we had to ascend as the track to Jianchang led along the next valley, running north and south parallel to the one we had just left. Alum stone was bought from 30 li away to be calcined at this coalmine. The valley had steep walls and narrowed below Baiguowan. The stream rushed down rapids between huge boulders or wound its way through scree beds, and most of the villages consisted of only a few houses, there being no soil to sustain any more people. We were once again in the torrid subtropical zone. A mountain ridge with two summits, Heshang Shan, jutted out into the cultivated basin at the mouth of our valley, projecting across it at right angles as far as the Anning He, which flowed south westwards along the western foothills of the Longzhu Shan to the Yalong, joining the latter close to its debouchment into the Yangzi. At this altitude the largest trees were two "banyans" — figtrees with stout trunks and spreading crowns: one was *Ficus cuspidifera* with thick rhomboidal leaves marked by prominent veins and the other was *Ficus superba* with narrower leaves and dense clusters of fruit on short shoots. They really belong to regions far to the south and west; here they were solitary, growing near villages or small shrines and specially cared for. Their old trunks arose from flattened aerial roots and branched low down. Some of them had cavities filled with masonry.

Not far below Gongmuying the track reached the Anning He itself. Its valley, the Jianchang, soon narrowed but although its sides were fairly steep it was cultivated everywhere and there were numerous villages. Granite outcropped on the valley floor and the stream from Yimen tumbled down to join the river through a ravine of mica schist, crossed by an iron chain bridge high above the water. In some parts the paved road ran close to the river, squeezed between it and the rice fields which took up all the accessible space, but elsewhere it climbed up the hillside to a height of as much as 200 m, as at the village of Luoyao, where the valley curved at the debouchment of a large side valley which entered from the southeast, close to a high mountain. In some stretches the track had been washed away by floods but instead of rebuilding it the Chinese had simply put up a neatly chiselled plaque with the inscription: *"Until the year such-and-such the road was here, but the water washed it away"*, and left the task of treading out a new route to the caravans themselves. The Chinese are great enthusiasts for memorial plaques: nearly every bridge has one, with the names of the donors who contributed to its erection. To immortalise their names was their first consideration, just as we ourselves in post-war Austria are now seeking to revive orders and titles. Many of the villages consisted only of one narrow covered street, and the paving stones were so uneven and slippery that it was better to dismount so as not to risk the horse's legs. At each end there was a gateway, often with steps leading up to it. The traffic was very heavy, though consisting almost entirely of porters on foot and travellers in carrying chairs. On both sides of the valley there were talus fans and terraces, and at Dechang it opened out into a broad plain, at the mouth of a fair-sized valley running down from the low pine-clad range between the Jianchang and the Yalong valleys. As it approached Dechang this range became higher and narrower and looked more like a mountain chain.

Dechang was a little town on the right (west) bank of the Anning He. A broad chain bridge crossed the river between crags crowned by gate towers. The boards in the middle were wide enough to allow one to ride, but halfway across the bridge began to sway from side to side so alarmingly that my horse hesitated and I was afraid of falling against the open lattice-work at the sides. The inns in Dechang were so bad that we had no choice but to seek accommodation in a temple. Its aged warden would not admit us without permission from the police chief. However, when the latter was at last found the warden became as friendly as he had previously been surly. In Dechang there was a Chinese Catholic priest who invited us in good Latin to visit him, and also a government school run by an Evangelical mission. Classes were conducted in English, but to judge by the tests which the teacher proudly showed us the standard was certainly no higher than that reached by any "boy". The Chinese priest thought little of him. *"Est nomen scolae"*, he said and grumbled bitterly about the Protestants.

On the heights of the mountain range to the west there were enticing patches of green and from its crest we hoped to command wide views over unsurveyed country. We therefore selected an easily attainable summit at the far end of the valley debouching near Dechang — not the highest, but one on a spur projecting towards the Yalong. As soon as the police chief heard of our plans he pretended to be horrified, and said that hostile Yi tribesmen lived there. Every Chinese official trembles at the mention of their name. The Yi are bold and fearless, and hate the Chinese, and the latter are certainly masters of the art of making themselves hated. But while strolling in the fields beyond the city gates I was told by a Chinese woodcutter that there was nothing to fear from the Yi up in the hills, and from what

the missionaries said to us it seemed reasonable to expect that our experiences on the Longzhu Shan would be repeated. Once the police chief saw that we were determined to stick to our plan he gave us four of his policemen and a man with a letter of recommendation for the furthest Chinese village, Gebankou. Not long afterwards he departed surreptitiously, having made the town too hot to hold him. It was not far to Gebankou, and on 5th April, in the afternoon, we set out as planned. The soldiers declared that they would not go past the village, because it was the boundary of their district and the territory beyond it belonged to Yanyuan; but this was a lie, and when we ignored them and rode on, two of the heroes came with us. The valley, which here ran southwards, was filled with scrub and bushes and we took the minor track through it instead of the direct route which ran through barren country. We found the new *Corylopsis velutina* with downy leaves and yellow catkins, *Rhododendron siderophyllum* and, higher up, *R. pubescens* [10]. Other finds included *Rubus henryi* with linear-lanceolate leaves covered beneath with white felt, *Iris japonica* with flowers in panicles, and large patches of *Primula cyanocephala* [11] on moist bare soil. I rode up a 3150m summit called Houziya on the main ridge. It still carried pine and oak forest (*Quercus aquifolioides* [12]) and commanded wide vistas. The Yalong itself was not visible because the slopes steepened near the valley bottom but otherwise the view to the west was most rewarding. The hillsides were dotted with Yi villages. Cultivation was carried almost to the summit and all the people were friendly. One man asked after the Chinese padre in Dechang, whom he knew. Another was driving a buffalo over the mountain, its front hooves fitted with shoes plaited from cord to prevent it from slipping on the wet clay. The Yi who came up from below were all more or less drunk. They all indulged in schnapps which they bought from the Chinese, but drink never made them illhumoured or spiteful. Below the red sandstone of the crest granite and mica schist were exposed near Gebankou. Next morning I visited a little grove of *Cunninghamia lanceolata* on the side of the valley. This is the most westerly outpost of that conifer. The woodland floor was devoid of plants, and was carpeted by its fallen twigs and broad pointed needles, like a pinewood at home.

Leaving Dechang we travelled along the left bank up the wider Jianchang valley, which runs due north. Its river terraces were partly covered by broad, slightly convex talus fans which here and there almost blocked the valley and forced the Anning He to swerve from side to side. In some places the talus fans were themselves cut through by wide deep stream beds, as at Huangshuitang, where in 1911 Legendre and his party were robbed of everything

---

[10] Now included in *R. spiciferum*.

[11] Now *P. denticulata* subsp. *alta*.

[12] *Q. semecarpifolia*.

they possessed. On the east side these streams came from a range of sandstone mountains well over 4000m high, with steep sides and deep clefts and dome-shaped or rather bell-shaped summits, the most southerly of which we had already seen from a side valley above Luoyao. The Yi, originally the rulers of this territory, had been driven into the mountains by Chinese settlers who now inhabited the valley. But they came down from the hills not only to sell and to barter but also from time to time to rob, extort and carry off boys as slaves. The entire valley floor was cultivated in the Chinese style, with terraced rice fields, hedges and rows of bushes in semicircles round the alluvial fans. Among them were pomegranates, oranges, *Aleurites fordii* grown for its wood oil, and *Sapium sebiferum*, the tallow tree, with small rhomboid leaves like those of an aspen, used for the same purpose. *Castanea mollissima* was abundant in the wild state, as was *Gleditschia sinensis*. Pastures with scattered bushes, notably the spiny *Caesalpinia sepiaria* with golden yellow flowers, covered the arid soil. Subtropical xerophytes such as *Bombax malabarica*, *Opuntia monacantha*, *Euphorbia royleana* and *Bryophyllum calycinum* were scattered here and there.

Most of the villages consisted of several groups of houses, often widely separated, surrounded by a few trees. They gave the broad valley floor an irregular dappled appearance which confused the picture. Because the elevations and slopes were so slight, the valley was difficult to survey, though sketching was easy enough. Whether from stupidity, a desire to please, or the sheer superficiality which is part of the Chinese makeup, people whom the traveller meets on the road, when asked the name of the locality, give the first reply which comes into their heads, often the name of the village where they had spent the previous night half a day's journey away, while local inhabitants working in the fields are often unable to name the next village across the river. At Luanfenba the steep-sided valley broadened into a former lake basin and the river flowed over a sandy bed, here and there splitting into several channels. The unremitting wind whirled the dust aloft, obscuring the view and cutting grooves in the sand dunes, which were quite substantial and covered large areas. Above Daxinba the narrow terraces along the valley sides faded out and the mountains rose gradually at an oblique angle to the valley, separated from it on the right by foothills. On 8th April we reached Xichang. Although we approached it by crossing a low col instead of following the outlet stream from the lake, the green vegetation and perfume from the bean fields round the blue lake made a pleasant contrast to the dusty road in the Jianchang valley.

Xichang, or in the local dialect Lingyuan, the chief town of the district, spread out on the northern margin of the plain. The gates were well guarded against surprise attacks by the Yi and no one with a weapon was allowed to enter. Schneider's bearer passed through separately from his master and the guards confiscated his Mauser, though they gave it back to Schneider at once. Xichang was the seat of the bishop to whom we had been recommended.

Monsignore de Guébriant was a shrewd and wealthy man. The Jianchang mission was entirely his work. The large new cathedral had been consecrated at Easter and by the autumn the whole mission with all its outbuildings was finished. He and his priests, notably the procurator Father Burnichon, were held in high regard by the Yi, who embraced Christianity wholesale without understanding what it is. Yet when the Naxi prince of Guabi came through Xichang while waging war against the Yi he likewise named the bishop as his sponsor, though he did not have himself baptised. The bishop was on friendly terms with the mayor and promptly found us lodgings in an unoccupied house not far from the mission. There was also a Protestant mission, directed by Pastor Jensen and Dr Humphrey, teetotal Americans whose standards of cleanliness were in marked contrast to those of the Catholic mission. Reciprocal invitations from the two competitors, though they were personally on friendly terms, often gave rise to comical situations. We called upon various Chinese dignitaries besides our landlord, among them the general and a commissioner who had just arrived on a visit of inspection, both of them very young men.

The northern buttress of the Luosi Shan, the range to the east of the Jianchang, was visible to the south of Xichang as a broad hummocky mountain, separated from the lake by a wide tract of much eroded foothills. Sometimes its snow-capped peaks sparkled in the sunshine, sometimes they were wrapped in wisps of cloud, but more often they were almost totally obscured by atmospheric haze or dust. We soon realised that it was the highest and hence the most attractive mountain within reach of Xichang. Against the advice of self-styled experts we set off unaccompanied, the promised guide having failed to appear. On both Davies' and Legendre's maps we saw a village named Shaguoma, situated to the east of the mountain at 2480m. This seemed to be the best starting point for the ascent and we hoped to reach it in one day's march. We had an escort of four soldiers, whom we ordered to walk with the caravan while we rode in front. We set off on 14th April along the west bank of the lake, its blue waters ringed by vivid green fields intersected by lines of dull green willows, among which were the mud huts and timber houses of the villages. The surrounding hills and mountains were totally bare, the red of the sandstone being the predominant colour, though it was still sparsely covered by dry yellow steppe vegetation. The only exception was Lu Shan, the temple mountain on the west bank, where the light green pine forest had not been felled. The temples were built in steps, rising steeply one above another on the side of the hill facing the lake, as is the Chinese custom in such places. Schneider rode part of the way up so as to exercise his mettlesome nag, which had been too long in the stable, and this gave our muleteer a pretext to say that someone or other had told him that we had ridden up to the temples and he was to wait at the bottom. We wanted to halt in the next village, but the pack animals with our lunch were not there, and it took a long time to find the caravan. Whether or not the incident was purposely contrived, our mafu had achieved his aim and we had no prospect of reaching our destination, but instead had to spend the night at Dashiban, the last village on the lake. From there the road climbed gradually over Mount Shaoshan at 2675m and down into the valley of Puge, which runs south east to the Yangzi. So deceptive are heights and distances in this barren country that no one would think the pass lies more than 1000m above the lake, yet the figure on Legendre's map is in agreement with mine, though he puts Xichang too high. Halfway up was a military post, a little fort protected by barbed wire. Woody plants were to be found only in a few channels. In the main they were the same as on the Houziya, though beneath them was a magnificent terrestial orchid, still leafless, with large solitary flowers of delicate pink with yellow ridges on the lip. It was *Pleione yunnanensis*. The original vegetation had been a low growing bamboo (*Arundinaria racemosa*), now flowering profusely in a little bog where it was interspersed with alders. Marsh marigolds, a tiny blue gentian (*Gentiana robustior*) and a dainty white burnet barely 20 cm high (*Poterium filiforme*) were the first spring flowers in bloom in the bog, which consisted partly of a true bogmoss (*Sphagnum subsecundum* var. *khasianum*). The track ran down into the broad uppermost basin of the Puge valley, where cultivation was less intensive. The little village of Shaguoma was located there, but much higher up the slope to the right we saw a large Yi village, where the local ruler was said to reside. Our best course was obviously to call on him, and despite vigorous opposition from our servant Li we headed in that direction.

The village (Wudajing) was surrounded by a wall which, though built of earth, was considerably above ground level in front of the village and might well have been defensible. The people assembled outside the gate and watched us in silence. The gate was so low that we had to dismount. Most of the houses were built of earth, but some of timber and bamboo, and all were roofed with the latter. The headman's house was recognisable at once, but he was not at home. As Li was trembling in every limb and the Yi spoke only a few words of Sichuan dialect negotiations were difficult and our search for accommodation at first met with little success. But the headman soon appeared, made a deep obeisance and invited us to stay in his house. His cows and buffaloes were driven behind the manger and our horses were installed. The whole house consisted merely of one room with two doors and no windows; only the women's sleeping quarters were partitioned off. There was no furniture except a chest with a lock and some straw mats. Our camp beds were set up in the middle and a fire was kindled on the hearth, which was ringed with carved stones. Tea was offered, and our servants enjoyed it, but we had brought our own provisions. The new and unfamiliar operation of pressing plants provided a spectacle for the village people, gathered round in a wide half-circle of sturdy brown figures. They were much more respectful than the importunate Chinese; they stood up when the headman went through and fell back in obedience to a simple gesture from him. The

Yi were never seen without their pleated cloaks. They wore their hair plaited into a horn in front or bound in a kind of turban. The women wore long pleated skirts reaching down to the ground and a head-dress in the style of a grandmother's bonnet. They all smoked long bamboo pipes. Some of the headman's female relatives had long ear pendants, but otherwise there was not much jewellery to be seen. On taking our leave we offered him money. He refused it at first, but when we said it was for his children he changed his mind. Our men and the soldiers soon made friends with the Yi. They made fun of their heavy cloaks, and the Yi responded by trying to hang them on their shoulders as they sat round the fire. In the overcrowded room, with pigs, hens and dogs crawling between our beds and the baggage, our night's rest was not exactly undisturbed, although there were no bedbugs or other vermin.

In the morning we did not make the early start customary among European mountaineers, because the Chinese lie in bed late and take a long time to cook their breakfast. Despite our urging it was eight o'clock before we set off. Once again we rode, as even for mountain climbing a horse saves energy and enables the rider to do far more that he could on foot. Steep slopes of parched turf led up to one of the many shrub-covered crests running down from the summit. The track which we had to take was visible from afar as a deep channel in the scree where logs had been dragged down. Nearly all the shrubs were rhododendrons, and at that altitude the blossoms were at their peak of perfection. Bushes adorned with flowers in soft white or various shades of pink seemed to light up the tall grass and elsewhere formed an unbroken cover over large areas of the steep mountainside. Here and there were the dark crowns of *Tsuga yunnanensis*, a conifer with leaves like those of a yew, and from about 3300m upwards there was a fir (*Abies delavayi*), at first occasional but becoming more and more abundant and above about 3700m forming splendid forests. This sombre woodland filled a wide cirque which was the uppermost trough of the valley on the south side of our crest. Cradled within it was a lonely mountain tarn, and as this was the dry season its shoreline was a ring of brown boulders. Some Yi tribesmen, up there felling timber, appeared and greeted us with bows. We had almost reached 4000 m when we halted for the midday rest, much needed by man and beast alike. The crest like the slope consisted of piled up boulders overgrown with fir trees, but the horses were led over it without difficulty. All the other ridges were bare, every tree and bush having been cut down and the grass which replaced them having been burnt, allegedly to improve the grazing and kill reptiles. Beyond a hollow was the gently sloping triangular summit; viewed from below it had seemed to be the highest point. Schneider stayed on our crest and headed towards the main ridge, but I was more interested in the hollow with its seemingly untouched vegetation, and climbed down into it through a fire-ravaged forest, clambering over fallen trunks lying in deep leafmould. I was determined to explore it, although our guide maintained that we would be unable to reach Xiqi by nightfall, and disregarding his protests I climbed up the ridge. It was not a serious obstacle and even the horses got over it without any difficulty. They were much smaller and lighter than our own and yet we were continually amazed at their sure-footedness. The Chinese, however, were dogged by ill-luck and Li appeared to be genuinely affected by mountain sickness. This part of the forest was entirely wild and untouched: tree rhododendrons, firs and rowans, an understorey of small bamboos, trunks soaring up to the sky, fallen giants overgrown with moss prostrate on the ground, everything festooned with lichen in strands several metres long. How noble and splendid are the works of natural decay compared with the squalor and devastation wreaked by the hand of man! The herbaceous plants were all dry and withered; only the stemless *Primula sonchifolia* was beginning to open its bluish flowers, sheltered within a resting "bulb" of fleshy bud-scales. A narrow track up a steep slope carpeted with leafmould led to the northern ridge, a flat grassy top where I was able to remount my horse. There was still some snow in drifts up to a metre deep on either side of the crest. The rhododendron bushes here were lower and other kinds appeared, notably the new species *Rhododendron cucullatum* (*R. roxieanum* var. *cucullatum*) growing in dense thickets 2 to 4m high. Beneath it various alpine plants were recognizable in their withered state but as a few scattered firs extended right up to the summit it would be wrong to speak of a high alpine zone. Just below the summit I met Schneider, he having already reached it via the eastern crest. I could have ridden all the way to the top, but my horse was tired, it was half past two and there was work to be done up there. I therefore left the horse behind and hastened up the last part of the ascent on foot. I set up my camera and tripod at once, but the biting wind from the west nearly blew it over, and great care was needed to avoid deviations from the correct level when taking a set of panoramic views for photogrammetric mapping. The view was most informative but during the ascent some clouds had gathered to the north, so that Xichang was barely visible and did not register on the plate. Towards the east I could see far into the country of the independent Yi, a fascinating blank on the map which was to be filled in partly by

this survey and partly by the journey which we planned to make next. Grouped together in the south were the stumpy towers of the range running eastwards from Dechang as far as Emei Shan; like the mountain we stood on they were of sandstone but some 200 to 300m higher. To the west the Jianchang valley was hidden by foothills, and only to the northwest could I see part of its sandy valley floor. The range beyond the valley was hidden in mist, as were the Tibetan snow-peaks behind that, though in good weather they would certainly have been discernible. To the northwest, not far below the summit, there was another small tarn in the forest, and here the fir trees gave away to bare slopes at a lower altitude than on the east side. The aneroid read 4250m, but corrected for temperature and the record at our base in Kunming the actual height must have been a little more, around 4300m; I had never expected to climb my first 4000m peak on horseback! There was a small rounded summit perhaps a few metres higher not far along the ridge, but time was getting short, the descent to Xiqi was 2600m and the distance to our destination was unknown though certainly considerable. Dusk was falling as we reached the valley which led northwest to the Anning He. Its eastern side consisted of limestone with a gentle easterly dip. Our men hurried on ahead, but there was nothing to prevent us from collecting specimens of the interesting shrubs which were in flower. There were not many villages, and the valley had two deceptive bends which made it seem very long. At last we saw men with paper lanterns sent by the village headman to meet us. More and more of them turned up until they made a regular torchlight procession, and as we entered the temple our soldiers presented arms and stood stiffly to attention. The headman, a friendly and intelligent man, soon arrived and of course he wanted to have his photograph taken. Next morning his wish was duly granted and he was photographed first with one friend, then with another, then inside his house and in all his finery, but I took care not to pull back the sliding cover of the cassette. For the interior of the temple, however, I expended a colour plate. A strenuous half day then took us over the low saddle to the south of Lu Shan to the lake and back to Xichang on 17th April.

Chapter 4. In the Land of the Black Yi

Trade goods — bog meadows of the Ziliba pass — landscape of Daliang Shan — feuds — an opium commissioner — a hot spring — remnants of the primaeval forest of Suosuo Liangzi — distant views

In Xichang the bishop had meanwhile been making arrangements for our journey to the "independent" Yi (Lolo) in the Daliang Shan range. The Chinese called them "black-boned" (Hei Yi) and feared them like the plague, and among Europeans they have had a bad reputation since the murder of

the English traveller Brooke [13], though he admittedly

---

[13]John Weston Brooke 1880-1908. In 1908, accompanied by two friends, Lieutenant Brooke slipped out of Ningyuen (Xichang)

tried to force his way into their territory without proper preparation or the necessary experience. The Chinese ventured into Yi country only by special agreement and then only singly, but a few years earlier after many fruitless attempts they had succeeded with the aid of the Naxi people of Guabi in establishing an official with a small garrison at Zhaojue, some 50km east-north-east of Xichang, and made safe the road between them. We chose this route for our visit because we had not much time to spare and because it was still unmapped, although three Europeans, to say nothing of the missionaries, had already travelled it. As the Yi did not use money we took goods for barter, including cloth, ribbons, salt and a small cask of rice spirit, though as soon became evident someone had forgotten the tap. As they were said to be extremely covetous of guns, we thought it wiser to leave our rifles in Xichang, and we gladly dispensed with our escort, who would in any case have been useless. We set out on 20th April taking with us, apart from a few of our own men, only one extra, a "white" Yi (Bai Yi) from the mission staff as interpreter, since the black Yi spoke no more than a few words of Chinese.

The Daliang Shan ("high cold mountain") sweeps up in a stupendous slope to a height of 1800m above the Xichang basin and, further north, rises directly from the valley of the Anning He. Bare and featureless from a distance, it is in fact furrowed by countless channels and ravines. At Daxinchang, behind a low ridge parallel to the eastern side of the lake, is the meeting point of three valleys coming from the south east, and here the real ascent began. In the lower part of the eastern valley there was a long scree fan extending down to the foot of the slope, and the dusty track zigzagged up it. Up at Shuangxunba we reached another valley running in the same direction, and after a further stiff climb we came to Alami, our first night's halting place, in a side valley at 2900m. The inn was a Chinese house and half its roof had collapsed, but the rest of the inhabitants were Yi, who offered us gifts — a hen and a young goat — and asked us to put in a good word for them with the authorities. Two of them were held as hostages to guarantee the safety of the route and though they were exchanged every four months they were now needed for agricultural work. A small pinewood and higher up a few scattered firs and broad-leaved trees were all that remained of the mountain forests which, to judge from the huge rotting trunks half buried in leaf mould, must once have stood here. The shady woodland and the damp forest floor carpeted with moss and shade-loving plants were now only a dream, though they had left vestiges in the form of humus, in some places resembling alpine peat. Otherwise the plant cover

consisted chiefly of ugly low-growing thorn bushes — the narrow-leaved *Berberis sanguinea* and *Quercus spinosa* — with a few rhododendrons scattered among them. Higher up on the Ziliba pass there was alpine sward at 3250m, and here things began to get more interesting. The grassland was no longer a steppe but a real meadow, although neither grasses nor flowers had yet unfolded. Round its margins were low bushes, just over 20cm in height, covered with blue flowers which completely hid the small scaly grey leaves. It was *Rhododendron intricatum*, one of the few species with flowers of that colour. We had reached the watershed. On all sides, barely 200m above us, were rounded tops covered with turf and pine tanglewood. The brooks, two of which we crossed in another boggy patch, flowed south east.

After crossing a somewhat higher col we went on slightly downhill. Sheltered by the steep sides of an eroded channel, a glade of rhododendrons had grown up along the sides of the a stream. They formed small trees up to 6m tall with long narrow leathery wrinkled leaves, their undersides coated with white felt, and heads of magnificent pink blossoms. It was *Rhododendron denudatum*. At a similar spot near the village of Luoluokou we found *Rhododendron rex* in flower. The trees were small and slender, and did not match the stately giants on Longzhu Shan, but their low stature made their leaves look even larger. Proceeding eastwards we soon came to the edge of a deeper valley running north and south. A river of some size ran along its broad green floor, flanked by meadows and marshes, making a much more pleasing and natural impression than the rice fields of Chinese peasants, for whom the climate was too cold. The sides of this valley had also been clear-felled, but far away on the mountain range to the north we saw remnants of forest apparently consisting of the firs which we had already seen growing singly. The whole terrain is made up of red sandstone with only a gentle dip, and the Daliang Shan is not a dome formation but simply a broad elevated mass cleft by longitudinal channels. The track ran north-north-east and crossed the valley near Lanba at 2700m; at the side of the valley there were abundant springs, welling up at the foot of the convex slope where it dipped beneath the recent infill on the valley floor. Our native bogbean (*Menyanthes*) flourished in the bogs, and a heron was strutting across them. The bird is sacred to the Yi, and one of them, who had come simply for the sake of the trip, turned towards it, folded his arms and bowed down.

Before climbing the next ridge we passed through a fair-sized village called Suosuokou. The houses were huddled together on a spur projecting from the slope, and were surrounded by an earth wall. At the wayside was a post with a crossbar and lashed to it was a young dog, yelping pitiably. Among the Yi this is the symbol of a feud. When we passed again later it was yelping no longer. Any attempt to put an end to its suffering might well have cost us our heads. At the top there was a watch-tower, already in ruins though built only a few years previously. We rode past the splendid forest of Suosuo Liangzi, apparently the only untouched woodland in the district; we had no time to stop, but we put it on the programme for our

and travelled northeast to Chao-choh (Zhaojue). There they met a friendly chieftain and were passed on from one tribe to the next. On 24th December, while discussing payment for passing through a chief's land, Brooke *"in a friendly way laid his hand on the chief's shoulder..."* Touching was a deadly insult among the Lolo. The chief drew his sword and struck a blow at Brooke, who parried with his arm. He drew his revolver and shot the chief, but the tribesmen killed him on the spot. Fergusson, W.N. *Adventure, Sport and Travel on the Tibetan Steppes.* London,1911.

return journey. We spent the night at Xikuai, in the house of the headman, a friend of the mission in Xichang. Like the others, his house had only one room and I had to put up barricades round my campbed to prevent the hens and pigs from scratching up the mosses which I had spread out beneath it to dry. This village was situated in another valley system, in a broad river bed, dry and not so green. To the north the river bends sharply back and is recrossed by the track which leads straight eastwards over a large ridge and an undulating tract beyond that. Then, running in a curve to the north in a deep gorge, it breaks through the mountain range between the Muji Liangzi 450m above it to the right and the much higher mountain, possibly reaching 4000m, above Zhaojue. On the undulating ground just mentioned, which extends from the north into the broad valley as far as the south bend of the river, is the village of Sanwanghe, a small Chinese settlement with an army post and ricefields below it. The valley resounded with the lamentations of the Yi in their nearby village and on the hill opposite, where they were cremating a body on a large pyre in the pinewood. Everywhere the rock was red sandstone, but beneath it, where the river broke through, grey clay-slate mud shale was exposed, and down in the Zhaojue depression there were multicoloured marls above it. The village, surrounded by a large quadrangular wall of new masonry, was situated in a barren plain not far from the main branch of our little river as it comes from the north. After joining a few kilometres further down, the waters hurried onwards through a seemingly narrow valley towards the Yangzi, into which they finally discharged almost one degree further south; from this point onwards, owing to the deeply incised channel eroded by the Yangzi, the landscape gradually became somewhat more impressive. We arrived in Zhaojue at midday. Because the magistrate was entertaining a visiting commissioner whose function was opium eradication, there was no room in his small yamen, but he found us accommodation in the temple.

The opium commissioner had not so far found any opium poppies in this part of the Yi territory, but someone suggested that there might be some in the next valley. However, the soldiers were afraid to go there. The officials apparently regarded this "expedition" as having fulfilled their task of purging Yi territory of opium, and now asked whether they might come with us, as they felt they would be safer from the Yi in our company. We therefore agreed to set out together next morning at 8 o'clock. It rained all night and in the morning the mountain above the village was covered with snow. After waiting till 9 o'clock on that cold morning (23rd April) we sent one of our men into the yamen. The answer he brought back was that the soldiers had not yet finished their rice. This was more than we could stand, and we set off with a Yi as our guide. Travelling north east, we climbed over a little ridge, pausing to collect plants among the scanty remnants of a mercilessly destroyed forest along the valley bottom of a little stream and on the slopes on either side. The presence of *Epimedium acuminatum* confirmed that the spot had once been forested. Before us was the Lemoka valley, traversed by a small river which entered from the north west and

left through a narrow defile at the north east. The river curved to the east but the view along it was blocked by several ridges which were not as high as Longtou Shan [14], visible on clear days from Yibin far away on the Yangzi. We had previously seen this mountain in the direction of our route and I planned to get as close as possible, since its position had been fixed by observations from the Dongchuan-Yibin road and would provide a datum for my survey. We had been down on the plain for some time when the officials at last appeared high above us, escorted by the garrison of thirty two men from Zhaojue, and announced their arrival by blasts on a trumpet. However, we made our way towards the hot spring which welled up from the limestone above the river. Like all the watercourses here, the river was easily waded, and its banks were edged with tamarisk bushes (*Myricaria germanica*). We estimated the temperature of the spring as 45°C. A stone wall completely submerged in the warm water was covered with a distinctive growth of algae, especially *Cyanophyceae*. The brick-red *Hypheotrix coricea*, in tough gelatinous layers as thick as one's finger, enveloped the entire wall, while a blackish *Scytonema* and the dark green *Phormidium pseudotenue* filled the running water itself. We stopped there for lunch, and while we were eating our meal the Yi living or working in the vicinity gathered round us, squatted on the ground and eyed us inquisitively. As if they had been dogs, they snatched up the chicken bones which we threw away and gnawed the scraps of meat left on them. It is not surprising that d'Ollone [15], who with de Guébriant was the first to set foot on their territory and traversed it as far as the Yangzi, called them "*les derniers barbares*". Black with dirt, their appearance was far from reassuring, and yet we found them perfectly easy to get on with, far easier than the deceitful Chinese.

I next climbed the nearest ridge south of the defile. Called Wushi Liangzi, it is an outlier of the higher range Woheletie, and rises 325m above the river basin, itself a little under 2000m above sea level. The route then continued to the right beneath Longtou Shan, which was so close that I could make out the scrub oak which clothed it. The projecting brow was not its highest summit, but merely a mass of stratified rock sloping down steeply to the south and east and, as the photogrammetric survey showed, certainly no higher than 3700m, though deeper into the range there is a domed summit which might reach 4000m. To the south east there is a group of mountains higher than the Longtou Shan, but they probably lie beyond the Jinsha Jiang. To the north there is also the range which we had already seen, running more or less east and west. Though some travellers report snow-capped peaks there is no question of anything of the kind. Its shape makes the Longtou Shan the most notable mountain of the district. The Wushi Liangzi was the first limestone mountain which we encountered, coming from the

---

[14] Height 12,820ft = 3907m on ONC H-11.

[15] d'Ollone, Henri, *Les derniers barbares — Chine, Tibet, Mongolie*. Paris, 1911. English translation, *In forbidden China 1906 - 1909*.

west as we did. The barberry which we had seen near Kunming, *Berberis wilsonae*, a small shrub with closely veined leathery leaves, made up the stiff thorny scrub, together with a holly-leaved oak, *Quercus gilliana*, which we had seen in many places since leaving Xichang.

The soldiery marched back into Zhaojue close on our heels, and next morning one of the officials came to complain that our horses had smashed the wood-framed window at the rear of the temple. Of course it was not the horses that had done this but the mafus, who claimed that they had been unable to find any other wood for their cooking fire. The official would probably have said nothing about it had he not wished to show that he was aware of our having decamped.

Next day we began our return journey along the same route and got as far as Xikuai. We met a Frenchman, Monsieur Guérin, an official of the Indochina Railway Company, to whom we had lent a few pack animals from our caravan so that he could travel to this spot. He had not yet encountered any snow, a fact which shows that the snowfall, now continuing at this lower altitude as rain, had come from the east or northeast, as in winter. In Xikuai we assembled a good collection of ethnological specimens including pipes — tiny musical instruments made from three pieces of bamboo, split and carved — food bowls, covered drinking cups with three or four small bamboo tubes through which the drink is sucked up, necklaces, ear pendants and articles of dress. We also purchased swords, crossbows, the head of a 6m long lance and other military gear including heavy cuirasses made of boiled leather, and the chief's brother had his photograph taken in one of them[16]. These articles are still in use and are not antiquated or obsolete; to this very day the various tribes carry on feuds and fight bloody battles, often leaving as many as fifty dead. Most of them were ornamented with round scrolls and flourishes in red, yellow and black paint. This art had survived even among the subjugated Yi in Yunnan, and most of the Chinese saddles offered for sale there were Yi handicraft. As we had run out of trade goods we paid for our purchases with an agreed weight of silver coins, for they melt down the dollars and convert them into jewellery.

On 25th April, just as the rain stopped, we at last reached the primeval forest of Suosuo Liangzi and set to work. The forest lay at an altitude of around 2600-2850m, filling a little gorge and covering its sides as far as the crest of the main ridge. It belonged to a type which we had not previously met — or at least not in such a well developed state: temperate zone mixed forest. There were comparatively few evergreen trees, including two large-leaved oaks, *Quercus glauca* and *Q. engleriana*, hollies, *Pinus armandii* and *Tsuga yunnanensis*; deciduous broad-leaved trees predominated, notably a maple with large rounded leaves (*Acer franchetii*), aspens, the elm-like *Zelkowa serrata*, *Sorbus hupehensis*, *Pterocarya insignis* with pinnate leaves and long hanging catkins, still bearing last year's dry fruits each with a pair of broad wings, birches (*Betula albosinensis*) and

willows. Shrubs included *Deutzia longifolia* and *Viburnum erubescens* with large white flowers flushed with pink. *Rhododendron denudatum* was a common tree in the forest and small bamboos grew here and there. The forest floor and the rotting trunks were thickly covered with mosses, and when I finally climbed down to the bottom of the gorge I found various shade-loving plants in flower, some of them small and dainty such as the white *Anemone flaccida*, *Eutrema yunnanense*, *Sanicula serrata*, *Polygonum*, a golden saxifrage (*Chrysosplenium davidianum*), the new *Primula crassa* with coarse hairs, *Viola moupinensis*, the green flowered *Paris thibetica* and *P. polyphylla* var. *stenophylla*, and others coarse and juicy, such as the aroid *Arisaema lobatum* and two remarkable green-flowered members of the lily family, *Tupistra viridiflora* and *Rohdea urotepala*, the latter a new species; both have fleshy flower spikes and broad lanceolate leaves, but those of *Rohdea* have undulate margins. On a ledge on a small cliff I found a new herbaceous paeony with large bright red flowers (*Paeonia oxypetala*) and near the stream, for the first and only time during my travels, *Cercidiphyllum japonicum*, far from its usual range. According to E.H. Wilson it was the largest broad-leaved deciduous tree he found in China, but here there were only a few flowering shoots sprouting from the stump where it had been felled.

We spent the night at Lanba. Crossing the Ziliba pass next day, we found many more flowers than on our outward journey: the densely hairy *Anemone rupestris*, the dainty *Ranunculus ficariifolius* and *Primula faberi* with its narrow yellow blooms. *Carex rara* ssp. *capillacea*, the main component of the sward, had opened its inconspicuous flowers. On the bank of a stream *Euonymus oresbia*, a shrub with stout quadrangular upright green branches, was in blossom, though it would be some time before its leaves unfolded. To vary the route we took a track to the left down through Yameiti. The rain had cleared the air and I climbed a ridge to enjoy the distant view. Range upon range, the mountains stretched into the distance in superb clarity, first the lower chain between the Anning He and Yalong rivers down as far as Dechang, then the steep jagged peaks of the range which projects from the south into the great bend of the Yangzi, then further away towards the north broad triangles and obelisks thickly covered with snow, some of which, as these mountains are over 5000m, must surely be glaciers and névé, and lastly, directly north and somewhat closer, the huge pinnacles around the source of the Jianchang itself. We spent the night in Daxinchang and by midday on 27th April we were back in Xichang. We handed over our spoils to the missionaries to be forwarded by the next caravan to Kunming; I had now despatched six crates of plants. For my survey I staked out a baseline above the town and on 2nd May a second line to the south of the top of Lu Shan. During this visit I came across a little wood lying in a hollow. Being largely undisturbed it was not without botanical interest. I tried out a new pony and we bought it. I also took a boat across the lake to fish for the plankton and the flowering pondweed (*Potamogeton*). The tall aquatic grass *Zizania aquatica* (American wild rice) is cultivated here, and its young sprouts make a tasty vegetable.

---

[16]See Rock, Joseph, *The Ancient Na-Khi Kingdom of Southwest China*, Vol 1, 222 and Plate 82.

Chapter 5. Yanyuan and the Yalong District

Runaways and deceivers — the rainy season begins — bamboo thickets — government buildings — salt works — karst mountains — the first high alpine flowers — the prince of Guabi — savannah woodland — the Wali goldmine — rhododendrons in flower on Mount Chahongnyocha

F requent thunderstorms now heralded the onset of the rainy season. One day there was a sudden downpour with a violent squall which ripped the paper window, swept the accumulated dirt off the frames and spread it all over my room. As my chests were open and various objects had been laid out for packing, everything was left filthy and wet through.

For the next stage of our journey we had to recruit fresh staff. Schneider's head servant Li was plainly the most competent and we therefore left all the shopping to him. Being almost unsupervised he diverted to his own pocket all the "squeeze" — the considerable sums of money he made by cheating his masters — and the others got none. One dark night my servant Yang, who was totally useless as an interpreter, together with the mafu Lo, who spent all his time gambling and neglected the horses, and our cook Tang, who did none of the shopping and resented having no opportunity to make money by dishonesty, all defected at once. Five of our coolies now offered to take over the cooking and we selected one of them who promised to do it better and more cheaply. As mafu we chose one of the caravan leader's men, while the bishop promised to find a "boy" and send him on later. Then came the head mafu, the caravan proprietor whose services had been procured for us by the German postal official in Kunming, and demanded money as his supplies were now exhausted. There should have been enough to last for several months longer, and we now saw the disadvantage of having made a large advance payment. He had hidden the money in his chest at home and felt confident that rather than turn back halfway we would pay up. However, thanks to the help of Père Burnichon as interpreter, we were equal to the situation. We handed him the money, but only as a loan secured against his horses, saddles and everything else he possessed. He began to recite the litany of Chinese curses, and claimed that he had had to buy horses before setting out and had used the money for that and other purposes, but in the end he was obliged to admit defeat.

We wanted to take the straight track to Guabi via the waterfall on the Yalong at Luowa, but when the aged guide whom the bishop had sent us set eyes on our baggage he declared that that path was too narrow and we would have to take the main road to Yanyuan. On 6th May we travelled south westwards along the far side of the broad valley of the Anning He as far as Hexi, and on the following day we crossed the Gaoshanpu pass at 2500m over the range which separates the valley from the Yalong. To the north and south the range was not much higher than the pass; on its east side it consisted of slate overlaid by extremely friable granite with narrow vertical

bands of diabase and quartz embedded in it. Not one specimen of the granite remained whole: they all disintegrated immediately into sand. The caravans had worn a vertical trench many metres deep and the slopes were furrowed by countless channels. Down from the pass on the western side the range and the Yalong valley 1250m beneath it consisted of red sandstone and mica schist with a steep westwards dip. The steep slopes offered no space for anything more than small-scale cultivation, and we saw only a few little groups of houses before reaching the village of Delipu where we spent the night. The room was crawling with cockroaches of two species: *Periplaneta americana*, long, narrow and reddish brown, and *Polyphaga yunnanensis*, shorter, broader and grey. Next morning I found that they had muddled up all the lichens which I had laid out to dry and had carried off the gelatinous species. The Yalong ran for a stretch of 6 km straight from the west towards us. On the opposite bank there was a little grotto of tufa among the contorted mica-schist rocks; overlying them, high up in the mist-shrouded peaks, was a layer of limestone. Datong was situated at the western end of the river bend. That afternoon I climbed a rocky ridge which gave magnificent views northwards over the sharp steep-sided crests which hid the Yalong, and west-south-westwards into the lateral gorge. Our route led along its narrow floor, mostly on limestone. The ferryboat at Datong was large and commodious, being provided for the numerous salt caravans which crossed here on the way from Yanyuan (its name means "salt springs") to Xichang. The large white blocks came from the brine pans in the shape of truncated cones. Cut in half, they were lashed to the saddle frames and transported without any packing other than a few dirty rags.

Opposite Datong there were tin diggings in alluvial conglomerate, from which large amounts of sinter had seeped out. The scrub and bushes of the Yalong valley did not have much new to offer us, but the side valley was more rewarding. Here we found *Randia lichiangensis*, a leggy shrub with small flat sulphur-yellow flowers, *Alangium chinense* with toothed leaves and rolled-back cymes of scented white blossoms, *Vitex yunnanensis* with large flowers despite its low stature, *Adina asperula*, a new species of tree belonging to the *Rubiaceae*, *Desmodium handelii* with silvery leaves, also a new species, as was *Senecio yalungensis*, a climber with a white felty coating, and *Vitis trichoclada*. A detour into a little side valley on the left near Lumapu yielded the yellow flowered *Paeonia lutea*. It had hailed the previous evening and at 10 am next morning there were still drifts up to 3cm deep; no wonder the plants were sadly battered. Continuing in the same direction past the mouths of several fairly large side valleys entering from the south, we reached Hanzhou at noon on 10th May. From here we wanted to travel northwards through what promised to be interesting terrain — along the western slopes of the Yalong valley system and then over the mountain range to Guabi. Since the mafu made excuses to avoid having to take this minor route, I rode ahead of the caravan and Schneider behind. Following my nose, I kept on along the path, which was in quite good condition despite the recent rain, but before long I saw the guide behind me turn off on to a slippery sidetrack between the terraced fields. The caravan trotted after him and in a few minutes four of our loads were lying on the ground several terraces further down, while their horses went tumbling after them. Schneider at once ordered a withdrawal, but the mafu gloated at the success of his scheme. He must have conspired with the guide, for stupid as the latter was he could certainly not have mistaken the path.

Next day, starting from Dugonpu in the southern branch of the valley, we climbed a little summit called Dajin (3400m) on the southern sandstone ridge. Although it was rather arid, we found more rhododendrons (*R. ledoides, R. rarosquameum*) together with *Dipelta yunnanensis*, a shrub resembling the garden *Weigela* with flowers pencilled with red and orange, and *Decaisnea fargesii*, a small tree related to the barberries, sparsely branched, with large pinnate leaves like those of *Ailanthus* and below them loose pendent racemes of large long-stalked green bellflowers. The northern slopes were covered with a jungle of bamboo and scrub, among which were a few lilacs, willows and *Corylopsis velutina*. I traversed the dense vegetation on the steep mountainside for the most part on hands and knees in order to approach a few trees which had caught my eye, but it was labour in vain as they were of no special interest. However, I was rewarded by numerous mosses growing beneath small rock overhangs, notably the new species *Anacolia sinensis*, which resembles our large and beautiful moss *Bartramia hallerana*. Fortunately the bamboos were not of the kind that lacerate the hands and I was able to cling to them, otherwise the traverse would have been really difficult. The old stems snapped with a noise like breaking china. I got home covered with stripes like a zebra after struggling through part of the bamboo which had been destroyed by fire, but happy to have gained some topographical data, although the highest mountains, such as Dahutu, a precipitous summit reaching about 4300m visible up the valley to the north, had their upper parts shrouded in cloud. Small villages were scattered here and there even in the highest parts of the valley, some of them being Yi settlements. As we approached the Liangshanpu pass at 3350m on the main ridge the slopes became less steep, though they were covered only by sparse scrub. From there the track continued gently downhill along a valley flanked on the right by limestone strata with a westwards dip to Yanyuan, which we entered on 12th May.

The inn in the centre of the town was not bad, though it was rather too open and the populace were exceedingly inquisitive. A bucketful of water thrown through the door at intervals was the only way to keep them back, and as even this had only a brief effect Li tried hot water as well. The magistrate was friendly and invited us to dinner, but he too was insatiably curious and could not see enough of our things. When he heard that we were on friendly terms with the missionaries in Xichang he asked whether we could possibly intervene on his behalf so that he could take action against the Yi, who had recently resumed their old habits of robbing travellers on the road between the two towns; the bishop, so he said, always protected them. The Government Commissioner whose acquaintance we had made in Xichang was so anxious about them that, when we met him on the road, he had brought an escort of no fewer than two companies of soldiers. The dinner was followed by the usual request for photographs. One of his subordinates, whose nose was deep blue in colour, said that he was ill and was soon going to die. He therefore begged us to immortalise him by a photograph, and two years later his relatives presented themselves before the German consul in Kunming and asked for the picture. I took more pleasure in photographing the spacious yamen, which was typical of a Chinese government office and law court. Passing through the gate one entered a large courtyard with prisons on either side. The prisoners were tightly crammed into low sheds, smoking and chatting to their visitors through the wooden bars. A few were exhibited in individual cages in the courtyard, each with a wooden "kang" round his neck; among them was an opium smoker, whose crime was inscribed on this collar. Behind the yard was the courtroom with a long table raised on a dais and covered with a cloth. On one side of the table stood a brush holder made of tin in the shape of an outstretched hand, and beside it were some wedgeshaped plaques inscribed with the judge's subpoenas which were used to summon witnesses. A huge Chinese dragon was painted on the wall at the rear. Passing to one side of the courtroom one entered a smaller courtyard behind which was the magistrate's reception chamber and finally his residence. When newly built, such a yamen, as indeed a newly constructed temple, looks neat, colourful and orderly, but after a year has gone by the cheap unseasoned timber begins to warp and the whole structure becomes loose at the joints, twisted and draughty. Everything is covered with thick layers of dust and dirt which no one bothers to clean off; the paper windows are tattered and full of cobwebs and, in short, the building slips into the state of neglect and dilapidation which one sees everywhere in China.

On 15th May we at last set off for Guabi. Our guide took us first due west to Maogeyanjing, a town at least as large as Yanyuan, and though the detour seemed unnecessary it gave us the opportunity of seeing the salt works. The brine was pumped up through boreholes about 7m deep from below a stratum of limestone conglomerate and evaporated in iron pans in covered sheds. Sixteen buckets yielded a fine white conical salt block weighing about 70 kg. Lijin (excise) was charged at a high rate, and the amount paid was stamped on each block in red. Plenty of it was smuggled, of course, and the population of Maogeyanjing, consisting largely of smugglers and other riffraff, made a somewhat sinister impression. We were therefore glad to resume our journey northwards to the river, though the people whom we encountered there, at Meiya, were no more attractive.

The Yanyuan basin is made up of limestones, marls and gravels and lies at an altitude of 2600m. Three substantial rivers run through it from north to south, cutting channels about 100m deep. Only along these riverbeds and their tributaries was the land cultivated. There were small hamlets and numerous scattered farmhouses, the larger farms having white towers, surrounded by rice fields and vegetable gardens, but the river gravel was covered by scrub — dense thorny bushes of *Pyracantha crenulata*. Further northwards the country was more barren, but the view became more extensive. To the south the basin was bounded by the Bailing Shan, about 4000m, a jagged-topped range of sandstone with a westwards dip. To the north the country rose gradually, from a distance appearing more or less smooth, culminating in the broad massif of the Lingu Liangzi which reaches 4660m. To the northeast the cleft limestone peak of Dahutu towered above a deeply furrowed mountain range, and to the northwest the less lofty Zala Shan projected into the basin. The track led over a broad undulating karst surface, on which several plants were coming into flower, notably *Hypoxis aurea* resembling a *Gagea*, the low growing *Iris collettii* with skyblue petals and a yellow beard, and the orchid-like *Roscoea cautleioides* [17] with dark violet flowers. The golden yellow stars of *Stellera chamaejasme* [18] were common, as they were everywhere on the steppe, but otherwise the terrain was as desolate as a Dalmatian *"polje"*. The only sound was the creaking of buffalo carts, and from afar the surrounding mountains did not look inviting. Here and there ran deeply cut stream channels, though their sharply demarcated rocky margins were discernible for short stretches only and were not easy to trace in their entirety, especially as they often took the most unlikely courses, sometimes running straight through a small hill. We spent the night in the first Xifan [19] (East Tibetan) settlement, a village named Kalaba. We had to use our tent, as their low log-houses were overcrowded with people and animals. The sturdy tribesmen were most polite and friendly.

Here began the real ascent into the mountains. The terrain became as rocky as the karst landscape

of Trieste, clothed with scrub among which were a few pines and oaks, and pitted with countless dolines. As the floors of these steep-walled depressions were not farmed, they were filled with temperate broad-leaved forest. Gaining access with some difficulty, we explored one of these dolines just beyond the village, and found *Acer davidii*, *Lonicera setifera* with coarsely toothed leaves, *Prunus perulata*, a cherry with vanishingly small petals, and, in the rocky swallow-hole at the very bottom, some rare mosses. Given time and opportunity, this would have been a good place to study the reverse succession of vegetational zones in dolines. There was a solitary arboreal juniper (*Juniperus formosana*), but once again the first discovery to relieve the monotony was a haul of mosses which flourished in the shade of some gigantic spruces, firs and oaks growing round a little sanctuary on a col at 3325m. From there the track went downhill a little and we saw in its full splendour the mountain range which from afar had seemed so smooth and featureless. The path continued along a narrow crest which separated two valleys: on the left the valley of the Reshui He, which rose here, and on the right the valley of the Malutang running towards us from the northeast. The latter was a U-shaped glaciated valley, here over 300m deep, with Yi villages on its floor; higher up a narrow spur divided it into two branches. Below us it curved to the southeast and entered the plain through a still narrower gorge. Isolated limestone pyramids towered up from its depths almost to the same height as our viewpoint. To the north steep rock steps, stretching from side to side, descended from Liugu Liangzi into the valley. We continued northwards over the broad main ridge and crossed it at 3625m. A magnificent forest valley, filled with spruces, oaks and pines, including *Pinus tabulaeformis*, a darker equivalent of *Pinus yunnanensis* of lower altitudes, here somewhat similar in habit of growth to the stone pine, together with pale green larches, birches and willows, led steeply down to the Litang river. We did not traverse it, but turned right to the little village of Lingu at 3350m inhabited by friendly Yi tribesmen black with dirt.

Next day (18th May) I climbed Houlong Shan, the main summit of Liugu Liangzi, while Schneider went hunting "wild horses", though he did not see any and was not even able to find out what they really were. From the saddle which we had crossed the day before I rode eastwards over an almost level plateau, past a shepherd's hut where there were some Xifan people with their yaks. After reconnoitring the main peak from an elevated knoll I rode towards it. The undulating plateau had been deforested for pasture. Despite the dryness of the soil due to the sharp drainage provided by the limestone, the abundant summer rainfall had allowed the accumulation of a deep layer of humus and weathered soil which carried a rich growth of plants, though at that season most of them were recognisable only from the withered remains of the previous year. However, the large solitary scarlet flowers of the low growing *Incarvillea grandiflora* were everywhere. Just appearing here and there were *Iris kumaonensis*, the blue *Corydalis curviflora*, the red *Pedicularis rhynchodonta*, the bluish-flowered

---

[17] Though the forms of *Roscoea cautleioides* in cultivation have yellow flowers, purple forms are also found in the wild. (Cowan, J.M. *A Review of the Genus Roscoea*. New Flora and Silva, 1939, **11**, 17-28.)

[18]*Stellera chamaejasme* usually has white or pink flowers, but there is a yellow form as well. (Bull. Alp. Gard. Soc. 1988, **56**, 21).

[19] "Xifan" was used with various meanings. Loosely, it was applied to various peoples of Tibetan affinity; in Yunnan it was often used specifically to denote the people now called Pumi. (S.G.H.).

Anemone coelestina with wedge-shaped leaves covered in silver wool, *Primula sinopurpurea* with red flowers and golden meal on its leaves, the closely similar *P. sinoplantaginea* with smaller leaves and hardly any meal, *Rhododendron intricatum*, *Mandragora caulescens* and a few others. Spreading among them was a luxuriant and interesting assortment of mosses including *Tetraplodon urceolatus*, a species which usually grows on dung. Here it was flourishing on birds' pellets and even on the twigs of the shrubs, among which were *Lonicera litangensis*, still leafless though its greenish sulphur-yellow flowers were just opening, and *Juniperus squamata*, forming a tanglewood close to the ground. At 4215m the last few pines faded out, but a dense tangle of rhododendron forest, in which I again found *Primula sonchifolia*, continued as far as the screes, boulders and crags of the crests. I continued on foot to the main summit of Houlong (4325m), which plunged down in a steep precipice to the north. Although there were still a few snow patches, several plants were beginning to bloom, among them cushion crucifers including the white *Braya forrestii*, *Solms-Laubachia minor*, a new species with large pink flowers, a yellow wallflower (*Cheiranthus acaulis*) and the minute *Lagotis incisifolia*, both of them new species. The distant panorama was clear and most instructive, although the sky was cloudy and the light was poor. To the north the view extended as far as the superb jagged peaks near Kangding (Tatsienlu), an unbroken stretch of high alpine terrain in which much still remains to be discovered. Closer vistas were obscured by lower summits nearby. I returned to Liugu for the night.

Favoured by good weather, we rejoiced in the superb landscape as we descended towards Guabi. The shortest route via Luowa along the steep rocky slopes was said to be impracticable for caravans and we had to make a wide detour. Guabi lay in a steep-walled basin filled with forest and girt on most sides by limestone cliffs; far below, on a ridge among the woods, we saw the yamen with its out-buildings and encircling wall. In the background were the triple peaks of Yinimi, a knife-edge of pale grey rock about 4345m high. The path led down into a small valley beyond Heiluge and then up again for about 500m to the yamen, which was situated at 2775m. The prince, who had been expecting us for several days and had had the path to Luowa repaired, received us with a gun salute, fired off in the yard just behind us, though luckily not before we had dis-mounted. His thin features bore the marks of an opium user. He introduced his small son Fritz and showed us a certificate from the German consul who was the boy's godfather. His residence was a solidly constructed building, mainly in Tibetan style, and had glass windows which had been carried from Kunming. Despite his opium smoking he was still quite intelligent and tried to live in European style; he ate bread, which his cook had learned to bake by watching the French consul's cook in Chengdu, and he entertained us to a meal at which we used knives and forks and were offered a special native delicacy — a gelatinous alga, a small *Nostoc* species from a high alpine lake, served in sweet sauce. His children's Chinese tutor, who had also been invited, made desperate efforts to cut his portion of sucking

pig with the back of his knife. The soldier who had been our escort from Yanyuan was an impudent fellow who had begun to make trouble during our journey and had apparently stolen some small items of equipment. He asked a young Yi shepherd to come with us as a guide, and when the boy said he could not leave his flock he gave him a beating. Now he got his comeuppance; he approached the prince and demanded not just a gratuity but opium as well, and was brusquely thrown out. The latter, being a native prince recognised by the Chinese government and entrusted with the duties of a district official (tusi), was entitled to one tenth of the revenue from the goldmine at Wali, down on the Yalong. A few years earlier, in his capacity as tusi, he had been called upon to take part in subjugating the black Yi, and he had employed a Chinese painter to commemorate his battles with them in a ceiling fresco. His troops and the Yi were vividly and delicately depicted in a range of colours, but in true Chinese perspective, in impossible positions and with absurd exaggerations.

We began by exploring the vicinity of Guabi. The air was far from moist, the hygrometer reading during the day being mainly around 30% relative humidity. The mountainsides were so steep that the altitudinal zones of vegetation were everywhere obvious to the eye as bands of different colours. The subtropical zone down at Heiluge consisted of species with small grey-green leaves such as *Acer paxii*, *Cornus oblonga*, *Quercus spathulata* and the new *Q. cocciferoides*, *Vitex yunnanensis* and *Melia toosendan*. Next came the warm temperate zone of pale green pine forest with *Quercus dentata*, closely resembling our pedunculate oak, then the temperate mixed forest zone, darker green and more varied in colour, then the cool temperate zone of pine forest, the trees, dark green or almost black in colour, standing out sharply against the pale limestone of the high alpine zone. At the time of our visit in the third week of May it was the understorey of the pine woods which made the finest show, a medley of large, richly colourful flowers, including the low growing narrow-leaved shrublet *Rhododendron ledoides*, the splendid purple *Salvia pinetorum* (a new species), *Pleione yunnanensis* and *Roscoea chamaeleon*. Especially round the yamen, the holly-leaved oak *Quercus aquifolioides* had grown into trees at least 25m tall, and here its leaves, coated with brown felt, were round and thornless. Hidden in the forest were deep chasms and bottomless pits in the limestone, and the mosses which lined them attracted my special attention. The pinnate-leaved *Cleistostoma ambiguum* in flat carpets, *Meteorium helminthocladum* with fleshy cylindrical leaflets, *Meteoriopsis reclinata* and *Trachypodopsis crispatula* with squarrose foliage crept over the rocks, their branchlets shimmering like gold. *Neckera bradyclada* was greener and formed similar cushions, but *Pleuropus fenestratus* was much lower. Two climbers, *Lonicera yunnanensis* and *Marsdenia oreo-philia*, scrambled among the trees.

The lake from which the edible *Nostoc* had been gathered was high in the mountains amid huge forests two days' journey distant and accessible only on foot. It certainly attracted me, but before deciding whether to visit it or a high peak of igneous rock which beckoned from beyond the Yalong and which I would not otherwise have had time to explore, I made a reconnaissance on horseback. On 22nd May, accompanied by my two coolies, I set out along the track which we had originally wished to take via Luowa. It ascended through the next side valley (to the north) of the Xiao Jin He[20], which flowed past in a deep gorge some distance away from Guabi. We saw a Naxi (Moso) village and several Yi villages among well preserved forests. The Naxi are related to the Tibetans and were the first tribe that we encountered in China who treat their forests with any respect; the Yi have learnt the practice of heedless devastation from the Chinese. A limestone pinnacle, in shape exactly like the Matterhorn, towered over the valley, the sides of which consisted of clay-slate with a steep northerly dip. However, it was no more than one corner of the long rock cliff of Yinimi. To the left the stream disappeared under a limestone slab, and failed to reappear lower down the valley. The track led up along the north side of the valley beneath the rock cliff just mentioned, over the two cols of Chumehe (both about 3475m) and then down into the Meiziping valley which ran down to the east. Several spurs between the upper ramifications of our valley were clothed with low growing pine scrub, while holly-leaved oak, forming a high tanglewood exactly like that on Longzhu Shan, covered wide areas and made a dense canopy hung with long strands of beard moss over the narrow sunken track, which had been eroded to a depth of some 4m in the soft clay slate. Such arid vegetation had little to attract me and I decided to join in the alternative trip with Schneider.

Next morning, May 23rd, we set out northwards along the side of the valley, at first 800m above the river. The mountain range which forces the Yalong to make its great loop to the north here rises steep and unbroken to a height of 2700m above the river. The splendid domes of Mount Yinimi soared to a giddy height above the track in a series of tremendous rock slabs. Beyond it, grey limestone peaks, no lower in altitude, gleamed under the blue sky, though the range undoubtedly reaches its greatest elevation at its northern end just south of the great bend in the Yalong. Along our path the rock consisted of clay-slate and probably phyllite, and formed a cliff so steep that even birds would have needed crampons, yet the gradually descending track was quite broad and easy for the caravan, although we sometimes slipped on slate debris in the steep eroded sections and stirred up clouds of dust. The vegetation was of great interest. The inconspicuous patches of scrub, yellow-green or grey-green in colour, consisted of subtropical sclerophyllous evergreen species such as pomegranates, *Pistacia weinmannifolia, Olea cuspidata, Quercus cocciferoides, Itea yunnanensis, Photinia lasiogyna, P. berberidifolia* and *Parasyringa sempervirens,* forming a genuine maquis. In some places there were deciduous or even evergreen shrubs with small leaves, many of which here again belonged to the savannah forest community, including *Randia*

lichiangensis, Terminalia franchetii with thick round silky haired leaves and yellowish catkins, *Abelia schumanii* with pale pink bellflowers, *Spiraea tortuosa* with contorted branches and small leaves, *Acacia yunnanensis, Albizzia julibrissin, Ostryopsis speciosa,* resembling hazel but with the undersides of its leaves now clothed with white felt, and scrambling over them all *Rosa lucens,* with white blooms in profusion. In other spots pea-flowers with silver leaves (*Campylotropis*) and aromatic *Labiatae* still dry and withered, formed a *tomillares*[21] community, other members of which included *Vitex yunnanensis* and *Styrax langkongensis.* Apart from certain species restricted to the area, this community consists of plants which are generally found much further to the south in great abundance as indigenous species far away in the dry valleys of the north west Himalaya. Here, however, and in the adjacent valleys, they have managed to survive, as also has the herbaceous flora including the sulphur yellow *Arisaema flavum* with a short pot-bellied spathe, the slender blue *Iris nepalensis* and the sulphur yellow *Anemone millefolium* with finely cut leaves. *Vallaris grandiflora,* a climber with dull yellow flowers 4 cm across stinking of mice, sprawled among the bushes, and the rosettes of *Sedum ambiguum* with flat-topped heads of pink flowers were plentiful on the rocks. As we had with us one of the tusi's men, everywhere we went we received gifts from his own people and the Chinese traders and innkeepers who were subordinate to him — hens, eggs and so on. At that time we always had one or two goats attached to the caravan, though naturally they cost us more than if we had bought them. On the second day, at a hemmed in spot in an arid yellow-grey landscape dotted only with dismal dwarf scrub, we reached the confluence of the Xiao Jin He (in Tibetan Li Qu) and the Yalong Jin He and crossed the latter by a ferry just below it. *Excoecaria acerifolia* was common here, a bush with lanceolate leaves and upright spikes with tripartite fruits and yellow anthers above. The thorny *Cudrania tricuspidata,* which we had seen in the hedges round Yanyuan, opening its yellow flowerheads on stalks which exuded milky sap, flourished on the slope above the wind-rippled sands of the river bank, and on the sand itself we found the small yellow poppy-like *Dicranostigma franchetianum.* A little further down the valley, above a steep scree fan, was the large mining village of Wali, at that time not yet marked on the maps, though already visited by several Europeans. The gold was extracted through tunnels driven deep into the scree fan, and we were shown a nugget as large as a man's fist worth 1200 dollars. Green slate, clay slate and quartz were the auriferous rocks. Once again the Chinese inhabitants were thoroughly repulsive. The magistrate was friendly and tried to be of service by speaking Japanese. The director of the mine was supposed to speak French, but in reply to our request : *"Nous voudrions bien voir la mine d'or",* all he could say was *"Mine d'ol, qu'est ce que est ça?"*

---

[20] The Litang river is called the Xiao Jin He in its lower reaches. (S.G.H.)

[21] *Tomillares* is a Spanish word meaning an open community of knee-high shrubs with aromatic leaves.

A stiff climb up the left bank took us to a little Yi village called Molian at 3100m. Looking downstream along the Yalong we saw the enormous slopes of eroded limestone between which the river is confined. We found *Rodgersia sambucifolia*, a juicy herbaceous plant about one metre tall with small numbers of large pinnate leaves, and here for the first time we saw its whitish flowers, grouped into large flat-topped heads. Another find was the deep red, almost black, *Primula anisodora*. Molian lies on a caravan route to Kangding and next morning we followed it through a superb forest of soaring *Tsugas* and firs (*Abies chensiensis*) no less than 50m in height, together with *Taxus wallichiana*, oaks, *Pinus yunnanensis*, *P. tabulaeformis* and, most notable of all, *P. armandii*; beneath them were cherries, limes, maples and other broad-leaved trees, all festooned with long strands of golden green mosses. The rocks and the soil itself, densely colonized by bamboos, were carpeted by the same mosses and by broad sheets of translucent filmy fern (*Hymenophyllum corrugatum*). Little streams murmured in the forest, and on one of them was a prayer mill. Soon we came to large piles of mani stones and a wooden arch with inscriptions in Tibetan. The Xifan tribesmen living here were under the influence of the lamas. In the village of Yachekou in the next lateral valley to the north of Molian we had a hospitable reception, so we left the caravan behind and went up into the mountains, taking only the tent and the bare essentials. The houses presented a remarkable appearance, all the window frames, door posts and other woodwork being decorated with impressions of hands printed in white chalk. The path soon reached the true fir zone, here *Abies delavayi*, and then led onwards through birchwood, bamboo and deep leafmould pastures in which we found *Thermopsis alpina*, a semishrub with soft stems and yellow flowers, and masses of iris leaves. It continued below a crest through rhododendron forests to the peak which we had seen from Guabi — Chahongnyocha in the Yi tongue. I rode in front, repeatedly compelled to fend off one of my escort who wanted to make the climb easier for himself by hanging on to my horse's crupper. Looking for a campsite with a water supply, I soon reached a col at the crest. Armoured with rock slabs, the peak towered steeply above us and plunged down into deeply cut gorges, their sides marked by recent rock falls. Westwards these gorges led back to the Yalong, but on this side they were sadly disfigured by burnt forests. As the path on the ridge still climbed steeply upwards and as what lay beyond was out of sight, I looked round for a depression which might contain water, but failed to find anything of the kind. It was getting late and we had plenty of plants to press, so we decided to go back to a hut which I had seen below the track. Yaks were grazing there, so there would certainly be water. In it lived an old hunchbacked Tibetan with a goitre — almost universal in those parts — and his equally aged wife. They were extremely friendly, and he produced a nondescript implement which he thought might be useful for pitching the tent, and later offered us yak's milk and cheese. This idyllic spot was at an altitude of 3600m. Next day, 27th May, the sky was overcast, but we set out early to climb the peak. On the deep layer of soil which covered the steep mountainside we found the robust, sweet scented *Primula leucochnoa* [22], a new species with purple flowers, growing among carpets of *Potentilla leuconota*. *Lysimachia pumila* with pink flowers was spreading by runners over the bare earth, while dwarf, densely twiggy rhododendron shrublets (*R. flavidum* and *R. impeditum*) with yellow and violet blossoms grew in close-packed cushions. Everywhere the forests were bordered by larger species of rhododendron with flowers in various shades of pink, chiefly *R. rubiginosum*, now in full bloom. Before the new leaves unfolded, the dainty blossoms, growing in closely packed unbroken masses, completely covered last year's leaves, though the bushes grew in dense thickets taller than a man and many times as broad. The sight was a riot of colour, quite indescribable in mere words. I made haste to ascend a minor summit at 4300m to survey the vista, as the clouds began to lower and had already enshrouded the main summit, which, armoured with black rock slabs, rose some 150m above me. The sharp points of the slabs hung down almost like icicles. Here there was no way up, and though the other side might have been practicable, it seemed more rewarding to spend the afternoon in exploring the vicinity of the campsite. The first flowers were just opening: *Androsace rigida*, the tiny *Oxygraphis glacialis*, *Mimulus nepalensis*, a *Sanicula*, *Potentilla coriandrifolia* var. *dumosa*, golden saxifrage (*Chrysosplenium*), and at the tree limit, forming almost impenetrable tanglewoods, *Rhododendron cucullatum* [23], which we had seen on Mount Luosi Shan, its globular heads of white flowers seeking a place in the sun above the flat canopy of narrow, dark green leaves, their undersides with a brown felty covering, borne on short stalks made seemingly thicker by their coating of woolly felt. Like the whole range, the arête consisted of slate with numerous quartz veins; here it had a north-east dip. Towards the north the ridge became visibly broader and flatter. That afternoon I spent some time collecting mosses and lichens near the hut, at the margins of the bamboo thickets, each of which contained about a hundred stems over 3m tall. As it rained unceasingly and as our stock of drying paper was running low I had to restrict the numbers of specimens which I took. Nevertheless, my haul was varied and interesting, especially as the district had never before been visited by a botanical collector and hence even the distribution of forest trees was still unknown. Indeed, hardly any cryptogams had previously been collected in any part of Yunnan. The rain continued next day during our return to Wali. A patrol had been posted at the ferry to check that passengers were not smuggling out gold. Their commander, stupidly enough, tried to stop us, as the magistrate in Wali had not given us the passes required by Chinese citizens, thinking no doubt that as he had furnished us with an escort of two soldiers there was no need for any other credentials. When Schneider seized him by the collar

---

[22] Now *P. melanops*.

[23] Now *R. roxieanum*.

and threatened him with his riding whip he remained outwardly calm and unmoved, but was totally speechless. We remained in Guabi for two days, during which Mount Chahongnyocha was blanketed with snow and the temperature dropped to 8°C, but then the fine weather returned.

On 1st June we went to Eti, the tusi's second residence, much older and smaller than his first and somewhat further up the valley, but situated not far above the river on an old sinter terrace beneath some rocks of limestone conglomerate from which a karst spring yielded an abundant flow of water. While we were there some of the prince's "soldiers" appeared, having swum across the river with inflated goatskins under their chests[24]. That evening there was a dance in the courtyard of the yamen. The people danced round the fire and leapt over it, to the accompaniment of some quite tuneful singing. Forming a chain, sometimes with their hands on one another's shoulders, sometimes holding hands, they moved in jerks stamping on the ground, while the first man played a tolerably melodious tune on a set of pipes. There was also choral singing which reminded me of the songs of the Cossacks from the Caucasus. Then they linked their arms and danced a varied succession of measures, squatting, hopping on one leg and crawling, and finally leapt over the fire.

On 3rd July we ascended the slope to Guandian, the highest village, enjoying ever more splendid views up the valley. Here, in fallow fields, the first edelweiss was starting to flower — *Leontopodium dedekensii* with thick leaves covered in grey wool. The Xiao Jin He valley was obscured by Mount Lama Shan, an isolated pyramidal mass on the other side of the river, really part of a limestone spur

running down from our mountain range into the clay-slate area, the river having cut a sharply curved S-shaped ravine through the spur. Here and there among the Naxi tribesmen we encountered slaves — peculiar dark-skinned people of short stature whom Legendre calls "negritos". Most of them were goitrous and feeble-minded, and one of their favourite pastimes was pull a thread or a straw back and forth through the mouth or across the chin[25]. The Linbinkou pass above the village was at 3175m. On the southern side there was a U-shaped glacial valley with numerous spruces, lilacs, holly-leaved oaks and other trees. Springs were abundant but the stream which they fed had dried up and the long valley floor, which was marked by numerous depressions due to incipient cave-ins, ended blindly in a ridge. Later during our descent I found a swallowhole in the limestone, hidden among the bushes, and I measured its depth by throwing a stone into it. After striking the sides twice it finally reached the bottom in four seconds, a time which corresponds to a depth of 80m. Below Kalaba we used a stretch of track distant from our outward route, but soon turned southeast straight towards Yanyuan, crossing cultivated valley bottoms separated by broad rubble-strewn plateaux. At one spot, not far from the village of Longtanghe, the side of one of these plateaux displayed some extraordinary rock formations caused by weathering. They looked almost like the carvings of a Gothic cathedral, with earth pyramids, flutes and ledges arranged in long horizontal groups. On 5th June we were back in Yanyuan.

---

[25] These may well have been people of Drung ethnicity; they were a backward people living in the remote northwest border region of Yunnan, who were often enslaved by other ethnic groups (S.G.H.).

---

[24] See Rock, J.F. *The Ancient Na-Khi Kingdom of Southwest China*, Plate 134.

Chapter 6. To Lijiang via Yongning and Yongsheng

We take charge of the caravan — subalpine pastures and scrub — rainstorms — the lake and lama monastery at Yongning — landscapes resplendent with flowers — leeches — a feeble-minded prince — a chain-bridge over the Jinsha Jiang

Having sent off a few crates of herbarium specimens by a packhorse caravan to Huili, we left Yanyuan on 11 June to explore the mountain ranges of western Yunnan. Our route led along the river to Meiyu and then north-westwards over an infilled basin and a low ridge, the latter being the southwest extension of Mount Zala Shan. We then came to a sizeable mountain chain, tectonically perhaps the southward continuation of Mount Lama Shan; it juts out to the south from the Litang watershed and forms the western boundary of the Yanyuan basin. That morning the mafu once again delayed our departure for several hours by various underhand tricks, and that evening, disregarding our wishes, he sought quarters in another village, so that we had to send a messenger in darkness and rain to fetch him to the place where we had arranged to stop — the village of Duer Liangzi, which was on the east side of the low ridge just mentioned. Back in Yanyuan he had held his tongue, as he knew that we could easily call on the magistrate's help, but now he again started to ask for more money. This time it was more than we could stand. Schneider took charge of the caravan and assumed direct responsibility. He got rid of the rascally mafu by leaving him two pack animals, and kept the remaining twenty three for us. All the same we had been cheated out of at least six hundred dollars, and we also had to settle debts amounting to fifty dollars which the mafu had run up with our coolies and other people. Two of his men defected with him, and he declared that he was returning to Kunming to claim the money from his employer — though it appeared that no such person actually existed. The next valley was a broad depression which reached its lowest level along its western ridge. It was filled with karst heath, normally arid, but now putting out green foliage and flowers of many colours. Some of the plants, though dressed in sober hues, were of arresting form, for example *Arisaema consanguineum*, the thirteen points of its palmate leaf, like the spadix projecting from its green spathe, being drawn out into slender threads 5cm long. A few deeply incised U-shaped valleys ran down from the north, but not much of the water in their streams reached the plain. On the western side was the Xifan village of Hungga at an altitude of 2900m, somewhat above the outer margin of the Yanyuan basin. In this terrain erosion produced grotesque appearances, both large-scale and small. I measured a runoff channel hidden among the bushes: over a long stretch it was 7m deep yet at ground level only 30cm wide.

The route which we took on 13th June led at first steeply up the mountainside — far too steeply for our caravan's comfort. Among the bushes were the tall stems and yellow blossoms of *Incarvillea lutea*, on bare patches of sandstone we saw the prostrate *Potentilla ambigua* with its large yellow flowers. Before long we entered the mixed forests of the temperate zone, which were now approaching their annual climax. Thanks to the abundance of conifers and the fresh green leaves of deciduous trees unfolding in the spring, these mixed woodlands were much less monotonous than primeval tropical forests. All shades of green were represented, and the trees varied enormously in habit and leaf size. There were small-leaved cherries and maples with large, lobate leaves (*Acer multiserratum*), both having wide crowns; silver-leaved poplars with foliage in loose narrow crowns and various species of *Sorbus*, notably *S. vilmorinii* with pinnate leaves. Soft-needled firs (*Picea likiangensis* and others) overtopped the broad-leaved trees, while the sombre green yews and *Tsuga* had broad spreading branches. The thick leathery leaves of the tree rhododendrons and the evergreen oaks made a dark background which showed off the flowering shrubs to perfection. Many of the finest plants which adorn our gardens come from the forests of Western China, including paeonies, various species of *Philadelphus* and *Deutzia* with white and pink blooms, *Syringa yunnanensis*, the splendid pink *Neillia longiracemosa* and several kinds of *Berberis*. Scrambling over the shrubs was *Clematis montana* with sheets of white flowers. Thick pads of dark lichens (*Lobaria*, etc.) covered every projecting branch, especially the dead wood, and pale beardmoss (*Usnea longissima*) hung down from the trees in strands several metres long. Further into the dark interior of the forest green and golden mosses festooned the twigs and branches, while other species formed thick cushions on the trunks. However, the most striking feature of the montane forests of southwest China is the bamboo. It formed the understorey everywhere, and at the forest margins and in clearings it grew in many-stalked clumps 3 to 4m tall with short twigs bearing whorls of pale green leaves. In the shade were plants such as *Smilacina lichiangensis*, not unlike lily of the valley, *Lappula dielsii* with forget-me-not flowers, and *Arisaema lobatum*. Flourishing on open pastures outside the forest was *Neillia gracilis*, a dwarf shrub with racemes of single pink flowers, and *Triosteum hirsutum*, a lush herbaceous plant with evil-smelling glands.

As we climbed up we soon emerged from this zone on to one of the crests of the Da'erbi ridge, which is about 3km across and consists of stratified limestone in horizontal contorted beds. Here we had a splendid view of the Yanyuan basin and paused to take photographs. Its river curved round to the south and ran far into the distance before cutting through our mountain range, which reached its highest point in the north where it joined the main chain. In the troughs formed by the buckling of the limestone strata vegetable mould had accumulated to great depths, and here, at an altitude of 3775m, bordered by willow bushes and clumps of pine with rhododendrons and bamboo, were tracts of turf resplendent with low growing herbaceous plants in full flower. The vegetable mould was derived from the thick roots of numerous different species and from the weathering of the outer leaves which sheathed their buds, and despite its dryness it yielded beneath the foot. Growing between the blue mounds of *Rhododendron hippophaeoides* was *Incarvillea grandiflora* with its asymmetrical pink trumpets; beside it were the yellow bells of *Nomocharis lophophora* [26], which might be taken for a *Fritillaria*, the purple blooms of *Salvia pinetorum* and the tubular purple flowers of *Morina delavayi* in dense inflorescences. Held up on erect stems were the stars of *Anemone demissa*, *A. coelestina* and *A. rupestris*, together with the orange yellow blossoms of *Taraxacum eriopodum*. *Mandragora caulescens*, its short juicy stem topped with a tuft of hairy leaves, put out long leafless spreading flower stalks, often in great numbers, ending in large nodding brownish-green bells. The thickets consisted of willows (*Salix tenella*) with *Sorbus vilmorinii*, *Lonicera chlamydata*, *Sibiraea levigata* and other shrubs. At their margins and extending deep into their shadowy interiors we saw tall slender plants of *Meconopsis forrestii* with blue flowers, a *Corydalis* (probably *C. cheirifolia*) and the yellow *C. yunnanensis*, more than one species of *Smilacina* with racemes of whitish or greenish brown flowers, and *Arisaema wilsonii* with purplish brown spathes up to 25cm long.

As we began the steep descent on the west side another superb vista opened before our eyes. The rain had cleared the air, and only in the distance were the mountains high enough to tower into the clouds. We gazed down over a broad depression filled with wooded crests all of much the same height (3500m) and all built of almost horizontally stratified rock. Between the crests were patches of uneven ground, and the landscape was incised by the narrow valleys of the rivers which traversed it. Further away was a range projecting above the forests and breaking off sharply at a corner to the south of Yongning [27]. Behind that was a tall mountain of paler rock, probably Xuechou Shan in the Yangzi loop, and to the left there were a few dark spires belonging to the gigantic Lijiang range, the rest of which was hidden in mist. Before us to the west an impressive rounded summit rose out of the depths; it was Shizu Shan and marked the position of Yongning, our next destination. Passing two Yi villages, the track plunged steeply downwards, losing 1200m in altitude, and then ran almost level for some distance between screes and huge boulders along a dried up stream bed, where it would have been suicidal to have stayed on horseback. Pelted by thunderstorms, we arrived as dusk was falling at the lonely ferry which crossed the Wolue He where it flowed between cliffs of limestone and tufa in a gorge with an attractive shrub vegetation. The Yanyuan river (Yanjing He) joins the Wolue He here, and they run northwards together to the Litang. I felt ready to take an oath that this would be the last journey I would undertake in remote mountains, little dreaming how well I was to get to know the rainy season in the Yunnan Alps. About an hour later we reached the village of Wolue He, too tired to do anything except stack our rich booty in separate piles, one for each place. If one

omits this task, the memory will be clouded by even a single night's sleep. The work of arranging the specimens between paper we left, however, until the following morning.

Next evening, after a steep climb up paths on slippery clay, we reached Fumadi, another Chinese village, though the surrounding population was Yi. Riding onwards over a broad ridge covered with spruce forest, at an altitude of 3300m, we were left in no doubt that the rainy season had begun. The ridge was built of limestone and sandstone, and the rocks were so hard that the streams had barely cut into them. A short distance further on the meadow flora at this fairly lowlying spot had now developed to a stage where the blue *Strobilanthes versicolor* was flowering in abundance though the plants were still quite low. With it were the blue flowers of *Iris bulleyana* together with a small golden brown orchid, *Oreorchis erythrochrysea*, a new species. On the descent we passed through almost pure woods of *Pinus armandii*, a tall pine with bluish green needles and cones 20cm in length and 12cm in diameter. Beneath it was bamboo undergrowth. Further down we encountered a fair-sized grove of *Mahonia alexandri*, each trunk rising to about 3m before branching, and carrying large spiny pinnate leaves and multiple racemes of yellow flowers. Two streams, coming from north and northwest, joined here. The scattered Naxi village of Gaitiu lay in a cultivated though rather dry basin. We soon left the stream which came from Yongning, curving round in a wide branch to the north, and ascended gradually up a tributary which was the outflow from the Chuosuo (Lugu Hu) lake. Here on the sandstone, and later even more frequently, we found some distinctive woods composed of aspens, *Pinus yunnanensis* and the large-leaved *Quercus dentata*. The trunks of these oaks were often completely clothed with *Drynaria delavayi*, a fern which looked as if it were an enlarged version of our polypody with broader fronds. However, beneath these fronds it bore faintly lobed epiphytic leaves, already brown and withered, which closely covered the tree trunks, their function being to collect water and nutrients for the thick creeping rhizomes. Before long the valley levelled out and its floor became broad and flat, filled with black marshy soil which supported rich green meadows. The slender yellow *Iris forrestii* grew in large clumps among tall red primulas now coming into flower. This plant – *Primula beesiana* — is one of a section found in southwest China. All its members have tall scapes with several superimposed whorls of flowers, in some species flat and open, in others bellshaped, ranging in hue from pink to carmine. The wide valley skirted round the left of the lake, and on a lateral stream we saw the yamen of the Naxi prince of Chuosuo, a timber farmhouse where the old gentleman, to whom we had an introduction from the prince of Guabi, gave us a friendly reception.

Next day (17th June) we watched the rain from our rooms, which had been papered with sheets from an English newspaper — chiefly pictorial advertisements — and dried our pressed plants over a fire in the covered gallery outside the house, while a large brown pool in the yard threatened to flood into it. On 18th June the sun came out again and we went out on Lake Lugu Hu in dugout canoes. Set among forested hills, its waters were deep blue, and

---

[26] Now *Lilium lophophorum*.

[27] There were two towns called Yonging, this one in Yunnan and another in Sichuan (SGH).

the stones and even the bubbles coming up from the bottom shared the same hue. Festoons of algae swathed the submerged limestone, and my task was to collect them for preserving in formalin, and to fish for plankton. Floating on the water in large masses were the handsome white flowers of the new *Bootia crispa*, each on a slender stalk, and when we explored the boggy meadows we found much of interest. From the meadow itself, where the ground was fairly firm — although my horse sank up to the knees before I realised what was happening — down to the water's edge there were three distinct zones: first a ring of *Iris forrestii* with *Anemone rivularis*, an *Artemisia*, *Erigeron praecox*, *Potentilla griffithii*, *Poterium filiforme*, a *Festuca*, a little violet and our own bird's-foot trefoil; then on the black soil masses of silverweed, shepherd's purse, plantains, three small knotweeds (*Polygonum*), sedges, *Lysimachia parvifolia*, *Gnaphalium multiceps*, *Salvia plebeia*, a little gentian and *Pedicularis densispica* — a plant community much the same as that on the banks between the ricefields; and lastly, on the wet mud, *Rorippa islandica* (*R. palustris*), *Senecio oryzetorum*, *Chenopodium* spp. and *Bothriospermum tenellum*. Growing in the dykes were *Acorus calamus*, marsh marigold, water crowfoot, arrowhead, water plantain and *Hippuris*. At the northern side of the lake sandy clay-slate, alternating with bands of light brown marl and shale, dipped gently northwards, though interrupted by limestone reefs, and on Shizu Shan — a mountain of impressive shape — overlain by massive beds of limestone. Next day we took a track which at first went up past some Xifan villages on to the mountain; then it curved off to the left over a little saddle into a valley with a dry streambed, leading gradually downhill into the Yongning basin. The boundary between Sichuan and Yunnan ran through the lake, and we were now in the latter. Low spurs projected into the basin, and abundant springs rose at their extremities; here again we found boggy meadows with a rich flora, notably a new smooth-leaved dock, *Rumex yungningensis*. The local ruler, a friend of the tusi of Guabi, had sent two mounted men to meet us and we soon arrived at his village, a long line of large log-houses at the foot of the mountain, cut in two by the river which broke through from the south and was crossed by a large Chinese bridge. The paths were deep in mud, and it was another halfhour before we reached the large monastery, situated just on the far border of the plain.

We were received by the abbot of Yongning, a man of giant stature dressed in the red habit of a monk, his enormous skull smooth shaven (Fig.6). He was of Naxi origin but completely Tibetanized. His office was hereditary; two of his sons were being trained as lamas. The monastery was built in the form of a quadrangle with the temple in the middle. In front of it was a courtyard with beautifully decorated stone fountains, but the massive masonry of the temple and its golden pinnacle towered above all the rest. Its huge door was concealed by curtains, and dim light penetrated into the interior through a few small windows high up and through the gaps in the brushwood which filled the space beneath the

roof. The great image of Buddha in the middle was new and there was nothing else of much value. The lamas lived in cells in the outer buildings of the monastery, which were girdled by wooden galleries at first floor level. They were said to number some two hundred, but only twenty were present at the time, the rest being away on summer holiday, collecting money or on other errands. We were housed in the main building next to the abbot's quarters. The balcony in front of our rooms was adorned with a large wall painting of Lhasa, where the abbot had studied for ten years. The lamasery was situated at the foot of a steep, more or less free-standing hill some 550m in height, consisting of sandstone with limestone outcrops. Its name was He'er and I climbed it next day. Clear weather enabled me to survey the entire surroundings. Everything was green: the meadows and the fields of oats and barley down in the basin at 2725m, through which the silver thread of the river wound in broad meanders; the heath pastures, an open plant community with few grasses but rich in sedges and low growing herbs, which covered Mount He'er and all the low rounded tongues or spurs projecting into the plain on its distant side; and above them the forests, in which the fir zone stood out sharply as a blackish line at the very top. There were a few cliffs and peaks of pale grey limestone, notably the south-facing precipice of Shizi Shan to the east and the three rounded summits of Mount Waha towering above the forest to the south. To the north east a dark chain of pointed spires separated the whole of the sunken woodland area from the Litang river valley, in which Muli lay, and to the north, gleaming under fresh snow, was Gonshiga (4900m), a steep summit beyond the forests, on which I was destined to set foot next year. The wooden huts of the Naxi and Xifan villages blended inconspicuously into their surroundings at the edges of the plain. At midday, after my return, I was suddenly attacked by dysentery with fever and faintness, which prevented me from climbing Mount Waha but which soon disappeared without any after-effects. The Naxi[28] people of this district constituted a separate tribe and called themselves Lüdi. Their language was closer to that spoken in Guabi than that of Lijiang, and their understanding of the latter was far from perfect. Besides the abbot they had a temporal head who resided at the other end of the village, and still further away there was a Chinese official with a few soldiers, who was said to find life here not particularly agreeable, though he was to all appearances on good terms with the lama. We visited them both. I measured another baseline on the plain for my map. Schneider bartered a rifle, a clock and some other items with the lama in exchange for ethnological objects, while I was given a little flat-nosed dog for the promise of an Autochrome photograph. On 23rd June we set off once more, to journey along largely unknown roads via Yongsheng to Lijiang.

---

[28] The Chinese call them Moso, a name which is faintly contemptuous and is disliked by the tribal people (H-M's note).

The track ran southwards on to a low elevation to the east, bypassing the river valley which entered the plain through a little curving gorge. The vegetation was now hastening with giant strides towards its climax, or, to put it more correctly, in attaining their climax the tallest plants overwhelmed and hid their shorter neighbours in a continuous display. The whole forest was lit up by the low trees of *Rhododendron decorum*, covered with heads of large beautifully shaped white flowers (Fig.7). The low growing anemones had withered and were now overshadowed by taller herbaceous plants 20cm or more in height, including a tall dark red sage (*Salvia castanea*), the scabious relative *Morina delavayi* with prickly hairs on its leaves and carmine-red flowers several centimetres long, several species of lady's slipper, notably the dull purple *Cypripedilum himalaicum* with flowers almost the size of a man's fist, and *Leontopodium dedekensii*. In little hollows and dolines and between the bushes tall-growing herbaceous plants were shooting up and forming a third tier or storey, among them several species of *Ligularia* with large ovate or kidney-shaped leaves and long panicles or racemes of golden yellow flowers (here chiefly *L. vellea*) and our native *Chamaenerion angustifolium*. When we reached the river once more it was splashing down tiny waterfalls over outcrops of almost horizontally bedded limestone into blue pools in a delightful forest valley flanked by a low range to the east and the much higher slopes of the Waha chain to the west. Before long we came upon some boggy meadows separated from the river by a line of sea-buckthorn trees (*Hippophae*) and *Euonymus lichiangensis* with winged stems. The meadow flora was superb: red primulas and louseworts, the yellow *Iris forrestii*, the blue *I. bulleyana* and *Strobilanthes versicolor*, *Euphorbia nematocypha*, large and bushy, white anemones and *Aletris*. In these delightful surroundings, situated as picturesquely as a village in the Alps, was Mudijin, the Xifan village where we were to spend the night. The valley then narrowed into a gorge filled with forest, bamboo and magnificent flowers. Flourishing mainly under the bamboos was the gorgeous *Nomocharis mairei*, its flat white flowers flecked with purple and its inner petals delicately toothed. But now in the rainy season we encountered some of the annoyances of this zone: tiny biting flies (?*Simulium*) and a species of leech with longitudinal brown and green stripes which lay in wait on herbaceous plants or bushes, stretched itself out, as thin as a hair and as long as a man's finger, towards the passer-by, and in an instant attached itself to one's clothing or the horse in its quest for blood. Its bite was quite painless and was only just perceptible if one was watching it closely. Yet the wound went on bleeding for almost half an hour, so that everything was smeared with blood — indeed, that was the most revolting part of the business. That afternoon we emerged from the Yongning valley system over a little col at 3450m clothed with birch trees with an undergrowth of willow. From here we had a fine view of the southern summit of the western range, a summit which we had previously identified from afar and which Gervais-Courtellemont had christened "Pic Le Guilcher", though quite unnecessarily, as its name — as was reported to me from the other side — was

Alo[29], or in Chinese Yue Shan. During the gradual descent, peering between the pines, we had our first glimpse of the snows and glaciers of Mount Yulong Shan (Yulong Xue Shan). Emerging for a few moments between the clouds, still far away beyond the unfathomable depths of the Yangzi gorge, it seemed to greet us from on high. Threading our way between deep funnels in the karst, we arrived that evening at Piyi, situated in a basin which drains eastwards into the main arm of the Woluo He. Our direction was still in the main south-south-east, and we went on across another fair-sized basin and past two side valleys higher up. Towards evening we reached the Woluo He itself, below a large village called Baodu, running north-east down a narrow valley. All round there were villages where Chinese and Naxi lived side by side. The former must have migrated from far away, for they had built large bucket-wheels in the river, of a kind which I did not see again until my later travels in Hunan. Ninglang, where a district official was stationed, was located to the south of Baodu near the end of an elongated basin where rice was grown and coal was mined high up in the mountains on its eastern side. The river narrowed again and made a seemingly paradoxical bend, the angle of which received a substantial tributary from the east. We soon came to the river again and went up its east bank to Xinyingpan, where a nephew of the tusi of Guabi was the ruler.

We could not get much sense out of the fellow, who was obviously feeble-minded, but we stayed with him for two days, using the first (27th June) to climb the mountain above us. The second day we were kept indoors by wretched weather — hail mixed with rain, overmuch of which found its way into my lodging in the temple. A track led past a small lamasery below Hongguwo summit, which seemed from below to offer the best vantage point, and then over the ridge accompanying the valley to the east. Nowhere was there any trace of a mountain path branching off from it, but somehow I had to reach the summit. I therefore climbed boldly into the long grass, leading my horse and threading my way between fallen tree trunks. When I emerged into the open again and mounted my horse, I was horrified to find that the pouch containing my aneroid was missing. However, my coolie had picked it up, though without saying a word, and now handed it back to me. Fortunately the instrument was undamaged and even its setting was unaffected. The summit at 3475m was covered with pine scrub and proved totally unsuited for my purpose as it offered no view to the east. All that I could see were two high mountains near Yanyuan, and I used them to fix its position. As there was no time to climb another summit, I had to be content with the western half of the panorama. A few dark rocky spires belonging to Mount Yulong Shan had been visible for a short time from much lower down, but now the whole mountain was shrouded with cloud, and as far as Alo all that could be seen was mountain landscape of the same appearance. It was somewhat

---

[29]Alo is Mianmian Shan, north of Yongsheng and northwest of Langshu Zhuo.

lower than the summit where we stood, and consisted of sloping plateaus, rounded ridges and here and there a level triangle, all built of more or less horizontal alternating strata of limestone and sandstone, with a filling of multicoloured marls in a few depressions. This territory, from Da'erbi to Yongning in the west, and as later became apparent, far beyond Jinsha Jiang to the south, is, superficially at least, the geologically least disturbed part of the Yunnan highlands. That night there was some shouting caused by the capture of a thief who had entered the yamen and taken a few harnesses and other items from our boxes. Next morning another was caught in the act of making off with Schneider's raincoat, so that in the end we had to insist that the "prince" should give us a written undertaking to assume responsibility for everything which might be stolen from us by his "law-abiding" people. The plant life had nothing special to offer apart from some fine trees of *Cornus capitata*, now in full bloom, a mass of sulphur yellow, this effect being produced by the four bracts which surround each of the tiny flowers. We also found a tall slender overhanging shrub with pink flowers — *Campylotropis polyantha*.

We left Xinyingpan without regret, though not before I had measured another baseline. We followed the main east branch of the valley up to its origin and found that the simple picture of the route given by Jack[30] was totally incorrect. The source of the river Woluo He is situated here, just above 27° of latitude. Crossing a col at 3075m, we came to a tributary flowing southwards. It followed the same Hongguwo range until it joined a little river which crossed the forest-clad sandstone range from east to west, though its valley was not deeply incised. Running along a stream, the broad ancient cobbled roadway, now completely ruined, led upwards, overgrown by oaks thickly covered with *Drynaria*. The mottled begonia-like leaves of *Parasenecio forrestii* flattened themselves against the mossy forest floor and *Saxifraga chinensis* was opening its flowers with their long deflexed tips. It was pitch dark when we reached our lodgings in Boluoti, the most southerly Xifan village. It lay beyond a second river, parallel to the other, which seemed to drain separately into the Jinsha Jiang. On 30th June, after our guide had slunk off into the forest in the rain, we at last made our way there, travelling south-westwards up and down across three side valleys running down to the river, and deviating round a higher group of peaks. From a crest we at last had a clear view far towards the south and west. The Yongshang basin lay 500m below us; it was really a broad shelf bounded on the far side by a slightly raised edge. Crossing it were a few deeply incised streams which ultimately united and cut their way through the marginal ridge, before running down into the still larger Sanchaun Ba 550m lower down. Today there were again changes in the flora. *Antiotrema dunnianum*, a member of a new genus of Boraginaceae, grew in the undergrowth of the pine forests, and the splendid new *Trigonotis heliotropifolia* beside a brook. Much lower down we

met some woody climbers: the dull purple *Paederia tomentosa* and *Millettia dielsiana*. Once again we made a long day's march, spending the night at Yongsheng on the further edge of the basin, at 2300m.

Yongsheng was a large town and a busy trade centre. We decided to take a rest day to catch up with the task of drying the pressed plants, a duty which had been somewhat neglected in the last two days. In the event it was done almost too thoroughly. Several hours after nightfall I noticed a pungent reek, more powerful than the ordinary smells of a Chinese lodging. I went to investigate and in the next room I found a stack of drying paper half a metre high, with the whole of one side smouldering; a coolie had set it on fire with his pipe. Père Guilbaud, a French missionary who like so many of his confrères was an ardent collector of beetles, paid us a friendly visit. However, we could not afford a prolonged stay and on 2nd July we set out again in the rain, first downhill in wide loops beside the gorge of the stream with its red limestone (presumably ferruginous) to the densely populated Sanshuan Ba. Its stream debouched into the Doluoti river but we did not follow it any further. Instead, the track continued in a westerly direction and ascended into a small valley, finally leading down to the Jinsha Jian beyond the Naxi village of Dawan, a day's journey from Yongsheng. From the highest col we had a magnificent view of the snow peaks of the Lijiang range, but not until we had descended some way, to a level where the subtropical vegetation had now assumed a green colour, did we emerge from the mist again. *Phyllanthus emblica* was ripening its apple-shaped yellow-green fruits, which the Chinese eat despite their acidity. Here I recorded the highest temperature reading of the year (31.5°), and it was also the lowest altitude that we had reached for some time. At water level under the iron chainbridge at Zi Lijiang it was only 1440m. Sixteen chains side-by-side, with two to serve as guard rails, stretched between two rock platforms 20m high, spanning the Jinsha Jian where it narrowed to 80m. The planks were very insecurely fastened and the whole bridge swung so violently that not more than two horses were allowed on it at a time, a rule which the watchmen on the tall towers above the gateways at each end of the bridge enforced by signalling. On the far side the miserably ill-paved track climbed up again. A brook plunged out of a ravine in several waterfalls over red limestone rocks. Down the valley towards the south the walls of the river gorge continued almost vertically as far as one could see. Leading up a steep stairway on a rock face, the track offered magnificent vistas. We had to engage several extra men to help with the loads, but our ponies were unbelievably surefooted and not once did we have to dismount. One thousand metres above the river the hillside became less steep and we soon arrived at the village of Duinaoke. On 4th July we ascended gradually through woodland to the pass at 3125m and then down on steep cobblestones into the Lijiang basin. It was raining yet again, and although the hedges were gay with fragrant honeysuckle, abundant white roses and tall golden yellow St John's wort, the dirty town seemed to offer an unfriendly reception.

---

[30] Jack, R. Logan, *The Back Blocks of China*, London, 1904.

Chapter 7. Lijiang and Mount Yulong Shan

Vicissitudes — the Naxi village of Nguluke — geology and summer flowers of the mountain — weather conditions — heaths and meadows of the glacial lake basin and the glacier stream Baishu — splendid primulas in the marshy meadows of Ganhaizi

Lijiang lies in a picturesque site at 2475m at the foot of two hills forming the end of a mountain range which projects from the north into the broad basin of a former lake. The outermost hill is quite low and is cut off by a stream diverted through the town; on it stands a glittering temple between tall cypresses. The basin is bordered by mountain chains running north and south. To the south west a lateral ridge branches off from a pointed peak, Weibi Shan, making a transverse barrier across the basin and forcing the western stream, which forms a lake there in times of flood, to swing round into the eastern part, where it joins the stream just mentioned and another coming from the north east, and turns towards the south. To the north we could at first see nothing but black clouds, through which we now and then caught glimpses of rock slabs and an icy summit, so high above us that from the lower parts of the town it towered far above the quite considerable northern hill. Not until some days had gone by did we see the "Pik" — in Chinese Yulong Shan (Precious Dragon Mountain [31]) — in its full splendour, and then only in the early mornings. It is chiefly this mountain that has made Yunnan famous among botanists and gardeners. First visited by the French missionary Delavay in 1884 and subsequently explored by Forrest, whose expeditions have extended over many seasons, it has yielded hundreds of species new to science and has provided some magnificent high alpine plants for our gardens. I did not intend to stay there long, but I wished to get a general idea of the flora and in particular to collect the cryptogams, which had never been studied at all; Schneider wanted to spend the midsummer weeks there.

First, though, we had to remain in the town for ten days, and endure various annoyances. In response to a letter sent in advance, the district official had procured accommodation for us in a fair-sized private house, but two days later we had to move into another as our coolies were too many for the proprietor. The population of Lijiang consists chiefly of Naxi (Na-khi), who are the local tribes of Moso [32], together with Chinese and Minjia, and also numerous representatives of other mountain peoples residing in the town. At the same time as our arrival the Austrian explorer A.K. Gebauer [33] entered Lijiang from the opposite direction. He had unfortunately been unable to carry out his plans, as the official in Deqen (Atuntze) — a man notorious for his hostility to foreigners — had prevented him from travelling to the Salween, and the official in Luchang had previously made it impossible for him to go any further upstream along that river. The information he gave me and his stroke of bad luck later became the inspiration for my most ambitious enterprise, a journey of which I still had no inkling at that time. We spent some pleasant hours together and replenished deficiencies in one another's kit. Then, one dark evening, a telegram from Kunming brought news of the assassination at Sarajevo on 28th June 1914. I knew Archduke Ferdinand tolerably well, having once escorted him for a day and half [34], and it was certainly a good thing that he never came to power, but the circumstances of his murder were such that we could not but fear for the consequences. I met Père E. Monbeig, who was journeying to Kangding (Tatsien-lu) to make enquiries into the death of his brother, also well known as a botanist, who had recently been murdered on the road from there to Batang. He too gave me useful information and, two years afterwards, reminded me that I had predicted the outbreak of war to him at our meeting. Li had a fight with a couple of soldiers over a woman and got badly beaten up.

We received valuable help from the Evangelical missionary A. Kok, a Dutch citizen who was working here with his wife and two deaconesses. During Kok's negotiations with the general, who finally gave orders that the two soldiers should receive a severe flogging, the latter mentioned that President Yuan Shikai had just imposed a ban on cartography by Europeans and he accordingly attached a soldier to our household as a spy. His presence naturally did not deter me from carrying on my surveying and map making; all it achieved was that I worked more surreptitiously than before and took great pains not to comply with the general's request to notify him of my departure in advance,

[31] Usually rendered as Jade Dragon Mountain.

[32] Moso are now regarded as a local tribe of Naxi. Most of the Naxi live in or around Lijiang (S.G.H.).

[33] Having set out from Burma on 12 January 1914, Anton K. Gebauer travelled via Tengyueh (Tengchong) up the river Schweli (Longchuan Jiang), crossed the divide to the Salween and went upstream to Tschenka. From there he crossed to the Mekong, reaching Weihsi on 27 March. All the passes were blocked by snow, but in the early summer he travelled to Atendze (Deqen), hoping to enter Tibet, but he was stopped by the Chinese. On the return journey he passed through the Liso village of Aiualo, later visited by Handel-Mazzetti, and crossed the Lenago pass to the Yangtze, arriving in Lijiang where he met Handel-Mazzetti. Leaving on 7 July, he returned via Tali to Tengyueh, where the British consul told him that war had been declared. After reentering Burma he was interned and spent the rest of the war in India, being repatriated in 1919. He brought back all his collections, including route surveys from Tschautou on the Schweli to Lijiang. *Anzeiger der kaiserlichen Akad. in Wien*, 1914, **51**, 101, 307 and 338. *Anzeiger der Akad. der Wissenschaften in Wien*, 1920, **57**, 11.

[34] See biographical memoir, page ix.

made so that he could provide me with letters of recommendation to the district officials and supply an escort of soldiers. In subsequent years this ban was reimposed several times. Tang Rirao, the dujun (military governor) of Yunnan, gave special effort to its enforcement; the Chinese newspapers were often full of it, and officials were strictly forbidden to give any of the available maps to Europeans. Instead of being glad that we were doing the basic work for a survey of their country — the results of which we would certainly not have withheld — they forbade it. And what have they themselves achieved in the field of modern cartography? China is probably the only country which has never carried out a comprehensive survey. There are good large-scale plans of the immediate environs of some of the larger towns, including Kunming, in crude lithographic reproductions. All other maps are hopelessly distorted, being compiled partly from reports of district officials and partly from reprints of European maps, and as any notion of copyright is quite unknown in China there is no legal remedy. Wherever they have inserted additional material it is full of crass errors; for example in a new map published by the Yunnan militia — based on Davies' map — the blank area between Weixi and Jianchuan is filled in, but the river from Weixi is shown as if it joined the Yangbi Jian — an impossibility sometimes depicted on our ancient maps, which make a river divide into two branches only to rejoin several hundred kilometres further on. It is therefore the duty of every serious explorer to put the matter right, provided he has the necessary skills and a little time to spare, whether the rulers like it or not. We were very glad to move on 15th July on Forrest's recommendation to the village where he lived, Nguluke or in Chinese Xue shan cun[35], 15 km away to the north-north-west at the foot of the mountain range.

So gentle was the upward trend of the plain, which consists chiefly of talus with patches of tufa here and there, and so enthralling was the ride along the gravel track, that it came as a surprise to find that the ascent from Lijiang to the highest parts of Nguluke was as much as 350m. The village consisted of substantial half-timbered farmsteads each built round a square farmyard, generally with living accommodation on one or two sides and stables and byres for horses, cattle, goats and sheep on the others. Above these were storerooms, topped with wooden racks for drying corn. The farms lay in three groups on the gently sloping talus fan which begins to ascend not far beyond the large market village of Baisha. Forrest[36] had rented a house, and during our stay in the village he was most friendly and helpful, drawing on his deep fund of experience to give me much good advice for my future journeys. The spacious lofts, though often smoke-filled and — to me a more serious drawback — open to the rain, were always my favourite quarters in

Naxi houses. The men dressed more or less in Chinese style, though they usually wore a felt hat and when out in the fields a thick felt weather-cape exactly like the shepherds in the Tyrol, and the women were clad in pleated skirts reaching down to the ground. They often had a small temple but in the village there was no real priest or medicine-man, though in many houses one found their books of magic spells written in strange hieroglyphic script[37]. It was by no means obsolete and was still in use at that time; in 1915 Kok showed me an account for the construction of a house which a carpenter had written out for him in Naxi characters. The men were keen hunters; some of them had homemade matchlocks, but most of them used crossbows with arrows tipped with poison from the root tubers of various species of monkshood, notably the twining *Aconitum delavayi*. A little scratch was said to kill a bear at once; the huntsman then ran up and cut out the flesh round the wound before the poison made the whole carcase uneatable. At that time the people of Nguluke consisted largely of "botanists"; since 1904 Forrest had employed them as collectors, and many of them, owing to their intelligence, keenness, feeling for form and not least their knowledge of the mountains, had given outstanding service. They knew the various plants which grew there better than he did himself, so he told us. So it came about that every evening of my nine day stay in the village they thronged into my house, invited or uninvited, spread out their spoils in the yard and held what developed into a regular plant market.

Yulong Shan rises at first gradually out of the plains. Wooded spurs project eastwards a few kilometres from the main ridge. Between them are old talus fans covered with heath vegetation, though above 3300m these merge into troughs filled with luxuriant meadows. Only to the south of Nguluke, where the height of the range is considerably less, does it plunge almost directly into the plain. At the foot of the mountain there is little solid rock exposed. What there is consists of limestone in which I later found fossils — poorly preserved corals of as yet undetermined age. This rock is almost everywhere covered with talus and conglomerate. In the alluvial cone of Nguluke there are substantial rounded blocks of volcanic stone of diabase type, resembling lava in structure and containing inclusions of limestone with crinoids. These come from high up the mountainside, a considerable part of which, including the crest itself, consists of dark diabase. To judge from the inclusions, this may have originated in a very ancient eruption; on the summit of Ünlüpe (4950m), which looks straight down on to the village, the diabase abuts in a sharp vertical line against the pale limestone lying to the north. Most of the houses were built of this volcanic stone in various shapes and forms, commonly spheroidal masses of radial structure. To the right, nearer than Ünlüpe, stands Hosayigo, a white trapezium rising steeply from its scree slopes to a peak at 4400m. To the north it continues as Sabä, a rugged crown with countless notches and recesses, while the main ridge, a jagged crest climbing higher and higher, curves in an arc towards the west. Although its exact

---

[35] Both names mean "Snow Mountain Village". At 2860m, it is the highest village on the slope above Lijiang.

[36] George Forrest, 1873-1932, botanist and plant collector. Worked in Yunnan from 1904 until his death. J. Macqueen Cowan, *The Journeys and Plant Introductions of George Forrest*, Oxford, 1952.

---

[37] See Bacot, *Les Mosos* (Handel-Mazzetti's note).

relationships are not discernible from below, the main summit of Yulong Shan, a superb ice pyramid 5450m in height, known to Europeans as the Lijiang peak and to the Naxi as Satseto, is directly visible between Hosayigo and Ünlüpe. A gigantic rock pinnacle, Chaloko, projects outwards from it to the east in the same line as Hosayigo-sabe.

The very next morning I rode through steep pine forest up the path visible from the village. Before I had gone far I saw the elegantly shaped white flower heads of *Pterocephalus hookeri* and the red blossoms of *Nardostachys grandiflora*, a genus related to our valerian. Spread out beyond the steep crest between dark fir-woods was a meadow called Ndwolo at about 3500m, covered with an unbroken sheet of flowers, the most conspicuous being *Strobilanthes versicolor*, with large blossoms, usually blue in colour, not only at the top of its one metre stalks but in panicles on all parts of the plant. With it was the single-flowered *Trollius yunnanensis* and, in drier places where the soil was not so deep, the tall *Cimicifuga foetida* and *Veratrum stenophyllum* together with the yellow *Draba yunnanensis*, fully comparable in size with our *Biscutella*, and others. Scattered here and there, their many stems sticking up like broom and their twigs spreading into an umbrella shape, were various shrubs, especially willows, lilacs, spiraeas (*S.arcuata*), *Philadelphus delavayi* and *Berberis dictyophylla*, their branches covered with dark grey mosses (*Orthotrichum hookeri*, *Hypnum hamatum*) and with grey and brown lichens (*Parmelia cirrhata*, *Oropogon loxensis*, *Leptogium menziesii*) in thick crusts and balls. But the tall vegetation harboured the first leeches and from there onwards, far up the mountainside, they lurked in their thousands to prey upon the unsuspecting wanderer. We went on up a steep slope through a strip of forest where lichens were even more abundant and came upon a rocky stream bed where the white heads of *Juncus allioides* dangled in the spray on their thread-like stalks, and the white flowers of *Saxifraga chinensis*, their petals elongated into ribbons, hung down in one-sided pairs from scapes dotted with red glands. We went up over stony turf past bamboo thickets beneath which a low-growing bramble (*Rubus lutescens*) had opened its large yellow flowers, accompanied by red and yellow *Pedicularis* in growing abundance. At 3700m there was another level spot, a boulder-filled corrie completely overgrown with lush sappy vegetation — tall yellow *Ligularias*, *Salvia flava* with yellow flowers spotted with violet, giant *Potentillas*, blue aconites and delphiniums, the pinkish-violet *Megacarpaea delavayi* and the mightiest of all louseworts, *Pedicularis superba*, its quadrangular stems as thick as a man's finger and nearly a metre in height, its leaf whorls fused into sac-like sheaths at their bases, and its numerous flowers, 4cm across, of a delicate translucent pink with a violet tinge like our *Orchis purpurea*. The last traces of the path faded out and at 4125m we passed the last few scattered firs, yet the higher we climbed the more glorious was the alpine flora. The steeply sloping meadows were ablaze with brightly coloured flowers vying with one another in size and splendour between clumps of grass, chiefly fescues, sedges and *Kobresia* species. There were Cremanthodiums (*C. nobile* and *C. campanulatum*), some with yellow

flowers like those of *Arnica* and others brownish-black, the gland-studded *Saxifraga nutans* with racemes of yellow flowers and many others of its genus, primulas in enormous numbers, crucifers such as the graceful *Dipoma iberideum* in various hues, Potentillas, dainty Parnassias, the low growing *Dracocephalum speciosum*, the forget-me-not-like *Microula hirsuta*, innumerable orchids such as *Orchis spathulata* and the vanilla-scented *Gymnadenia delavayi*, the yellow-flowered *Cyananthus macrocalyx*, edelweiss (*Leontopodium calocephalum*) with wide flat stars, but yet again the finest of all were the red louseworts with their fantastically shaped flowers — *Pedicularis delavayi* with long narrow corolla tubes and *P. elwesii* with large heads — nearly 10 cm across — of densely packed blooms on almost leafless stems. Long white screes, never entirely at rest, extended down the mountainside and they too had their own peculiar vegetation. *Pleurospermum foetens* and *Trachydium hispidum*, umbellifers with huge taproots, pressed their elegant rosettes of leaves tightly against the stones, together with *Meconopsis rudis* carrying large nodding blue flowers on tall stems covered with prickly bristles; *Eriophyton wallichianum*, looking like a deadnettle clothed in white wool; several species of larkspur, yellow, blue and violet, and *Hemilophia pulchella*, a small crucifer with pink and white flowers. *Anemone rupicola*, the undersides of its leaves suffused with violet, pushed its thread-like rootstocks up between the stones to unfold in loose mats on the surface. At 4250m, in depressions where the snow had lingered, we encountered yet more primulas of the utmost beauty: *P. pseudosikkimensis* with large pendent sulphur-yellow bells and *P. pinnatifida* with compact spikes of small blue flowers. With them were a low-growing dark violet sage (*Salvia evansiana*), the tall pink *Allium victorialis* and others. All these alpine flowers gave off marvellous perfumes — a scent of honey from the blossoms and a spicy odour from the glandular hairs. The perfume from the dried specimens still pervades the herbarium parcels ten years afterwards. Our own alpine flora cannot match the splendours of this range and my later travels in Yunnan convinced me that Yulong Shan is the *nonpareil*, the finest of all floral mountains, unrivalled in its glory both scenic and botanic. I cannot imagine anything which could possibly excel it. The work of Delavay, Forrest and Schneider (I do not include my own, as mine was only a short exploratory visit without any attempt at thorough study) has already yielded some five thousand species of flowering plants from its highest slopes down to the river at its foot, and these, coming from an area only fifty kilometres square, comprise almost as many species as the flora of the entire Balkan peninsula. On that day, however, my enjoyment was rudely interrupted; it began to hail and then to pour. The rain ran in at my neck and out at my boots; that was only the first of many days on which I got wet through.

But even when the sky was blue, the village basked in warm sunshine and atmospheric humidity fell to 35 per cent, Jade Dragon Mountain was seldom without its cloud cap. Nearly every day, seemingly from nowhere, a cloud would gather round the peak and a violent thunderstorm would ensue; Forrest once counted sixty lightning flashes in a minute. This heavy precipitation, invariably falling as snow, produces intense glaciation, and together with the steepness and instability of the slopes this is the reason why the treeline and the high alpine floral zone are at far lower altitudes here than in most other mountain ranges of Yunnan and southwest Sichuan, which though similar in situation are less isolated and do not have such lofty peaks. The unforgettable riches of this high alpine flora, brought together and preserved on this range in a concentrated or "potentiated" assembly, are presumably explained by the moistness of the mountain climate in conjunction with the geological diversity of the rocks and the open, free-draining soils. In the rainy season low cloud and drizzle are frequent in all parts of Yunnan, and the Lijiang range does not shelter any of the surrounding country — with the exception of the depths of the Yangzi canyon — from this precipitation. Even on freely permeable gravel soils it is enough to allow the local equivalent of heath vegetation to flourish luxuriantly. Such vegetation is seen at its finest along the track leading northwards at the eastern extremity of the range towards Baishui (Whitewater).

On the 18th July I rode out in that direction. At the margin of the former lake bed, which continues northwards for 5 km from Nguluke, thickets of holly-leaved oak were crowded between blocks of conglomerate left by the receding glacier. At that time of year there were relatively few plants in flower on the stony soil, but in spring there would be *Incarvillea grandiflora* and in autumn a narrow-leaved sky blue bellflower, *Cyananthus argenteus*, lying prostrate on the ground. At the edge of the forest we came upon the caravan route from Lijiang to Dagu and Yongning, and soon reached the chasm with its underground watercourse which drained the glacier in ice age times and which now emerges at the plain and flows along its eastern boundary to the town. Coniferous woodland predominated, with much spruce and *Pinus tabulaeformis*, though with an undergrowth of holly-leaved oak in many places. In shady spots there were dense stands of luxuriant perennials up to a metre in height, including *Strobilanthes versicolor*, *Rodgersia pinnata* and a tall meadow-rue, *Thalictrum delavayi*, carrying broad panicles of countless mauve flowers with quite large petals. Old moraines, now tree-covered, ran down from our left, and the trail climbed over them to its highest level (3110m). Beyond it stretched a beautiful green meadow with sinuous indented margins; just above it began the forest, its lower boundary defined by a precisely horizontal line. The subsoil consisted of pebbles cemented together into conglomerate and it was obvious at first sight that the meadow had once been a lake. Indeed, its Chinese name [38] Ganhaizi (dry lake) seems almost to imply some geological insight, though it is probably derived from the fact that it sometimes fills when the snow melts. Owing to the permeability of the soil it has remained treeless, and in some places it was so dry that only a few herbaceous species flourished, notably *Anaphalis chlamydophylla*, which looks like one of our everlastings and covered large stretches with its straw-textured silver-white flowers,

and *Leontopodium dedekensii*. Everywhere else, however, there were flowers of all colours, even among the heathy undergrowth in the surrounding pinewoods. Among the most striking were the dainty little *Gueldenstaedtia yunnanensis* with sky blue flowers, the pink-flowered *Triplostegia glandulifera*, related to our valerian, the yellow *Viola delavayi*, the white *Androsace erecta*, *Drosera peltata*, an insectivorous plant with indented halfmoon-shaped leaves covered with red glands, Swertias in various colours, the prostrate creeping *Lysimachia congestiflora* with yellow flowers, the tall *Pedicularis polyphylloides*, a coarsely hairy plant with creeping purple-red stems extending widely, each stem bearing rows of red flowers, the erect *P. integrifolia* with entire leaves and the taller, stiff, much branched *P. tenuisecta* with finely cut leaves; the tall herbaceous *Scutellaria likiangensis*, salvias, morinas, asters, various species of *Saussurea*, resembling our knapweed but with leaves like those of our silverweed covering the ground and long stiffly erect flower spikes; *Spenceria ramalana*, a plant as beautiful as it is interesting; the tall bristly blue *Onosma paniculatum*, *Roscoea cautleioides* with orchid-like flowers in shades of violet, pink and yellow and various true orchids including lady's slippers and *Habenaria glaucifolia* with fleshy leaves tightly pressed against the ground and large, curiously shaped green flowers with rolled sepal tips; and also forming rosettes, but in this instance up to half a metre in diameter, the composites *Jurinea forrestii* and *J. berardioidea* with sessile flowerheads, the first having several in a cluster and the second having individual flowerheads between the leaves. Slender sedges and rushes heightened the similarity to a meadow, among them the lax-flowered *Cyperus sieberianus* and the narrow-leaved *Fimbristylis diphylla*, together with *Juncus allioides* with its white flower heads. Satseto emerged from a backdrop of dramatically sunlit clouds. A sharp crest presented its eastern flank towards us, its upper rocks plastered with snow and fluted with snowchutes, its lower part an ice slope, and then swung round to the right to end in a monk's cowl dome. A colossal randkluft (marginal cleft) ran along its foot, and the névé basin which fed the glacier was barely visible from below, but the icefall of the glacier's snout hung down the slope as far as the highest trees. It looked as if it might be possible to climb the ice wall from the glacier on to the crest, but I do not know in what season the weather conditions might enable even a first rate mountaineer to attempt it. Nothing disturbed the majestic calm of this lonely uninhabited place; the only sound was the murmuring of the glacier stream heard from afar as it plunged over the precipice and hurried to join the Yangzi, running through a gorge which it had cut to a depth of 125m not far ahead of us. The path led down through the woods to a stone bridge. The milk white brook flowed over its bed of sand and gravel between dense thickets of willow, much of it covered by moss, while birches and various conifers including larches clothed the slopes which descended steeply down to the valley floor, rather narrow but perfectly level. In this spot, untouched by man, beneath the towering crags and snowy heights of the mountain range, every step revealed a new aspect, each more magnificent than the last.

---

[38] The Naxi name is Gaba.

Two days later I went up the mountain again, at first taking the same path as on the first occasion, but then straight up the steep grassy slopes to the highest corrie below the Ünlüpe crest. Once more I revelled in the glories of the alpine flora, but yet again my enjoyment was rudely cut short. It began to rain and then to pour. My porters thought it was unsafe to continue on the slippery turf in their straw sandals and in thick mist without a guide it seemed unwise to venture further in unreconnoitred terrain. A little further down I therefore took a steep track leading southwards, so as to reach the volcanic rock which forms the southern part of the range. Here too there was a rich flora, including clumps of *Lloydia oxycarpa* with yellow flowers like lilies, the white *Allium yunnanense*, the dusky blue *Codonopsis bulleyana* and many others. The bright yellow lichen *Acarospora discurrens* (a new species) with its radiating storage branches made a splendid contrast against the black rock. I climbed up over a little col and down the next gully. I had sent back my leather gaiters with the horse so as to make climbing easier, but my waterproof cape brushed against the dripping leaves and was soon full of leeches. When I got home I found eight of them on my legs. They had wormed their way through my stockings and, distended with blood, had been unable to get out again.

On 22nd July I at last set out in search of the plant which in recent times has perhaps attracted more attention than any other flower from Lijiang, namely *Primula littoniana*, though as later transpired it had a prior name — *P. vialii* — by which it must now be known(Fig.8). Here it grows only in a few spots — in a bog on the range to the east opposite Nguluke and at the second "dried up lake" near Ganhaizi, on the direct route from Lijiang to Zhongdian. This last place was reached on the downhill slope facing south-west, where the small *Primula yunnanensis* with one to three flowers grew in masses by the wayside, especially on sandstone, together with the low-growing *Rhododendron sinolepidotum*, its large deep-red flowers contrasting vividly against the white limestone. Lying in a boggy meadow in a depression on the ridge was a clear pond called Haleko. Beyond it, 200 m further down, the path led into the large depression of Ganhaizi. Not far off was a Naxi village divided into three groups of houses. Even on the mountainside, just as in the immediate neighbourhood of Nguluke, the spring-fed bogs were gay with flowers. Among them it was surprising to see the blue *Cynoglossum amoenum* growing luxuriantly, the yellowish grass-

of-Parnassus *Parnassia wightiana*, a dark *Phlomis* (*P. atropurpurea*) and a tall bog edelweiss (*Leontopodium calocephalum* var. *uliginosum*). The limestone conglomerate was adorned by *Didissandra sericea* with thick whitish woolly rosettes of deeply furrowed leaves and dainty nodding umbels of blue flowers with variable markings. But the highlight of the day was the boggy meadow itself, which lay at an altitude of 3130m and drained into a lake with no outlet. Our search did not take long: beside the little stream, which had cut through the black soil down to the gravel bottom, we soon found our primula — indeed its colours guided us to it. It is hard to say whether it is the most beautiful of all primulas, but it is certainly one of the most imposing. Its stout scape reaches a height of 70 cm, and is topped by a spike 15 cm long and 3.5 cm across. The upper part of the spike is coloured scarlet by the unopened calyces and the lower part is a cylinder covered by the violet-purple flowers, somewhat deflexed. There was no need to pick and choose the subject for a colour photograph. Wherever I set up the camera there was a gorgeous background — a rivulet, the meadow itself in all its hues, the narrow band of the lake, and the dark pinewoods, below which the flower meadows, so thickly covered with *Strobilanthes* that from a distance their colour was blue-grey, sloped down to the lake floor. A herd of shaggy black yaks grazing in the distance would have reminded even the nonbotanist that he was not in some pretty corner of our own Alps, but quite near Tibet. And yet, only two years later, when I came back from the Nu Jiang to Lijiang, the forests seemed to have dwindled to a shadow of their former selves.

On 25th July I returned to the town, determined to dry and despatch the vast amount of herbarium material which I had collected — indeed I did not greatly care if some of the packages got scorched — and to prepare for my next journey, again into little known country. Unfortunately the caravan leader who conveyed the tins to Kunming must have dropped one of them into the water, or perhaps the rain seeped in through a badly soldered joint. Two years later, when I opened it, I found its contents spoilt and rotten, but still I was glad that most of the material came from the Lijiang area, which had already been thoroughly explored, though alas other dried plants collected near Wali and on the journey from Yanyuan to Lijiang were also spoilt.

Chapter 8. To the Zhongdian Mountains

New staff — in the Dagu basin and across the Yangzi — outbreak of World War — arid gorges — Bede and the sinter basins — ascent of Shusuzu — through the forests to Xiao Zhongdian — the Piepen Alps — abundant plant life at 4650m — I break off my journey and return to Chuxiong

When I left Lijiang on 29th July I had a completely new staff, apart from two of the three mafus who came with me together with the best of the pack animals — nine in number — which Schneider had picked out for me. The interpreter was "Jean", a man whom Père Salvat had sent us from

Dali. He was hard of hearing, cross-eyed, slow on the uptake and no longer young, but as he was capable of displaying energy on occasions he was not entirely useless, although I was thoroughly disgusted by his filthy appearance — even by Chinese standards he was exceptionally dirty — and this adverse impression was not in the least mitigated by his constant harping on his adherence to the Catholic faith. The only advantage of employing Christians was that as they were totally dependent on the missionaries they were unlikely to abscond or commit any crass misdeeds. First of all I had to drum into him that he was now in the employ of a rabid nonsmoker and must not come into my room smoking tobacco, but any attempt to rid him of other truly Chinese habits would have been fruitless, and he continued to spit on the ground and wipe his nose on his hand, after doing which he would smear the product in a broad streak first on the doorpost and then on his felt shoe, and would then bring me my mug of tea, with his fingers stuck deep into it. Reading aloud from a grubby old book, he struggled to expand his knowledge of French. His vocabulary was larger by about a dozen words than that of Wang Wenjing, the fellow whom Herr Stiebritz had provided in Kunming and who, though equally stupid, had possessed the inestimable virtue of cleanliness, for which reason I had taken him on as our cook. Yafcha was lazy and found the journey too long for him, and I had already chucked out the other coolie; instead of them I took a man called Ben (Pen), also supplied by Salvat, who turned out to be very satisfactory, and a Naxi by the name of Yang, who was useful as an interpreter though unfortunately not capable of much physical labour.

I had resolved to go as far as Zhongdian and from there (Xiao Zhongdian) on to Xiao Weixi on the Mekong, working in the mountains everywhere along the route. I chose the track via Dagu, a ferry located in the first third of the Yangzi loop, in order to explore Bede, which according to Bacot was the sacred place of the Naxi people. The first night stop was Nguluke, where I once more took leave of Forrest and Schneider, though arranging a rendezvous on the Baishui Bazi for the next day; I wanted to journey to it by way of the mouth of the huge gorge which runs down from the main summit, as this was something I had not yet seen. Forrest had described the route for me, but I turned off too soon and went up the wrong track. Then, finding no path leading into the gorge, I turned back and simply followed my nose until I finally reached the right spot — one of the enormous moraine ridges which lie beneath the lower part of the gorge. The glacier melt-water, a fair sized stream, seeped into the sand between them, re-emerging much further down. The mountains were hidden by cloud, and I got only a few glimpses of the remoter parts of the gorge, where it is hemmed in by screes and vertical rock-faces with waterfalls tumbling down them. I had intended to continue along the track to a campsite above Ganhaizi — a heathy flat at the foot of the mountain below the glacier — with a view to visiting the latter on the following day. The caravan, however, went on past the campsite and missed the rendezvous. As things turned out this hardly mattered, since it rained almost all that day. I therefore pitched my tent beyond the Baishui on a little patch of meadow where a small Tibetan caravan was already encamped at the foot of a cliff. As we later heard, at that spot and on that very day another caravan had been robbed of seven horses and

their loads by bandits — army deserters, of course. The next day's march led north east round Mount Yulong Shan, first uphill, then steeply downhill to the Heishui (Black Water), then after a stiff ascent on to the mountainside detouring round several side valleys where tributaries ran down into the valley system which debouches into the Jinsha Jiang at Dagu. Up on the mountain the path ran for much of its length through splendid forest and bamboo, dripping with moisture, where *Aralia* trees were now flowering. The tops of the firs and pines were red with the flowers of the parasitic *Loranthus caloreas,* while their lower parts were grey with hanging strands of beardmoss, *Usnea longissima.* Apart from a few huts on the Heishui, the Xifan village of Lukuzhe was the first habitation I had seen since leaving Nguluke. From there the path went further up the mountain, finally leading down a steep descent to an arid plain of conglomerate, traversed by a few quartz dykes discernible as small low ridges, where Dagu is situated near the river.

The Jinsha Jiang flows between vertical cliffs — not very high — composed of very fine yellow conglomerate and has an extremely steep fall. Unfortunately all the mountains were hidden in cloud; not until that evening when I was in my lodgings did I get a glimpse of part of the big glacier that flowed down from the north summit of Yulong Shan into a valley which ran towards us between two parallel chains of rock hills, cut through part of the conglomerate basin and debouched into the river upstream of the ferry. It was only during the descent that I had a view of the walls of the huge gorge to the south west — almost vertical rock precipices on both sides of the river. With the water level as high as it then was the little ferry looked far from safe, and the fares — 7 cents for each person and 14 cents for each horse and each load — were far from cheap. The boatmen began by rowing upstream in a slight countercurrent, then they took hold of a projecting rockface and finally one of them seized a rope stretched along the rock and, pulling hand-over-hand, dragged the boat some distance further upstream. The boat then shot downstream, but plying their oars vigorously the ferrymen guided it to the other bank where it landed between enormous rocks. The porters then had to carry the loads on their backs for some way, and for this purpose they had to be untied from the pack frames. All this meant that my caravan took fully six hours to cross. However, there were all kinds of beautiful xerophytes begging to be collected, such as *Aristolochia delavayi,* which stank abominably of *Bifora,* several species of *Asclepiadaceae, Abelia gracilenta* in full bloom and other members of the *tomillares* formation, which consisted chiefly of *Buddleia caryopteridifolia, Caryopteris forrestii* and *Trailliaedoxa gracilis.* In the patches of steppe or grassland I found the poppy-like *Anemone glaucifolia,* together with *Ruellia drymophila, Cyperus niveus, Phtheirospermum tenuisectum* and others. My lodging was a wooden house in the nearby village of Zaba. Though it looked charming it was the worst bugs' nest I ever spent a night in. Next morning I counted some fifty of these vermin in my sleeping bag and blankets — and there were still a few survivors that evening. I sent the caravan along the straight track which led along the steep arid side of the Jinsha Jiang valley, but I told my guide to take me further away to the left. Our route passed through pinewoods via the village of Yunuo and that afternoon we reached Haba, a collection of houses scattered on a gentle slope between several tributaries of the Haba He, each of them bordered by a luxuriant growth of moisture-loving shrubs.

I was busy putting plants in the press — among others I had found the leafless *Phacellaria ferruginea* growing parasitically on *Loranthus caloreas*, which is itself a parasitic shrub — when a man entered the yard, wearing a European belt with pouches. After speaking to my men he came up to me and pulled out a letter. It was from Schneider and brought terrible news: "Just received a telegram from Kunming, that Austria has declared war on Serbia. Situation in Europe very grave. Keep in touch with me." I had felt uneasy ever since that evening in Lijiang, and now the blow had fallen, a terrible blow for a convinced pacifist, and it was my Fatherland that had declared war. No, surely it could not be my beloved country, my honest fellow citizens, but only our deluded rulers. From the wording of the despatch I could not see any reason to turn aside from my task, but it was enough to destroy my peace of mind and sap my contentment in fulfilling my duty to remain true to my profession as long as possible. How can any man maintain the inner calm necessary to carry out scientific work — let alone enjoy it — when he is tormented day and night by mental images of mass murder and devastation, hunger and wretchedness, the ruin of lives devoted to science, and the slaughter or mutilation of colleagues, friends and relatives? Besides this overwhelming distress I had a lesser worry; nearly all my supply of petrol had leaked out, but as it did not have to last much longer its loss hardly mattered.

I rode on next day with a heavy heart, once again through fresh green pine forests, travelling some distance away from the river valley, along the foot of the tall round-topped mountains, clothed with dark woods of firs and pines, which continue northwards from Haba Shan. I crossed a low saddle and went gently downhill along a little brook into the valley of the Bapaji, the Bede river, the track running along its right bank. From the valley I had a view into the Yangzi gorge; beyond the river there were the mouths of two large caves in the reddish-grey limestone cliffs of Xuechou Shan. Further up our side valley its walls became quite steep, but on our side there was a gently sloping terrace about 100m above the valley floor. On its slope, among terraced rice fields, was our next halting place, Washua, and above it at an altitude of 2500m were the seven villages of Bede. Fifteen kilometres from the Jinsha Jiang and situated on small spurs, they were clearly visible from a distance, although they consisted solely of small brown wooden houses, with tall racks for drying grain projecting high above their roofs. The whole stretch of country was still within the pine and oak wood zone, and two shrubs with large, stiff, somewhat prickly leaves — *Photinia prionophylla* and *Itea yunnanensis* — were frequent. Moisture-loving shrubs were also abundant on the terrace at Bede, as they were at Haba. *Debregeasia longifolia* (*Moraceae*), a shrub with narrow leaves, dark green above and coated with white felt beneath,

often festooned with climbing roses, arched over the muddy, stony paths, hemmed in by fences, and compelled the horseman to duck his head. Everywhere among them were the large golden yellow flowers of the shrubby *Hypericum hookerianum*, while the dark yellow racemes of *Elsholtzia flava* were less conspicuous. All the water courses were bordered by vivid green turf. Shuijia was the name of the group of houses in the centre of Bede (corrupted by the Chinese to "Beidi"), where I found suitable accommodation among the Naxi. As everywhere in these parts, they were perfectly friendly. The undersides of the roof tiles above my balcony were painted with their hieroglyphs — otherwise seldom seen except in their books of spells. At first the mafu was unhappy because he could find no beans for the horses, and the oats which the villagers brought were unknown to him. "We must see if they'll eat it", he said. "I'd like to see the horse that won't eat oats," I replied. Before long he returned, amazed; "Oh yes, they like it very much."

Despite Bacot's [39] claim, Bede is not *"le lieu saint des Mosos"*, and Kok, who knew the district well, likewise denied that it had any such significance. Nevertheless, it ought to be declared a sacred place for lovers of nature. Above the villages and at the foot of the sombre forest which covered the mountainside was a speck of white which caught my eye when I was still far away. Even on moonless nights it gleamed in the light of the stars. I had a presentiment of what I was to find, even though I had completely forgotten Bacot's casual mention of a "dépot calcaire", and I visited it that afternoon (4th August). A little cold stream trickled down into deep pools of gorgeously blue water between sinter terraces bedecked with flowers. Lower down, by the deposition of lime on exposure to the air, it had formed superb sinter basins(Fig.9). This wonderful natural phenomenon was of unusual extent, the whole array being some 40m in height and several times greater in breadth. The outer walls of the largest basins were up to 2m in height, while others, especially in the lower parts of the group where the slope was less steep, measured only about 20cm. The basins themselves had curved outer margins, in some cases forming a complete semicircle, and varied greatly in diameter, but none of them was very deep. All of them were empty of water, on that day at least, yet the lime-sinter was wet through. Although I made repeated attempts to chip off a few pieces I was obliged to retire empty-handed, my chisel blunted, my hammer cracked and my fingers grazed. I should very much have liked to collect a specimen showing the wonderful pattern of fine horizontal corrugations on the outer surface of the terraces. Fortunately my photographs displayed them beautifully, besides enabling me to make a photogrammetric reconstruction of the entire group. A few bushes were beginning to invade the formation from the sides and from below, and nearby there were some ancient terraces of the same origin, grey, crumbling and overgrown. To judge by the laminations visible on exposed rock faces at the

---

[39] *Le Tibet Revolté*, p. 308.

sides of the track, the whole of the terrace formation on which Bede stands must have originated from water flowing out of the mountain — and the ground beneath Washua also.

On 5th August I visited Shusuzu, the mountain above the villages. It is the corner of the Piepen range, which extends towards Zhongdian. Because my guide did not fully grasp my sign language I got no higher than 4000m, but it was a delightful excursion and afforded occasional views for photogrammetric purposes beneath the clouds, which were not much higher. Dusk fell early on the return journey, and my pony, though usually awkward and ungainly, balanced as steadily as a circus horse on the narrow dykes — often less than a foot wide — between the rice fields and the ditches, some of which were very deep. Only once did he slip down into a rice field, and I did not even lose my seat.

I was informed that the route to Xiao Zhongdian was very narrow and bad, and that to carry my wide crates I would have to take six local pack animals without Chinese saddles of the lift-off kind. I agreed to do this at the incredibly low price of 35 cents. Opposite the sinter basin we began a steep ascent up the side of the mountain which I had climbed the day before, first through pine and oak woods, then firs with bamboo undergrowth, until we reached the broad undulating plateau which joins the Piepen and the Haba Shan ranges. The forest stretched as far as the eye could see, though mist covered all the higher ground, and the upper halves of the firs were covered with grey beard-lichens. During the midday halt at Xiao Niuchang I collected a rich booty of mosses and lichens from their trunks, including the delicate *Calicium sinense*, a new species of pin lichen which grew in dense patches bearing tiny fruiting bodies resembling toadstools, each on a shiny black stalk, curved or straight, a few millimetres long. Further on we came to mountain pastures extending up from the pass at 4125m to a crest 175m above. They yielded a splendid haul, including the deliciously scented *Cremanthodium campanulatum* and *C. helianthus*, *Ligularia pleurocaulis* with long racemes of nodding bellshaped flowers, the stemless *Phlomis rotata* with rosettes of four large spatulate leaves pressed against the turf and short sessile spikes of violet flowers, the new *Saussurea wettsteiniana*, its drooping heads of violet flowers hidden beneath nests of large pale green bracts, and other species new to me. The crest itself was covered with rhododendron tanglewood, and along its borders was the heather-like *Cassiope selaginoides*, still bearing a few of its white bells. The surrounding peaks of rock and scree were not very high. They were built of alternating layers of limestone and sandstone, with coal lower down. I was just getting ready to take photographs when the mist came down again and a bitterly cold wind sprang up. The descent from the pass led steeply down through a narrow, deeply worn track in the phyllite rock to the camp site at Da Niuchang, on a pasture in a wooded valley opening to the west, where I pitched my tent at 3800m (7th/8th August). Fine penetrating rain persisted all night, and the next day's weather was almost as bad, yet I went on collecting and photographing, notably *Pedicularis siphonantha* with red tubular flowers 6cm long, growing in masses round the pools in the bogs.

Sheltering under my coolie's umbrella, I took numerous photographs during the next few days, and the results were not at all bad. We continued at more or less the same height along a ridge at the western side of the range, but nowhere did I get a good view of the landscape. In some places the wretched track was almost blocked by fallen tree trunks, but it led through superb coniferous forests, over boggy streams and across turf bedecked with flowers. In the woods the herbaceous plants struggled vigorously to reach the light, among them the tall, sappy, thick-stemmed *Pleurospermum davidii*, the slender *Pedicularis vialii*, a metre high, with long thin racemes of small flowers, half white and half pink, and then the tallest of all gentians, *Gentiana stylophora* (now *Megacodon stylophorus*), as high as a man, with pendent greenish sulphur-yellow flowers 9 cm long(Fig.11). Then the path went downhill in steep zigzags, where traffic and water had eroded the track to a depth of several metres. The bottom was too narrow to put both feet side-by-side, and the horses had to raise their legs high off the ground to place one hoof before the other. They stumbled down this ravine, our crates bumping against its sides, while bamboos and prickly-leaved oaks covered with beard lichens made a roof above our heads. After crossing the valley which ran alongside to the right and climbing over a small spur, we reached a broad vale, up which we went to a large farmstead called Alo where we were to spend the night. Now thoroughly soaked, I was welcomed by the Naxi Tibetan halfcastes who lived there and accommodated in a clean room. They at once brought burning logs on an iron tray, but because of the smoke I declined this with thanks, for by slipping into my sweater I was soon able to get warm and dry. The house was built in genuine Tibetan style: there was a narrow yard which together with the stables around it was occupied by the animals, the filth being to some extent mitigated by strewing twigs of holly-leaved oak on the ground. The living quarters, where their food was cooked in large pots, were on the upper floor, which was surrounded by wooden galleries. Their beds were on benches or storage chests all round the wall, and there was even a spotlessly clean lavatory which my Chinese servants showed me with amazement.

The valley ran parallel to the main road from Lijiang to Zhongdian, debouching into the Zhongjiang He at Tuguancun. I followed it, ascending gently north west through spruce woods where the under-growth was among the finest of its kind that I have ever seen. There were tall slender louseworts (*Pedicularis* spp.), various large-flowered cranesbills including the new *Geranium calanthum* with flowers of the same shape as our *G. phaeum*, the slender narrow-leaved *Lilium macrophyllum* (*Notholirion macrophyllum*) with a raceme of small greyish pink flowers, and *Cacalia palmatisecta* (*Senecio palmatisectus*) in vast numbers, its abundant finely cut palmate leaves and large panicles of narrow pendent golden yellow flowerheads with reddish brown bracts making a charming picture. Among the climbers was *Clematis fargesii* with flat snow-white flowers 6 cm across, and along the stream there were large bushes of our sea buckthorn, *Hippophaë rhamnoides*. The stream rose in several tributaries from the northeast of the mountain and my route led over a flat col only 3500m high, at the side of which was a doline between limestone rocks. We passed a little village called Latsa where our branch of the valley swung round and continued in the opposite direction. Even before we crossed the col the forest was beginning to give way to meadow, and on the col itself, apart from a few patches of holly-leaved oak, the meadowlands reigned supreme. They were relatively dry and belonged to the heath meadow type. Their sumptuous and gorgeously colourful array of flowers completely displaced the grasses and reminded me a little of the forest meadows of East Bosnia, but in colour and form the flora of the Zhongdian highlands was incomparably more splendid, luxuriant and exotic. There were several magnificent garlics, notably *Allium polyastrum* with tall broadly winged stems and numerous rather small flowers and *A. macranthum* with large nodding bells which give it some resemblance to *Butomus*; also *Linaria yunnanensis*, its skyblue flowers pencilled with yellow; *Saussurea wettsteiniana*, taller and more lush at this lower altitude, numerous other species of *Saussurea*, and many umbellifers including *Heracleum nepalense*, closely similar to our *H. montanum* and a small *Angelica* (*A. scaberula*) with purple flowers; *Leontopodium franchetii*, a mat-forming edelweiss with small starry flowers on thin stalks and close-set thread-like leaves with sticky glands; *Dracocephalum isabellae* with clusters of large violet labiate flowers, panicled blue gentians and dainty bellflowers, and once again masses of the splendid clustered yellow *Ligularia pleurocaulis*. The rest of the day's journey was said to be no more than 15 li, but as the mountain people were never able to agree on distances stated in Chinese li, a midday rest was considered necessary and we halted on the gentle downhill slope. On the right there were some fine peaks towering above the forest, and I immediately decided on a plan. I turned to the mafu, pointed out one of the broad and easily accessible side valleys running down towards us, and told him that it was our objective for the morrow. The main valley curved down towards Xiao Zhongdian, and opening into it were two further side valleys, both with good tracks leading up them. I accordingly cancelled my previous instructions and told him to take one of these routes into the mountain.

Xiao Zhongdian lies close to the Zhongjiang river in an old lake basin, some 2 km from the outermost foothills of the Piepen range, which the track had just traversed. The stream which I was following ran across the lake bed and had cut a little ravine with vertical walls of gravel and conglomerate, in which it formed a waterfall. I arrived early that afternoon, unloaded my specimens and left them there in Wang's care together with part of the caravan. Next morning, taking only the bare essentials — tent, campbed, paper for pressing plants and three days' provisions for man and beast — I set off up the side valley into the Piepen range. Even before the point where the valley forked I found interesting plants growing among the stones in the spring flushes by the wayside: *Pedicularis longiflora*, the yellow counterpart of *P. siphonantha*, a hybrid *Primula vittata* x *poissonii* and, unexpected as an inhabitant of a bog, an edelweiss, *Leontopodium souliei*, which resembles our *L. alpinum* more

closely than does any other Chinese species. Nearby, on turf beneath pines, there was an eyebright, *Euphrasia regelii*, with little pale violet flowers with a yellow throat. I was in front and, as previously arranged, when I came to the fork in the path I hung strips of red paper on the trees to mark the route for my men, and then rode on to continue my work. The valley was similar to the one at Alo, but the forest meadows though less extensive were moister and the vegetation was hence even taller and more luxuriant. Moreover, the valley soon reached higher altitudes, at which new species began to appear. There were tall blue larkspurs and monkshoods, violet *Nepeta* species, a sage with bicoloured flowers in violet and yellow, sorrels, tall spurges, and between them some of our meadow grasses and sedges, here growing in clumps a metre in height. Overtopping them was the teasel *Dipsacus chinensis* and scrambling through the herbage were two dull violet and yellow-green bellflowers, *Codonopsis rotundifolia* and *C. macrocalyx*, with milky sap and a revolting odour, while bamboos bordered the surrounding woodland. Where the soil was drier the dominant plants were *Morina* (red and white), and various rank *Ligularia* species with large thick leaves and long thick spikes of large yellow daisy flowers, together with louseworts of many colours. In the forest I found a new yellow-flowered species, *Pedicularis aequibarbis*, with multiple stems 2m high. The equivalent of our butterbur, *Ligularia transversifolia*, a new species with flowers in corymbs and giant leaves with centrally attached stalks, grew along the banks of the stream, which was so deep that it came up to the horses' bellies and wet my feet every time I crossed it. I was more than ready to halt, but the caravan was nowhere to be seen or heard, so I sent Jean after it. He of course found that the dim-witted mafu had forgotten his orders, missed my direction markers and gone back along yesterday's route. Meanwhile I found two fine rhubarbs growing at the side of the stream, *Rheum officinale*, taller than a man, with leaves nearly 1m in diameter, and the smaller *Rheum alexandrae*, its large pendent bracts, at first pale, already turning a beautiful red. Both grew on gravel subsoil, their massive rootstocks projecting above ground level and embedded in peat which had been formed by the decomposition of their withered leaves, supplemented by the other herbaceous plants, willows and dwarf rhododendrons which flourished and decayed between them. To get closer to the highest mountains I turned into a lateral valley on the right. It ran parallel to the main range, and though stony and wet it was easily negotiable. It led through fir woods, between willow bushes covered with lichens (*Lobaria*) and juniper trees, up to a fairly large flat expanse of turf dotted with *Pedicularis*. It seemed too early to camp there, and I went on, but the path stretched out endlessly without passing any reasonably open ground, dusk began to fall, and I thought I would have to return to the turfy patch we had seen earlier. However, we met a Tibetan on his way down from cutting wood and in response to our signs he indicated that we should continue uphill. Before long we did in fact reach a tolerable though rather cramped site and I pitched my tent in darkness and incessant rain at 3880m. That evening and next morning the temperature was 6°C.

The 11th August, the anniversary of my memorable ascent of Meleto-dagh in Kurdistan, seemed a good day to undertake at last a really high alpine expedition. At the treeline (4125m) there were a few shepherds' huts and growing abundantly around them two shrubby *Potentillas*, the yellow *P. fruticosa* and the white *P. veitchii*. Among them was another tall *Ligularia*, similar to the one I had seen earlier, but with its flowers in broad corymbs instead of spikes (*L. cymbulifera*). Lots of people had gone up on to the screes to dig for roots, and higher still to tend their yaks. There were several scree-filled corries below weathered limestone towers, but nearly all the peaks were in cloud, and though first one and then another briefly emerged it was impossible to tell which was the highest; however, there was certainly no great difference between them. The bed occupied by a glacier in some former ice age was obvious at first glance from the moraines left by its snout and the *roches moutonnées* of its *névé* basin. I climbed up towards the highest pass I could see. The flora of the scree slopes was very fine: a low growing *Corydalis* with large pale violet flowers (*C. hemidicentra* — a new species) had a thick, deeply buried root from which numerous thready stems pushed their way between the stones to form loose mats of tripartite seagreen leaves pressed against the slope; the yellow *Potentilla articulata* grew in dense cushions, its leaves, also tripartite, divided into linear erect parallel segments; *Primula dryadifolia* had rosettes of smaller leaves closely resembling those of our mountain avens (*Dryas octopetala*) and short scapes each carrying several splendid reddish purple flowers; the yellow *Saxifraga drabiformis* formed loose cushions; with its white flowers, *Arenaria lichiangensis* was reminiscent of the Oriental species of the genus; *Cobresia stiebritziana* (a new species) was an inconspicuous cushion plant resembling *Carex firma* of the Alps; swaying in the breeze among them were two new species, *Arenaria weissiana* and *A. fridericae*, together with some plants of the Papilionaceae family; *Aletris nepalensis* and *Polygonum sphaerostachyum* extended up to this altitude from lower levels; and there were several species of Meconopsis, some single-stemmed and others with multiple stems, both low growing and very tall, with nodding blue poppy flowers. Even more splendid was the flora of the snow patches, a term which denotes the depressions where snow lingers late and by its weathering action creates soil rich in humus which is protected against being washed away. There were masses of the tiny *Primula cyclostegia* [40], a counterpart of *P. minima* in the Alps, but single-stemmed and having much smaller leaves with yellow farina below and bluish violet flowers, also *P. lepta* (*P. apoclita*) with a spike of florets like a grape-hyacinth; a tiny *Ranunculus*, seldom more than a centimetre high (*R. micronivalis*, a new species); *Sibbaldia parviflora*, the dwarf willow *Salix lindleyana* and others; and at their margins, where they were bordered by the dwarf *Rhododendron cremnophilum* (*R. primuliflorum*), here approaching its upper limit of altitude, were the splendid dark

brownish violet pendent bell-shaped flowerheads of *Cremanthodium campanulatum* on short scapes above rosettes of leaves like those of *Adenostyles*, among cushions of liverwort. Beyond the col there were a few small snowpatches on the northeast side; they might actually have been permanent. At the top (4650m) the scree flora was hardly less rich and even more interesting. Growing between golden moss cushions (*Tetraplodon urceolatus*, *Barbula asperifolia*) was *Wahlbergella apetala* [41], a catchfly with inflated spheroidal calyces; two new louseworts, one of them (*Pedicularis parvifolia*) minute and the other (*P. pseudoversicolor*) resembling our native bicoloured *P. oederi*; *Solms-Laubachia pulcherrima*, belonging to a genus of Cruciferae discovered near Lijiang, grew in patches arising from a rootstock so deep as to defy all attempts at excavation; and *Saussurea leucoma*, swathed in thin wool, with short thick columnar stems closely beset with pinnatisect leaves, each stem ending in a disc of violet flowerheads. The mountain top was again enveloped in cloud and offered no better views than the col I had already reached, and instead of climbing the 5000m peak I decided that I could spend the time more advantageously in botanizing and taking colour photographs (Autochromes); despite the cold wind they came out quite well. On my return I steered towards the larches which formed the treeline at 4250m on the other side of the little valley leading down to my camp. When I reached them I began the descent to the brook, down scree slopes which offered further novelties. At boggy spots along the stream the bushes of *Potentilla veitchii* with their nodding white bells were particularly fine, and flowering among them were blue *Swertias*. Returning next day along the same valley to Xiao Zhongdian, I was fully occupied in studying the profuse and fascinating population of mosses and lichens which flourished on the trunks of the pines and willows, on rotting wood and boggy ground.

I spent two days in Xiao Zhongdian. It was a fair-sized Tibetan village of large wooden houses, painted in reddish colours, with grain-drying racks projecting above their broad gables. From a distance of farmsteads bore some resemblance to the peasant farms of our Alps. In the vicinity there were numerous water-driven prayer wheels, prayer flags and obos, the last being piles of stones on which prayers such as "Om mani pemehum" [42], "om wagi scheri mum", "om baser peme hum" and other longer phrases had been carved. Situated as it was on a main route, the village was quite animated; caravans were constantly passing though, and to a foreigner's eye the sight of these sturdy Tibetans, with their brown faces, their jewellery of silver and jasper, their long hair hanging down in wild locks, was always fascinating. They were clad in robes of grey or red, leaving the chest exposed and girdled round the waist to make a container for most of their

[40] Now *Primula bella* var. *cyclostegia*.

[41] *Lychnis apetala*. See Polunin, O. & Stainton, Adam, *Flowers of the Himalaya*, № 194.

[42] Usually transcribed as "Om mani padme hum".

personal possessions — food, money, a bowl for their meals, a tobacco pouch, a prayer wheel and their weapons — and they wore felt boots(Fig.10). Some of them used yaks as beasts of burden and it was these splendid though extremely nervous creatures which brought firewood into the yard of my hostelry. The people were most friendly and much better mannered than the Chinese; though they peeped shyly round the doorposts to see what I was doing, those on one side gestured to their friends on the other to tell them not to block my light. I bought a sheep for one and a half dollars to provide us with meat for a few days. However, the village was not really suitable for a longer stay as the only person who spoke Chinese was one old woman. Tibetan-speaking Chinese traders sometimes passed through and my interpreter said of one of them: "*Il parle cinq tibétains*", meaning that the trader spoke five of the native languages. In this district Man hua ("the language of the tribesmen") primarily means Tibetan, and as he had heard me call it "*tibétain*" he extended the meaning of the word to cover all non-Chinese languages. From the trader I obtained the information I needed for the next stage of my journey to the Mekong, which I hoped to resume on 15th August.

That was not to be. On the evening before my departure the messenger I had sent to Zhongdian came back with a telegram from Schneider reporting the conflagration which was sweeping across our "civilised" Europe. How much more truly civilised was life in this peaceful wilderness! As it was generally believed that Europeans in China would be in jeopardy in the event of war, as Schneider's telegram indicated that he was returning and as, whatever the moral position, there were no grounds on which a military court would conceivably have exempted me from my impending call-up, I decided to turn back. That evening I repacked my baggage so that in the event of any delay I could travel ahead with three pack animals to carry the collections and the essentials for the journey. The track ran alongside the Zhongjiang He, first on the gravel terraces of an old lake bed where the river had cut only a shallow trench, then over several smaller lateral terraces separated by wooded spurs and hills, above a hot spring and past large scattered Tibetan villages situated among green meadows and fields framed by gentle wooded slopes, along a row of dolines which stretched in the same direction between the two valleys, onwards through unbroken woodland, at one spot coming so close to the edge of the ridge that it afforded a vista — unfortunately only partial — of the vale of Alo, and continued as a corduroy road up and down through bamboo scrub and boggy woods to the little temple at Minya, where it once more led to the steep side of the Zhongjiang He gorge, which was quite deep even here, though the mountain range beyond it was nothing more than gently undulating woodland country. A little further, on a spur projecting into one of the river's loops, we came to our campsite at Yijianzhen, a forest meadow full of leeches.

Next morning the horses were covered in blood, though fortunately none of the leeches had got into the tent. One of the horses had run away and could not be found despite a long search; I thought it must have fallen down the rocks, possibly into the river.

I therefore left behind two crates of paper, which was now superfluous, as collecting was the last thing I felt inclined to do in my present mood, and in any case I had to travel on without stopping. On top of all this turmoil came Schneider's messenger bearing my call-up telegram from the German consul in Kunming and with it the first bad news of the fighting. When I set out the messenger, who should have waited for my reply and payment, had disappeared, as had my guide from Xiao Zhongdian after having taken a small advance payment. They probably planned to rifle the crates, and must have been sadly disappointed to find nothing more than paper inside them. The crates and the missing horse were subsequently found by two of Forrest's collectors, whom I had encountered on the Piepen range, and returned to Schneider. The track continued along the heights; here and through almost the whole of the valley the rock was mica-schist. Forest stretched as far as the eye could see; a few hundred metres almost vertically below us the mountain torrent raged in its gloomy ravine. The country was magnificent, but in those unhappy circumstances I was in no state to enjoy its beauty. The path ran down to the Yi village of Tuguancun, in the Alo valley close to its mouth, then up again to a wretchedly bad stretch where it consisted solely of water-filled holes separated by high narrow transverse banks or ridges of clay. The pack horses tried to keep on the ridges but inevitably slid down into the pits between them, splashing mud high into the air. Though they fell repeatedly, they were unscathed. From a col I had a good view of the lower part of the still unsurveyed valley, then came a steep descent to a tiny Chinese village called Luoxiwan, 800m below. From there it was a further day's march along the turbulent mountain river to its confluence with the Yangzi. The main ferry was a short distance upstream at Yuluo. Towering above the village, Satseto, here stupendously steep, loomed now and then through the mist. Next day the route ran first through dry fir woods on the side of the valley, then through a pretty little glen filled with bamboo scrub and mixed forest, in which a yellow Gesnerad (*Oreocharis forrestii*) had found lodgement among the ferns high up on the branches of the oaks, while lower down its blue counterpart (*Didissandra cordatula*) grew in large numbers on the tiled roofs of the houses. The climb up to the col at Ganhaizi was 1400m in all. It was hot and the horses found it such an ordeal that I had to unload two of them, let them rest and give them a feed of rice before bringing them along behind, but nonetheless we reached our intended camping place at Ganhaizi. Next day I lunched with Schneider and Forrest at Nguluke. To me at least, Forrest said that he had no words strong enough to condemn England's declaration of war. Schneider took charge of my plants and promised to complete the task of drying them. That evening I reached Lijiang, where I discharged Yang, and the next day (20th August) I set off for Dali.

As if in mournful farewell the snow-capped peak was free from clouds, though it had been obscured for a fortnight. It was thickly plastered with new snow and seemed to ask: "Why are you forsaking the beauties of nature for the savagery of mankind?" At Lashiba the track curved to the southwest and went uphill; it then ran down into a broad valley which ran southwards, its head separated by a low col from the great bend of the Yangzi. There was a stench of carrion, probably from the carcase of a pack animal putrefying among the bushes at the wayside. It prompted thoughts of the war-polluted air of the battlefields, and even the sweet scent of the rose bushes which bordered the track did nothing to dispel them. Towards evening the mist dispersed, leaving a clear view westwards over jagged peaks to Laba Shan and north-westwards up the Yangzi. As if to tease me, the clouds lifted even from the summits of the northwest continuation of the Yulong Shan, which I had wooed so long and never before glimpsed. They too approached 5500m in altitude. Steep, snow-crowned pinnacles towering above the clouds, they are the two guardians of the Jinsha Jiang, which has cut a gorge almost 3600m deep between them. The vista came as a painful reminder during my unhappy retreat, yet it was so enchanting that despite my earlier decision I once more set up my camera for a photogrammetric survey. From then on the terrain was less striking. Between Xiaying and Niujie there was an exceptionally hot spring, welling up at the foot of a limestone crag and feeding several artificial pools. I collected the algae and an evil-smelling *Chara*, which formed extensive brown sheets, lime-encrusted and dried up, where the water spread out over the level ground. At Dali the Cang Shan range was veiled in cloud. I called on Père Salvat and found him as friendly as anyone could have wished, but even he had nothing to go on but the false reports put out by the British consul-general. I discharged Jean, and felt glad to see the last of the dirty fellow. As the telegraph at Lijiang had been cut off, it was not until I reached Dali that I was able to send a telegram to my consul; knowing that England had declared war I realised that the order to proceed to Hongkong was no longer appropriate, but as a soldier I had to obey until it was countermanded. The reply — sent on to me at Xiaguan — was useless; it referred me to the Austro-Hungarian consul-general in Shanghai, and I could not expect a reply from him until I arrived in Chuxiong, six days further on. I therefore resumed my journey, in a reflective state of mind. The main road through Yunnan was no better, and indeed in some places worse than many of the "minor" routes. Where it was paved, the surface had long ago disintegrated: some of the stones had been trodden into the ground and others had disappeared leaving gaping potholes full of mud and water. Wherever a rivulet crossed the road it made a bog into which the horses plunged up to their knees, and wherever it was built of soft sandstone flags the pack animals

had worn a narrow groove or had even hollowed out a sequence of separate steps, one for each hoof, with the result that if a horse started off on the wrong hoof it was sure to fall, unless its rider could immediately force it to step back. In such stretches the rider who values his horse's legs — and his own ribs — is well advised to dismount. On the exit roads from every sizeable village there were beautifully carved triumphal arches and neatly executed stone tablets in memory of officials who had "not misappropriated the funds". Here and there I saw the "scales of justice", a beam with a ring at one end and a hook at the other, fixed to a tree or a post, and above it a notice proclaiming that on that spot a thief had been flogged. From a distance, viewed from higher ground, the medium-sized settlements, with their straight main streets flanked by one-storey houses, reminded me of the villages of the Vienna basin. The inns were comparatively good and the people were not excessively inquisitive, as they had seen European travellers often enough. What I did find most unpleasant, however, was the smoke, allegedly containing arsenic, which Chinese travellers used to repel midges; I often offered them ointment instead, when the smoke got up my nostrils. Between Xiangyun and Yunnanyi there was a minor incident: accompanied by shouts from numerous peasants at work nearby, a large, almost white wolf came trotting slowly on to the road. I leapt down from my horse and drew my Browning. It crossed the road a few paces ahead of me, but as there were people on the road beyond I had to take care and missed him. He laid back his ears, made a few leaps and vanished behind a hummock. If I had been in another mood I would have tackled him in a different style. The terrain and vegetation were somewhat monotonous. Each day's march was no more than the distance normally covered by a fast caravan, but my pack animals had had 14 days' work without a break and found it a severe ordeal. Two were limping, another had huge boils, one of which, situated on the withers, suddenly burst, sending out a jet of pus which persisted for several seconds, and a fourth had attacks of colic which my mafu dealt with by inserting a hollow needle of European manufacture at the navel and drawing off fluid. Had I not felt that I was subject to the exigencies of martial law I would not have allowed such sufferings to continue unchecked, especially as the animals were my own property. But the explorer's imperative "onwards!" is in itself a kind of martial law and anyone who is unduly squeamish should stay at home — and certainly not travel to the Orient or to China.

Chapter 9. From Chuxiong via Huili to Yanyuan and back to Kunming

Resumption of work — flowers of the steppe — salt mining — low lying country of the Yangzi valley — on Mount Longzhu Shan again — lush subtropical flora on the Yalong — the caravan's mishaps — autumn on the Huangliangzi (4075m) — back through the Jianchang

W hen I arrived in Chuxiong on 31st August I went straight to the telegraph office and was relieved to find the consul-general's reply awaiting me: *"Return impossible, recommend remain China".*

There was now no time to retrace my steps and resume my original plan. I was not willing to be swayed by hypothetical fears that the war might imperil the safety of Europeans in China — at least not until there was real evidence of such danger. I therefore decided to make for the nearest accessible high mountains, namely those around Yanyuan in Sichuan, so as to study the high alpine flora in the eastern part of that district — which had not been sufficiently developed on our first visit in the spring — and compare it with the flora on the western side. But first I had to spend four days in Chuxiong to give my caravan a rest, to buy new paper and have it folded and to prepare for the next stage of the journey. I had engaged a second coolie as a collector; next morning he was nowhere to be found and ultimately turned up in a drugged state from opium. In Guangtong I therefore took on another named Jin Jingwen, who proved extremely useful. As the tent would not be necessary in the district I planned to visit I sent it back to Kunming together with the dried plants in the charge of a mafu to whom I sold the two limping ponies. One of them he resold at once for a good profit, and by the next day the other was no longer limping. I got in touch with Herr Weiss [43], the German consul in Kunming who had been appointed in April, and at last received news of the war more favourable to our cause. I also visited the Chuxiong magistrate, an old gentleman who pretended to be greatly astonished at my having come without an official escort. He kept reverting to this topic even when I remarked on the cleanliness of his town, but ultimately he provided the usual escort of one or two soldiers, and caused no further annoyance. On the evening of 4th September I successfully photographed an almost total eclipse of the moon from the yard of the inn where I was lodging — quite a tolerable hostelry right in the middle of the town.

To reach Yanyuan I had to continue along the Kunming road to a point beyond Guangtong [44] and then turn northwards to Huili. Delivered at last from the nightmare of call-up for military service, I now felt able to devote my attention to the plants, and there was indeed much of interest, for late summer, in the rainy season, is the flowering time of the grasses and herbaceous perennials of the steppe.

More or less uniformly distributed, in some places densely crowded, but nowhere matted into wide areas of unbroken turf, the erect grasses of the steppe grow in many-stemmed clumps. *Heteropogon contortus* has long sharp hygroscopic awns, and after the seeds drop they curl up into bundles which often remain hanging on the stalks for a long time; *Themeda triandra* has several handsome wedge-shaped pendent spikelets on long stalks; *Cymbopogon nardus* has tufts of narrow spikelets covered with silvery hairs; similar in appearance but always tinged with red is *Andropogon delavayi*, usually just as abundant and just as striking; and the brownish-green *Arundinella setosa* has its panicles arranged in whorls. The average height of all these

grasses is 70cm, and the perennials and dwarf shrubs of the steppe grow to the same level; scattered in small numbers among them is the beautiful *Erianthus fulvus*, a grass with a coppery-red sheen, which grows to more than twice their height. *Osbeckia capitata* (*Melastomataceae*) is a sub-shrub which has a thick woody stock but is otherwise for the most part herbaceous; it has small opposite leaves and gorgeous large pink flowers with long yellow stamens projecting from them. There were several low growing true shrubs of the pea family, mostly like broom with racemes or spikes of flowers in various shades of red and pink. The orchids included *Habenaria loloorum* with dense spikes of small yellow flowers, *Spathoglottis fortunei* with lax racemes of larger yellow flowers pencilled with brown, and *Bletilla yunnanensis* with pink flowers. There were various species of *Swertia* with numerous blue or violet bell-shaped flowers in pyramidal panicles, and *Cyanotis tuberosa*, a blue "Tradescantia". On the shady banks of the sunken tracks there was a luxuriant growth of herbaceous plants and ferns, notably two species of *Hedychium* — a genus related to ginger — with long spikes of large, short-lived flowers — white in *H. spicatum* and white with brickred markings in *H. acuminatum* — and two twiners, *Ipomaea hederacea* with large purple flowers and *I. hungaiensis* with numerous smaller yellow flowers; also the white *Thunbergia fragrans*, mimicking our bindweed, the bean-like *Pueraria peduncularis* and *P. edulis*, and the inconspicuous yams *Dioscorea bulbifera* and *D. submollis*. Growing among them was the tall grass *Rottboellia exaltata* with disintegrating cylindrical spikes, and the less conspicuous *Setaria forbesiana*. *Themeda gigantea*, a grass up to 4m tall, grew along ditches and streams. Along the route, especially between Chuxiong and Guangtong, the hillsides were clothed by forests of pine, *Keteleeria* and evergreen oak, together with *Castanopsis delavayi*, a tree with faintly silvery leaves and clusters of soft spined fruits. On the ascent to our first night's halt at Guangtong I found the small parasitic but non-twining *Peperomia reflexa* growing on a *Castanopsis* trunk. Just as I was somewhat noisily setting up the tripod to photograph it, a mounted officer dressed in the rather womanish plain clothes of a Chinese civilian came riding round the corner. He was obviously horrified, asked my servant what I was doing and tried to tell me that I had no right to take photographs in China. When he saw that I was not going to take any notice of him, he shouted the command *"Attention"* — probably the only European word that he knew. On the descent into the next valley I found *Magnolia delavayi* now in full bloom, though its huge scented white flowers — like partly open chalices almost hidden among the profusion of its large leathery leaves — can be seen in ones and twos at other times of the year. At this spot I quitted the Kunming road and followed the stream northwards.

Here, on the southern slope of the watershed between the Red River and the Yangzi Jiang, was the salt-producing village of Alaojing, and further to the northeast, beyond the 2400m ridge but still on the upper reaches of a stream flowing back to the Red River, was a salt-works town called Houyanjing. These two places, together with Heijing situated on

---

[43] In 1908 Weiss made a journey from Chengdu to Tatsienlu and into Tibet. He was the first European to cross the 4100 m Dangling pass in the Silhatshan chain. See Limpricht, W. *Botanische Reisen in den Hochgebirgen Chinas und Ost-Tibets*. Berlin, 1922.

[44] In 1960 Guangtong ceased to be a Xian and was included in Lufengxian (SGH).

the Longchuan Jiang further northwest, supplied all the salt required in the capital of the province. In Houyanjing I was given some substantial lumps of grey rocksalt. However, the finished product, produced in the same way as at Maoguoyanjing in Sichuan, was pure white — the best salt that I saw in China. The towns themselves, densely populated by coolies, were extraordinarily dirty, and the dark stone walls of the tall government buildings, the smoke-blackened brine works and the piles of brushwood, cut for fuel and stacked higher than the houses, left a gloomy impression. Botanically, the track over the sandstone ridge was of some interest, even though nearly all the forest had been felled; on the moist soil watered by the abundant summer rain the shrubs evidently grew up again quite swiftly. At the roadside there was a rich vegetation of willowherb, teasels (*Dipsacus aster*), *Carex cruciata*, valerian, *Pedicularis polyphylla*, *Phtheirospermum chinense*, resembling a lousewort, and two species of *Polygonum*, one of them a sprawling climber. Butterflies with grey-white chequering (*Arichanna jaguararia*) had settled in large numbers on a flat rock by the road, and they sat so still, with their wings flattened against the rock, that I was able to take an unhurried photograph. The large long-tailed light green butterfly *Actias selene ningpoana* also occurred in the vicinity.

My route continued north-northeast across an upland tract intersected with valleys and covered by the usual forests. In the *Lithocarpus* woodland I made one or two delightful finds, including the small tree *Schefflera delavayi* with large grey-green palmate leaves, which I saw here for the first time with (still young) flowers. In the garden hedges of the scattered villages *Erythrina arborescens* was putting forth scarlet clusters of butterfly flowers among its large trifoliate leaves. It was quite a narrow track, but even in that lonely country the route was indicated by marker stones at the forks and crossings and although often overgrown by scrub they enabled us to find the right path. As we went down into the little basin of Yangjie I encountered plants of lower altitudes, among them begonias (*B. sinensis* and *B. henryi*); *Petrocosmea nervosa*, a violet-like Gesnerad; and the slender twining *Streptolirion longifolium* with waxy pink stem tips ramifying at right angles into racemes with flowers of the same colour, the lower, seedbearing flowers each resting on a large bract. The shade required by these plants was provided by various climbers — *Tripterygium forrestii*, *Porana mairei* and *Cynanchum otophyllum* — and the non-woody twiners *Apios carnea* and *Codonopsis forrestii*, which scrambled over the bushes and smaller trees, often bending them down by their weight.

Yangjie, our fourth night stop after leaving Chuxiong, sticks in my mind as one of the worst lodgings of my travels, where I had to climb a breakneck ladder into a tiny, smoke-filled attic, sweltering hot and full of fleas although it was situated above the stable. Just after leaving the village the track turned down into the Majie basin, a large depression filled with marl, gravel and sand. The *Keteleeria* woods continued for some distance on this subsoil, that species and the prickly *Juniperus formosana* showing signs of damage by a leafless mistletoe with jointed stems, *Arceuthobium*

chinense, Then came a zone of grey thorny scrub, but down in the basin there was nothing but barren steppe. The floor of the depression was intersected by countless dried-up watercourses — in the Arab countries of the Near East they would be called wadis — and displayed earth pyramids and other formations produced by weathering. The sky was overcast and I doubted whether photographs of this broken and confused landscape, used in conjunction with the reverse views to be taken next morning from the low ridge beyond Yuanmou, would be clear enough for a survey of the basin. But that night it rained; next day everything was shrouded in mist and photography was out of the question. Below Majie we reached the Longshuan Jiang (Dsolin-ho) flowing towards us from Chuxiong. Late that evening, while I was in my lodgings in Hailuo, there came a knock at the door. It was Guérin, a Frenchman whom I had met in Xichang that spring. He had been recalled for military service and had had to leave the Yi country; he subsequently lost his life in the war. We got on very well together; next morning one of my packhorses died — the one which had been treated for colic — and as I had to lighten the loads I was able to give him some minor items of equipment.

The route now trended gradually downwards, the river valley became rocky and more deeply cut, and there were outcrops of granite as well as mica-schist with quartz. It harboured a rich xerophytic flora including *Didissandra cordatula*, the sky-blue *Commelina kurzii* and masses of *Cyperus niveus*, a sedge with white inflorescences. At midday we came to the ferry over the Jinsha Jiang at Longjie. The boat pitched and rolled in the fast running river, and the men had difficulty in calming the animals, which they did by splashing water in their faces. On the far side of the river the ground was flat and sandy, and there were large colonies of the tall grass *Erianthus trichophyllus*, a new species with large silvery panicles. The path ran northwards up a dry ravine, and then wound steeply up its eastern side on to the ridge which bordered it. Once again, there were some interesting woody plants among the scrub: *Clematis delavayi*, not a climber but an erect shrub with small leaves with silvery hairs, and *Brandisia racemosa*, its overhanging branches carrying small clusters of long scarlet flowers which gleamed in the last rays of the setting sun.

Jiangyi was 1000m higher than the river, and for the next three days the track led along the eastern edge of a low chain of barren sandstone hills, where there were veins of coal and copper, and over the equally dismal tableland from Tongan to Huili. One of the inns was so dirty and festooned with cobwebs in such profusion that I felt impelled to take a photograph — with suitable lighting — simply as a record. Several grassland orchids were in flower and beside a brook, on rock slabs kept moist by spray, I found the tiny pink-flowered *Utricularia orbiculata*, but otherwise this stretch did not offer much of interest.

In Huili I had a rest day and on 16th September paid another visit to Mount Longzhu Shan to learn more of its flowering plants, as they had not been sufficiently developed in the spring. Elaborate preparations were not necessary, as I already knew the route. The magistrate gave me just one soldier, as guarantor rather than escort, a fellow who had no badge or insignia to proclaim the dignity of his office and was without headgear of any kind. Two packhorses sufficed for my kit. As it was the only route up the mountain I followed the track we had taken in March. Up on the ridge some children were watching their flocks, and one of their foals trotted along after my horses almost as far as Jifangkou, with a Yi girl behind it. We caught the foal, intending to hand it over to the shepherdess, but she was afraid to come near. As we went further and further downhill she became more and more dismayed, until at last she timidly approached, snatched the halter and ran off with the foal.

The range of flowering plants which I saw during the ascent was miserably poor, and a visit to the summit next morning yielded very little more. One plant of special interest was the twining blue *Aconitum bulbilliferum*, a new species of monkshood and the only one of its genus which has bulbils in the axils of its upper leaves. The low-growing but robust orchid *Satyrium ciliatum* with inverted flesh-pink flowers and deflexed bracts of the same hue was frequent, and *Codonopsis forrestii* with its saucer-shaped blue flowers scrambled among the golden tufts of moss on the shrubs and bamboos. Since the summit region of Mount Longzhu Shan (3675m) was unforested — whether because of its volcanic rock, its exposure to wind or more probably because the trees had been felled — it seemed higher than it really was; in fact it is considerably below the high alpine zone, and the absence of limestone has discouraged the evolution of a diversified flora. The mountain's most pleasing feature was the array of mosses and lichens, and on closer study it furnished many specimens to add to my earlier collection. Lower down the late flowers of the heath meadows were unfolding in profusion, but I noted hardly anything which I had not seen before. One new find, however, was *Hydrangea macrocarpa*, with a downy covering on the undersides of its leaves, but its flowers had gone over.

In Huili I soldered up my herbarium specimens in tin boxes and left them with the innkeeper. On 20th September I set out for Yanyuan, taking the track marked on Davies' map via Puwei (Pudi-dschou), though having no inkling of the problems which the pack animals would face on this route. After an ascent of only 800m it crossed the rather bare crest to the south of Mount Longzhu Shan and plunged down into the deep valley of the Anning He. Alongside a stream the track had sunk below ground level, and no one had bothered to mend it. One of our horses slid straight into the mud-filled channel and sank belly-deep into the mire, from which we had some trouble in extricating it. *Oroxylum indicum*, a small scantily-branched tree belonging to the Bignoniaceae, with large bipinnate leaves triangular in outline and woody pods 70cm in length dangling from long upright stalks(Fig.12), was growing there among luxuriant spreading umbrella-shaped bushes of *Phyllanthus emblica*. Intending to collect some of the pods, Pen climbed up the tree, unwound his turban, tied the trowel to it and threw it at them. On the first attempt he missed his aim and made a gash in Jin's head. Jin promptly picked a few leaves from the wayside plants, among which

I noticed *Medicago lupulina*, and used them to dress the wound.

Next morning we crossed the Anning He above Panglingkou. It was quite narrow, but, viewed from the ferryboat, it created a strange impression, rushing down towards us in a short level stretch, smooth and brimful, and then foaming over the large round boulders which made its steeply inclined bed. Our route then ran northwest, climbing gradually up a broad cultivated valley. The huge subtropical *Bombax malabarica* was growing near the houses. Then came a little ravine; I was busy with various tasks, and when I caught up with the caravan the mafu had halted although it was only half past five and he was far short of the intended halting place, and had unloaded outside a house where we could not possibly spend the night and where there was no space or forage for the horses. The people said that three li further on there was a village with several inns. I told him to load up again and rode on with my men in front of me. The guide whom we took with us ran off when we reached the next house, but we found a substitute in another house further on. They were simple peasant houses; the occupants would not take us in and were not exactly friendly. As it was a cloudy night it soon grew pitch dark, but at last in a village called Banshan a friend of the Protestant missionaries in Xichang invited us into his house, which proved quite passable. There were no inns there. The caravan finally arrived at half past nine, guided by men with torches who had been sent to meet it. Excepting the bundle of pressed plants, all the loads were wet through, allegedly because they had fallen into the water when a wooden bridge collapsed. Next morning was therefore spent in drying them, and it was midday before we set off for Puwei, after the local police chief, summoned by cannon shots to some official function, had sat down beside me, peering out of the corner of his eye at my tattered travelling coat, and we had both shared a ceremonious reception.

The track led through a little ravine where the dainty *Didymocarpus stenanthos* was growing on the sandstone rocks, through oak forest where the undergrowth was full of the imposing *Begonia taliensis* with large red-bordered leaves mottled with white and divided into pointed lobes, over a low col covered with pines and finally along a valley to Puwei. The col lies on the watershed between the Anning He and the Yangzi, an inconspicuous ridge of red sandstone less than 2000m in altitude, flattened and divided into irregular tracts, though down in the valley the rock is grey in colour and there is a low ridge of limestone blocks which demarcates the small plain of Puwei. Next morning, as we passed the recently harvested ricefields, the dry stubble made an extraordinary crackling sound as it burst and split in the warmth of the sun. In some places it was audible from the track, and when I stepped on to the ricefield and bent down it was almost continuous.

The route now ran down along the steep valleyside, first on the clay-slate which is always found in the deep river valleys and later on micaceous quartz-diorite. Near the Yalong the track became very bad and narrow, but in the humid air the plant life was subtropical, rich and unspoiled. This was the only occasion in that year on which I encountered such greenhouse conditions, although the temperature at midday was only 23°C. Bowed down by enormously numerous though individually delicate leaves and panicles, the slender hollow whorled stems of *Andropogon assimilis*, a grass several metres tall, arched over the hillside. The bushes (*Cinnamomum delavayi*) were interlaced with the sprawling *Mussaenda simpliciloba*, a new species, its narrow orange yellow flowers made conspicuous by snow white bracts, together with the twining *Polygonum aubertii* with profuse yellowish white panicles, and *Streptolirion volubile*. With my Browning pistol I shot a large eagle-owl which foolishly loitered near the track in broad daylight. That evening it was skinned and salted, and the skin was tied on to one of the loads to dry, though unfortunately it was torn to shreds later when the load fell off. We halted for the night at Lanba on a ridge before the Yalong. The caravan was again late in arriving, and the load containing the kitchen crate, campbed and blankets was missing. It had fallen off at some rocks where the track was built up into steps, and had tumbled down into a stony gully, and as dusk was coming on the men had left it there. The horse had been held back by its bridle. I was happy to find that Lanba had recently been burnt to the ground, and the bedsteads, straw mats and eating utensils belonging to the Chinese villagers were consequently brand new — and if necessary one can always live on rice. However, the accommodation was so cramped that I had to share the room with the coolies. Apprehensive that they might adopt a somewhat antagonistic attitude to my demand to make more space for me in the room, and probably remembering that I liked to sleep outside Chinese houses, Wang had the impudence to say to me: "Sleep just outside the door", though the eaves gave hardly any shelter and the blackness of the sky heralded an approaching rainstorm.

Next morning the first task was to recover the lost load. The kitchen box was shattered into a thousand fragments, but we found everything. The cooking pots were somewhat dented and the provisions (sugar, tea, bread, etc.) had been soaked by the rain. While supervising this work I noticed a tree which I had seen before in similar places on the Yalong and above the bridge at Zi Lijiang. Its round leaves had a greasy lustre and here to my delight I found its inconspicuous pendulous spikes with reflexed fruits, which enabled me to identify it — after my return to Austria — as *Hymenodictyon flaccidum*, a rare species of *Rubiaceae*.

At midday I rode ahead of the caravan to the ferry over the Yalong, somewhat less than two hours distant. The path was very narrow and in several places I had to widen it with my ice axe, the haft of which had long ago been split by such misuse. I waited at the ferry under a spreading banyan tree, at a spot from which I could see far back along the route. Sandstone strata with bands of quartz were exposed in a vertically compressed sequence from north-northeast to south-southwest. To pass the time I put a thermometer into the windblown sand beside the river. Heated by the sun, its temperature was 46.5°C. Four o'clock came and there was still no sign of the mafu. There was now no prospect of getting everything across the river, and as there was no accommodation at the ferry I had to go back and

see what was wrong. I found him sitting on the path; after stopping to widen a narrow place he had unloaded the horses and settled down to cook his rice. This was the only time that Wang displayed any spark of vigour: he gave the rice pot a kick and it went rolling down the hillside. I told the scoundrel that he would certainly not receive any gratuity for good conduct, but I should really have given him a good thrashing. We had to go back to Lanba, where Wang subsequently admitted to me that that very morning the mafu had said that if I went in front he was not going to follow, as the path was so bad. The next day (25th September) I stayed behind the caravan and though the boxes had to be unloaded and carried in two places all went well as far as the ferry at Datiaogu. Moving with oriental slowness the ferry carried first the five loads, myself, Wang, the two plant collectors, the "soldier" and my pony; then after bringing three pack animals the boat went back with the mafu to fetch the remaining packhorses and the servant's horse. As soon as they reached the bank the boat, which had already been taking a good deal of water, sprang a large leak. "Then mend it", I shouted across to them. "Non, total cassé," was their answer, as interpreted by Wang. It was now 5.45 pm and dusk was gathering; to proceed with the whole caravan was out of the question, and the inn was three quarters of an hour's journey further on. I had to let the two mafus go off with the horses. We left two loads in a little hut near the ferry, took the other three on our shoulders and marched on. Unaccustomed to such work, I nearly flattened my Adam's apple against the lid of the box. One of the loads was dropped — a quite unnecessary mishap — but although it was now pitch dark we found it again. I went in front, leading the horse and feeling my way until I reached a corner of the rock face where the path was too narrow to pass. There was nothing for it but to set up my campbed on a level patch, and send a man to the inn to fetch pine-wood torches and rice, as my matches were in the boxes and I dared not open them in the rain. Several men came back carrying lighted brands, but without any food, simply because someone had stupidly forgotten it. At last the rain stopped for a moment and I crawled into my waterproof sleeping bag, though the downpour continued all night and my blankets were soaked by rain which leaked in through the neck opening. My men stretched something over the pole of my mosquito net and crept under it. As some stretches of the track were too narrow for packhorses, several porters came early next morning to carry my big crates. We divided the smaller items among our three pack animals and marched on. The porters brought me five duck's eggs which I ate ravenously, having had no food since noon the previous day.

At a fork in the path just beyond our camp site one of the loads slipped off the saddle and the horse lost its balance, toppled backwards and somersaulted down the stony hillside towards the river. However, it soon got on its legs again and stood there quietly, quite uninjured. The sack containing paper for pressing plants rolled into the Yalong. At first it floated near the bank, circling slowly round and round. Swift as lightning I unbuckled my camera and leapt down to fish it out with my iceaxe, and in so doing I lacerated an Aleppo boil[45] on my right forearm; it had appeared as a belated souvenir of my stay in Mesopotamia, though it usually gave me no trouble. The sack drifted out into the current and was carried downstream; the soldier ran back along the path and rescued it at the ferry. In the meantime the horse had grown restless and when the men tried to catch it it broke away, fell over again and gashed its neck. Although the wound was trivial and I applied an aseptic dressing at once, in the prevailing Chinese filth it turned septic and the horse remained unfit for work for many days. At last we all arrived at the inn at Pojue and dried our kit in front of the fire. The two mafus turned up that afternoon, bringing the other horses. I turned my attention to the vegetation. Various shade-loving plants had found shelter under the tall grass *Andropogon assimilis*, notably the pink *Justicia procumbens* and the blue *Dicliptera cyclostegia*, both belonging to the *Acanthaceae*, *Petrocosmea nervosa*, a plant with deep blue flowers and thick round leaves related to the "African violets", and the dainty *Selaginella braunii*.

From Pojue to Datiaogu the Yalong flowed from west to east, and higher up it curved in a semicircle round a talus fan at the mouth of a fairly large, thinly populated lateral valley which ran down from the north east. In the course of further erosion both the tributary stream and the main river had cut down through the talus fan into the underlying sandstone to such a great depth that several landslips had occurred on the hillside opposite the lateral valley.

Our route led close to the rockface exposed by such a landslip up on to a ridge covered with pine forest and then down into a side valley of the Yalong. During the descent we had to repair a suspension bridge over a deeply eroded channel and hack away the sandstone. The leading horse broke through the bridge and fell backwards several metres on to some rotten timbers. It was unhurt, but to get it up the steep hillside was no easy task. The crates which it was carrying had remained on the bridge. We had to take off the loads and even the saddles before we could lead the other horses across, holding on to their tails on the uphill side. Stretched over the stream between two posts was a rope by which travellers could pull themselves across in times of flood; this was the only occasion on which I saw such a ropebridge in purely Chinese territory. Next day the path continued north-westwards along the steep side of the lateral valley. The slopes were clothed by the same luxuriant subtropical vegetation, among it *Saurauia napaulensis*, a small well-shaped tree with large, beautifully veined dark green leaves and loose racemes of fleshy spherical fragrant rose pink flowers. At a narrow corner where the path went round a tree my best horse, carrying the heaviest boxes, lost its balance and crashed down the rocks into the stream. It was stone dead, though without any external injury, and its death cost me some 80 Austrian crowns at the prewar rate. The crates lodged undamaged in the trees and were soon rescued. What were we to do? To turn back meant facing the same hazards once again and abandoning

our goal, but if we went forward we might hope for something better. So the two mafus loaded the boxes on to their backs, one of them, a broad sturdy fellow, without difficulty, the other with much panting and muttering, and we marched on. Soon afterwards another horse fell down a little waterfall in a rocky gully — an almost vertical drop of about 10 metres. However, it was unhurt and immediately stood up and started grazing. The pack-frame was shattered, but the load caught on the rocks and was saved. Finally the horse carrying my tin boxes rolled down the slope into a rice-field, and as they had already sustained so many dents the watery mud leaked into them, seriously damaging their contents. At the village of Shiwanhe I engaged two porters for the boxes from the horse which had been killed and another for Pen, who was suffering from rheumatism in consequence of camping without shelter in the rain.

We proceeded up the gently ascending valley, which soon became narrow and rocky. The scene was wild and romantic. The stream raged between splendid cliffs of limestone, on which, arising from cushions of tufa-forming moss (*Hymenostylium curvirostre*), there were curious stalactitic formations, resembling irregular bracket fungi though some of them had little sub-stalactites hanging from them. Here, growing in subtropical grassland at an altitude of 1450m, was the largest of all species of edelweiss, *Leontopodium artemisiifolium*, a metre tall, with loose star-shaped flowers up to 12cm in diameter. Below Zaluping the valley forked. Growing there on the rockface were two handsome Gesnerads, the juicy *Rhynchoglossum obliquum* and the white-flowered *Boea paniculata*, a new species. Before long the path quitted the steeper main eastern fork and climbed to the west to Niuchang, a tiny nest where we found shelter for the night. From there the path climbed steeply along the stream through *Lithocarpus* woodland with a richly assorted understorey of shrubs, reaching an altitude of 3640m. Blooming on the sandstone slopes above were masses of the mat-forming *Leontopodium subulatum* together with the deep blue *Cyananthus delavayi*, also growing in mats. The stems of *Astragalus prattii* spread out in all directions from its thick rootstock, and lying prostrate everywhere was the remarkable *Pedicularis cymbalaria*. At first glance its flowers appear to be golden, but on closer inspection they are seen to have a pale pink lower lip flecked with purple and a light brown hood marked with purplish brown veins. There was *Saxifraga strigosa*, a slender plant with numerous bulbils in its leaf axils, and other species with conspicuous flowers, such as *Sedum beauverdii*, with foliage resembling that of a haircap moss. The flowers of *Leontopodium calocephalum* var. *uliginosum*, growing in wet spots on the other side of the mountain, made patches of white visible from some distance. On that day (30th September), as on the previous few days, rain fell almost incessantly during the march to Yanyuan; only in the low lying part of the basin was the weather clear.

My next objectives were a limestone mountain to the north, about 4300m high, which had been

---

[45] Oriental sore, the lesion of cutaneous leishmaniasis, caused by *Leishmania tropica*.

pointed out as "Huangliangzi" [46] in the spring, and one of the many sandstone peaks in the vicinity. Owing to the rain none of them was visible, and no one understood the sketch which I drew from memory, but before long I found a soldier who knew Mount Huangliangzi. After a rest day I set off for the ascent, estimated to need three days, starting out along the track by which we had returned from Guabi and making for the yamen of the Yi prince at Gubaishu, who was moreover the tusi(government official) of the territory I planned to visit. He presented me with two hens and a lump of excellent butter; in exchange I gave him one of my 3.50 crown watches. Just as I was ready to set off again, he produced a hotly spiced meal for my men and me. Though I had a Yi as an extra guide, this delay meant that we got only as far as Shanmenkou, where we found accommodation for the night in a small Chinese farmhouse. I seemed to remember that somewhere hereabouts we had to turn off into the mountains, but visibility was poor because of the persistent rain and in the featureless karst landscape there were no landmarks that I recognized. The route along which the guide led me was already at variance with the plan, but as he assured me that the Huangliangzi was very high and that from it one could see as far as the Dechang district, I assumed that it must be part of the main crest. Since I had no positive alternative plan to offer, I agreed to his proposals. The steppe which grew on the deposits in the basin resembled that found at lower levels, though it was much less rich in flowers (the only plentiful plants in bloom were Swertia species), and the reddish Andropogon delavayi was dominant, other steppe grasses being almost entirely absent. As we went up the gentle slope towards the mountain the steppe gradually changed into a heath meadow community, rich in blossoms of many hues, which brought back vivid memories of the karst heath which flourishes under closely similar conditions in Illyria.

Towards midday I reached the descent on the far side of the mountain and followed the left bank of the Malu Tang, dipping far down into the side valleys and climbing out of them, past a Xifan village and several Yi villages. Before reaching Baitiaohe, where we were to spend the night, we came out again on to the river, which here emerged from a deep U-shaped valley between huge limestone cones and broke through a narrow ravine into the surrounding lowlands. The U-shaped valley, which was not very long, was formed by the junction of two gorges, separated at first by an extremely narrow crest which had to be climbed. From its inner end, at the foot of the mountainside, the path led down again into the western gorge below the east side of Mount Houlong Shan[47], which plunged down very steeply. This was the mountain which I had ascended in the spring. The blue gentian relative Crawfurdia fasciculata, scrambling high up over bamboos and shrubs, was common here, and

tall Saussurea species were flowering at the edge of the dense woodland thickets.

That evening, climbing once again out of the valley, I reached the bamboo huts of the tiny Yi village of Huangliangzi, situated at 3325m on the mountain of the same name and just within the district of Guabi. The summit, which I reached on 5th October in heavy rain and sleet, consisted of clay-slate, together with limestone in the last 200m, and touched 4075m. The vegetation was already autumnal; there was much edelweiss (Leontopodium calocephalum) together with Anaphalis and numerous large flowered gentians, the fine blue bells of Allium beesianum, Delphinium forrestii and others. Part of my task was thus accomplished, namely to examine the flora of the acid rocks. Despite the rain a few Autochromes and other photographs were successful. Back in the hospitable Yi hut I dried myself in front of the fire, over which potatoes were simmering in a large iron pot for my evening meal as well as theirs. It was a small but cosy lodging.

"So this is what the wicked Yi are like, when I actually come and see them, even though the Chinese officials are always warning me about them," I said with a laugh, and Wang interpreted.

My mafu was so careless that he would certainly have set fire to their hut if it had not been so wet; when he went out to attend to the horses he took a bundle of bamboo culms which he had lit at the fire and which flared up as he stood at the door. From this spot I could easily have climbed Houlong Shan again, but in the unrelenting rain the ascent would have been no pleasure, and furthermore I had a large collection of plants which could not be allowed to remain any longer without changing their paper, more especially as the trip had already taken three days longer than I had planned. I therefore made my way back along the same valley, declining with thanks an invitation to visit Guabi which the prince sent by two messengers to Mabahe when he heard that I was there. I crossed to the right bank of the river, followed the route over the crest which we had taken in May, and then took the better path — the route which Schneider had used in the spring — arriving after dark at the Xifan village of Huapolu. From there, by crossing the Malu Tang at a ford, the journey back to Yanyuan can be completed in one long day's march. The people said the water was too deep, but having heard such stories before I ignored them and went down to the ford. Once there, however, I realised they were right. The people down there gestured to indicate that I would have to swim and explained that the water had been breast-high even the day before. The sight of the broad stream left me in no doubt. I therefore had to go back some distance southwards as far as the bridge at Meiyu, the people of which I recalled as being rather unpleasant. That morning, however, the mafu from Lijiang, claiming to be ill, had once again taken fully a hour to pack the two loads, and it was therefore so dark when we arrived that hardly anyone noticed me and I found quite agreeable accommodation. I finally got back to Yanyuan after six and a half days, happy to be in good health and free from even the most trivial or transient ailments despite continuous travel in the rain and all the discomforts it entails, despite splashing through

---

[46] Heng-liang-tzu Shan (13,000ft) on Rock's map.

[47] Hou-lung-shan (14,500ft=4421m) on Rock's map, (15,300ft=4665m) on Davies' map.

countless streams in boots that were falling to pieces, and despite riding for days along tracks that were bottomless morasses, a sport which, in October at an altitude of 2500m, is certainly no pleasure.

Dahutu, the limestone mountain which I had originally chosen as my goal, now unveiled herself partially from time to time, but she had donned a mantle of snow and the season was in any case too far advanced to permit the desired comparison with the flora of the western side. Furthermore, the reports of the war now circulating in Yanyuan, having been transmitted via the mission in Xichang, were, if not exactly false, so depressing in their tenor that they killed in me that spark of enthusiasm which is necessary for vigorous exertion in such weather. I therefore decided to go back to Hexi along the route by which we had come and then to return directly to Kunming. Pen was still unwell and I had to send him back to Dali in the carrying chair. I took some pleasure in sending home the allegedly sick mafu; he invested all his cash in clothes and headgear, made himself ridiculous by appearing for several hours daily dressed in a khaki suit cut in European style but so hopelessly ill-tailored that it hung loose from every limb, and suddenly declared that he actually knew nothing about horses, having formerly been nothing more than a simple soldier. As for the soldier who had been sent as my escort from Huili, I had at his wish taken him up Mount Huangliangzi in Pen's place, and he now wanted to remain with me, as no one in Huili wanted him any longer. These "government representatives" were evidently nothing more than casual labourers. Through the good offices of the town clerk (the xianzhang) I had engaged a new mafu with a horse to replace the sick mafu and the animal which had been killed, but when we reached Hexi he decided not to come with me to Kunming; instead, he sold me the horse — without the bridle, the sale of which would bring bad luck. I filled his place by using the "soldier" from Huili as my mafu, so all ended well. The Yi tusi visited Yanyuan occasionally, and eyed me shyly from the back of the courtyard. However, when I invited him to tea and cake, he asked me for medicine for one of his people, and when I hinted that his butter had been very much to my liking I found myself the richer by two lumps of it, and indeed, my attention alerted by his original gift, I had purchased from the Xifan people a large lump of butter, a delicacy which the Chinese disdain.

After resisting with some trouble the importunate pleadings of the xianzhang, who wanted me to sell him my Browning and send it from Kunming by Wang, I left Yanyuan on 12th October. I retraced the route which I had taken in May, and collected some interesting late-flowering plants growing in this stretch of the Yalong valley which, bordered by higher mountains, is very much drier. I reached Hexi in four days and had a friendly reception from Père Labrunie, who had meanwhile been stationed there. I accepted with alacrity an invitation from the bishop to visit him in Xichang. I now realised that old Father Burnichon was a dyed-in-the-wool French fanatic. Bishop de Guébriant was too shrewd to reveal much of what was passing through his mind; he expressed regret for Austria's "continual defeats, even at the hands of the Montenegrins; a powder magazine must have exploded there". He said

nothing about Prussia, but his thoughts were all too evident. I took the opportunity of calling upon the missionary Mr Wellwood and his German-American wife, who was extremely downcast by the news she had just received of the battle of the Marne. After returning to Hexi the next evening, I took the track leading along the right bank of the river to Dechang. In the gorgeous autumn weather which had now set in it afforded magnificent vistas of the talus fans and river terraces along the Jiangchang valley and the superb range of sandstone pinnacles — around 4500m in altitude — on the opposite side (east). Visibility was far better than in the spring and my photographs were much more successful, especially as I had now corrected a fault in the camera which I had previously overlooked. This time I found the inhabitants much more friendly than on my first visit, but I had not entirely forgotten the need to rant and rave[48], though such conduct was totally foreign to my mature. In contrast to their offhand attitude towards the modest and unassuming traveller, these people — even the most repellent of them — react quite otherwise to the man who arrives with a large retinue, his coming proclaimed in advance by couriers sent to all corners of the land, and who makes the whole village resound with fearsome cursing and scolding in military style. The blue dye for clothing fabric was now being prepared throughout the country. Around Huili it was extracted from *Perilla avium*, and at Dali I subsequently saw *Strobilanthes cusia* planted for the same purpose beneath the shade of bamboo canopies. The leaves were soaked in water for five or six days in large pans waterproofed with lime (at Dali in wooden tubs) and then strained though cloth. The vats used for dyeing the fabric stood open in the streets and were among the chief sources of evil stenches.

I continued my journey in the customary daily stages, stopped at Huili to pick up the crate which had been stored there, loaded it on my servant's horse, which he had in fact never used, and proceeded along the direct route to Kunming, halting repeatedly to take more photographs of the scenery and to collect plants, some because I had not seen them before, some because my existing specimens showed them in earlier phases of development, and others because they seemed to display polymorphism or other features of interest. From now on I lengthened each day's march, for at the end of October the frosts begin on the Yunnan highlands and my favourite sleeping place under the open roof outside the bedrooms became uncomfortably chilly, and at this season a prolonged search for flowers was not worth the trouble and expense. The direct route passed to the west of Sayingpan, cutting off the bend in the river by crossing the col at Gandeng in a sandstone ridge, then traversed the valley at Erdaohe and rejoined our outward route on the saddle above Luoheitang. In the inn at Luoheitang an old man was dying, and the carpenter making his coffin was busy all night hammering and sawing outside the door of his room with the maximum of

---

[48] He said nothing about this on his earlier visit to Dechang (Chapter 3).

noise. This time I did not take the detour via Suge, but went straight on from Santang to the Qiaotianshang. Ten days after leaving Huili I arrived in Kunming, where Herr Stiebritz and his family most hospitably offered me board and lodging.

Map 3

Handel-Mazzetti's routes in the Mekong, Salween
and Irrawaddy gorges 1915 and 1916

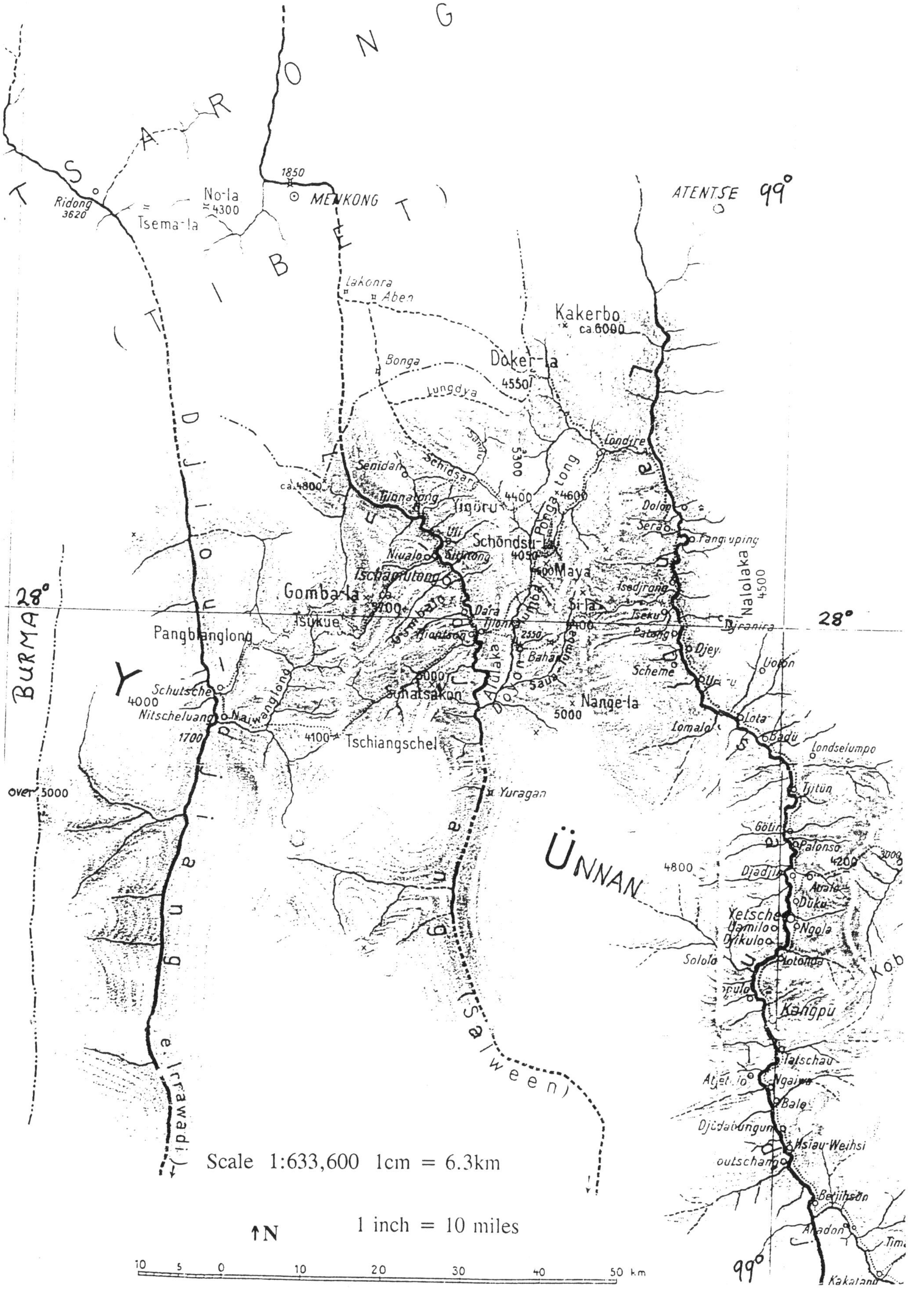

TSARONG

Ridong 3620

No-la 4300

Tsema-la

1850

MEKONG

TIBET

ATENTSE 99°

Lakonra

Aben

Bonga

Kakerbo ca.6000

Doker-la 4550

lungdya

ca. 4800

Senidah

Schidsan

Londjre

5300

Tjunatong

Iigoru

4400

Dongatong 4600

Dolon

Serao

Fanguping

Uli

Schöndsu-la

4050

Niualo

Sitkrong

4600 Maya

Ischamutong

Dara

Tsedjrong

Nalolaka 4500

Gomba-la

3700

Sila

Tsiken

28°

Tsukue

Tjonce

4100

2550

Patongo

Djranira

28°

Pangblanglong

Tjantson

Baha

Scheme

Djey

Uioton

Dulaka

Saua

Djiru

500or

Sohatsakon

Nange-la

5000

Lomalo

Lota

Badü

Schutsche

4000

Nitscheluang

Naiu

4100

Tschiangschel

Tijtün

1700

Londselumpo

Yuragan

Götin

Palonso 4200

3700

4800

Djadjil

Apalo

ÜNNAN

Duku

Xetsche

Uamiloo

Ngola

Dyikuloo

Solola

Plotonda

Kob

Gpula

Kangpu

BURMA

Tatschau

Atjet.10°

Ngairu

Bale

Djidaiungum

Hsiau-Weihsi

outschamo

Berjihson

over 5000

die Irrawadi

Gujlu (Salween)

Anadon

Tim

99°

Kakatanu

Scale 1:633,600   1cm = 6.3km

↑N   1 inch = 10 miles

10   5   0   10   20   30   40   50 km

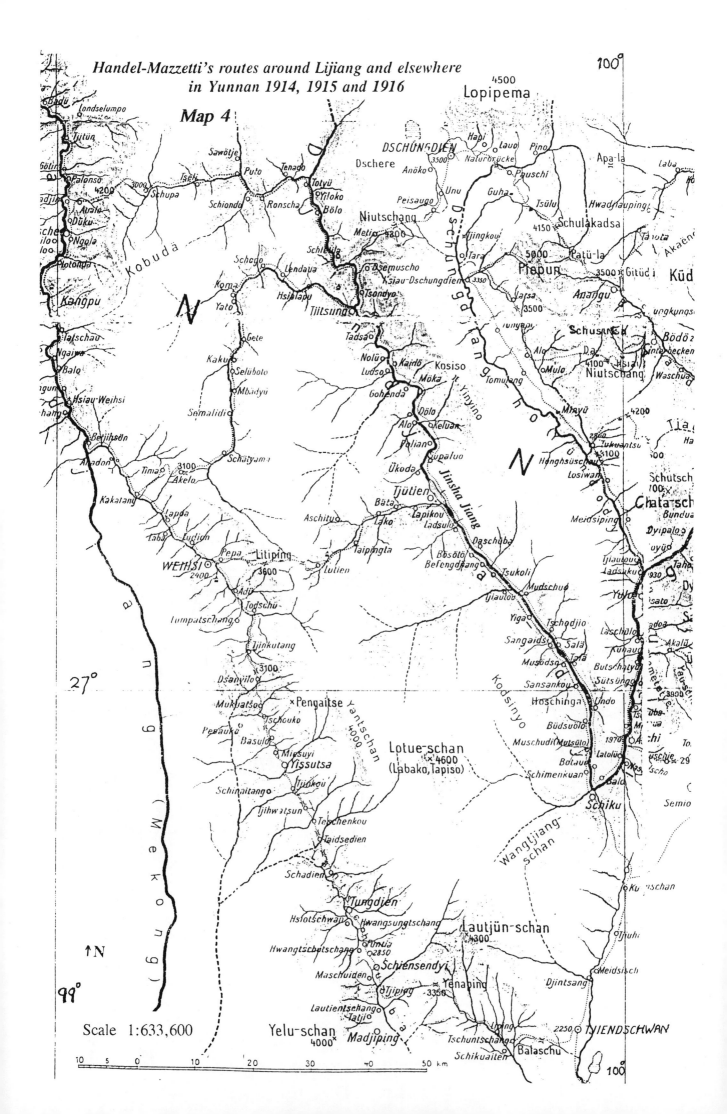

Handel-Mazzetti's routes around Lijiang and elsewhere
in Yunnan 1914, 1915 and 1916

Map 4

Scale 1:633,600

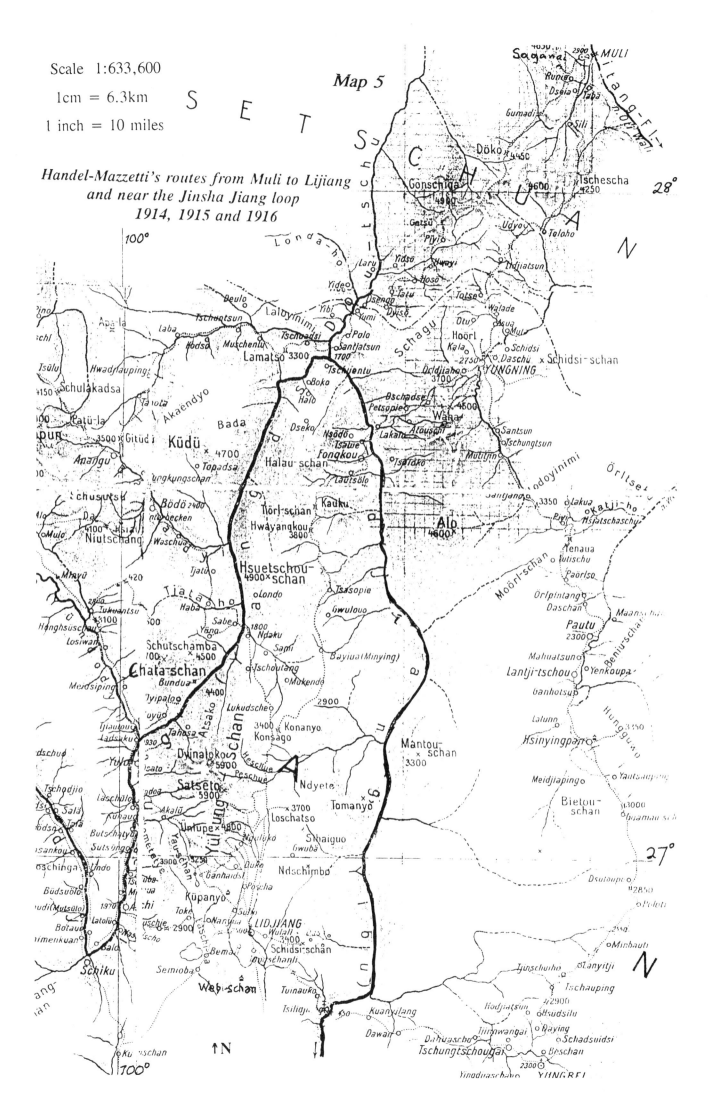

Scale 1:633,600

1cm = 6.3km

1 inch = 10 miles

Handel-Mazzetti's routes from Muli to Lijiang and near the Jinsha Jiang loop 1914, 1915 and 1916

Map 5

Reproduced from the map of

NW Yunnan and S Sichuan

drawn by Heinrich Handel-Mazzetti

based on the map of Yunnan by Major H.R. Davies
and Handel-Mazzetti's own triangulations,
route surveys and photographs taken in 1914, 1915 and 1916.

Scale 1:633,600 1cm = 6.3km 1 inch = 10 miles

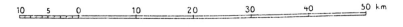

⊙ ○   *towns and villages*
◑, ◔   *ditto, with missions*
 ℅   *scattered settlements*
 ¤   *places named but not visited*

 ≙ *monastery*   ▪ *hut*   ✖ *bridge*
 ×ᵢ *peak*   ≍ *pass*
 ⇝ *waterfall*   ⦅⦅⦅ *glacier, snowfield*
 ‥-‥ *international frontier*   ·-·· *provincial boundary*

 .... *Handel-Mazzetti's route*   altitudes in metres

PART II 1915

To the Tibetan Border

Chapter 10. Winter in Kunming

The German community — Schneider's departure — enemies and neutrals — features of the locality

The German community in Kunming had been augmented by the arrival of several refugees from Tonking. There was Herr Hieber from Speidel & Co in Haiphong and Herr Stutzke who had been in charge of the machinery of a rice mill in that city. Herr Treptow of the British and American Tobacco Company was now permanently resident in Kunming. A German-Swiss family, Herr Otto Schoch with his wife and two children, had moved from Tonkin for similar reasons. Fräulein Fense, who looked after the consul's children, had arrived from Mengzi, and there was an Austrian, Herr Pawelka, an official in the Chinese Maritime Customs, who had formerly served as a cavalry officer and whose knowledge of horses was to save me from various mistakes. The consul Fritz Weiss and his family kept open house, and there was no excuse for boredom. The main subject of conversation was of course the war. Through the German Overseas Service we received the German news reports in full, and set against news from enemy sources they naturally painted a far more favourable picture than I had hitherto dreamt possible. *"One moment exulting, the next quite cast down,"*[49] might have summed up our mood, though for my part I found the matter far too tragic for jubilation. As always I sought solace in the world of nature, though most of my time was spent in developing eleven hundred photographs, making excerpts from my diaries and preparing my scientific findings for publication.

As my buff piebald pony had such an awkward gait that it was no pleasure to ride I sold it together with the pack animals, retaining the bay which I had bought from the mafu, a strong and lively beast though very small. At Christmas Schneider returned via Fengqing and Yimen after a journey from Dali to Pupiao on the Nu Jiang (Salween) and gave me a handsome grey which Li and then he had ridden on the way back. Though it ultimately proved not sturdy enough to carry my weight it held out for the next expedition into the mountains. I spent Christmas Eve — the second of my exile — with Stiebritz and his family. A long-needled pine made a somewhat unsatisfactory Christmas tree; in later years I used a *Keteleeria* tree instead. Little did I dream how many Christmases I was yet to spend in China! (Fig.14). In the New Year Schneider took leave of us and travelled with Stutzke to Yibin and down the Yangzi to Shanghai, where he sailed to America to take up a post he had been offered at the Arnold Arboretum. Happily, we were able to keep in touch, and his letters were of great assistance in my subsequent scientific work.

Never before had any war caused such sad disruption of personal contacts between individuals, and even in China our relations with nationals of the Allies became more and more strained. On meeting one another in the street, men who had formerly been the best of friends would at first still exchange greetings; then they would merely raise their hats; later they would simply nod, and finally each would look the other way. With the French missionaries I remained somewhat longer on friendly terms and even Dr Vadon, though he slipped back into his opium smoking immediately after returning from a course of treatment in Paris designed to cure him from the addiction, never forgot his humanitarian duties: at a time when smallpox was prevalent in Kunming he vaccinated everybody, and he never refused to sell me the medicines which I needed for my journeys. Neutrals were few in number — a few Americans, a Swede in the Post Office and the Norwegian missionary Eduard Amundsen, the only one who still associated with us as freely as with the rest. However, he was working for the English Bible Society and it was his genuine and impartial neutrality which later, through the intervention of Mr Goffe[50], the British consul general, was to cost him his job.

Every second day, or in bad weather less frequently, I went out riding for a few hours into the hills which rim the Kunming basin. Except on the occasional days when snow was lying, there were a few flowers to be found there throughout the winter. I enjoyed many outings with Herr Schoch, an energetic walker. He displayed great interest in botany and in the summer of 1915 independently collected some four hundred species, a set of which he entrusted to me for identification. Although the immediate vicinity was almost entirely denuded of forest apart from the groves round the temples, there were certain aspects of the landscape, notably its colouring, which gave me great enjoyment. Indeed it was the very absence of the tree cover that disclosed the structure of the mountain as viewed from afar, and made plain the succession of the strata and their contortions with a clarity gratifying to the scientist's eye. To the northwest — west of Buqi — there was a layer of grey limestone rolled up almost into a circle. Mount Changchong Shan to the north of the city was built up of numerous dark grey limestone strata interbedded with volcanic rock and swung round so as to lie vertically, with a strike from NNE to SSW. Weathering had converted them to a karst landscape with rows of spikes and towers sticking up like fish bones. Lower down it was covered by bright red *terra rossa*, the residue of the dissolution of the rock. This succession of strata

---

[49] From Clärchen's song in Goethe's *"Egmont"* III, 2.

[50] Herbert Goffe complained to the Bible Society that Amundsen, who was in their employ, flew the Norwegian flag from the mission building, made no attempt to conceal his pro-German sympathies and imported stores for the use of the German consul. See biographical note on Amundsen, page 178.

sank down below the plain to re-emerge beyond the lake in the wild limestone pavements of the Xi Shan ridge, which terminated in a vertical scarp facing east(Fig.16). The hills to the east of the basin displayed similar but less distorted stratification, with a gentle eastwards dip. In the rays of the setting sun these hills glowed with a splendid peach-red tone, set off in due season against the plum blossom in the orchards or, at the beginning of March, against the peach blossom beyond Heilongtan and the gap where the railway entered the mountains. Along the cypress alleys which bordered the irrigation channels between the vivid green of the beanfields the evening sun evoked a display of colours unexcelled in its delicate nuances.

The myriad twiglets of *Cupressus duclouxiana*, covered with dull grey-green scale-like leaves, took on golden tones, as did the thin grey bark as it peeled off in longitudinal strips from their vertical trunks, which cast long shadows on the ground. In February the air was heavy with scent from the dense panicles of violet flowers which hung from the gnarled low-growing trees of *Buddleia officinalis*, while the soft green of the young, almost translucent leaves of the weeping willow (*Salix babylonica*) provided a sharp contrast and a reminder of spring colours at home. Lazily balancing on the treetops were huge kites and cormorants, black crows and more rarely white herons, while large flocks of starlings and quails appeared from time to time. One of the most attractive plants found in the neighbourhood was the cushion-forming *Lithospermum hancockianum* (*Lithodora hancockiana*), known only from Mengzi and from Kunming north-northeast as far as the Yangzi (Fig.15). Solitary plants were to be found in the Changchong Shan, but it was more numerous on the Laojing Shan situated in the Xi Shan range to the south. Its stems, leafless in their lower parts, are covered with blackish scales and reach a length of 30cm, ending in rosettes of stiff silver-grey leaves 10cm long; projecting from the centre of the rosette is a short tuft of long-tubed pinkish-violet flowers, their corollas almost 2cm in diameter. Aggregated in enormous numbers they formed flower-spangled hemispherical cushions half a metre in diameter, rooted in crevices and spreading out on the bare rock.

Chapter 11. To Manhao in Tropical Yunnan

The descent from Mengzi — a troublesome escort — rain forest remnants and savannah — tree ants — doctoring the sick — blind valleys and sinkholes

A major journey in the winter would not have brought results commensurate with the expense unless it were devoted to the tropical zone of Yunnan. My request for additional financial support had been met by the safe arrival of 3000 crowns[51] from the Academy of Sciences in Vienna, but as I had no idea whether I would receive any further grants I thought it best to err on the side of caution and made plans for the shortest and most economical trip. The point most easily reached was Manhao, on the Red River south of Mengzi[52] at less than 200m above sea level. Judging from the richness of the genuinely tropical vegetation which I had studied at the nearby Phomoi in Tonkin and seen from the train at Nanxi, even a short visit to Manhao promised to be extremely rewarding. If I went there I would be able to collect an abundance of material in a short time, return in two days with the spoils to the drier air of Mengzi and then to the favourable climate of Kunming, and thus avoid the necessity of drying plants under tropical conditions, where mould is so difficult to prevent.

Through the consul Herr Weiss I gave notice of my intentions to the dujun (military governor) and received from the latter a written reply to the effect that I might call upon the daotai (circuit intendant) in Mengzi to provide me with an escort of soldiers, as the district was at the time infested with bandits. Armed with this letter, I travelled there by rail on 20th February, and was hospitably received by Herr Andersen of Speidel & Co. My first call at the daotai's was fruitless as he was away in Kunming, and his deputy knew nothing of the matter. A telegram to the consul brought this reply: "*Authorities request you wait Mengzi*". The police commander promised to find me some good soldiers as soon as he received authorization, and sent a messenger to see whether there were any bandits on the road and to announce my impending arrival in Manhao.

"*If I'm kept waiting too long, I'll just go by myself*", I declared, for I certainly did not wish to waste time in the vicinity of Mengzi — territory which had been thoroughly explored by Henry[53].

"*No, you can't go,*" said he. However, there was no further argument; Herr Weiss made all the arrangements and on 26th February I set off with an Annamite servant as interpreter and cook, a riding horse, four pack animals and an escort of five police soldiers under an exceedingly swollen-headed corporal who tried to tell me that photography was not allowed, but I took no notice of him.

Once past the little town of Asanzhai the road climbed gradually out of the unattractive plain up a slope with a scattering of bushes. Higher up there was more extensive shrub cover and some bamboos with broad pale green leaves, but otherwise the flora of the steppe was still very similar to that around

[51]About £120 or $600 in 1915 values.

[52]Mengtz on Bartholomew's map, Meng-tzu on Davies' map. Davies went there at the end of his third journey, in May 1899.

[53] Augustine Henry (1857-1930), an Irishman in the Chinese Maritime Customs Service, resided at Mengzi from 1896 to 1900, collected plants for Kew and studied the Yi (Lolo) language. For details see his biography "*The Wood and the Trees*", Sheila Pim, MacDonald, London, 1966.

Kunming. At 2065m, 760m above Mengzi, we reached the pass or rather the crossing over the mountain range, which consisted of short, steep rock edges projecting from a broad ridge and running northeast to southwest. Everything was bare, but while descending the south-facing slope I found remains of luxuriant summer vegetation, notably teasels and *Artemisia* as tall as a man. The steep winding path, with steps in places, led down into a blind side-valley of the Red River; in fact the valley was a series of dolines without any exit. In it was the village of Shuidian, where we spent an uncomfortable night. Even after dark had fallen the corporal kept on grumbling and I had to impress on him that I wished to sleep. In the yard there was a water buffalo. They are ugly creatures at the best of times, and this one had lost its entire snout — torn away by the nose ring. This hideous sight was enough to put anyone off the hostelry.

Here, on a SSW-facing slope at 1300m, was the first of the tropical vegetation. All around me the "jungle" was being burnt, and the air was filled with blue haze and smoke which hid any distant prospect and falsified the perspective so that the descent — which was in any case nearly 2000m in all — seemed truly gigantic. Below Yaotou the paved road climbed over a low col to the east and led straight down the slope to Manhao. In some parts it was very steep and best negotiated on foot. Arriving at Manhao at 3 pm I had a friendly reception from the official and was accommodated in the police barracks. I immediately hung up my thermometer and hygrometer, but the corporal regarded them as a serious danger to the security of the State and fetched the official to inspect them. Fortunately, he was not such an idiot and showed me a thermometer of his own. Because it had been left hanging upside down it read 50°C, but by careful shaking I was able to put it right.

Until the railway was opened Manhao was the main entrepot for trade from Tonkin to Yunnan. When I was there many of its huts — mostly thatched — were falling down and even the telegraph was no longer connected, though dangling wires and broken insulators were still to be seen. I stayed there for six days, seeking out the scanty remnants of natural vegetation which survived in that sadly devastated district. Tropical rainforest was still to be found in meagre patches in a few lateral gorges, especially on the shady side along the right bank of the river. Among the Indian trees which I found were *Dysoxylon procerum, Markhamia stipulata* var. *kerrii* with broad downy brown pods 80cm long, *Stereospermum chelonoides* with narrower shorter woody pods, and *Brassaiopsis papayoides*, a new species. Beneath them grew *Alocasia odora*, an aroid with heart-shaped leaves of metallic appearance almost a metre in length. In contrast to Laokay, only 80km distant, there were no thickets of tall bamboo, though along the river there were extensive tracts of "jungle" consisting of wild sugarcane (*Saccharum arundinaceum*) with panicles beset with silvery hairs, tussocks of giant reed (*Arundo donax*), tiger grass (*Thysanolaena procera*) with large panicles of thousands of tiny grey-green spikelets, and *Themeda gigantea*. All these grasses grew in clumps, their close-ranked leaves and stems rising to 2-2.5m, though their panicles reached twice that height. Twining among them were *Thunbergia grandiflora* with large blue flowers, *Pueraria alopecuroides* with dense pink

spikes, and *Mucuna bracteata*. Especially on the south side of the valley the hillsides were covered with tropical savannah woodland comprising *Bischofia trifoliata, Colona (Columbia) floribunda, Mayodendron igneum* with flowers sprouting directly from its trunk, *Wendlandia tinctoria* sprinkled with small white flowers, one of the commonest species, and *Callicarpa macrophylla* with small white fruits. All these were intertwined with the ferns *Lygodium flexuosum* and *L. polystachum*. Most of these trees had small leaves and an open pattern of branches. On them, in large numbers, were ants' nests (*Cremastogaster artifex*) made from chewed leaves, looking like large hornets' nests. I cut one down with the twig on which it was fixed and placed it in formalin to kill and preserve the ants and, even more interesting, the larvae of a cockroach (*Phyllodromiinae*) which the ants had domesticated. Leafcutter ants (*Oecophila smaragdina*) were also common, and while collecting them, both here and subsequently, I was surprised that they never bit me. On the north side of the valley the slopes were steeper and the forest had been felled. In its place was subtropical savannah, just the same as I had seen from the train in the Naupan Jiang valley. It extended down almost to the river and up to an altitude of 1650m. One of the most striking sights was the umbrella shrub *Woodfordia fruticosa*, with narrow dark green leaves and clusters of fine scarlet flowers. Before I set off on a trip upstream on the other side of the river the official warned me not to accept anything to eat, for "*the people there put poison in the food*". This trip was one of the most rewarding, as the vegetation had suffered less from human interference than elsewhere. Arching over the path were shrubs with slender flowers (*Eranthemum polyanthum* and *E. nervosum*), and growing in the shade beneath them were fan-shaped patches of the vivid green *Selaginella pseudopaleifera*, a new species. At the corner of the next valley entering from the south the hillside was colonised by a peculiar evergreen shrub community dominated by *Taxotrophis macrophylla*, a prickly-leaved member of the mulberry family. Further up this side valley I once more encountered *Caesalpinia morsei*, a large leguminous tree with bristly seed-pods 20cm long hanging from its branches. The spoils which I brought back from my visit to Manhao were far less than might have been desired, chiefly because so little of the natural vegetation was still untouched, but the herbarium material, initially dried at Mengzi and then in Kunming, was successfully preserved, and colour photographs taken to show the principal vegetation types were also successful. Even down at Manhao the climate during my stay was not unpleasant: the temperature did not exceed 28° and the humidity was often a little below 50%.

Guards were posted at the exits from the town and they presumably had orders to see that I did not go out without an escort. On my outings I was always accompanied by two soldiers who had to give the corporal a report of my activities, especially the number of photographs which I took. On one occasion the corporal felt obliged to see for himself what I was doing. I lured him first straight up the steep hillside, up a woodcutter's track which was no more than a series of separate footholds, then through savannah woodland intertwined with thorny climbers and blackened by soot from a fire and finally into a deep pit filled with primaeval forest

accessible only by clambering down from one handhold to the next. There he had to sit and wait, muttering curses, his uniform torn and soiled, while I browsed upon the delights of the tropical flora. This quenched his curiosity and no doubt gave him plenty to tell his cronies about the crazy doings of the "waiguoren" (foreigner). Every evening I was confronted by sick people who expected that the five medicines at my disposal would cure them of every imaginable ailment. Skin diseases of all kinds were common, notably a condition characterized by circular patches 2-3cm in diameter, at first red and later forming blisters which discharged black fluid. It was apparently a refractory complaint, for the patients displayed old scars of similar shape on various parts of the body (? ringworm). I followed the adage *"even if it does no good, it will do no harm"*, with the result that next day they all declared themselves better and wanted more, or in some cases had discovered yet another ailment, so that before long my stocks were nearly exhausted.

The official invited me to a meal; he evidently wanted to show that he could do everything in European style and perhaps for that very reason he held it in the open entrance hall of his house, where the soldiers and other rabble crowded round the table. He had the board laid with forks and open clasp-knives and began the meal with horribly oversweetened black coffee. The repast itself was excellent, but was accompanied by teacups — fortunately nothing larger — of revolting beer seemingly at the same temperature (25°C) as the hot spring outside the village, and wine which had turned to vinegar months before. It ended with mouldy litchees and a huge glass of the same excessively black coffee, vile enough to infuriate anyone.

For reasons to do with the pack animals I had to travel on market day and I therefore left Manhao on 6 March, having received from Mengzi only three instead of the five horses I had expected; luckily I was able to get two more at the market in the next village. I took the same route as on my outward journey but travelled more slowly, wishing to spend a whole day in the district round Yaotou and Shuidian. We made our midday halt at 660m, where the first stream crossed the track, and there I found a remnant of primaeval forest which yielded a goodly haul. Growing beneath *Melodorum chloroneurum* (a new species) was a small *Pandanus*, a large fern forming nests on the tree trunks (*Asplenium nidus*), *Rhaphidophora decursiva* (*Araceae*) climbing up the rock-faces, and in rock crevices along the stream itself, the clubmoss relative *Psilotum triquetrum*. The figtrees *Ficus hispida* and *F. roxburghii* which put forth their fruits from the old trunks were particularly numerous. Higher up we saw a party of fifteen to twenty people on a hill top a few hundred metres away. The soldiers claimed they were bandits, said they were thirty in number and loaded their rifles, whereupon the people promptly made off, a few

carrying lances, but most of them with bales of hay on their backs — not part of a bandit's conventional equipment. Between Yaotou and Shuidian, at an altitude of 1100m, there was a deep sinkhole at the foot of a cliff. Where the stream tumbled into the hole the limestone was worn so smooth that one had to take care not to slip into it. Splendid tropical flora grew all round: *Brassaiopsis papayoides* (*Araliaceae*), a handsome little tree with a whorl of large circular simply lobed dark green leaves, wild bananas, *Veronia volkameriaefolia* (*Compositae*), a small tree with spreading panicles of large violet-blue flowerheads, and many others. All of them were overgrown with woody creepers, predominantly *Tetrastigma planicaule* (*Vitaceae*) and Japanese hops, though the latter is not woody. Because of this dense tree cover there were not many herbaceous plants, but in less shady spots I once more found the lush, sappy *Alocasia odora* with its white spathes. Being somewhat drier, the steep sides of the gorge were overgrown with thorny lianas (*Caesalpinia*) together with flowering creepers, *Senecio scandens*, *Jasminum bifarium* and *J. polyanthum*, which weighed down the less robust shrubs and made an impenetrable tangle. There was of course a dragon who had his lair in the sinkhole, and while I was looking round my men tried to fool me by imitating his roars. Shuidian was situated at 1300m among the uppermost slopes of the tropical savannah zone. Between the fields there were still a few large trees of *Duabanga grandiflora*, its twigs bowed down from its dark spreading crown by the weight of the flower heads grouped at their tips; each flower consisted of a heavy calyx of juicy sepals enclosing a corolla of dainty white or yellowish petals. A common sight in the wayside hedges was the sprawling climber *Blumea chinensis* (*Compositae*) with yellow flowers, later turning red. Among the bushes were *Leucosceptrum canum* (*Labiatae*), a large shrub with thick upright spikes of beautiful violet-blue flowers projecting from a layer of white fur, and *Oxyspora paniculata* (*Melastomaceae*), a shrub with pink flowers. In the savannah woodland itself the best find was *Sterculia henryi* with dainty racemes of carmine flowers. On the pass I wanted some more plants of the small *Primula sinodenticulata* and gave orders for them to be dug up.

"What, just ten of them?" said the little mafu, whom I had engaged for such work, "I'd like to go on another trip with *him* for my master". "If *you* only knew what real work is", I thought. On 8th March I arrived in Mengzi and, after missing the train owing to the breakdown of arrangements for transporting my baggage to the station and after further delay caused by the railway — one of my bales of plants was mislaid for a day en route — finally got back to Kunming on 13th March.

Chapter 12 Over the Highlands to Lijiang

A cave — landscape, colours and atmosphere — Taohua Shan near Yanfeng — chopped off heads — in Delavay's territory — Ji Shan — forests of the Heishanmen range — rhododendrons, mosses and toadstools — distant views

It was on 26 April that I set out on my next journey into the mountains. The decision to start had not been easy, as it meant cutting myself off from all news at a time when Italy was on the brink of declaring war [54]. But it was my duty to employ my time in scientific research which might bring honour to my Fatherland, and any feelings of homesickness were promptly dispelled by revulsion at the events unfolding in Europe. The arrival of a fresh remittance from the Academy of Sciences in Vienna in the sum of 6000 crowns [55] freed me from financial anxieties, and a letter of recommendation from the provincial authorities addressed to all districts on my route ensured smooth progress as far as Lijiang, where the real work was to begin. I took a track which ran to the north of the main road to Dali so as to collect the spring flora of the Yunnan highlands and replace the material from 1914 which had been seized by the English while in transit to Austria. I also wished to visit the basin between Dali and Yongsheng, the classical territory where Père Delavay originally discovered the riches of the Yunnan flora. My party at first comprised Schneider's man Li, one of his best coolies, Wu Suoling, Li's kitchen boy Zhafa and a caravan of eight pack animals with three men who had accompanied Schneider on his return journey from the Nu Jiang (the Salween) and had gained his approval. I paid the usual price of 50 cents per beast per day, and 20 cents for each rest day; my food cost me $12 monthly, a bargain which could hardly be bettered. I took only a small amount of canned food as an iron ration, and consigned the tent and its accessories, together with a number of paraffin cans, cut open and flattened to be soldered up into tin boxes for pressed plants, to a caravan travelling to Lijiang via Dali. The tent reached its destination after much delay, but the metal was never seen again.

After a farewell dinner at the consul's a short half day's march through light rain brought me once again to the edge of the plain near Buqi, where I had been in March 1914. On the very next day I found something of interest. The track to Fumin ran over the tall narrow limestone ridge which shut off the lower end of the Qiaotianshang valley basin and was itself pierced by the sizeable stream coming down the valley. A steep rock cliff provided homes for numerous nesting birds and towered over the mouth of a cave which led westwards and joined the stream running from Ercun to Fumin. The track continued downhill along this stream through a limestone ravine. High up on its smooth walls some spots of deep pink caught my eye; I thought it must be a primula, but how was I to get at it? The stream, rushing between knife-edged boulders which had tumbled into its bed, was easily crossed, but the plant resisted my attempts to shoot it down. I fired off some twenty cartridges, but only two flowers and two leaf rosettes fell to the ground. While searching for the pieces, however, I found a stem which must have fallen at an earlier date and had put out a flower. The plant turned out to be *Dendrobium crepidatum*, a magnificent orchid with an orange-yellow lip edged with white.

In Fumin there was a handsome stone bridge over the Pudu He. Then the track led along the left side of the valley and turned into a side valley filled with richly assorted shrub vegetation up to the top of the ridge. Flowering between and beneath the evergreen oaks were *Magnolia delavayi*, *Platycarya strobilacea*, a tree related to the walnut with fruit cones like teasels, surrounded by a ring of yellow male catkins standing up like candles and releasing their pollen; *Catalpa duclouxii*, *Albizzia julibrissin*, *Schefflera delavayi*, *Decaisnea fargesii* and other interesting species. On the col at 2475m, a windswept expanse of sandstone lying upon marl and limestone, there was a low maquis characterized by *Thea speciosa*, *Myrica nana* and *Rhododendron irroratum*, the last having pale yellow flowers with brown markings. The track led gently downhill to one of the many villages named Majie (horse market), situated to the south of Luozi on a stream running through the latter. Passing a wretched hovel, I told my men to ask the name of the place. A ragged fellow begged for alms. "What are you thinking of? From a foreign gentleman!" Wu Suoling barked at him in his gruff voice, and he shrank back.

For the next four days we travelled westwards across irregularly dissected sandstone uplands, a tangle of mountain ranges. In places there were plateaus bounded by steep scarps; some of the valleys were quite deeply cut and at their upper margins there were red sandstone bastions standing up like castles. The country was at first quite attractive, with vivid green woods of *Keteleeria* and *Pinus yunnanensis*, a tree with long needles which gleamed in the blazing sun and stirred in the gentle breeze which freshened towards noon, but after a time the landscape began to pall and the flora offered little variety. We were on a salt route leading down to Heijing, situated at 1600m in the Longchuan Jiang — hot, arid and filled with prickly pear (*Opuntia*). Before descending from the heights, not far from the point where the track crossed last year's route from Guangtong to Yuanmou, I encountered for the first time *Rhododendron simsii*, growing in the depths of small channels among bamboos. Its superb purple flowers, large and delicate, were sold in large amounts in the market at Kunming.

---

[54] Italy declared war on Austria on 24 May 1915.

[55] Equivalent to £240 or $1200 in 1915 values.

From the top of the next ridge I had a broad vista over the highlands to the west, but it was mottled with cloud shadows and unsuitable for photography. However, its configuration was plainly quite different from the terrain which I had just traversed, for the strata were greatly disturbed. They were not arranged in plates or blocks and did not form continuous ridges, but were cut up into a medley of short crests and low summits, mostly triangular in outline though not very steep. Next came a valley and another gentle ridge, on which the fragrant *Ternstroemia japonica* was in flower, a low evergreen shrub with pendent flowers which, though not exactly small, are inconspicuous because they are of whitish, ochre yellow colour and are often brown at the edges. For my midday halt on the second day I was once more in a fair-sized town — Mouding (Dingyüen). This time I found the people friendly. Even their importunity was not so unpleasant, perhaps because I could see its ridiculous side. I sat in an inn in Mouding, eating the food I had brought with me, besieged by gaping onlookers who were amazed at my beard. Then they fetched one of their number, and showed me that he too had some bristles on his face; presumably I was intended to gaze in astonishment at him. After a short time I said to the man who had fetched the bearded one: "All right, now you can go away again". Another one said to his child: "Look, he's eating bread", and tried to touch my loaf, but as always I refused to allow that.

Continuing along the same track to Dayao, marked on Davies' map, I found that the course of the streams was in need of major corrections. In fact the path does not follow the main river valley, but crosses two valleys running northeast, by climbing over low cols at 2250 and 2225m between them. In Qinchangguan I had a visit from the local doctor, an unwashed old man who took his metal pipe out of his mouth and invited me to have a few puffs — a truly Chinese notion of hygiene. Before reaching Dayao I had been soaked to the skin by a cloudburst and was glad to spend a rest day there on 7 May, sorting out the pressed plants. The surrounding landscape consisted chiefly of multicolored marl strata and although somewhat higher in altitude it was a labyrinth of channels and basins between shapeless hills. Subtropical *Pistacia* scrub extended for a considerable distance into the tableland. One more day's march brought us to Baiyanjing (Yanfeng), along a route which trended downwards through shrub communities which differed in composition and contained a wide range of species. My eye was caught by a vivid blue stratum between the layers of marl. A specimen was identified by A. Köhler as the rare asbestos mineral crocidolite.

Yanfeng was another salt town, stretched out along a narrow, shut in valley. The colour of its muddy streets was reflected in the dark grey salt which was despatched from the town in small uncut sugarloaf cones. The Chinese women wore a headdress of a kind which I saw nowhere else. It consisted of a narrow black cloth rolled up and wound round the head to form a horizontal ring or covering, not unlike the blue headcloth worn by some people in Sichuan and Zhaotong in Yunnan, but much narrower and more neatly rolled. Shown on Legen-

dre's map to the northeast of the town is a mountain 3500m [56] high which I wanted to climb. I never had a view of it either at close quarters or from afar, as the rain started to pour down again, but this did not prevent me from reaching the big temple at 2775m after two halfday marches. That evening the rain stopped for a while and I went up to the summit (Taohua Shan), which was certainly no more than 300m above the temple. The mountain was built of sandstone and was covered with oaks. It did not yield much of a haul, but there was a few novelties, notably *Cinnamomum pittosporoides*, perhaps the largest flowered species of cinnamon, and two yellow primulas, *P. flavicans* and *P. ulophylla* [57]. During the ascent I encountered a swarm of termites, a grey-brown species of *Odontotermes* 2cm in length or 5cm including the wings, which came flying along in large numbers and then immediately shed their wings. That evening I was present at a Chinese religious ceremony and so far as I remember it was the only occasion of its kind that I really enjoyed. The mist swirled across the temple forecourt, and when the Buddhist priest intoned his wailing chant and beat the huge gong the effect was indeed most impressive.

Back in Yanfeng I spent another rest day sheltering from the rain, and on 13th May set off down to Guanfang, where I intended to cross one of the major tributaries of the Yangzi and continue directly across an unsurveyed tract to Pianjiao, 30 km north of Binchuan. On the slippery valley sides below Yanfeng I saw — for the first and only time in China — notices with the words "Woodcutting Forbidden" and this was probably the reason why the subtropical shrub cover and the woodlands in the gorges were so well preserved there. Large shrubs of *Radermachera sinica* (*Bignoniaceae*) were particularly striking. The slope was covered with bushes of *Styrax limprichtii*, which looks like broom but has flowers like little white bells; there were various species of jasmine with white or red flowers, perfuming the air with their fragrance; *Alangium chinense* flourished in the ravines, overgrown by *Pueraria yunnanensis*, a woody climber belonging to the pea family, with massive flattened knobbly stems and hanging racemes of scented white flowers. The river was so high that the ferryman would not attempt to cross it that day. However, the delay was not unprofitable, for below the ferryhouse, at only 1500m, I found yet another novelty, *Croton caudatiformis* (*Euphorbiaceae*), a small tree with upright spikes of yellow flowers. After crossing the river next morning I found that no one there had heard of Pianjiao. I could not find a guide and had to take the main road up the river and then along a lateral valley via Midian to Binchuan. This detour brought its compensations, although the track consisted of cobblestones dumped at random, for it provided a rich haul especially in the damp gorges below Midian. Along the river bank and on the west-facing slope there

---

[56] ONC H-11 shows two summits, one of 3085m 17km NE of the town and the other of 3662m 33km to the NNE. Perhaps Handel-Mazzetti climbed the wrong mountain.

[57] Now *P. ambita* and *P. bracteata*.

were trees with luxuriant foliage, including *Rapanea yunnanensis*, *Rhamnus nigricans* (a new species), *Eriobotrya prinoides*, *Photinias*, willows, *Adina asperula* with globular heads of rose pink tubular flowers and the scrambling *Mallotus philippinensis*. Mainly on the opposite side of the valley there was dense savannah woodland with arid patches of oak. In my field notes written on the spot I used the descriptive phrase "veil forest" more than once. In such woodland the countless twigs of the overhanging trees and spreading shrubs have for the most part a loose and open pattern of small leaves and delightfully fragrant flowers — *Delavaya toxocarpa* with pink blossoms, *Phyllanthus emblica* with minute yellowish green flowers and the thorny *Gymnosporia royleana* with even less conspicuous florets — and even where they are profusely interwoven with creepers — *Dalbergia mimosoides* with hooked tendrils and slender flower panicles or *Trachelospermum cathayanum* with scented white flowers — they do not form a dense canopy of foliage, but merely a transparent veil of tracery suspended a few metres above the ground. Furthermore, but for this detour I might have encountered a band of army deserters, allegedly some thirty strong, who had plundered a caravan there four days previously. Two of them had been captured, and their heads, with a suitable notice, had been hung up in cages above the road; the others had fled into the mountains. Above Midian the valley broadened once more into the familiar landscape: groups of green bowls between low rounded hills clothed with pine forest.

The pass at the head of the valley was no more than a shallow notch in the sandy conglomerate which made up the range of hills — a rock which I often encountered thereafter. Just beyond it we entered the broad dry valley in which Binchuan and Pianjiao are situated, a dried up lake basin overlying conglomerates where the land had been so assiduously "cultivated" by the Chinese that it was utterly deforested and barren. Here and there among the arid steppe were steep stony banks which, in the wet weather prevailing on that day, were coloured dark green by the unfolded rosettes of *Selaginella involvens*; in dry weather they roll up and are hardly visible. *Acacia farnesiana*, growing among the rounded boulders of a stream bed, was a pleasing discovery, but it did little to cheer up the dreary landscape. At last we reached a track where the going was easier and I was able to travel at a better pace than a bullock cart. After five days' journeying we arrived in Pianjiao, where I stopped for a day's rest. Instead of the subtropical air there was a cold north wind. Despite careful search I found practically nothing of botanical interest. I had a call from the French missionary, Father Degenève, a brisk and energetic young man. He had just returned over the mountains from a visit to Huangjiaping, where he had been obliged to have a path cut through the vegetation and had then galloped down the hillside on his mule. The poor fellow had to live entirely in Chinese style and was overjoyed to meet another European. I invited him to dinner and even though a huge cockroach fell from the ceiling on to the dinner table and nearly landed in the dish, he was so delighted with the potted chicken which Li placed before us that he thankfully took the remains home for his breakfast. The information he gave me, taken in conjunction with what I could see from below,

caused me to give up my plan to climb the mountain to the east of the town, said to be only 10,000 ft high. Instead, I turned my attention to Ji Shan, a famous place of pilgrimage which Davies marks on his map but without giving the altitude. It lies north east of Dali, beyond the lake, and has a somewhat lower summit with some temples still further north east. From my present location the best starting point for the ascent was Huangjiaping. The journey to that town brought me out of the territory of the Yi people. During my travels I had not seen anything of them except in the markets; however, in Heijin by a stroke of good fortune I bought a girl's multicolored headdress decorated with silver plates and inlaid bone buttons.

On 19th May a long day's march from Pianjiao to Huangjiaping took me along the next parallel valley, through country which though dry had a rich flora. The lower slopes were covered with numerous plants of *Selaginella involvens* growing beneath scattered bushes of the sticky *Dodonaea viscosa* and the dainty *Phyllanthus emblica*. Then, in grassland on a low ridge, I found the tiny blue gentian *Gentiana napulifera*, seldom more than 3cm tall but often having more than a dozen juicy tuberous roots 5cm long, and a spurge, also with thick storage roots, the new species *Euphorbia porphyrastra*, made conspicuous by its purple bracts. Just a little further, on limestone at the edge of the forest, there was a wild fig (*Ficus superba*) together with *Firmiana maior* (*Sterculiaceae*), distinguished from the well known cultivated tree [58] by its large pink flowers and larger leaves and fruits. After this long march I took the opportunity of calling on Père Guilbaud, whom I had met in Yongsheng. He had come over from Dali, where he was now stationed, on a visit to Dapingzi, an hour's journey from Huangjiaping and well known as the village where Delavay [59] formerly resided. He was fanatical in his enthusiasm for the French cause and less restrained than any of the other missionaries in his biased comments on the war. Some time later, when I was better informed about the war, I felt I had no choice but to write to him setting out our point of view, and when we met some time afterwards he refrained from speaking about such matters. His place in Yongsheng had now been filled by Salvat, whose large-scale opium smuggling operations had been discovered by the authorities and who had therefore been transferred from Dali, a much more agreeable post.

Sending the caravan a little further on, I myself set out with my men and two pack animals to ascend Mount Ji Shan. We went back a short distance along the route we had taken two days earlier, then turned to the right up the mountain and on to the northeast ridge. Further on, just below the ridge, we came to a fair-sized temple at the foot of the steep ascent to the summit. I went inside, and on making the customary offering I was asked to write my name in a well-kept visitors' book, in which I

---

[58] *F. simplex*, which has small yellow flowers.

[59] Père J.M.Delavay lived at Dapingzi for nearly ten years and ascended Zemei Shan (on horseback) no fewer than sixty times.

found the name of the French explorer Bacot[60]. That evening (May 21st) I went up to the summit, for although the weather was not good there was no certainty that it might not be even worse on the next day. The track zigzagged up a scree on which I found *Aristolochia yunnanensis*, a twining plant with large flowers, *Deutzia longifolia*, its flowers tinged with pink, *Berberis* spp. and various others, and then steeply upwards on to a scarp of green diabase. Here there were steps hewn out of the rock, and in one section the route was guarded with stanchions, chains and handrails like a tourists' path in the Alps. After ascending for 325m I reached the summit at about 3200m. At the top was another temple richly decorated with beaten copperwork; there was a second which I had passed on the way up and a third which clung to a narrow rock ledge over a dizzy precipice; in the rays of the afternoon sun its white glint was visible from Dali 30 km away. The vista was far from satisfactory as all distant prospects were obscured, but from the summit I had a striking view of the temples, twenty in number, scattered on the southeast side of the mountain towards Binchuan; the lowest of them displayed a huge obelisk. To the northeast the mountain range continued in a massive, almost horizontally stratified block of limestone. Although not very high — about 300m — its simplicity of form and the steepness of the cliffs bounding it on all sides made it an impressive sight. Beneath it was red sandstone, which also formed the lower part of Ji Shan, and beneath that was dark green dahamite. Neither in the surface configuration nor in the tectonic structure of the higher parts of the range was there any suggestion of the "Yunnan arc" which, according to Deprat, runs through this district. Scattered pines and yews crowned the crest; lower down there was *Lithocarpus* forest and holly-leaved oak scrub, and below them aspens and willows spread their delicate foliage. The summit ridge ran east and west, and was the only place where I found *Vaccinium delavayi*, a dwarf shrub resembling bilberry, and *Gaultheria cardiosepala*, which looks like *Erica*, both of them grew on humus soils among cushions of moss. The tall rhododendron bushes (*R. rarosquameum* [61]) were a splendid sight, densely covered with large, somewhat asymmetrical pale pink flowers flecked with purple, while their leaves had not yet begun to unfold. Here and there were solitary trees of *Magnolia taliensis*, 3m in height, with large pendent patulous snow-white flowers, also appearing before the leaves were fully developed. From our overnight lodging the descent led first along the mountainside, then from a col north westwards over the opposite slope to the east side of the range which runs northwards from Lake Er Hai.

It was my intention to climb at least one mountain in that range, which forms the western boundary of the Yangzi basin and is called Heishanmen in its southern part and Ma'an Shan in its northern. In Jiangying I rejoined the caravan, happily ensconced

in the worst house in the place. The track led northwards over an undulating forest-covered tract at roughly 2300m lying at the foot of the mountain range; it is probably a remnant of a basin-shaped portion of the Yangzi valley, which is now much more deeply incised. As shown by a rock exposure which I encountered during the ascent, it is built upon a recurring sequence of thin layers of limestone, marls and sandstones with a northerly dip. I branched off to the left from the track and travelled for two hours to the village of Xiangshuihe, so as to spend the night at the very foot of the mountain range. The tribe living there were Bai, tall, powerfully built people, and friendly enough with the exception of their headman: Li had to hold my letter of recommendation under his nose, pull off his hat and give him a few digs in the ribs to impress upon him that he had no right to refuse to allow me to buy provisions. On the afternoon of 24th May I paid a visit to the still untouched river gorge above the village, where the best finds were *Cephalotaxus fortunei* and *Philadelphus delavayi*, the latter in full bloom, together with several species of gooseberry, red currants and wild rose, and also *Lonicera setifera*, a honeysuckle with leaves which are almost lobed. Next day I again had to face the difficulties of the rainy season, which had set in once more in earnest. Not one of the mountains was to be seen, and when I said that I wanted to climb the highest summit in the vicinity (the name Ma'an Shan[62] did not come to my ears until some time later), my guide simply took me straight up a woodcutter's path which was very steep and completely overgrown. My pony managed it very skilfully, though my coat got ripped and the branches tore off my hat and scratched me. The path finally came to an end at 3400m in an impenetrable thicket of rhododendrons, among them *R. bureavii* with red-brown felt on its leaves, and *Pieris japonica*. The spoils were somewhat disappointing, though there were some interesting cryptogams, notably the fungus *Calostoma junghuhnii*, its eggshaped pale olive-brown fruiting bodies, 1.5cm long, with red stripes radiating from the opening like a poppy capsule, growing in the leafmould of the evergreen oak wood. This part of the range consists of green diabase, the same as that which I had just seen on Mount Ji Shan and previously on Longzhu Shan near Huili in Sichuan, whereas Heishanmen to the south, which had such an important place in Delavay's work, is a limestone mountain. During the descent I lost my footing and sat down on the slippery clay more often than I care to remember, and finally got back to my lodgings completely soaked.

Next day we travelled northwards along the shallow depression to the east of the mountain range, crossing several valleys between whale-backed ridges, many of them topped with limestone. They extend out from this mountain range and unite here in the trough running parallel to it. At one time they were much deeper, but now they are filled with talus, and the ridges project like cliff-girdled peninsulas out of a uniformly ascending slope. At noon I

---

[60]Bacot, Jacques. *Dans les Marches Tibétaines....1906 - 1908*. Paris,1909.

[61] Now *R. rigidum*.

---

[62] ONC H-10 shows an unnamed range north of Lake Erhai, the summit at 4046m.

passed through a large village called Songgui where the Bai were holding an interesting fair (Fig.18), and spent the night at Diansuo, 12km south of Heqing, with the aim of reaching higher and more promising altitudes on the further crest, which had now come into sight. I wanted to get on to the main road from Dali to Heqing and travel along it to Heqing to spend the night. During the ascent the mountains were visible as far as the vicinity of Yongning 140km away. The Lijiang snow peak, dull and devoid of lustre, towered into the cloudy leaden-grey sky, attended by its companion beyond it and to the left, both coated with fresh snow, like solid silver above the sombre mountains at their feet. Wisps of cloud drifted here and there between them, and in the sunless atmosphere, where everything was dripping with moisture, it created an extraordinary impression of melancholy splendour. Mount Haba Shan came into view beyond the great bend of the Yangzi, looking as if it were the chopped off tail of the Lijiang range. The track passed through pine forest with small trees of *Rhododendron irroratum.* Its succulent flowers were being gathered in baskets for eating. We climbed on to a low saddle and then traversed a steep valley filled with jungle [63] and woodland consisting of *Tsuga* and oaks (Fig.19). Among them was a new tree rhododendron (*R. persicinum*) with smooth white bark and dense clusters of large flowers, a splendid peach-red in colour. We crossed the main crest by the Zuningkou pass, only 3400m in altitude. As there were no paths to the summits, as the guide claimed that there was no prospect of reaching the main road and getting to Heqing on that day, and as the plants up there were still greatly behindhand in their unfolding, I thought it best to have a good look round in the "jungle" and then to return via the first saddle and take the shortest route to Heqing. At the edge of the "jungle"

on the saddle we had just reached — which was in fact on the main crest just north of Ma'an Shan — there was a little glade surrounded by gnarled trees of holly-leaved oak.. Hanging from their branches among cushions of moss and streamers of lichen were ferns, notably *Polypodium lineare* with thick, narrow ribbon-like leaves, and similar species which I already knew. Along the stream, flowering beneath the oaks, the dark purple *Lonicera adenophora* and the bamboos, were masses of *Lappula dielsii* with splendid blue flowers like big forget-me-nots, together with the large blackish purple *Arisaema elephas* (Fig.17) with a long awl-shaped spadix, the common *Paris polyphylla* and other large-leaved shade-loving plants. I took a number of photographs of the vegetation but two of them were failures, because a Chinese mechanic, well-meaning but ignorant, had oiled the balljoint of my tripod and it would not lock securely. I collected a large haul of cryptogams, and after a long day's work finally reached the hostelry in the dark.

Next day I continued northwards, first along the elongated basin in which Heqing lies, a cultivated tract bounded on both sides by mountains with a westerly dip. At its southern end the Dongshang river coming from Lijiang cuts through a gorge to find an outlet to the nearby Yangzi. Then the track led over a rocky riegel [64] apparently covered by an old moraine, which the river traverses by a short ravine, then on to the western flank of the Lijiang basin at its south eastern extremity, over a small projecting spur into the basin itself. On 28th May I arrived in Lijiang, with a splendid collection of plants, many of them, because the season was so much more advanced, quite different from those I had gathered in 1914, and gazed once again on the giant peak — a sight to quicken the pulses of any mountaineer.

---

[63] Handel-Mazzetti uses the word jungle *(Dschungel)* not in the current sense of primeval forest, but in the original sense of the Hindi word *(jangal)* — as adopted in Anglo-Indian usage — of ground covered by rough grasses including bamboos.

[64] A low transverse ridge of resistant bedrock marking the exit from a cirque or separating rock basins along the floor of a glacial valley.

Chapter 13. Exploring the Mountains near Lijiang

A banquet — early summer flowers on Mount Yulong Shan — a viewpoint at 4500m — the giant face of the main peak and its glacier — symptoms of mountain sickness — Mount Yao Shan near Ganhaizi — the moraine cirque and the Luoqu gorge

In Lijiang I again enjoyed enthusiastic help from the Dutch missionary A. Kok. He advanced money when my remittances failed to arrive punctually, he introduced me to the new district official, with whom he was on excellent terms, and — most important of all — he promised to take regular barometer readings as a basis for correcting the altitude observations taken on my subsequent journeys. Unfortunately he was not able to carry out this task for the whole period, and the altitude observations taken in the Mekong and Doker-la districts in 1915 were not corrected against his readings. Through the good offices of one of his men I was able to take colour photographs of three pure-blooded Tibetans from Qagchêng (Xiangcheng in Chinese), members of the notorious tribe whose lamas had plotted the murder in 1915 of Père Th. Monbeig, a missionary with an interest in botany. Tibetans are reluctant to allow their photographs to be taken, and this prejudice is not easy to overcome as they believe that being photographed will "extract the soul from the body". The district official was a highly intelligent youngish man, a law graduate of Tokyo University, versed in European manners though having no command of any Western language, but still wholly Chinese in his ideas on the administration of justice: he had not progressed beyond the idea of extracting confessions by flogging. He at once invited Kok and me together with some Chinese friends and officials to a banquet at 9 o'clock in the morning. The two of us arrived at 9.30 and were of course the first.

"Yes", he said "if you make an appointment with a European for 9 o'clock, he will be there on the dot, but you'll have to send for your Chinese guests at 10 o'clock".

It was the best Chinese meal of which I ever partook, though my appetite was rather spoilt by the sight of the head cook, a dirty ragged coolie who appeared now and then at the door. The meal began with pastries and bottled fruit and Chinese macaroni with salt and pepper, both set out on little tables along the walls; then the following cold dishes, served simultaneously on a large table in the middle of the room; candy sugar, chicken livers and chicken skin, wheat porridge, pig's liver with turnips, honey cakes, chicken gizzard with cabbage, pumpkin seeds, duck eggs with ham, ginger sauce and paprika; then a number of hot dishes, served in succession: catfish, roast chicken in fat, two kinds of lake fish, seaweed with eggs, two sorts of pastries, sweet rice-meal sauce, and rice wine to drink and finally tea, accompanied by bean curd, "Mixed Pickles" and rice.

The people of Lijiang were somewhat excited and restless. The dujun had ordered soldiers to be levied, and as the Naxi people had the reputation of being quiet and submissive he planned to raise large numbers from the Lijiang district. The official divided the district into twenty parts and called for twenty recruits from each. But there was a "professor" who took a stand against the levy and had notices posted to the effect that the number of soldiers required was only two hundred instead of four hundred, and that the rest of them should go home. As might be expected, all of them reckoned themselves as being unwanted and set off for their homes. There was even talk of setting fire to the yamen, but the official got wind of it and had the professor put behind bars. All was then quiet. These events did nothing to create hostility towards foreigners; on the contrary, many sought to enter their service so as to escape the levy.

As my tent had still not arrived, I at first planned to climb Yao-Shan, easily accessible via Ganhaizi, so as to make a survey. We should have to start from Ganhaizi before dawn to photograph the western side of the snow-capped range before the summits became veiled by cloud. I disclosed my plan to the prefect and he sent two soldiers to accompany me, but they made themselves a nuisance by their idiotic conduct. On one occasion a Tibetan caravan was approaching us along the road, which here on the plain was wide enough to take three horses abreast. They halted it by holding up their rifle butts. The horses recoiled in terror, turned sideways and finally got jammed in an inextricable tangle which blocked the entire roadway. Such antics helped no one, and it was only when I refused to tolerate their misconduct and ordered them to let the Tibetans pass by in peace that I was able to resume my own course along the road without being pushed into the rose hedges. In any case the Tibetans, being well mannered and experienced travellers, were always willing to give way and would, if necessary, turn back along the track for a considerable distance.

Next morning Ganhaizi was shrouded in mist and rain and I had to withdraw, my aim unachieved, but I had at least got to know the first part of the main road to Zhongdian and enjoyed the flora of the pine heath — chiefly *Roscoea* and *Iris*, now in flower — and the abundant shrub vegetation, notably the tall *Indigofera pendula* with long lax racemes of handsome blossoms in a delicate shade of pink hanging down over the sunken road. In the splendid meadow near the lake, where I had seen *Primula vialii* the year before, hardly anything was yet in flower.

On 4th June I went again to Nguluke and moved into Schneider's former dwelling, a low and ill-ventilated attic, dimly lit by two of his photographic plates scraped clean and fitted into the roof as skylights. I was received with great friendliness, but when Li arrived he met with general consternation and black looks. I resolved to keep a closer eye on his activities so that he would have no opportunity of doing anything which might upset my good relations with the villagers. He must have had an uneasy conscience from the previous year, otherwise he would not have kept the main gate into the yard closed at all times; even the side gate he opened only on request. The Naxi villagers of Nguluke were indeed no longer the same as they had been when Forrest first arrived eleven years earlier. They were traders and horse copers — apart from farming, their main occupation was now the rearing of horses and mules, though they made no attempt at selective breeding — and towards botanists their attitude had become more mercenary. In 1914 Li's wrongdoings had goaded them to such a pitch that they had apparently voiced the intention of attacking Schneider one evening and giving him a beating, though Kok talked them out of it by reminding them of the far more severe beating which they would then receive in the yamen. Li had made himself objectionable in several ways. Goods which they did not wish to sell he simply snatched from them without paying; he forced his attentions on a Chinese woman living in the village, he smoked opium and committed various other offences, for all of which the villagers believed that his master must be largely to blame.

This year, as in 1914, most of my forays up the flanks of the mountain ended in pouring rain. The subalpine meadows at 3500m, later to be covered by the tall, lush *Strobilanthes versicolor*, were still adorned by several species with large and sumptuous flowers — the low growing scarlet *Incarvillea grandiflora*, the blue *Meconopsis delavayi* and the curious *Roscoea cautleioides* together with various inconspicuous crucifers and other plants growing among a small sedge, *Cobresia curvirostris*. Lilacs and other shrubs were flowering at their margins and in the woods were several species of lady's slipper orchid, among them the dainty *Cypripedium ebracteatum* growing in deep moss. It has two large, almost circular leaves spotted with brown, flattened against the ground, and between them it puts forth a succulent, waxy blossom speckled and striped with purplish brown (Fig.22). The Autochrome plates produced a faultless picture, even though the guarantee had expired fifteen months before. The hollow in which it was growing ran down from a rock face riven by a deep cleft, which was in fact a pothole washed smooth and rounded by water, visible from afar as a black void among the bushes. By staking out a measured baseline on the gravel plain of the former lake bed below the village I achieved a triangulation survey of the range, and at last obtained accurate altitudes for the summits; my figure for the nearer (south) main peak, Satseto, was 5450m[65]. Above the village, far above the cleft just described, was a tall rock face running obliquely across the steep slope; from what I recalled of Forrest's description it should be a good place for flower hunting. A woodcutter's track, each foothold separately hewn out, led steeply uphill from the south to its upper edge, and from there we saw the Lijiang plain spread out like a map at our feet. From the top the path went straight down the rock face, which was clothed with shrubs, notably *Daphne aurantiaca*, a small, densely branched bush with numerous egg-yolk yellow flowers, moulding itself against the rocks, its stems often compressed into flat bands. Growing in large numbers among the bushes was the scarlet-flowered *Roscoea chamaeleon*, the finest of its genus. By midday I was down at the village again,

and that evening, as promised, the district official came out accompanied by Kok. By taking advantage of my activities, he hoped to get a view of his Yulong Shan from close quarters.

He brought fine weather with him, and on the morning of 11th June the sky was clear. Escorted by a large party we rode up through pine woods to the "great meadow", as we usually called it (Ndwolo), through a band of firs, then up a steep grassy slope with patches of bamboo, threading our way between rock outcrops along a stream until we came out above a huge rock mass shaped like a man's head, a landmark visible from far and wide. Beside it was the source of the streamlet. The stones were padded with cushions of moss which I had already collected in 1914. However, I gathered further material, notably the crinkly-leaved *Ptychomitrium tortula* with clusters of short-stalked spore capsules, with the purpose of distributing herbarium specimens of these splendid examples of the local mosses and — for the first time, I may say — of drawing the attention of botanists to the rich cryptogam flora of south west China, since its phytogeographical importance is no less than that of the flowering plants, which have already been studied by several research workers.

Up there, at 3700m, we dismounted at the edge of a tarn surrounded by boulders overgrown with spiraeas, berberis and honeysuckles together with a luxuriance of herbaceous plants. I discarded my heavy leather gaiters and, after checking that none of us had picked up any of the leeches which had already attached themselves to the horses' pasterns and the men's bare feet, we resumed the ascent on foot. Soon the last fir trees were below us, and we were climbing up steep grassy slopes between limestone crags. Only a few flowers were open yet, but these were exceptionally gorgeous: *Primula secundiflora* with dense umbels of pendent blooms of deep carmine, *P. sinopurpurea*, similar but with purple flowers, the large yellow flowers of *Meconopsis integrifolia* and, in loose scree, the yellowish green bells, flecked with red and suffused with violet, of *Fritillaria delavayi*. The higher we climbed, the finer was the view of the green plain of Lijiang, with the neat brown timber houses of the Naxi villages scattered among hedges, the town itself with limewashed houses between its two hills, and beyond it the gleaming white obelisk erected beside the road from Heqing on the apex of a low spur projecting into the plain. Range upon range, the mountains rose up higher and higher as far as Ji Shan and Cang Shan near Dali, and indeed far beyond, though there they were of lower altitude and less jagged outline. On rock faces the larger rhododendrons of the tree-line were still in flower (*R. adenogynum*), and spilling out of the crevices were rough-leaved cushions of a crucifer, *Solms-Laubachia pulcherrima*, studded with large pale blue flowers. Naturally I had to instruct the official in the elementary principles of mountaineering — not to talk continuously while ascending and other rules which we take for granted. He was soon far in the rear, assisted by a soldier who unwound his head-band and used it to tow him uphill. After entering the cirque (Pelchua) behind Hosayigo peak, a towering white scree-skirted trapezoid which belongs to the parallel chain close to the eastern side of the main

---

[65] The height is now considered to be 5596m.

range, I lost sight of him and of the entire landscape below me. I could no longer see far ahead since the sky had clouded over and the high crests were hidden by mist. However, I was not willing to abandon my plan and climbed onwards in the direction which Forrest had indicated in his description. I soon came to snow, still unthawed from this level upwards. Wu Suolong's feet, shod only with straw sandals, began to freeze and he turned back, wishing me joy for the rest of the day. While I climbed up to the next crest — the northern border of the cirque — the official sat down to eat; nevertheless he had guts and soon resumed the climb, still towed by the soldier.

Another plod through the snow, and at midday I reached my goal. Reclining on the slabs of a sharp crest beneath a rock tower, we gazed down into a giddy abyss in which we saw the cleft and fissured snout of a glacier, with moraines running steeply down from it, a tiny round green glacial tarn, and the last black straggling lines of firs in the Luoqu gorge, which separated our viewpoint at 4500m from the main summit, Satseto (Fig. 20). The mist continued to rise and fall; sometimes it revealed glimpses of an immense rock face opposite us, but sometimes it engulfed us entirely and hail pelted down. Would it lift and unveil Satseto in its entirety, if only for a few moments, and allow me to make a permanent photographic record of that splendid high alpine scene? The camera was screwed on to my ice axe ready for action and would need only minor adjustments to frame the picture as soon as the mist cleared. Tension mounted; would it remain persistently obscured, as it had been that morning when I was low down? Would I have to make the ascent again, with no greater certainty of success? Before long Kok arrived, followed more than an hour later by the official, still being towed. Once again he brought good fortune: after a few minutes the mist lifted and unveiled, from top to toe, one of the most splendid mountain views that mortal eye has ever looked upon. Directly opposite, barely more than a kilometre distant, the south face of Satseto, 1800m in height, rose up almost vertically before us, grey and fissured, marked only by a few flecks of yellow-brown or black. Hanging glaciers clung to every ledge and recess, the lowermost split by crevasses into gigantic ice blocks. Above the precipice was a steeply sloping basin of permanent snow; beyond that gleamed the ice domes and pinnacles of the crest wreathed by wisps of cloud, and high above them the peak itself, a superb white cone crowned by snow cornices. The summit ridge swept down to the left in a series of curves to join Ünlüpe, a jagged rock chain merely 5000m high, which curved round to the south east to bound the Pelchua cirque and tumbled down in a mighty precipice to the right towards the rocky pinnacle of Chaloko, which stuck out far towards the east. Almost without a pause, ice avalanches and falling rocks thundered down the cliffs, while little waterfalls threw themselves over high rock steps from the left into the gorge.

The natural forces which build the mountains of the earth do not yet permit Yulong Shan the majestic calm of an ancient alpine range, for the mountain is not finally shaped and completed. It belongs to the "land of deep corrosions" [66] where erosion and reconstruction are still as active as they were in the Alps after the ice age, though indeed for other reasons. From the point where we stood the rock face plunged vertically down into the gorge in an unbroken drop of 800m, traversed only by a few fissures. Our men voiced their awe and wonder in astonished shouts of "Oi oi oi" which blended into a somewhat discordant chorus. We were indeed a strange assortment of races, though representative of this part of China: a Dutchman, a German, Chinese, Naxi, Bai and Xifan. Before starting the descent I took another photograph of the view to the east, so as to have a record from this side of the moraine cirque spread out beyond the gorge. A second and larger depression extends, sharply demarcated, into the low ridge which runs parallel to the snow range, to the east of Baishuibazi and the Baisha plain; it may well owe its origin to an even older glacial tongue. We climbed down swiftly, and found our horses waiting for us on the "great meadow". However, I had sent mine all the way back and by making a faster descent on foot I partially escaped the hailstorm which soaked the rest of the party. The official was rescued — though too late — and given a meal in the little temple at the village. I had invited the guests to join me in my attic room, but so much rain streamed in through the roof that straw had to be heaped on the floor to mop up some at least of the pools of water. All of us felt the after-effects of the thin mountain air in the form of headache or tightness in the head, which was still quite perceptible though no longer really unpleasant. For weeks afterwards everybody in Lijiang talked about the heroic deed of their prefect, who — though no one knew quite why — had climbed the mountain on foot. However, I now recognized more clearly than ever that any attempt to reach the summit would be practicable only when perfect weather could be relied upon, in other words in late autumn, but by then deep snow would probably make it impossible to pitch camp at a sufficient altitude and might imperil the success of the whole enterprise.

Next morning the official was called upon to settle a legal dispute. The villagers of Nguluke wanted to build a mill on their land beside a stream which, further down, flowed through Baisha, but the people of Baisha would not agree to this, since they earned part of their living by grinding corn for Nguluke as well as their own. As the official set out, accompanied by about half the population of the village, to view the locality, some people from Baisha came and asked him to postpone the inspection until he had visited their village. What they wanted, of course, was to offer him a better meal than the people of Nguluke could provide. However, he strung them along by saying: "I'll come back again later"; and then decided in favour of Nguluke. In the following year, it seems, the Baisha villagers took revenge on their neighbours by insinuating that they had been involved in a case of robbery with violence which occurred near Ganhaizi.

---

[66] This phrase is the title of the last chapter of Frank Kingdon Ward's book *The Land of the Blue Poppy*, Cambridge, 1913.

On 13th June, a fine day, I explored the little wooded peak of Yao Shan (3825m) near Ganhaizi, my previous attempt to reach it from Lijiang having been thwarted by rain. The view of the more distant part of the range and its continuation beyond the Jin-sha Jiang was quite instructive, but cloud hid the summits all day. I remained there, my camera at the ready, passing the time by collecting the lichens, mosses and liverworts which encrust the trunks of the firs and rhododendrons which grow on exposed windy crests at high altitudes. The view to the south and west was perfectly clear as far as Dali and Weixi. On the steep turfy mountainside I caught two young poisonous snakes and preserved them in formalin. Werner later identified them as a new subspecies: *Ancistrodon blomhoffi* var. *monticola*. The dark red tree paeony *Paeonia delavayi* was in full bloom, but there was not much else, and the day's haul consisted chiefly of cryptogams.

I then made several visits to the old terminal moraine below the great gorge, Luoqu (Fig.21), with the aim of photographing the gorge and the precipices below the summit of Satseto from the east side. After several attempts spoilt by mist I was finally successful. I had realised from the outset that there must be a vista which would repay some perseverance. A professional photographer could take dozens of pictures from different points along the moraine ridge and besides depicting the various groups of peaks could compose individual views with weather-beaten pines and larches, twisted into pleasing shapes, in the foreground; yet I believe that some of my efforts were not entirely without merit. To find these two species — pine and larch — together is most unusual. This was one of the few places where xerophilic pine forest and mesophilic mixed forest grew side by side, sharply demarcated from one another, on the same soil, dependent only on the aspect of the slope. Here, at 3400m, *Pinus tabulae-formis* and holly-leaved oak scrub covered all the south and south-east facing slopes of the moraines and also the crests themselves, while *Larix potaninii*, accompanied just below the crest by spruces, firs and miscellaneous broad-leaved trees, covered the slopes facing all other points of the compass.

Another day was devoted to the huge gorge itself. The sandy plain of Saba — marshy in some spots — lay between the moraines and was covered by short open turf. Towards its margins there were shrubs — the yellow *Potentilla fruticosa* and *Sibiraea levigata* with erect spikes of brown flowers. Further into the gorge the track entered coniferous forest, which here consisted of pines and spruces (*Picea likiangensis*), a most uncommon combination which was due to the juxtaposition of sharply differing conditions for their growth. The well drained, arid talus subsoil favoured the xerophytes, while in some places where the moraines — about 150m in height — approached each other more closely there were patches of level ground which were kept cool and, being at a fairly high altitude, offered conditions much more to the liking of the spruces. In the mossy, turfy hollows there were numerous dainty orchids such as the small red and white *Oreorchis oligantha* (a new species), the golden brown *O. erythrochrysea* and the tall pink *Calanthe delavayi*, together with the lax *Pedicularis axillaris* with finely divided leaves and long flower stalks, our own *Pinguicula alpina* and several lilies, notably *Lilium taliense*, which resembles the Turk's cap lily.

Before long we were passing between two huge precipices, one to the north plunging down vertically from Tschaloko summit and the other to the south from the jagged-edged rock dome of Saba. Up to a line exactly level with the moraine ridges the ice-worn rock surfaces were so smooth and polished that no trees had been able to find lodgement, whereas higher up fair numbers of pines had rooted in the fissures. From a distance the whole scene presented a superb example of glacial action, an ice age landscape unique in its perfection. Here, at the foot of the rocks, the traveller still sees the deeply incised grooves and scratches scored by the passage of the glacier. They commence high up on the walls and slope downwards along the course taken by the ice. In cool moist corners and in shady spots at the edges of bamboo thickets, woods and scrub there were dense stands of lush large-leaved herbaceous plants such as *Cardamine polyphylla* with fine flesh-pink flowers, *Smilacina* spp. with panicles of little bells of green or brown, and white-flowered *Eutrema lancifolium*. The strips of woodland at the foot of the rocks became gradually narrower and more difficult to penetrate, while the stream bed grew broader and more chaotic. I soon had to leave my pony behind and thread my way between rounded boulders as large as houses.

The recent moraines, brought down by the crevassed hanging glacier on the south face of Satseto, were no longer very wide. With some trouble I climbed round their exceedingly steep flanks, composed of fine sand cemented into a solid mass, and here, at an altitude of only 3625m, I collected some gorgeous alpine plants, notably a large-flowered low-growing wallflower, *Cheiranthus forrestii*, with a wonderful perfume, a large sand-wort, *Arenaria fridericae* [67] and others. So once again I returned with rich spoils. As in 1914, every evening the natives brought large quantities of plants to the farm where I was lodging. I accepted more or less everything which they collected, for I still had an uneasy feeling that my financial support from Vienna might cease or that further expenses might mount up, and for this reason I was glad to have material which I could convert into herbarium specimens and sell as duplicates.

---

[67] A new species which Handel-Mazzetti later named in honour of his mother.

Chapter 14. To Mount Haba Shan

Tibetan caravans — an impassable track — the most westerly Yi villages — alpine leafmould pastures — a camp among rhododendrons — far ranging views — flora of a 4450m summit

At last the tent arrived and, after further delay caused by deliberate stupidity on the part of Li, who detested camping, was actually delivered to the village. I made enquiries for a caravan of five pack animals for an excursion to the snow-clad mountain at the north-west end of the range beyond the Jinsha Jiang. Besides making a botanical reconnaissance, I hoped to check the geographical information obtained in 1914 during my journey across the Zhongdian highlands in the rain. It should have been possible to find some horses in Baisha, but the local mafus declared that even for a dollar a day they were unwilling to take service with a European, for they knew such men all too well: they had travelled with the Frenchman Peronne [68], a musk trader from Dêqên, and he had always been hitting them. I was unsuccessful in my attempts to persuade them that not all Europeans were alike and that I treated my men very well, provided that they did more or less what I wanted, but in the end — though of course not without still further delay — I found the necessary horses in Nguluke.   Setting off on 19th June, I crossed the col above Ganhaizi, reached the river in one day and spent the night at Yulo [69], the ferry station on the near side. Next morning the ferrymen kept me waiting on the bank for over an hour; they were on the far side, saw a caravan approaching and wanted to ferry it across the river before coming for me. We shouted and whistled in vain; however, now I knew that the ferry was operated at public expense, and I therefore gave them no tip and let them return with empty hands and downcast faces. This achieved the desired result, and on the return journey they attended to me with the utmost promptness. Travelling in the same direction as ourselves was a Tibetan caravan. They used the enforced rest to make tea on the sand beside the river; men and women, who both do exactly the same work, sat in circles round the kettle, singing, laughing and teasing one another. During their frolics a mafu wench, as tall as a beanpole, turned the drinking water pail upside down over her partner's head. In total contrast to the Chinese, who cannot work without grumbling, sulking and uttering unspeakably foul curses, the robust, shaggy and yet elastic figures of the Tibetans seemed to be bubbling over with joy of living. Whenever I met them on the road they always greeted me with a clumsy curtsey, their hands held palm upwards before their chests. In those districts I never encountered the mode of greeting — sticking out the tongue — usual further north, except on one occasion on the Lancang Jiang from a man who had probably come from there. The peaks were of course shrouded with mist, and enquiries regarding the correct route came up against the usual difficulties. Down here it was in any case useless to ask about a track up the mountain; however, if there were a track from Lendo [70], the first village on the Zhongjiang He, leading over the range to Haba [71] — known to me from my travels the year before — then that must be the right approach. The people said there were two roads, a major and a minor, and the major road led over a mountain. I accordingly told my guide to follow that.

It led first into the great gorge of the Jinsha Jiang, high up above its left bank. The opposite side of the gorge was free from clouds for much of its height and offered magnificent views. If the track had curved to the left it would have taken me in the direction in which I wished to go, but presently it became clear that this was not the case, and people in the fields called to us that it would soon become too narrow for our loads. They were at once proved correct by the sight of one of the loads rolling down the hillside, though luckily it was rescued. This route through the river gorge to Dagu, though it did lead to Haba, was obviously of no use to me. I turned round and took the Zhongdian road. At Qiaotou [72] it crossed over to Lendo on the left side of the Zhongjiang He, and ran at first close to the river bank along vertical talus cliffs scooped out by the stream. In their lower parts the sides of this sparsely populated valley sloped steeply upwards, but higher up they flattened out, especially towards the southwest, forming a broad undulating wooded ridge about 3600m high, which separated it from the Jinsha Jiang running from south to north. Lisu and Xifan lived there in small, widely scattered hamlets, but the Chinese were confined to solitary cottages down in the valley. At Meiziping the track climbed more than 100m up the valley side in steep zigzags. It descended again into a deeply cut lateral gorge and then more gradually down to the river. There was plainly no practicable route branching off to the right (north east) anywhere as far as Tuguancun, two days beyond Yulo. Since my journey along this route in 1914 a hostelry had been erected there, a small bamboo hut in which we spent the night. On the Hongshishao saddle, which we had to cross to reach Tuguancun from the river, we met a caravan which had stopped to rest, but the men advised us not to

---

[68] Gustave [aka Gaston] Peronne, a musk trader, lived for over 20 years at Dêqên (F. Kingdon Ward, *"From China to Hktami Long"*, London, 1924, p.93). J.W. Gregory met him there in 1922. (J.W. & C.J. Gregory, *"To the Alps of Chinese Tibet"*, London, 1923, p.205).

[69] At Yulo (6300 ft = 1920m) the trail turns at right angles down to the Yangtze where a flat-bottomed ferry crosses it to the hamlet of Ggo-lo" (Plate 114). (Rock, Vol. I, p.255).

[70] Probably a non-Chinese name (SGH).

[71] "Handel-Mazzetti's name Tja-ta-shan can be traced to the unfamiliarity of the Naxi with the Chinese language. His guide, apparently ignorant of the real name of the mountain (Haba ndsher nv-lv), and being close to a rather important village called Ch'iao t'ou(Qiaotou) (bridge-head village), in which district the mountain is also situated, called it Ch'iao'tou shan, whence Tja-ta-schan". (Rock, Vol.I, p.255)

[72] There was a wooden bridge at Ch-iao-tou across the river Chung-chiang ho (Rock, Vol. I, page 256).

camp there because there were so many leeches. From the saddle I had a magnificent view — lasting just long enough to take a photograph — down the valley towards the western side of the two main peaks of the Yulong Shan, both capped with snow, but the mountain on this side of the Yangzi — my journey's goal — was hidden in mist.

Tuguancun was one of the most westerly Yi villages; it lay in a side valley which ran down from Alo and, after making a sharp bend which cut off the route over the Hongshishao saddle, debouched into the main Zhongjiang He valley close by. From Tuguancun there was a track leading to Bede; higher up it allegedly gave off a path to the snow-capped mountain. After some difficulty — and for a high price — we found a young man as a guide, as I was not willing to travel into unknown territory without one. The fields of the Yi — the first people to settle here — extended over low ridges separated by small streams. The burnt stumps of chopped down trees still projected above the ground and here and there a mighty trunk, too large to utilise or clear away, lay prostrate; between them grew oats, barley, buck-wheat and potatoes, the main diet of the tribes-people, whose low-roofed one-roomed bamboo huts were scattered among them. Behind the last of the huts the track entered the forest, which at first consisted of pines. Even at this altitude the plant cover was splendid and colourful. There were several species of lady's slipper orchid and of *Roscoea*, together with *Nomocharis aperta*, which has large saucer-shaped drooping rose pink flowers, and other species of the lily family. Other noteworthy plants included *Stellera chamaejasme* and *Morina delavayi*. Growing on the trunks of the pines was an orange-yellow fungus (*Cryptoporus volvatus*), as glossy as if it had been varnished, reeking of the cheapest schnapps. The natives ate it raw. In moist places there were strips of "jungle" vegetation where the steep slippery track was sometimes almost totally blocked by fallen bamboos and tree trunks, which gave the pack animals much trouble. Then it came out on to open sward gay with flowers of almost unparalleled splendour, in particular the deep rose-pink hemispherical umbels of *Androsace spinulifera* covering large patches, while *Veratrilla baillonii* had just opened its green flowers in dense panicles. On last year's dead stalks I collected two species of minute fungi. We stopped for our midday rest in an unoccupied shepherd's hut in a pine grove, and as soon as I had devoured the meal I stood up and began to scour the mountainside above us. Wherever it had found lodgement on the slopes, leaf mould had accumulated and on it grew a plant community, for which I coined the name "leafmould pasture"[73]. The brown topsoil consisted of weathered plant remains, roots and rootstocks, with leaves and especially the leaf sheaths which envelop the living stems and form a covering round the neck of the plant. On it grew dwarf shrubs, including *Berberis*

spp., honeysuckles, small rhododendrons and *Therm-opsis alpina* with large flowers like brimstone butterflies, all woven together in dense tangles. Among the shrubs various herbaceous perennials were now in flower, many of them so deeply rooted that it was hard work to dig them out intact. There were anemones, *Nomocharis lophophora*, *Potentilla stenophylla* with pinnate silvery leaves and the strange-looking *Mandragora caulescens*. *Meconopsis pseudointegrifolia* [74] is a robust plant a metre in height with a thick hollow stem covered with rough golden hairs, and numerous drooping poppy-like sulphur yellow flowers on erect pedicels. *Primula szechuanica* has delightfully fragrant sulphur yellow flowers, resembling those of *P. sikkimensis* but with petals bent sharply backwards and pressed against the tube — a peculiarity seen in very few species of primula.

Soon we reached the crest[75], from which we had a splendid vista towards the other side over the valley of the Bapaji, the little river running from Bede. Close to it lay Washua, its houses looking like toys. Twenty six km north-northeast was the arid bastion of Kudu (4700m), and to its right we gazed into the depths of the Yangzi gorge, from which the caves I had seen in 1914 stared up like two mis-shapen eyes. Beyond the gorge was the range ex-tending from Xuechou Shan (4800m) to Halao Shan. It is nothing more than an offshoot from the second main range ending in the Yangzi loop. The main range itself is cut through by the Yangzi between Xuezhou Shan and Kudu. I certainly wanted to climb one of the peaks and photograph the full 360° panorama for my map, but on second thoughts I decided to play safe, so I set up my camera on the pass and exposed a few plates, my fingers numbed by the cold wind. Unfortunately, like many land-scape photographs taken in 1915, they gave very poor results because the plates were old and stale. There was in fact a path leading to the broad ridge on the right, and I took it. The view was so glorious that even Li — no lover of mountains — was at first impressed, but now he sat wrapped in his Yi cloak shivering in the wind and complaining that he felt "*beaucoup froid*". However, when I suggested that sitting still was not the best way to keep warm he came after me, accompanied by Wu Suoling. After some two hours' march the track led into a hollow on the south west flank of the mountain, where I pitched camp in a delightful little spot beside a spring at 4175m (Fig.23). The ground was so boggy that I had to put flat stones under the tentpoles to prevent them from sinking into it. All round the tent were rhododendrons[76] with large white and pink flowers. Though gnarled and twisted, the bushes were quite tall, and their dead twigs were covered by

---

[73] "*Modermatte*". The English phrase is taken from Handel-Mazzetti's lecture *"The Natural Habitats of Chinese Primulas"*, given at the Fourth Primula Conference in London on 24th May, 1928. (J. Roy. Hort. Soc. 1929, **54**, 51-62)

[74] Now included in *M. integrifolia*.

[75] This was presumably the pass shown on Handel-Mazzetti's map (4200m). Rock calls it Hsüeh-men-k'an (13,800 ft = 4207m). Washua is 13 km distant from it.

[76] Handel-Mazzetti's photograph (Fig.23) shows rhododendrons about twice the height of his tent and the caption names them as *R. adenogynum*.

covered by tufted lichens, some black (*Alectoria acanthodes*) and others yellowish (*Nephromopsis delavayi*). Not far below were the dark green spikes of the firs — at their altitudinal limit — and beneath them was unbroken forest, filling a tangled lattice of valleys running in all directions and clothing the ridges between them. Farther to the northwest the sun was shining on the emerald green meadows which today occupy the dried up lake beds below Zhongdian (Fig.24). Low clouds scudded over the ground, while shafts of sunlight painted constantly changing patterns upon them and outlined their margins with gold. That day I had some trouble with the men. One of them, a former soldier whom I had taken on probation, hid in a nearby hut with the mafus and despite all my shouting would not come out and take his share of the work. Later he refused to groom the horse, saying that Kok had not told him he was to do that task, so I promptly threw him out. Li had a genuine attack of mountain sickness and I gave him some tablets for his headache. Next morning, when he let it be known that they had really worked, all the men clamoured for them, and I left them behind in annoyance.

On 23rd June I climbed unaccompanied to the crest and followed it south eastwards. It ran a sinuous course far above the tree line, not giving off many lateral ridges but marked by several minor elevations. Crystalline rocks and clay-slate, emerging below the limestone which outcrops on the mountainside lower down, were arranged in an extremely steep or even vertical dip running mainly north and south, though buckled in various directions. The vegetation on the windswept southwest side was obviously different from that on the more sheltered northeast slope. On the latter there were woody plants forming dense continuous dwarf shrub communities up to the crest line, especially willows, rhododendrons (*R. complexum*) and at the very top *Cassiope*, a genus of *Ericaceae* widespread in the Arctic and Himalaya with short erect stems like a clubmoss. This one was *C. selaginoides*. Where the crest ran in a straight line the shrubs on the northeast slope extended up to it and were cut off along an equally straight line at the crest, though it was far from sharply angled. On the southwest slope, however, the shrubs began much lower down, and the upper part of the slope was occupied only by a few non-woody plants, while the edges of the rocks (slate and calcareous slate, or calc-schist) were encrusted with lichens, many of them the same as those found in our own Alps. However, I was particularly struck by the rare *Acroscyphus sphaerophoroides*, a lichen otherwise known from the Himalaya and the Andes. It grew in patches as big as a man's head crowning the rocky spikes of the *arête* and was distinguished by its round erect grey-white stemlets, branching like coral. Every few paces I found something to collect, and some four hours passed before I ultimately reached a minor summit at 4450m. From it I could see the lower slopes of Mount Haba Shan[77], but its summit was hidden by a sharply defined layer of cloud about 500m above me. Any serious attempt to climb it was no longer feasible, and the summits in front of it were scarcely any higher than my own,

which in any case gave the view I desired. To the west and northwest stretched the forest-covered green Zhongdian uplands with a few meadows here and there; beyond them — and similar in appearance — was the broad mountain range which separated the Yangzi from the Laugcang Jiang, overtopped only by Baima Shan (5300m) near Dongzhuling nearly 150 km to the northwest, a sombre rugged peak with a few small glaciers. Beyond were the snowcapped mountains on the Tibetan frontier opposite Dêqên, all of them unfortunately hidden by a stratum of cloud. The broad expanse of the crest on which I stood was crossed by the track leading from Bede to Xiao Zhongdian, and beyond it, to the north, were the multiple summits of Piepen with its brown sandstone foothills. Further to the right were the mountains I had seen yesterday, around the northern part of the Yangzi loop. Still further off, I could see the countless peaks of the Tibetan districts of Quag-chêng and Gongling, near the road to Batang, some of them still topped with snow.

The plant community on the crest, which was built of primitive rocks, was much less varied than those found on limestone at similar altitudes. White and purple were the predominant colours: *Androsace delavayi*, resembling our *A. glacialis*, several primulas and saxifrages, the low growing *Rhododendron prostratum* with large deep purple flowers, and, somewhat similar in appearance, *Diapensia purpurea*, growing in dense cushions (Fig.25). This species, absent from Mount Yulong Shan, is characteristic of the high mountains further west. I gathered some beautiful mosses and lichens: several species of *Grimmia*, the new *Andraea yunnanensis* and our own *Thamnolia vermicularis*, which in China is used to make tea. That evening the men were of course restored to health, and Li's oven — an empty paraffin can — had been put to good use. Up on the mountain the cold wind blew unremittingly and during the night a downpour drummed against the canvas, while the storm threatened to tear the tent from its pegs.

My grey pony — the one I had taken over from Schneider — also had a nasty attack of mountain sickness while we were up on the ridge, and even after we had descended its recovery was slow. On the climb to the saddle between Tuguancun and Luoxiwan it was barely able to carry me and fell several times, not as I at first thought because the ground was slippery but in reality because of dizziness. On the descent, though not carrying any load, it began to reel and stagger so badly that it nearly pushed me off a bridge into the stream. In the end it was almost unable to go any further, and to protect it from rough treatment from the men I myself had to drive and shove it along. On the next day, as we continued our journey down the valley, it was still unfit for me to ride. On the following day I stopped at Yulo to photograph the distinctive plants growing beside a ditch — *Houttuynia cordata* with heart-shaped leaves and dense spikes of yellowish flowers above four white bracts, *Pteris vittata* and leaves of *Amorphophallus* — while the caravan went on. During the climb up from the Yangzi towards Ganhaizi the pony was almost impossible to curb and struggled so hard to keep up with the others that on the last stretch its strength once again failed completely. On the fourth day I re-entered Lijiang.

---

[77] 15,420 ft (4701m) on ONC H-10. Handel-Mazzetti gives its height as "over 5300m".

Chapter 15. From Lijiang to Yongning and up the Waha Range

Naxi caravans — a view of the Yangzi loop — mountain bogs — the arid Yangzi valley at Fengke — over the pass in the rain — lodgings at the abbot's — opposition from the magistrate — yak huts on Mount Waha — a high treeline — a mountain lake — difficulties of mapmaking

On the fifth day (9th July) it was still raining dismally as I left Lijiang, delayed by the dilatoriness of the Chinese workmen. My new caravan men were Naxi from the nearby village, whom Schneider had found satisfactory the year before. They brought no fewer than thirteen pack animals, for the districts through which I planned to travel were sparsely populated and in some parts we had to carry enough food and forage for several days. The price was low — $5 in all for each day on the road and $2 for each rest day — and I never had the slightest difficulty or demur from the men. As was plainly apparent from their frank and open looks, they were honest, energetic and willing; they never argued or answered back, and when the final payment was due they found the accounts in order and were content with their well-earned gratuity. In all these respects they were totally different from the Chinese. Their animals were fully capable of meeting the demands made on them, although not much better cared for than those of the Chinese. As plant collectors I took Wu Suoling and a Naxi from Nguluke, a man who had given Schneider such good service that he took him as far as Kunming. His name was Li (Lao Li or "old Li" with the prefix used among people of the servant class), and he was an intelligent and tolerably clean young man, who served me as well as he had served Schneider [78].

The track ran straight northwards across the talus-covered plain, passing Baisha and Nguluke. At the edge of the forest it joined the route which we already knew, leading from Nguluke to Baishui. There, at the edge of the glacial brook, we pitched our first camp. Next day I at first followed the track along which I travelled to Dagu in 1914, but soon I took a path along the crest. Starting from the Konanyo pass at 3400m, this ridge climbed up to a rounded summit on the right and then flattened out. Consisting partly of sandstone, it sloped down to another col at only 2900m, a col which joined the Lijiang range to the adjacent range of Mount Xuechou Shan [79]. That afternoon we pitched camp some distance beyond Konanyo on a splendid pasture

between mixed forests of larch and pine. Though still rainy, the weather had improved a little and from a small crest above the campsite I was able to photograph Mount Haba Shan, the snowclad mountain which lies beyond the Yangzi though in fact it belongs to the Lijiang range. During my journey to Tuguancun I had attempted to photograph it without success. From this side it presented a long rock crest falling away vertically on either side. The wind whirled the snow from its summit into spiralling eddies which rose like smoke from a chimney into the deep blue sky, and it made a superb picture, softtoned and seemingly translucent in the mountain air as it shimmered in the warmth of the sun.

Branching valley tracts ran down to the Jinsha Jiang from both sides of the low col. The valley on the left ran north-westwards, debouching into the river near Dagu. In its upper part it had steep walls on both sides, but lower down it spread out into a broad flat floor extending for some distance. The valley on the right, after traversing an undulating hilly tract into which it had cut a relatively shallow channel, ran south-eastwards and joined the other side of the river loop opposite the steep precipices of Mount Mantou Shan. Between the lowest slopes of Mount Yulong Shan to the south and Mount Xuechou Shan to the north the saddle was about 10 km broad, and at its northern border was Mingyin, a Naxi village with a Chinese lijin post for the minor road to Yongning. A little further on I climbed a steep wooded crest to the right of the road and found that once again my luck was in. Although I had not until then been able to get much idea of the lie of the land, my intuition had not betrayed me in leading me there. The spot offered a good view and for once it was unobscured by clouds. The crest projected some distance towards the river and gave a long vista up its valley. By this I do not mean that one could see the river itself at any point at all — it was hidden in its gorges 1800m below — but at my level and somewhat lower there were rocky bastions which pushed out their shoulders of gently tilted strata towards the river. These bastions belonged to the ridges which intervened between six steep lateral valleys running at right angles to its line of flow. Looking like painted scenery on a theatre stage, they intersected with a series of spurs running down from the western side of the gorge, a series which seemed to extend close to the range of mountains between Xuechou Shan and Halao Shan, parallel to it and much lower. Beyond the river gorge I could see the steep slope of the range which ran southwards from Yongning. It too was 4600m in height, but much less dissected by streams. It terminated abruptly in a splendid double peak which the people here called

---

[78] Hereafter sometimes referred to simply as Li, but not to be confused with the man of the same name who had served Handel-Mazzetti until now, and who is mentioned in Chapter 14.

[79] Xuechou Shan, otherwise La-bpu Ngyu, Lapao Shan or Mount Bonvalot (4800m) is the mighty limestone mass that fills the Yangtze loop.

Alo[80]. From this spot it was also clear why the direct route to Yongning ran high up across the mountains and avoided the river valley. Gwulowo, a Naxi village, lay some distance to the east of the track, spread out on a patch of ground sloping down to the next brook. There were only a few others, down near the river. Lambe was supposed to be one of the larger ones, and Lisu tribesmen lived to the south of it. Far away to the north, beyond the river gorge. I saw range upon range of mountains, some still capped with snow, in the vicinity of Muli, my objective, and near Gongling. To the south there were fine vistas of the northerly rock peaks of the Yulong Shan, two mighty parallel serrated edges with teeth resembling the summits of the Rosengarten in the Dolomites, declining gradually in absolute altitude as they ran northwards towards me, though hardly at all in relation to the surrounding landscape. High up on the range, cradled between the peaks, was a huge glacier, and today, for the first and only time, I enjoyed a more or less complete view of the snowfield which fed it. Seen from the north, Satseto, the main summit, displayed its structure of vertically tilted rock strata running north and south. I halted at Tsasopie, a Naxi village situated in the next side valley a short distance below the track, in a position which was the mirror image of Gwulowo in the preceding valley. I spent the night in an open room exposed to wind and rain, where my sleep was disturbed by the incessant barking of the farm dog. The outcome was a slight cold which gave me some discomfort for the next few days, although the rain was only intermittent.

In moist spots in the woods, where there was an understorey of bamboo, I found hydrangeas (*H. xanthoneura*) and *Meliosma cuneifolia* in full bloom. The latter is a tall shrub with tiny yellowish flowers grouped together in large panicles to make them more conspicuous. For most of the way, however, the track led through drier forest made up of *Pinus tabulaeformis*, a pine which ascends to great altitudes, and then ran down into the largest of the side valleys which we had to cross. Its tributary streams ran down from Xuechou Shan, the mountain on the left about 4800m in height. I caught glimpses of its bare limestone crests looking down from behind dark fir woods. I attempted to measure some of the stretches of the track with the Roxanditsch range-finder, but it soon became obvious that the instrument would work only when it was set perfectly horizontally; if it inclined a little to the left or right, the points would come together at completely different places and the readings would be totally at variance.

On the far side of the valley the track climbed up for some 500m to the Huayangge pass at 3775m. Beyond it and a little lower down, on a wet flowery meadow between larch woods, was the campsite Mahaizi, with steep limestone crests above it. That evening I spent some time fishing for plankton in the bog pool on the meadow. Although the botanist cannot carry a net as part of his everyday equipment, when the route leads past lakes or pools or the camp is situated near one it is always worthwhile to unpack the net. I positioned myself on a projecting salient of the bank and Lao Li stood on another, separated by the length of the cord. I told him to cast the net and then pulled it swiftly towards me. After a few casts I had a glass tube full of tiny animals zigzagging in wild confusion and doubtless an abundant phytoplankton as well, though these minute plants are not visible to the unaided eye. Inside the tent it was very warm, especially in the main compartment with its double roof and well closed flaps. Li, Zhafa and another man spread out their blankets under the canopy, which had been provided with sidewalls and a groundsheet, while my other plant collector and the two policemen sent by the Lijiang magistrate made themselves comfortable under the eaves of the flysheet, using branches for bedding, though much of this space was occupied by my saddle and other items which needed protection from the weather. The caravanmen made shelters by piling the loads close together, stretching covers across and crawling underneath.

Next morning there was hoarfrost on the ground and fresh snow on the mountaintops; a little further along the track they made a superb backdrop behind the meadows and the numerous pools scattered across them. There were so many flowers that their colours quite outshone the green of the meadows. Thronging together in separate patches were the white *Morina alba* with inflorescences resembling *Betonica* and narrow bristly leaves, *Primula sikkimensis* with sulphur-yellow bells and *Ranunculus pulchellus* with yellow flowers. In the bog itself, mirrored in the muddy brown pools, *Rheum alexandrae* was just coming into flower, its tall spires ensheathed in large bracts. At the bottom of these pools, which never dry out, I found a water fern (*Isoëtes hypsophila* — a new species). It grows in tufts of light green leaves resembling grass but soft and circular in cross-section. In the leaf axils there are sporangia which produce an onion-like expansion or swelling of the entire basal part of the plant. The track continued over another pass of equal height and then down for 1600m into the next parallel valley, through this and then for some distance along the side of the river valley to Fengke[81], where I

---

[80] 4800m on Handel-Mazzetti's map. Mien-mien Shan on Rock's map.

[81] George Forrest passed through "Fengkow" in 1914 and wrote to his sponsor J.C. Williams: *"Seldom in all my wanderings here have I struck such a barren and blistering hot country as the Yangtze valley at Fengkow. A descent and ascent of some 9,000 ft and all practically desert. We spent one night and the greater portion of a day camped on a sandbank, rocks too hot to touch, tents unbearable, climate like Rangoon in August minus the rain. If you can imagine that, temperature over 110 in the shade, brazen skies and the previous day we were at 14,000 ft.* (George Forrest. Journeys and Plant Introductions. Ed. J. MacQueen Cowan, 1952, Oxford University Press).

Rock states that it was probably at Feng'ko that Kublai Khan crossed with his army when he attacked Yunnan in 1253.

halted for half a day to get warm and rid myself of my cold.

In Fengke I was visited by a man whom Schneider had recommended because he spoke several languages. He offered his services and I agreed to take him on, but after vehement protests from his better half he did not reappear. The arid hillsides below the village had only a sparse scattering of shrubs, and where the turbulent streams from the mountain slopes above, coursing down in countless clefts and runnels, had washed away the yellow crust formed by weathering, the multicoloured primary and volcanic rocks, crumbling to dust where they outcropped, made garish contrasts. Down here even the Naxi houses had nothing better than flat roofs of mud. On the morning of the 15th July the rest of my caravan crossed the Yangzi by the ferry. Though quite a large boat, it rolled alarmingly in the middle of the fast-flowing river, which was narrowed at this point by a projecting mass of dark rock. On the far side we took the road uphill. Westwards it looked down over a conspicuous bend in the river. The side valley was a mere ravine, and the track had to ascend a projecting spur on to the valley side, which it followed for some distance before dropping down into the flatter upper part of the valley to the camping place on a heathy pasture at Zhazi.

Having climbed out of the arid depths of the river gorge we were once more in subtropical maquis consisting of *Pistacia weinmannifolia* with *Vitex* and *Ziziphus* bushes, succeeded at 2400m by bright green *Pinus yunnanensis* woodland. We climbed up through the next vegetational zones in rapid succession — a forest of the darker, short-needled *P. tabulaeformis* interspersed with oaks, and temperate zone mixed woodland, with much bamboo, running down into a little ravine. Here, on the limestone rocks, I found another blue Gesnerad, *Didissandra grandis*, its leaves edged by white down extending from the under surface, and collected two mosses growing in deep soft cushions; *Hymenostylium diversirete* with crinkled leaves neatly arranged in three lines, and the golden-green *Gollania robusta*. Both species were new to science and I never found them anywhere else. The pass was at 3700m; standing on a lush meadow we gazed over the Yongning basin, but low clouds hid the mountain tops and cast a gloom over the green landscape.

I sent a policeman ahead with my card, having deliberately instructed him to report first to the lama, my friend from the year before, and only then to the Chinese minor official, for I felt confident that the lama would help me in my plans for further journeys, while the official could only be obstructive. As we descended the track grew steadily wetter and became a mere line of holes where the pack animals had to pick their way between knife-edged blocks of limestone pavement protruding from the red earth, some of them hollowed out and perforated like carious teeth. The whole formation was overgrown with trees. I met a Tibetan in multicoloured costume who had travelled with a few laden pack animals from Kangding. He was just making tea and invited me to sit down on his splendid carpet, spread out by the roadside. The track across the Yongning plain was a bottomless morass, but at last we reached the

lamasery on 16th July, and the abbot once again gave me a friendly reception.

In the previous year, so he told me, the officials had arrived from Yongsheng and Lijiang with numerous soldiers and had tried to take his monastery away from him. However, he had plenty of men, including some from Muli and was not to be overawed. The officials thereupon withdrew, their aim unaccomplished. The local official resided an hour's journey distant in a village named Dashi and I did not meet him until a Tibetan holiday, when the abbot invited us both to a banquet at which — horror of horrors — he played a gramophone he had recently acquired. Next day I returned the visit accompanied by my servant and the lama. Sitting behind his writing table, the magistrate received us in a room which, simply because it was new, was clean and tidy. I had the place of honour at his side, Lao Li was beside me and the lama in a corner. I explained that I wanted to go to Muli and on to Zhongdian, and asked for a soldier with a letter of recommendation as an escort. During the conversation I enquired about Gongling and Xiangcheng, located deeper in the interior, but my mention of these places displeased the fellow so much that he tried strenuously to dissuade me from travelling to the north. Muli was in Sichuan, he told me, the people did not speak Chinese and the lamas were not well disposed towards foreigners.

"The abbot of Muli is a good friend of mine," said the chief lama.

"I am familiar with the reports of the Europeans who have been there — Amundsen and Davies — and they all speak well of Muli," I remarked.

"Yes, quite a lot of Europeans go there," said the lama, taking sides with me. I complained about the rain.

"It's always raining in Xiangcheng," said the magistrate," and a month ago robbers from Gongling plundered the temple at Muli."

"That's quite untrue," growled the lama. The prefect said he would have to write to Yanyuan in Sichuan to get a letter of recommendation.

"So far as I'm concerned you can write to Peking," I replied, "but by the time an answer comes, I shall have left Muli far behind me."

I stood up and took my leave, the magistrate regarding me with a long face.

My next aim was to visit Waha, the mountain south of Yongning which I had had to omit from my itinerary in 1914. After waiting yet another day on which it poured unceasingly, I set out on 19th July along a track which at first ran southwards from the village and left no option but to wade through the muddy waters of the swollen rivulet. Leaving the horse to pick its way, I bent forwards and pressed my face against its mane, this being the only way to creep beneath the overhanging rose thickets without losing my hat, having my clothes torn and sustaining deep scratches on my back. *Primula vialii* was now in flower everywhere in this district (Fig.8). Near Lijiang, where it was discovered, it occurs in only two sites, both on marshy meadows, but here it grows in a wide variety of habitats, flourishing in large numbers even among bushes of prickly-leaved oak, a shrub which prefers dry conditions. This is obviously its centre of distribution; in other directions there are scattered colonies as far as Muli and Yanyuan.

Leaving it on its left, the track departed from the shallow but steep-walled trench, out of which emerges the main branch of the little river from Yongning, and climbed steadily through woodland. The pack animals were soon exhausted from struggling along the slippery path and clambering over fallen tree trunks, and my grey had bouts of shivering, so when we reached a yak pasture at 4030m we pitched camp. As the site had not yet been occupied the turf was still untouched and repaid careful examination. Among the grasses I found some old acquaintances from our own Alps and nearby — *Trisetum sibiricum, Festuca ovina, Poa pratensis* and *Elymus nutans.* Next I found *Dracocephalum wilsonii,* resembling catmint but larger, and then to my great joy my *Taraxacum tibetanum* [82], like our own dandelion but having black involucral bracts each with a large horn-shaped appendage. Growing on bare earth at the edge of the meadow was the tiny *Draba elliptica,* in dense patches of seedlings. Then I crawled about among the rhododendron bushes and searched for cryptogams. The best finds were an orange-yellow cup-fungus growing on old yak dung (*Plicaria fimeti* var. *miniata*); a tiny ash-grey stalked fungus of the same kind scattered in large numbers over the rolled up rhododendron leaves lying on the ground (*Lachnum foliicola* — a new species) and the moss *Zygodon brevisetus* growing on fir bark.

Next morning I climbed to the top of the ridge accompanied by my collectors, the lama's two henchmen, both carrying rifles, and the soldier provided by the magistrate, though he thought it better to leave his rifle in the hut. The firs thinned out as we approached the treeline, though there were still a few rowans among them, and flowering beneath the trees were *Saussurea poophylla, Dracocephalum speciosum,* a sage with large but short flowers, *Gentiana puberula* and *Primula florida.* Higher up I found some deep holes in the limestone pavement which lay on top of the sandstone at the crest of the ridge. Between three bare summits, visible from Yongning, I reached the main ridge, which ran southwards. *Arenaria kansuensis* formed broad cushions with sessile flowers which look green since the petals are shorter than the sepals. *A. oresbia* carried taller stems with solitary large white flowers; *Lasiocaryum trichocarpum* (a new species) was an annual which mimicked a small forget-me-not; *Androsace euryantha* (also new) had large red flowers above dense carpets of leaves, and *Sibbaldia purpurea* had small flowers of darker hue; *Lagotis yunnanensis* with fleshy leaves and cylindrical spikes of small white flowers grew in marshy hollows. On the right there was a small tarn in a sharply incised valley debouching below Zhazi. Keeping to the left of the ridge, after a short distance I climbed down to another tarn, also on the tree line. Its outlet was subterranean and probably supplied the stream in the valley beginning just below and running down to

join the Yongning river. The tree line was surprisingly high, though because of a cloudburst I was not able to ascertain its altitude exactly. Subsequent calculation from the base in Lijiang gave a figure of 4325m. I was not yet accustomed to finding the tree line at such a high altitude, but in the continental climate of high mountain masses this is the general rule, as it is in adjacent parts of Sichuan. The water temperature in the tarn was 19°C; a *Batrachium* was growing there, and we startled a beautiful multicoloured wild duck. In these parts the ducks seemed to be treated as sacred or were at any rate protected, for when the men were telling me about them they made quacking noises and I, thinking they were imitating frogs, made signs that I would like to catch some, at which they protested vehemently. Fish are said not to occur here, yet their absence is surprising in view of Bacot's claim to have seen certain forms uniquely adapted to the extreme conditions in lakes which have only a brief ice-free season between Litang and Gongling at 5000m. The wonderfully fragrant *Primula yargongensis* was flowering in the bog, and large tufts of *Drepanocladus turgescens* sprawled down into the water. The scree slope above yielded a rich haul including the small *Thalictrum glareosum* (a new species) with recurved stems, almost buried in the shingle, *Saussurea leucoma, Cremanthodium* spp. and many others. The turf was short as if it had been mown, but this was the result of natural selection; it comprised only those low-growing grasses and herbs which persisted despite grazing(Fig.27). Among them were the small, mat-forming, softly hairy *Pedicularis microphyton* with long, tubular, yellowish white flowers flecked with carmine on the upper lip, *Phlomis rotata,* which I had already met, *Polygonum sphaerostachyum,* like our snake root but only a few centimetres high, and *Aster likiangensis.*

Cloud draped the tops and obscured all distant views and I therefore rested content with an altitude reading of 4500m. I had a violent headache, probably because of the prolonged stay at that altitude, and I was not altogether sorry to give up the idea of climbing one of the rather unpromising little summits nearby. Next morning, during the descent, I collected more of the numerous mosses and lichens growing in the leafmould and on the rotten trunks and stumps, more especially in the upper zones of the fir woods. Then, standing in a burnt patch of forest, I took another photograph of the Yongning basin. Indeed I took far more photographs than were really necessary for cartographic purposes, as each view seemed better than the one before, although it was difficult to find a spot to set up the camera where the charred trunks did not block some vital feature. Here the camera was at least standing on firm ground, yet I remember another occasion when I had to drive the iceaxe, to which the camera mount was attached, as high up as possible into the rotten wood of a swaying tree-trunk; then I scrambled up and adjusted the focus, climbed down again and released the shutter, taking care not to bump against the trunk and make it sway during the exposure. Such are the joys and sorrows of a photogrammetric surveyor in the field!

[82] *Taraxacum* was one of Handel-Mazzetti's favourite genera and had been the subject of his dissertation. He described *T. tibetanum* in 1907.

Chapter 16. The Land of Muli

The Chesha pass — the monastery town of Muli — a distrustful lama — interior of the temple — prayer wheels — up Mount Saganai in the rain — tales of bandits — the Li Qu valley — three days' march at over 4000m — ascent of Gonshiga (4750m) — Xifan people along the Shuiluo He — the Yangzi bend

The friendly relations between the lama and the official were purely superficial, and it now suited the lama to help me in my efforts to reach Muli. In the meanwhile he had sent ahead a messenger with a letter in Tibetan, and he said that the official would not be able to stop me.

"He is really just a child, and if he still raises objections I shall simply shout at him, and then he will certainly give way", said I, to the lama's approval.

The inhabitants were by no means friendly, and the mafu who had stayed in the town complained that he was unable to purchase anything; wherever he went, as soon as the people saw him coming with his sack they slammed their doors. Not until the lama had provided a man to accompany my servant was he able to buy the necessary food supplies. On the day before I planned to depart the official sent a soldier with an invitation to dinner for the next evening.

"What does he think he's playing at?" Lao Li said to him, "that's not the way we do things. When a European says he's departing tomorrow, that's just what he will do, and you can forget about your invitation to dinner. What I want is a letter for Zhongdian. The lama is already fixing things for Muli."

This produced the desired effect, and a soldier duly turned up on the morning of 23rd July. The abbot still insisted on being photographed in various costumes, but when the proposed subject did not appeal to me I simply left the cover of the slide-holder in place. However, I took pictures of his eighty year old father dressed as the living Buddha and of a mendicant lama with his yellow hat and praying kit, also a prayer wheel and a drum covered with human skin. Then I departed with my caravan, which had been augmented by one of the abbot's henchmen, a man who spoke Chinese, Tibetan, Naxi, Xifan [83], and Lüdi, the last being totally different dialects of the Naxi language [84].

The route led northwards across Naxi territory, through green valleys, over low ridges and between countless dolines, many of them concealed in sombre woods of *Pinus tabulaeformis* interspersed with holly-leaved oak scrub. Once beyond the Yongning basin it continued straight through into the province of Sichuan as far as Wujiao, the first Pumi village, where I set up my campbed under the eaves of a house, as the interior rooms were too malodorous for me. It was not until long afterwards that I realised that this revolting stench, which I often encountered in Tibetan houses, simply came from their meat-smoking operations and was really quite wholesome.

Next morning along came an old woman with bitten off (or torn off) oat stalks in one hand and a pile of horse dung in the other. On the basis of these *corpora delicti* she asserted that my horses had been trespassing in her oats, and claimed damages. However, as they had not been outside at all, we finally threw her out.

The next day's march took us at first slightly downhill along the lateral valley in which Wujiao is located, a valley which runs eastwards to the Yongning river. Then we went uphill to another tributary, its banks bordered with old trees of sea buckthorn covered with moss (*Didymodon corticola* — a new species). We continued up the hillside through magnificent forests, in some parts consisting of firs and numerous yews with an undergrowth of bamboo, and elsewhere of huge oaks, finally emerging on to the jagged mountain which bounds the valley of the Litang river. In many places the track was a deeply cut trench, used by riders at their peril. Tree trunks had fallen across it and once, having just ridden beneath one, ducking as low as I could and yet scraping my back on it, as I started to straighten up, I saw just in time that there was a second trunk beyond the first and only managed to dodge it by a hairs-breadth. If my forehead had struck against it, I should certainly have been swept senseless from the saddle. I pitched camp below the pass at 3950m at the foot of rugged limestone peaks full of caves and grottoes, beside a little waterfall and amid fir woods and *Potentilla* bushes. The Chesha pass lay 150m higher, between short mountain chains running north and south. The whole mountain consisted of such chains, but erosion attacking it from north and south has converted it into a range which for the most part runs east and west. The descent began through a high alpine valley where I gathered some botanical treasures: the tall purple *Saussurea longifolia*, the large *Aster yunnanensis*, *Codonopsis subscaposa* with white bellflowers marked with brownish-purple and *Campanula aristata* with tiny blue flowers. In a gloomy forest of firs and rhododendrons I found a new species of primula (*P. muliensis*) [85]. Its leaves were white beneath and its flowers, over 4 cm in diameter — among the largest of its genus — were spread horizontally to catch the light.

We turned left over a whaleback ridge and plunged steeply down through pine woods to the Muli valley. Clearings in the forest gave glimpses to the north. From afar Muli looked like a heap of pale stones flung down on the steep valley side. The Litang river ran past to its right in a deeply incised

---

[83] Xifan = Pumi (SGH).

[84] The Naxi language is related to the language of the Yi, and belongs to the Tibeto-Burman section of the Sino-Tibetan group. It has two major dialects (SGH).

[85] Now *Primula boreio-calliantha*. Handel-Mazzetti's tepid description of this "truly magnificent Nivalid" — he omits even to mention the flower colour (lilac, purple, mauve or violet) — is in marked contrast to Kingdon Ward's ecstatic depiction in "The Romance of Plant Hunting", 1924, p. 119-120 (under the name *P. coryana*). See also K. Ward, Gard. Chron. Ser. 3 lxxxii, fig. 35 (1927). It has never been successfully cultivated.

channel. Rugged crags towered to heights of over 2000m above it on both sides of the valley. Far upstream its course was delineated by intersecting lateral spurs, which compelled it to make seemingly minor zigzags. On that day, however, all the peaks were shrouded in low cloud. We camped for one more night down in the valley among aromatic *Artemisia* — one of the plants which made up the garrigue growing on the arid valley slopes. Below it was the lush subtropical bush of the humid river gorge. Next morning three hours' march brought us to the little town. The abbot's man had announced my impending arrival, and the headman of the temple was expecting me, a plump lama with a piercing gaze. His skin was smeared with rancid butter and he wore a red cowl which left his right shoulder and arm bare. The actual chief — I find myself slipping into the jargon used by Lao Li, to whom anyone with another man under him was a "chef" — was temporarily absent, having set out with two hundred men in pursuit of three hundred of his yaks which bandits from Gongling had driven into the mountains. I was accommodated in a house just outside the town. It had been built by a Chinese trader, but his business had not lasted very long. He had been murdered on the road to Kangding and his dismembered corpse had been despatched to his widow.

Muli had been built in a quadrangular plan but was without a perimeter wall[86]. Situated at 2800m, beneath forests of huge evergreen oaks overtopped by steep rock faces, it offered long vistas deep into the green valley of the Litang river. Its solid stone houses were roofed with shingles, and their small windows had frames with an expansion beneath and a little cornice above to keep the rain off. Two large temples, one at the upper and the other at the lower boundary of the town, served the needs of worship. However, the whole town was really a monastery, for it housed seven or eight hundred lamas, and the few lay inhabitants in their grey penitential garments seemed to blend into the background. I was surprised to find that the lamas, like all of them here, were red, and not, as one might expect from Davies' book, yellow. According to Rock, they belonged to the yellow sect of the reformed Tibetan church, but their only distinguishing mark was their yellow head-dress; usually, however, they went bareheaded. As for women, there were only a few in the small farms round about; they came in to sell eggs, vegetables or wood or barter them for tea. Travellers in the mountains had to carry a stock of tea to offer instead of currency when making small purchases, for away from the main trade routes the natives would not accept copper coins. In Muli the Sichuan coins worth 40 cents — often called "rupees"[87] by Europeans —

were in circulation. There were only a few Chinese living there — traders from Shanxi — and they had a miserable existence: they were not permitted to smoke their pipes except in the privacy of their houses, nor to open their mouths too wide, nor to adorn their dwellings with the customary greetings printed on red paper — not that these did anything to enhance the appearance of the houses. The only place where anything of the sort was to be seen was above the gate of the great lamasery itself. Here there was a dedication in large Chinese lettering from the dujun of Chengdu (the provincial capital of Sichuan), who had granted it to the native prince (the "tusi") in recognition of his peaceable conduct.

As evening came on the little town prepared for divine service. It was heralded by sonorous blasts on a horn, and the streets were immediately swarming with people. Red figures hurried towards the temple, and from it came murmured chanting, mingled with the sounds of gongs and drums. Choral singing, sometimes remarkably pleasing, was also to be heard, and after the monks had dispersed to their dwellings the noisy gabble of their prayers continued late into the night. It sounded like an endlessly repeated "katanatanöten nöten", but what the words actually were I was unable to ascertain. Not until 9 pm did quiet gradually descend. The Pumi language spoken in Muli had certain striking peculiarities, notably the sharp rasping "r" and some cadences resembling the second half of the well known song *"Dearest father, send me cash!"* I gave the headman of the temple a watch; though it cost only $2½ my servant told him that its value was $15. With an astonished cry of "a-i" he held it to his ear and listened to its ticking. Then he brought me an old alarm clock which no longer went and asked whether I could repair it. It was soldered into its case and there was no way of opening it, so there was nothing I could do, and my gift, simply because it was the only timepiece in the place, was *ipso facto* of greater value.

On the third day of my stay I called on him with the purpose of viewing and if possible photographing the temples. First of all I took a picture of an enormous prayer wheel in its own little house, with an old man turning it, but then the door was immediately shut. The lower temples were locked up, and the keyholder, so I was told, was a long way off, but the upper temple was open. We climbed up to it, but found it closed. On trying the door the large lock at its foot gave way of its own accord; it was evidently

---

[86] Owing to the deteriorating conditions in China a town wall has since been built (see illustration by Rock in the National Geographic Magazine XLVII, p. 466). Muli must be the only town to have been fortified in this way in the twentieth century (Handel-Mazzetti 's footnote).

[87] *"The Chinese rupee is a curious coin struck in Szechuan for Tibetan trade. The Tibetans of central Tibet trade mostly with India, and small traders take a sum of about 3000 rupees (£200) to Calcutta, where they buy Indian goods for sale*

in Tibet. Three thousand silver rupees are about one man's load, and, apart from the expense of carrying the money down, there is the danger of robbers. Consequently, the trader prefers to enter the British Post Office at Gyantse and send a money order to himself at Calcutta, which he does at a cost of one per cent. The British-Indian Post Office at Gyantse would not accept any but Indian currency; Chinese and Tibetan currency, therefore, depreciated in value in comparison with Indian. The Chinese sought to overcome this by coining a Chinese rupee which would be of value equal to the Indian rupee; but, of course, though similar in size, weight and almost so in pattern, it was still of no use at the Gyantse Post Office and fell in value to twelve annas (three quarters of a rupee), much to the annoyance of the Chinese. I found that on this eastern border the Chinese rupee, not being influenced by the British Post Office, had a higher value than the Indian coin." F.M. Bailey, China-Tibet-Assam, London, 1945. Bailey made the journey in 1911.

defective. The man who was escorting me said that we ought not to open the door without the lama's help, and I myself felt somewhat uneasy, since all the rest of the men had remained below. There were, so it seemed, plenty of keys, but the headman of the temple could not bring himself to permit photography within the sanctuaries. Other foreign visitors had stayed only one night or even less, he was reported as saying, but I had stayed much longer. At this I told my men to speak politely to him and to ask whether the watch was still going and whether he had remembered to wind it. This had the desired effect, and that afternoon I was permitted to visit the temples, though without my camera. First of all, however, I was entertained to a dish of tsamba, a Tibetan food made by mixing tea with butter and adding various kinds of flour and, in this instance, sugar. Then I had to purchase some lengths of silk as offerings, and incense candles, before we were allowed to proceed.

Black curtains edged with white concealed the huge doors of the three-storey building and lent it an air of mystery. On feast days enormous incense burners sent columns of smoke towards the heavens. Before entering the sanctuary we shuffled through a pile of bracken to clean our shoes. The Tibetans are totally different from the Chinese in their attitude towards their temples. No one in Muli would have dreamt of holding feasts or revels in front of the gods or of using the temples for play or merrymaking. The chambers were separated from one another by halls with wooden pillars, and their floors were strewn with red cushions and rugs to permit worshippers to kneel or prostrate themselves in comfort. Massive articles of copper and silver bore witness to great wealth. Figures made of butter on flat tablets of clay were being offered as sacrifices. Kneeling in front of each of the images of the principal deities were two lamas, reciting their rosaries in husky tones. My men paid their respects, but Lao Li, being a freethinker, was unmoved. The finest of all was a temple adorned with silk (Fig.28). There was a row of columns stretching up to the ceiling, all of them hung with layer upon layer of silk in various colours; the wooden pillars were swathed with similar fabric, and hanging down from all the galleries were silk-embroidered banners, side by side or overlapping. The colour scheme was not garish, but soft and festive, a light blue predominating. The religious books, each volume between wooden covers, were ranged round the whole room, set out in bookcases on rows of shelves. In a narrow hall at one side of the temple was long row of prayer cylinders with the well known inscription *"Om mani padme hum"*. From time to time they were set in motion, each revolution counting as a prayer. Close by was a group of prayer flags, narrow strips of fabric fastened to tall poles in order of length, each having the words *"Om mani padme hum"* printed upon it. Everywhere in the neighbourhood were swarms of obos, low pyramids of stone slabs with prayers chiselled upon them, each pile topped by a carved pole.

It was still raining hard and looked as if it would never stop, so I decided not to put off my trip to the mountains any longer. Next day, taking the tent and essential baggage, I set off towards the mountain to the west. I had been told that it should be possible to travel two days' journey into the range without risk from bandits, and I was attracted by the prospect of making a photogrammetric survey of the country towards Gongling and up the Litang river, which should be feasible if the weather was kind. When Lao Li heard that the route I had chosen was the one leading to Zhongdian he said he thought the lama was trying to get rid of me. Before we had gone far, however, we came to a path which branched off to the right and led steeply uphill. When we reached 3900m the guide declared that we had already completed the first day's march and that there was no water further on. I accordingly pitched camp and spent the rest of the day collecting plants.

Next morning (30th July) it was still raining but I went further up. I had eyes for nothing except the wonderful plants of the limestone screes, among them *Cremanthodium smithianum, Cyananthus formosus, Eriophyton wallichianum, Aconitum tatsienense, Corydalis calcicola, Hemilophia pulchella, Dipoma iberideum,* the little *Scrophularia chasmophila* with large greenish-yellow flowers, the new *Pedicularis lophocentra,* growing in mats beset with long-stalked red flowers, and *Valeriana trichostoma.* Up on a saddle known as Santante there was an unpleasantly cold wind, but otherwise the weather was quite agreeable, though unremittingly wet. I climbed a peak called Saganai (4525m), clothed to its very top with patches of turf, rhododendrons and willow scrub. Photogrammetric surveying was out of the question and I was able to take only one plant photograph, but I made some interesting discoveries including a small blue Corydalis (*C. trilobipetala,* a new species) and the well known northern *Saxifraga flagellaris* in a form with exceptionally large flowers. At the tree line, which on the south side of the peak was constituted, quite exceptionally, by *Quercus aquifolioides* scrub, I once more found some huge spikes of rhubarb, growing above a wall of rock slabs dripping with moisture.

On the return journey next day, acting surreptitiously to avoid detection, I pocketed some papers printed with figures of gods and spirits which were tied to trees and bamboo thickets near the camp. Lower down I also appropriated a few small, neatly chiselled stone slabs from an obo, and some little grooved balls, moulded from clay, which had been placed together with incense candles in rock crevices to propitiate the mountain spirits. On my return I found the young lamas at their lessons; half of them were sitting at the foot of a wall while the others stood in front of them, addressing the pupils and clapping their hands unceasingly.

I then discussed with the lama the route to Zhongdian via Eya, and soon afterwards Lao Li came to me, once more pale and trembling.

"Sir", he said, "don't go through Eya. A few days ago it was raided by sixty bandits from Gongling. They stole a hundred pack animals and killed some people".

Banditry was rife at that time, since the force of four thousand soldiers stationed in Gongling and Xiangcheng, having been paid with paper money — something quite unfamiliar to them — had deserted and occupied Kangding and Ya'an. The major caravan route leading from Heqing between Muli traders who told me that they had been obliged to return from Bawolong, travelling all night along secret paths, and in view of what they said I felt it would be unwise to make a journey from Muli to the north. However, I was in no position to judge the truth of the stories I was told about the bandits. Chinese servants are inclined to fabricate such tales if they are afraid or too lazy to go somewhere, especially in districts inhabited by "Manzi". They use this term or "Yiren" to denote all non-Chinese peoples, and indeed we Europeans were commonly called "Yangguizi" (foreign devils), until the authorities were compelled to forbid the practice. Even at that time children still used to call out "foreign devil" as I passed, and they certainly had not invented the insult themselves. Some time afterwards Kok said to me that according to information which he had received I could have gone to Gongling after all — the situation was not really so bad, even there. I had by now gained the temple headman's trust. He actually invited me to take pictures, and I succeeded in photographing the interior of the main silk temple, though even then there was a young lama who hurriedly tried to lock the door when he saw me approaching. Considering that the last white man to visit the temple — Jack[88] — was not permitted to cross the threshold, this was a gratifying achievement.

A climb down the arid hillside to the bridge over the Litang river — the Xiao Jin He in Chinese[89] — was less rewarding than my journey hither, although my route along the side of the lateral valley in which the town is situated was not at a substantially higher altitude. Low growing pale blue Gesnerads were flowering (*Didissandra bullata* and the taller *Rhabdothamnopsis sinensis*); others included the new *Primula barybotrys* with spikes of dark red flowers, *Sedum engleri*, similar to our own *S. maximum*, and *Vitex yunnanensis*; and the new *Quercus cocciferoides* was in fruit. The rock in the lower part of the valley consisted of clay-slate, compressed and flattened; it was said to be rich in gold, and in Muli I was shown articles carved from talc which had been quarried here. The bridge was a substantial structure built from wooden beams cantilevered out from each bank, arranged in such a way that each layer projected some distance further out than the layer beneath, until finally their ends came close enough for them to be bridged by a platform high above the water. This type of construction, completed by a handrail supported by a tall arch in the middle, is characteristic of medium-sized Tibetan bridges.

Having soldered up a box full of dried herbarium specimens and entrusted it to a trader for forwarding to Lijiang, I left Muli on 3rd August with an addition to my caravan, a schnapps-sodden crony of the lama. Since the soldiers had not brought with them the promised letter of recommendation for Zhongdian, I sent them back to Yongning with orders to ask the official if he would kindly make good this omission at once, but in reality it was a matter of complete indifference to me. As the weather was better I told the caravan men to pitch my camp on the Zhongdian road at the first stream beyond the branching of the track, and once more climbed the same mountain as far as the Santante col. Unfortunately I was again unable to photograph distant vistas, but I returned with some useful additions to my botanical collection and some good pictures of plants. The next day's march led from our hillside down into a beautiful woodland valley where the people, most conveniently for me, had just completed the reconstruction of a bridge washed away by the river. The luxuriance of the mixed woodland — one striking feature was the large-leaved *Populus szechuanica* growing near the stream — was matched by the lushness of the meadows which filled its clearings. The mules from a small caravan were grazing in the meadows and the vegetation — consisting almost entirely of herbaceous plants with hardly any grasses — was so tall that one saw nothing of them except their backs emerging here and there. The route continued south-south-west along the side of the wooded valley. As far as the Deke pass, which formed the watershed between the Litang river and the Shuiluo He (the river which runs into the Yangzi at the northern apex of its great loop), there were still a few scattered trees, although the pass was at an altitude of 4350m; between them, however, there was a flourishing high alpine flora. The slopes were dotted with silvery clumps of *Anaphalis yunnanensis*, a subshrub anchored to the clay-slate talus by its branching rootstocks. In moist spots where fine grit was exposed I found *Lagotis micrantha*, a new species, deeply buried in the gravel, its leathery leaves pressed against the ground and its spikes of violet flowers lying on the muddy shingle. Another find was *Crepis hookeriana*, its short stem expanded into a round swelling completely buried in the earth, with a rosette of numerous pinnatifid leaves pressed against the ground and in the middle a broad disc made up of countless narrow yellow flowerheads at ground level. Similar to it was *Lactuca souliei*, a small plant with blue flowers. *Saussurea stella* had the same habit of growth with linear grasslike leaves and flourished in the yak pastures, which covered large areas chiefly on the southern side of the pass. *Cyananthus macrocalyx* with yellow flowers also grew in them, together with *Anemone rupestris* and *Tanacetum delavayi*, only 1.5 to 5 cm in height, and here and there among them a small hairmoss (*Polytrichum*) was putting up its little "flowers".

[88] R. Logan Jack, a Scottish geologist, had been engaged by the Chinese government as an adviser on mining and was stationed at Chengdu. Owing to the outbreak of the Boxer rebellion, he and his companions were obliged to leave China. Setting out on 27th June 1900, they travelled south east through Ya'an and Guabi, reaching Yongsheng on 30th August. They went on through Lijiang, up the Yangzi, across to the Lancang Jiang and as far as Weixi, where they turned back as the route to Burma was impracticable. Then they travelled south through Baoshan and Tengchong, reaching Burma on 20th October. Muli is shown on his map (as "Mili Gen-chen"), but his route passed 60 km to the east. (R. Logan Jack, The Back Blocks of China, Edward Arnold, London, 1904). Though H.-M. was mistaken in implying that Jack had visited Muli, his memory was not entirely at fault. Major H.R. Davies spent a night there on 19th March 1900, but did not enter the temple. ("Yunnan", Cambridge, 1909, p. 242-243). Davies says that he was not the first European to visit Muli: Amundsen had been there in 1899 (Geographical Journal, June and November 1900) and wrote: "I believe M. Bonin also visited Muli in 1897".

[89] The Litang River below Muli is often called Xiao Jin He [Lesser Gold River] (SGH).

We pitched camp just beyond the pass and next morning I visited it again, for I realised that its riches were not exhausted and the weather was now more favourable for photography. The track ascended the ridge, following the crest which led southwards between the Yongning valley landscape and the Shuiluo He river towards Waha and Alo, continuing at altitudes well over 4000m. It was a good path, the very one which Davies had taken in March 1900, but in his map he depicts the course of the crest incorrectly; he travelled along it in a snowstorm and had obviously lost his bearings. The flowers were superb. The fragrant yellow *Cremanthodium cyclaminanthum* (a new species) grew in small patches of turf; in muddy spring-fed bogs I found the beautiful *Ligularia paradoxa* (also new), a comparatively small species with deeply cleft palmate leaves and greenish flowers, and *Swertia elata*, another new species, with blue flowers. Growing at the edges of the thickets was *Haplosphaera phaea*, representing a new genus of *Umbelliferae*, with single umbels of purplish-brown flowers, and *Corydalis radicans*, also new.

Scattered along the windswept ridge were groups of firs, patches of tanglewood and little thickets of rhododendrons — both shrubs and small trees — all growing on a variety of geological formations, mainly craggy limestone and soft igneous rocks, and presenting gorgeous pictures of unspoilt natural beauty. To the west, below the crest, among sombre firs and tree azaleas, were some little mountain tarns, as deep and clear as the lakes of the Bohemian forest. Looking into their green waters one could see massive brown tree trunks rotting at the bottom; every stone between them was clearly visible even from a distance. Growing in the soft mossy soil were some superb flowers, notably *Cremanthodium campanulatum*, *Doronicum stenoglossum* and, once more, *Primula muliensis*. There were some splendid and informative vistas, especially from a little summit projecting towards the east. I climbed it so as to photograph the range which I had seen when crossing the Chesha pass. From this side its numerous peaks seemed compressed and foreshortened. Beyond the broad green vale of Yongning I could see all the mountainous tract which extended to the south and southwest of Yanyuan. On the maps it was still a blank, but it was far too distant for any attempt to fill it in. During a somewhat belated midday rest I climbed a little summit to the right of the track in the hope of seeing the snow-capped Konkaling range, but I was disappointed. To the northwest there was indeed a chain consisting of dark rock, exposed to view up to an altitude where it was still sprinkled with numerous snow patches. Above this, however, it was completely hidden by cloud. Among the slate rocks of the peak I found *Sedum pleurogynanthum*, a new species with white flowers resembling those of a gentian. The little summit was situated at a nodal point; the main crest sloped down to a saddle beyond which it gradually rose again into a broad forested mountain named Shagu, but the track led westwards along a branch

ridge which terminated in Gonshiga [90], a mountain which projected towards the Shuiluo He gorge. It was one of the highest mountains in the district, and at its foot I pitched what proved to be the highest camp in all my travels at 4250m.

Next morning (6th August) I set off to climb Gonshiga. The mountain sought to hide itself behind a hedge of rhododendrons, but I was able to see that one of its three peaks was the highest and I made it my objective. I soon wormed my way between the gnarled trunks of the tree rhododendrons and reached a watercourse which flowed down through a little ravine to the camp site. Up here the stream was bordered by an abundant growth of roseroot (*Sedum purpureoviride*) and *Potentilla* bushes, their stems and branches thickly clustered with cushions of moss, notably a new species of the family *Pottiaceae*, a brownish moss with terminal fruits and small thin tightly packed spore capsules (*Didymodon handelii*). Also growing beside the stream, generally as isolated plants, was *Saussurea obvallata*, its succulent stems tipped with densely compacted flower-heads and enveloped by large pale leaves, resembling those of *Cirsium oleraceum* though more closely apposed. I climbed obliquely up scree slopes of calcareous clay-slate, where I again found *Arenaria kansuensis*, *Hemilophia pulchella* in a form with large yellow flowers, then *Saxifraga muliensis*, a new species with spreading runners, the narrow-leaved *Primula rigida* and the new *Saussurea katochaetoides* with broad, stiffly toothed leaves and a sessile flower head. The uppermost summit was a marble crag at 4750m; it was the highest point that I ever attained. Growing in its clefts and fissures was *Saussurea leucoma*, covered with white wool, and our own *Pseudostereodon pulcherrimus* forming golden-green cushions. The other plants ceased together with the clay-slate less than 50m below, yet up to that level there were still patches of turf comprising no fewer than fifty species of flowering plants, including the shrubby *Potentilla fruticosa* and *Lonicera hispida*, while *Rhododendron adenogynum* climbed up to 4600m.

Although the sun broke through at intervals, distant views were totally hidden; I therefore turned back and devoted my attention once more to the mosses, which flourished in great profusion of species in moist shady spots beneath boulders and on bare patches left by earth slides. Some were our own alpine species such as *Riccia sorocarpa*, *Distichium capillaceum*, *Encalypta ciliata* and *Campylopus schimperi*. Then there were new species (*Desmatodon setschwanicus* and *Tayloria pygmaea*). Growing on the rocks were *Grimmia subconferta* and *G. micropyxis* together with our own *Gymnomitrium revolutum*, two little yellow saxifrages (*Saxifraga triaristulata* and *S. elatinoides*) resembling *S. montana*, both of them new to science, and lastly *Aconitum pulchellum*, also new. On this occasion, possibly because of the denser air of summer, I had no

---

[90] This peak, about 30 km NNW of Yongning, is called Kan-ju-shan on Rock's map. Handel-Mazzetti's altitude of 4750m is remarkably close to the figure of 15,450 ft = 4770m given on ONC H-10.

symptoms of mountain sickness. I returned along the stream to the camp, ate my midday meal while the men packed up the tent, and then began the descent. The main track led down north-westwards through a short and very steep rocky valley to Weisha on the Shuiluo He river, but here I chose a detour to avoid bandit territory, a route which suited me since it led through stretches, admittedly not very extensive, of still unsurveyed terrain, while not diverting my steps away from anything else of interest.

Continuing south-westwards along the narrow crest we were drenched by a cloudburst, but as we went down the track leading off to the left we came to a shoulder from which we had a fine view of the forest-filled valley through which we now had to travel. In conjunction with a photograph from the lower end it was enough to fill in the map. Situated in small clearings on the hillsides were some Pumi villages, each consisting of a few stone houses. I stopped at the highest of them, Piyi (3250m), where my lodging was an open verandah and I was unable to dry my clothes properly. I sat up late that night putting my rich haul of plants into the press. Next day the narrow path led through the gorge and then along the opposite side of the valley — part of the slopes of Mount Shagu — up into each lateral ravine and then down again. The rain had washed it away in places and our guide had to send men ahead to repair it; our progress was slow. The valley was administered by Muli and hence belonged to Sichuan, not as the maps show, to Yunnan [91].

Battened upon by the lamas, the people were poverty-stricken. Men and women alike were clad in miserable rags. Nearly all the men wore pigtails and most of them had a knife and a snuffbox hanging from their belts. The women adorned their hair with chains of red and blue stones. Most of the children were completely naked, and all of them were streaked with dirt. Their houses were small and exceedingly dirty, and I thought it wiser to sleep in the outer room — and on the second evening in my tent — in preference to accepting their friendly invitations. My guide certainly understood how to enlist their speedy cooperation. On one occasion he shouted a command to a youth standing on the outskirts of a village, and when the young man stared at us open-mouthed, he immediately threw a stone at him. In another village he made all the young men of military age turn out and devote their labour to the peaceful cause of science.

At the mouth of the valley the track descended into the arid subtropical zone belonging to the outer part of the Shuiluo He valley. The scenery here was similar to that on the Yalong. The ridge between the river and its western tributary, the Londa He, was made up of vertical strata of phyllite. As we went on the villages became more frequent; Dsengo, inhabited by Naxi people, looked like a fortress situated on a knoll projecting from the ridge into the river valley. The people gathered in front of the villages to stare at us; the lower we went, the less clothing they troubled to wear. In this dusty oven I myself began to wilt, and gazed longingly at the sombre fir woods now far above us. But this was not the time to let such longings prevail. The subtropical flora was certainly of no less interest than the plants which I might expect to see up there, and its study was perhaps of greater value in understanding the botanical history of the country, and its past climatic fluctuations and plant migrations. Here I encountered a new species, Lysimachia reflexiloba, with white flowers, the tips of the petals bent backwards; also Primula bathangensis, a tall plant with racemes of yellow flowers, and then Scilla chinensis, Chlorophytum flaccidum and Croton caudatiformis in ripe fruit. I had to wait half a day in Yumi while a bridge washed away by the water was being rebuilt; in fact, when I reached the spot I had to begin by telling the men how to lay the planks. As we progressed the valley scenery grew even more splendid. The path climbed up the mountainside again, overhung by steep rock faces consisting of limestone overlying sandstone and phyllite dipping southeast at about 30°. These rocks rested unconformably on an older stratum of phyllite which was folded almost vertically. On the opposite side of the valley its wall also became steeper instead of flatter, and ahead of us we saw the sharp ridges and spurs round the northern side of the great loop in the Jinsha Jiang river, which I finally reached on 11th August at a village called Sanjiangkou.

91 On modern maps the valley of the Shuiluo He is entirely within Sichuan (SGH).

Chapter 17. Over the Zhongdian Uplands to the Mekong (Lancang Jiang)

Arid mountains and gorges — a detour via Anangu — scrub-covered tablelands — a vista of unknown territory — yak herds — a natural bridge — Zhongdian — with a Tibetan guard over the Nguka-la — the ferry over the Yangzi at Jizong — through unknown country to the Mekong (Lancang Jiang)

The Chinese proprietor of the ferry below Sanjiangkou at first demanded an outrageous price, but a jab in the ribs made him see reason and we crossed the Shuiluo He (Duo Qu) close to its confluence with the Yangzi, though the horses had to swim. Two men entered the water with inflated goatskins under their chests and helped those horses that were unaccustomed to swimming. Taking several at a time, they fastened their halters to a rope stretched between them and held their nostrils above water. All this took so long that having reached the far side we decided to take our midday break. This proved a lucky decision, for growing there was a twiner, *Ipomoea cairica*, scrambling up into the trees. As soon as the stem was cut the deep pink flowers, over 6 cm across, and the delicate palmate leaves began to droop in the blazing sun. However, I swiftly unpacked a bundle of paper and put specimens in the press before they had time to wilt. I did the same with several species of *Ceropegia*, namely *C. profundorum*, a new species with narrow leaves and large deep violet-brown flowers, the common *C. monticola* and the small green-flowered *C. muliensis*, which I found here only. The liana *Illigera mollissima*, which also grew here, belongs to an otherwise purely tropical family.

Our path took us along a narrow, steep-sided hogsback ridge interposed between a stretch of the Jinsha Jiang running from west to east and a tributary, flowing parallel to it, coming from Apa-la near Zhongdian to join the Shuiluo He barely 3 km north of the ferry. The narrow track along its southern face had to be repaired in some places before the caravan could pass, and if anything had rolled down the hillside it would have vanished for ever in the raging torrent. I climbed a little knoll on the ridge, near the saddle which carried the track to Chuazi, the last Pumi village, so as to take bearings on the principal features of the country around the bend in the Jinsha Jiang. Opposite the village, beyond the tributary, there was a vertical crest of hard limestone running north and south, outcropping as a narrow wall between the strata of soft slate which extended in the depths of the gorge. A much broader mass of limestone not far to the west of it formed Mount Lamacuo (3300m on Handel-Mazzetti's map), which was the continuation of the hogsback we had just traversed, though more than four times higher. The erosive action of the tributary to the north of this mountain had scooped out a ravine with vertical walls. Next day our path led up its southern side, a climb of almost 1500m, at some points dizzyingly exposed. Though constructed with some care it was exceedingly narrow and the four roadmen sent ahead of us with heavy iron pickaxes were kept busy chipping away projecting rocks at the corners to make the path practicable for my not unduly bulky loads.

Growing on the rocks were some interesting xerophytes: *Pertya phylicoides*, a composite with needle-shaped leaves; two silver-leaved shrubs, *Clematis delavayi* and *Desmodium cinerascens*; *Plectanthrus oresbius*, a little shrublet with a covering of ashen grey felt; *Wikstroemia androsaemifolia*, a robust plant with yellow flowers (a new species); the delicate *Primula aromatica* with elongated flowers, and near the top of the ridge a slender pyramidal cypress, *Cupressus duclouxiana*. The track crossed a col on the crest, which was over 3300m high, and went down its south side. From there we had a striking view of the basin of the Jinsha Jiang as it flowed from the west-southwest, and beyond it the Xuechou massif. One can only picture the depths of the canyon through which the torrent surges, squeezed against the foundations of the steep mountain mass of Kudu. Far above the waters are the margins of the gorge, running side by side along the western border of the shallow basin and marking the line where the river has cut its channel through the rocks. Further on the basin rose up into the Xuechou Shan — Dier Shan range, while far below, deep in the bowels of the mountains, the brown waters struggled to escape from the last narrow ravine, at a point marked by a sharp crest with two summits. The huge scale of the landscape, coupled with the simplicity of its form, left a profound impression, although here it was very dry and barren, the sparseness of its covering of scrub being probably natural and not the outcome of man's destructiveness. Compass bearings and photographs enabled me to make a major correction to the course of the river as depicted on Ryder's map. The track now turned back into a valley occupied by Naxi tribesmen.

Here, and on the following day where it ran across more or less undisturbed strata of limestone and sandstone, I found some interesting plants, notably the orchid *Pecteilis susannae*, an erect plant with fleshy or waxy white flowers having a spur 15 cm long and resembling those of the commonly cultivated tropical orchid *Angraecum sesquipeda*. Another find was *Dobinea delavayi* [92], a herbaceous plant a metre tall belonging to the *Anacardiaceae*. It was not uncommon in habitats favoured by the orchid. The people collected the leaves of *Gerbera nivea*, which are rather less than 20 cm long, sepa-

---

[92] *Dobinea delavayi* has certain remarkable features. Unlike most members of its family *(Anacardiaceae)* it is not a woody plant but a herbaceous perennial. The female flowers are carried in catkins resembling hops, while the white bracts of the male flowers are shed at a very early stage. The fruits are located in the middle of the bracts, or in other words the stalk of the fruit is fused with the bract. The thick woody rootstock, characteristic of a steppe plant, has an odour of pine resin. (Handel-Mazzetti's notes, originally part of the text).

rated the leaf stalk and central vein and used them to make fabrics.

Bandits were said to frequent the Apa-la, and the lama at Yongning had advised me to send men forward from the last village to reconnoitre and to take an armed escort with me, as the Chinese soldiers, if they encountered bandits, would promptly throw away their weapons and run off, or might even join forces with them against the master they had been ordered to guard. Partly for this reason, but chiefly because the route over the Apa-la had previously been surveyed by Ryder though there was still some unexplored territory between it and the area I had mapped in 1914, I branched off to the left from Laba and travelled southwards up the longest branch of the valley, climbing high up on to its western side and passing the Yi hamlet of Huajiaoping. Towering up on the opposite side, the arid limestone massif of Kudu presented its back to us, here known as Aka-ëndyo. Besides a boy who came with us from Laba, we had as our guide a Tibetan trader who dealt in drugs and medicines and who had taken the same route as ourselves from Muli, having failed in his attempt to get to Kangding (Tatsienlu). The narrow track led down to the stream and then steeply uphill beyond it. Lao Li's pony, as feeble a specimen of horseflesh as his rider was of mankind, started to flag, and suddenly, with a scream from Lao Li, both of them disappeared over the side of the track behind me. Lao Li landed on his feet a few metres down the slope, but the pony tumbled down to the soft marshy valley bottom, damage being confined to the shattered saddle. Lao Li had to walk all the way to our campsite at the next spring; though this was irksome the exercise was no doubt beneficial.

After a short ascent the route led along the hillside and then across the flat Gitüdü pass (Machangba in Chinese) at 3425m. The meadows of the pass took an hour to traverse and displayed the superb flora which I had seen on the Zhongdian plateau in 1914. Here and there were marshy patches with willows. As we went down into the Bapaji valley a splendid vista unfolded through an opening in the pine forest; far away to the south, but perfectly clear, was Mount Haba Shan, a soaring snow-capped dome looking like the Ortler seen from the north, with the range running southwards from Bede to join it, including the peak which I had climbed in June; closer to me was Shusuzu, an old friend from the previous year, and the reddish sandstone mountains between it and the Piepen summits. Beyond the river Bapaji at the foot of this range, a narrow strip of pine wood marked the edge of the river gorge; from there it was only a short day's march to the terraces at Bede. I crossed the Bapaji, turned to the right, climbed to the edge of the gorge and arrived at Anangu (Ananchang in Chinese), a flourishing mining town of some size. Though built in Tibetan style, its mixture of peoples included Chinese, among whom were several officials, and the chief of police kindly invited me to tea. He gave me two policemen for the journey to Zhongdian and since thieves were numerous in Anangu — as must always be expected in industrial towns — he sent another for that night. This man performed his duties as watchman by lying down outside my door and snoring

with all his might. Indeed, he did not awake until I got up, took a long strap and endeavoured to chase out a cock which had been hiding just above my bed and long before daybreak had put an end to my slumbers.

Next morning (16th August) I set off northwestwards from Anangu, taking the main route towards Zhongdian, the district centre. High up on the hillside to the left were the spoil tips from the silver and gold mines which had attracted the Chinese into these mountains. Soon we descended again to the stream, which flowed beneath a dense cover of large bushes of buckthorn (*Rhamnus virgatus*) and spindle-tree (*Euonymus lichiangensis*), the latter having four-angled twigs with longitudinal wings, and very narrow leaves and seedpod valves. This stream, the main affluent of the Bapaji, came from Piepen to the west-northwest. The track left it and climbed up the left side of the valley. The sandstone banks on either side of the track were coated with green — the sporelings of various small hairmosses. We came out on to a broad ridge clothed with patches of woodland interspersed by flower-filled pastures. Streams ran down on three sides — towards Bede, Laba and Zhongdian. The pass was called Patü-La (3925m); though it did not offer much of a view I was able to get my bearings without difficulty. After descending for 375m we came to a branch of the Zhongjiang He and halted for our midday rest at a spot where the river broadened a little. This branch ran due north from Piepen and encircled the whole mountain. While exploring a little bog nearby I noticed for the first time that a tiny plant growing on the bare mud — a plant which I had seen once or twice before but had dismissed as nothing more than a dense clump of seedlings — actually bore narrow fruitlets under its tufts of spathulate leaves with forward-pointing teeth, and these fruitlets arose from still tinier green flowers. Not until long afterwards did I realise that it was *Circaeaster agrestis*, one of the few flowering plants whose affinities and taxonomic status are still totally obscure [93]. The second tributary of this branch of the Zhongjiang He flowed down an equally gentle gradient between the corries at the foot of the steep face of Piepen. From its valley — continuing in the same direction — the path climbed up to the main pass at Shulakaza, which lay on a broad plateau. A ridge extending from it to the right looked as if it might give a good view of the country. I climbed it and was not disappointed. The larches and oaks which grew there did not prevent me from taking some useful photographs. Looking southeast along the line of the Bapaji I had a clear view of Xuechou Shan. To the left and somewhat closer was the mighty bastion of Kudu, some 4700m high, its banded strata dipping slightly northeast. To the right were the splendid peaks of Piepen, the other side of which had been the site of my final explorations in 1914. Its pale grey limestone pinnacles towered up from scree slopes and forests of dark green fir, sharply silhouetted against black thunderclouds, but

---

[93] Later assigned to a family of its own: *Circaeasteraceae*.

before long they were enveloped by white mist. Towards the north the Piepen range diminished in height, its last brown sandstone ridges projecting only a little above the undulating plateau which extended — over 4100m in altitude — between us and Zhongdian. Just beyond the pass I counted eight little tarns, gleaming like mirrors, but otherwise most of the terrain was covered with brown holly-leaved oak scrub. Its predominance, taken in conjunction with the unusual assortment of plants in the meadows, indicates that the Zhongdian district is really an outlier of the floristic region which borders on the high altitude deserts of Tibet. A similar area to the north of Kangding (Tatsienlu) is characterized by a band of holly-leaved oak extending over an altitudinal zone of 700m. However, it was the view to the north, over unknown country towards Xiangcheng, which gripped my attention. It was an inextricable tangle of minor peaks and folds, apparently for the most part consisting of sandstone, only a little higher than the plateau itself. This plateau, almost totally unforested, was furrowed by a few valleys running from west to east, belonging to the Shuiluo He river system. The landscape, as I saw it on that day, conformed exactly to a description of the Yaragong district between Batang and Xiangcheng as portrayed to me some time later by one of the missionaries. A survey or photograph from another spot might have enabled me to construct some sort of map, but such an opportunity was not granted. To the left the continuation of this mountainous tract, which probably does not exceed 5000m, was hidden behind Lopipema, a mountain situated not far to the northeast of Zhongdian. To the right, as I was descending from my crest, Gongga, a snow-capped mountain of at least 5500m near Gongling, emerged from the clouds for just long enough to enable me to take a bearing; it seemed to lie to the west of and outside the high rocky range which I had seen from the crest south of Muli.

Zilu was a small grazing ground for yaks situated on a stream flowing in the fourth direction, i.e., north-westwards to the Zhongjian He. That evening numerous herds of yaks, sheep and goats, each several hundred strong, belonging to the Zhongdian lamas, ambled slowly past my camp over the emerald green meadows, brilliantly lit by the setting sun. Among them were numerous hybrids between yaks and domestic cattle, representing a complete range of intermediate types. Though female yaks are not particularly good-looking, yak bulls are often of splendid appearance. Some of them were used as pack animals. They were extremely nervous, and when I encountered them they would often turn aside from the track in fright and clamber up or down the steep slopes, but they were thoroughly docile withal. The route continued straight on through evergreen oak scrub with sparse conifers over low ridges, then through mixed forest and deciduous bush along the valleyside, gradually descending to the Zhongjiang He. The little river wound its way quietly over its gravel bed between the lush meadows and arable fields of the wide valley floor; further up it disappeared behind Mount Lopipema, about 4500m in height. It was a mountain of soft outlines and rounded contours; its brown

sandstone soil was bare and exposed everywhere and its slopes had remarkably little forest cover — far less than would be expected in this district — probably because it supplied wood for Zhongdian and the numerous Tibetan villages. Their substantial, gable-roofed houses, distempered in red or brown, were scattered along the valley.

I reached the river at midday, at what proved to be a fascinating spot. The valley narrowed or, more correctly, the river had carved out a small ravine in the left side of its broad channel. Close to the river bank, welling up in a recess in a bed of stratified limestone, was a hot sulphur spring, accessible only by wading through the stream. Evidence of its previous activity was to be seen in the sinter deposits laid down like a flight of steps above the present-day outlet, where they formed a marsh with a thick growth of grasses and sedges and an abundance of orchids. Just downstream from the spring there was a natural bridge, about 20m in height and the same in width, beneath which the river flowed through an underground cave. The luxuriant vegetation growing above the spring owed its existence perhaps to the supply of sulphur and the abundant moisture, and possibly also to the frequent presence of man. The hot water (43°C) flowed swiftly through a manmade basin of stone, and any attempt to fish for plankton would probably not have yielded much of a catch. I tried to photograph the natural bridge and the course of the river downstream. It made a sharp bend and then, leaving its original channel, cut through some outliers of the plateau from which we had just descended. However, when I had pulled the cover halfway out the whole plateholder came with it, and I had so few plates left that I was unwilling to use another. The streams running down from Lopipema united in a channel in the valley bottom, separated from the river by transverse limestone ridges. Dry heathy meadow vegetation clothed the elevated sections between the meanders of the stream, which drained into the Zhongdian lake. A peculiar louse-wort, *Pedicularis tricolor* (a new species) was flowering on them in abundance; it is a low-growing, mat-forming plant with long tubular flowers having large, pale yellow, white-edged corolla lips and a reddish beak. Ahead of us gleamed the golden domes above the white walls of the two large lama temples. It had been raining intermittently and the track was indescribably muddy. It bore off to the left, and two and a half hours later we were in Zhongdian.

Situated at 3400m, it was a chilly place. Its streets were filled with a mixture of natural mud with Chinese and Tibetan filth, but I was comfortably accommodated in a large room in what had once been a Tibetan temple. The official at Yongning had not sent any letter of recommendation; the police officer asked to see my passport, felt my baggage for weapons and withdrew, satisfied but somewhat embarrassed, after realising that the suspected rifles were merely tentpoles. One of the chief worries of the Chinese was that Europeans might bring weapons for the "Manzi", as indeed happens on a large scale via Tibet. The district official invited me to a meal at which he staged various little happenings with the aim of blackening

Tibet and the Tibetans in my eyes. A Chinese burst in, greatly excited, and told us that two of his countrymen had been beaten up by Tibetans while they were on a mountain digging for roots — simply because the Tibetans wanted to keep the trade to themselves. He told me that the fish sold in Zhongdian — I had bought a large carp — was unfit to eat, since the Tibetans cut up their dead and threw them into the streams, or left them out for the vultures to consume. The Tibetans practised polyandry, he said, and smeared their bodies with butter, which was the reason why they stank.

"So far as we're concerned, your polygamy is just the same thing, and your people stink of garlic, which is much worse!" was my rejoinder.

"Are you perhaps thinking of going on to the Salween (Nu Jiang)?" asked the official.

Though the inhabitants detested him, he was certainly not hostile to Europeans and was most friendly towards me.

"That hadn't occurred to me", I replied, "only as far as the Mekong (Lancang Jiang)", well aware that I must not arouse even the slightest suspicion. There was a telegraph in Zhongdian; one message from him would be enough to wreck all my plans, as had happened to the unfortunate Gebauer in 1914. I learnt something of the situation in the world outside China, but news trickled through very slowly. I handed in my telegram at 9am. The telegraphist worked out the number of words and I paid for it. Then at 4pm he sent a chit with a message in English: "Please is it one words or two wds...?" and I finally received an answer four days later, though the distance was no greater than I could have travelled in four days at home. I had to go to the bank and draw money remitted by Kok, have my shoes mended and have a new pair of trousers made. All this took time. The ponies needed a complete rest. My grey had begun to limp, and had a sore on the shoulder where the harness had rubbed; this had been caused by the loss of the crupper, which had broken and been lost in a pool of mud.

I sent off my specimens in wooden crates, but one of them had no tin lining and the colour photographs taken at Muli and Shulakaza — remarkably successful considering the age of the plates — were spoilt by a green haze spreading in from the edges. All this kept me busy from 18th to 23rd August and because of wet weather I was able to make only one excursion — to the lake near the great lamasery. My guide or sponsor from Yongning took me there, though at first he misunderstood me and thought I wanted to visit the larger and more distant lake which Szechenyi [94] calls Omintsoka, and which receives the waters from the Zhongdian stream and its tributaries. The little lake was a miserable puddle, but on some limestone blocks nearby I collected *Saxifraga candelabrum*, a species with numerous glands, and in the heathy meadow I found *Saussurea romuleifolia* with grass-like leaves, *Microula pustul-*

osa and others; and on solid mud *Aongstroemiopsis julacea*, otherwise known only from Java. From there I sketched and took compass bearings on the few conspicuous landmarks which were to be seen on the low forested slopes on either side of the broad valley channel running south towards Xiao Zhongdian, so as to provide a view from the north of the terrain which I had photographed from the south in 1914. I was told that a band, some twenty strong, of the dreaded brigands from Qagchêng (Xiangcheng in Chinese) had been seen two hours distant from the town, and that all the one hundred soldiers of the Chinese garrison had been sent in pursuit of them, though they had gone in the wrong direction by mistake. The official therefore had no men to spare and as he had not much confidence in his soldiers he sent a message to the headman of the last village at the foot of the mountain along my route ordering him to supply a party of Tibetans to escort me as far as Meti, I having insisted, despite his efforts to dissuade me, on sticking to my plans for travelling due west to the Yangzi and on to Weixi.

I set off on 24th August with two police soldiers and a picturesque troop of Tibetans — five armed with lances and swords and two with firearms. At first we travelled south along the route towards Xiao Zhongdian and Lijiang. It ran at the foot of a low limestone ridge in a valley occupied by a few villages but otherwise rather barren. Large tracts were tinted blue by *Halenia elliptica*, a gentian relative with spurred petals. The stream flowed towards me and on to the Zhongdian lake. Then we turned off to the right and halted for our midday rest at the home village of my escort, a place called Beishaoge, where the men borrowed an ox to carry their kit. The western side of the valley was also extremely barren, consisting of a stratum of arid limestone, steep but not very high, running in an almost straight line, with gaps from which alluvial fans spread down towards the stream. Above it was a narrow shelf and above that the forest-clad ridge of the watershed between the Zhongdian depression and the Jinsha Jiang. Rising up from this, at the same latitude as Zhongdian, was Zhere, a low dome with a truncated cone resting on its eastern side, reaching about 4500m. I thought I could see waterfalls on its slopes. When we reached Beishaoge the uppermost stratum had already faded out and our route climbed westwards across soft clay-slate. There was a splendid view from a spot on the broad undulating ridge, which diverged from our route and ran southwards as far as a valley which cut into it to some depth. The view comprised the whole of the former lake bed as far as Xiao Zhongdian, bordered by gravel terraces and separated from the Zhongdian basin by a low brown ridge, beyond which the Zhongjiang He emerged from the transverse valley below the natural bridge. In the background were the eroded slopes of Piepen, unfortunately shrouded in rain, and the highlands to the north of it. Close at hand the terrain was covered with forests of dark green firs, many of them grey with beard lichens. In the clearings were waterlogged bogs, in which magnificent yaks were quietly grazing. Rhododendrons, willows and spiraeas flourished there, together with *Swertia calicina*, a plant 75 cm tall with pure white flowers 4.5 cm

---

[94] Szechenyi, Bela. *Im fernen Osten — Reisen des Grafen Szechenyi in Indien, Japan, China, Tibet und Birma, 1877-1880.*

Fig.17 *Arisaema wilsonii* (*A. elephas*) above Xiangshuihe. Chapter 12.

Fig.18 Market day in Songgui.
Minchia women; buildings in Chinese style. Chapter 12.

Fig.19 *Tsuga yunnanensis*
at 3300m below the
Zuningkou pass.
Foreground:
Rhododendron rarosquameum;
top right:
Loranthus caloreas.
Chapter 12.

Fig.20
The south face
of Satseto,
the main peak of
the Yulong Shan, 5450m,
viewed from
an altitude of 4500m.
Chapter 13.

Fig.21
Glacier snout,
moraine and talus bed
at 3700m
in the Luoqu gorge
on the south side
of Satseto.
Left: *Larix potaninii,
Betula forrestii.*
Chapter 13.

Fig.22 *Cypripedium ebracteatum* (now *C. margaritaceum*)
in willow and birch thickets above Nguluke, 3350m.
Leaves of *Oxyria sinensis*. Chapter 13.

Fig.23 Camp above Tuguancun at 4175m,
looking WNW over the Chongdian plateau.
Rhododendron adenogynum in the foreground. Chapter 14.

Fig.24 The ridge between Tuguancun
and Haba at 4450m, looking NW. Chapter14.

Fig.25 High alpines on the ridge
between Tuguancun and Haba, 4350-4450m, 23 June 1915.
Anemone demissa, Diapensia purpurea,
Cassiope selaginoides, Rhododendron complexum,
R. prostratum, Primula chrysophylla. Chapter 14.

Fig.26 Lüdi (Moso) women at Yongning
with children in Chinese dress. Chapter 15.

Fig.27 Alpine sward (yak pasture) at 4300m
on limestone soil at the tree-line on Mount Waha near Yongning.
Potentilla stenophylla, Polygonum sphaerostachyum,
Aster likiangensis, Phlomis rotata,
Pedicularis microphyton, Anaphalis sp. Chapter 15.

Fig.28 Interior of a temple at Muli. Chapter 16.

Fig.29 Grain drying racks on the huts in an unidentified village.

Fig.30 Rope bridge over the Lancang Jiang (Mekong) near Tseku. A mule is being hauled up. Chapter 18.

Fig.31 The Lancang Jiang (Mekong) gorge above Lota.
Water-worn potholes; maquis woodland. Chapter 18.

Fig.32 *Pseudotsuga wilsoniana*
on the Doker La. Chapter 19.

across, and the new *Saussurea uliginosa*. A huge Tibetan mastiff, black and shaggy, made even more terrifying by a collar of red wool, nearly pulled up the long stake to which he was tethered outside a yak-herd's hut; as long as we remained in sight he went on barking and leaping up, his bloodred eyes bulging from their sockets in his rage.

We had not much further to climb to Nguka-la, a pass at 4125m lying between crests about 100m higher. Among the plants growing in the fir woods were *Senecio pleopterus*, 1.20m tall, with large pinnate leaves and heads of three florets grouped into large corymbs; giant monkshoods (*Aconitum scaposum* and *A. franchetii*); two large delphiniums, both probably new species; and the white *Beesia calthifolia* (*Ranunculaceae*). The whole district was dark and sombre, an impression created not merely by the woods, but also by the dull green rock, which was a volcanic tuff, and the leaves of the rhododendrons (*R. recurvum*), while the overcast sky seemed to deepen the gloom. Though the slopes on the eastern side had been gentle, the descent from the watershed to the Yangzi was quite the opposite. The route led down a continuous stairway, laid out in zigzags yet nevertheless exceedingly steep, built from angular blocks of hard igneous rock. I climbed down on foot, scorning my police escort's outrageous suggestion that I should remain in the saddle. Nothing but the clink of horseshoes and the calls of the mule drivers disturbed the quiet of the primeval forest, dark green and dripping with moisture. A flowering currant (*Ribes acuminatum*) grew epiphytically high on the trees, the tiny *Polypodium sikkimense* in moss cushions on their trunks, and the new *Pimpinella muscicola* (now *Acronema muscicolum*), nearly as minute, in the moss covering the rocks. The cleft through which we were descending became less steep, and a pure growth of holly-leaved oak replaced the mixed woodland — which was of a type which might almost have been classified as moisture-loving. Remaining on the northern side of the valley, the track rounded a rocky corner and came to the village of Meti at 3125m. The people living in this group of houses were apparently Naxi-Tibetan halfbreeds, though another hamlet lower down belonged to Lisu. We continued our descent along the valley floor; though narrow, it was not very steep. High up on the side of the valley was a limestone stratum projecting as a sharp crest towards the Jinsha Jiang. Along the stream there were some dank secluded corners with a rich growth of shrubs including the elm-like *Euptelea pleiosperma*, and further down, where conditions were subtropical, *Alangium chinense*, *Chionanthus retusa* and *Machilus ichangensis*. The mountain beyond the river was much lower than the one we had just traversed, though at the bottom its slope was very steep. Making a double bend, the Yangzi came flowing towards us. We followed it downstream, and as we had already done a good day's march and it was starting to rain we sought shelter in a house in the little village of Tsondyo, a few kilometres further on. Water soon began to drip through the roof on to the mosses which I had spread out to dry and my other possessions. I tried to dodge it by shifting to another spot, but in the end I was forced to have one of the flysheets unpacked and spread over the shingle roof.

Next morning an hour's journey downstream through woods of pine and oak brought us to the ferry opposite a fair-sized village called Jizong. The river was a raging torrent, and the boat was of triangular shape so that it could be towed against the current. On reaching the middle, however, it spun round, and it took no fewer than fourteen oarsmen to propel it to the other bank. We landed some distance downstream, at a spot where an abundant spring welled up in the valley bottom, its outlet shaded by a grove of giant oaks and laurels. Ferns grew in profusion on the leafy soil under the trees. The stream had cut its way through a hollow tree-trunk, and the tree straddled the water as if on stilts. The trees were festooned with huge lianas (*Vitis* and *Celastrus*) dangling down to the ground and putting out roots. Some of them, weighted down by cushions of moss, dipped into the turbulent waters, which tugged at these natural ropes and made the tree-tops quiver. The task of ferrying the caravan took until noon, but, having found accommodation in the village headman's house, I spent the rest of the day sorting out my dried plants. Next day we resumed our journey along the large valley which debouches into the Yangzi valley at Jizong. Its winding course was the route to Kakatang, a village three days' march ahead, between Weixi and Xiao Weixi.

The valley ran at first north-westwards without any substantial gradient, breaking through three more or less vertical limestone beds. Infolded between mica-schist and, later, arkose sandstone, these ran parallel to the river further downstream. The valley bottom, in some stretches quite wide, was well farmed and there were several fair-sized Naxi villages. Their inhabitants were extremely friendly: when we were taking our midday rest near one village the people came out with presents for us. On both sides there were broad ridges about 500m above the valley floor. Leading over the northern side, branching off just before Shogo (Shyon-gung on Rock's map) where we spent the night, was the main road to Dêqên (Atuntzu) via Benzilan (Bangdsera), a route travelled by several Europeans, but my path now took me into unknown terrain. The volume of the little river was enough to prove that our valley could not really be as short as it is sketchily depicted as being on the maps. Within Shogo the track forked; my route followed the branch coming from the south. The elevation of the margins of the plateau on either side above the valley floor became less and less, the valley became somewhat steeper and then narrower, while the slopes were clothed with evergreen broad-leaved trees with scattered spruces and *Tsuga* instead of the pines which predominated lower down. From 2500m upwards, growing singly alongside the stream, were some huge dark pyramidal conifers, at least 50m tall. One species was a giant fir, but the other, with flat, sharp-pointed leaves marked by two white lines beneath and large green fruits about 3 cm long, each containing a hard seed, was *Torreya fargesii*, a relative of the yew. Among other interesting plants were *Actinidia purpurea*, an enormous liana; *Schefflera stenomera*, its palmately divided leaves having remarkably long narrow segments; the new *Penta-panax larium*, also belonging to the ivy family; and *Pterocarya forrestii*.

Shatyama (To-na-ko on Rock's map), where I spent the night before leaving the valley, consisted only of a few scattered Lisu huts, as did the nearby hamlets. The stream was still quite substantial and the villagers, so as to get across to their fields of buckwheat, had bridged it with a slender treetrunk, which had been barked, hacked more or less level along the top and provided with branches on both sides as handrails. It was far too slippery for my mountain boots, and I had to crawl across on hands and knees to botanise on the far side; I was glad not to have any spectators for this performance. Among other plants I found *Struthiopteris orientalis* and an *Angelica*. The valley continued south-eastwards, coming, as later became clear, from the Lidiping plateau near Weixi. Its total length is hence 80 km and the stream in fact flows in a shallow longitudinal channel on the crest of the watershed between low wooded heights. My route branched off to the west, entered the forest and then emerged on to a col, Akelo, at 3150m. The canebrake was full of mud-filled holes between exposed roots, and several of the pack animals tumbled over. Growing there was a large *Sphagnum* moss (*S. pseudocymbifolium*) and, in shady channels, a new species of aconite with vivid green flowers (*Aconitum chloranthum*). From our midday halt at the Lisu hamlet of Akelo (Ko-lo on Rock's map) I looked down the steep slope beyond and saw that the giant fir did not grow there. As I had not yet seen any of its cones I left Lao Li behind to procure some for me. From the material which he obtained I later identified it as *Abies chensiensis*. Below us lay the vale of Weixi, bounded on this side by the steep crest sloping down from Lidiping to Akelo and continuing north-west-wards for some distance before rising up into a higher elevation near Xiao Weixi, a village on the Lancang Jiang (Mekong). On the far side it was bounded by the Weixi - Lancang Jiang watershed. The val. was in the main a broad trough, divided across its width by spurs of sandstone, with some limestone here and there, projecting between lateral streams of varying lengths, with a medley of folds and minor peaks. We crossed the lateral valley on foot, turned right and climbed up to a flat boggy patch which was the source of the first stream flowing down the far side. Here we found a group of Chinese hamlets called Tima. My servant was delighted to see them, but I was somewhat less enthusiastic, for on entering the room which was offered to me the stench was such that I recoiled in disgust. The villagers were at first reluctant to let me have the altar room under the roof, allegedly because the lady of the house slept next to it, though when I insisted they gave way. Next morning, passing through an ill-lit doorway, I bumped my forehead so violently against the absurdly low lintel that I let out an involuntary cry, staggered and fell almost sense-less to the floor. The resulting occipital headache lasted until the following day. Descending the valley — in some places a ravine and in its lower part very steep — I reached Kakatang [95] on the "Da He", the "big river" of Weixi, and spent the night a few hours' journey downstream at Anadon [96]. Next day, 1st September, I sent Lao Li with the soldiers to Weixi to buy supplies. I told him to show the officials my letter of recommendation from Zhongdi-an and ask for a further letter to the Naxi tusi of Yezhe, but to refuse any offer of an escort.

---

[95] Ka-ka-t'ang--a "narrow, filthy conglomeration of huts and pigsties" (Rock, p. 303).

[96] "After a march of 30 li (from Ka-ka-t'ang) we pass the small Tibetan hamlet of A-nu-ndo, the Chinese A-nan-to......the principal crops are maize, millet, beans and tobacco; the leaves of the latter are tied to strings which are stretched under the eaves of the houses to dry." (Rock, p.304)

Chapter 18. The Lancang Jiang (Mekong) Valley

Secret plans — maquis and garigue — native tribes — rapids and water-gap gorges — new caravans — arbor vitae woods — rope bridges — the mission at Cizhong — Forrest's work — an accident — porters

From now on I had to proceed with caution if I was to avoid the unhappy fate of Gebauer, who had been prevented from travelling to the Nu Jiang (Salween) after the authorities had got wind of his plans for entering Tibet. I therefore had to keep my intentions secret even from Lao Li. I decided not to go to Weixi myself, but travelled downstream instead, reaching the Lancang Jiang that very day at a point below Beiqicun, the last village built in Chinese style. From here I continued up the somewhat monotonous, cultivated valley of the Lancang Jiang and arrived at Xiao Weixi in the early afternoon. I spent four days there, living in a cramped, smoke-filled loft. The temperatures (36°C in the living room) were the highest I experienced in all my travels in Yunnan. I enjoyed friendly relations with the missionary Lesgourgues, ate several meals with him and used his library. The poor fellow was utterly weary of missionary activities; thieves had broken in and stolen most of the property belonging to Monbeig, whose deputy he was, and the mission building was sadly dilapidated and dusty.

Lao Li, not suspecting what was in store for him, had done everything I had asked, and as the small detachment of soldiers in Xiao Weixi did not bother their heads about me, I resumed my journey up the Lancang Jiang on 6th September. The missionary having assured me that no one would attempt to detain me on a journey along this bank, I gave up any idea of slipping unnoticed across the river at that point. It was well that I did so, for, as later emerged, I would probably have met insuperable obstacles on the route along the right (i.e., west) bank[97]. The valley became more attractive, the hillsides were quite steep in some stretches, and minor bends in the river brought some diversity into the landscape. On the outer side of each bend there were steep cliffs of friable phyllite rock, while rice was cultivated on the flat ground within the inner side; in some places there was a gently sloping terrace with a steep bank at the river's edge. Elsewhere the river swept round a cone of rock debris at the mouth of a lateral valley, and the current had gnawed its way through the obstruction and then cut deep into the solid rock beneath. In other spots the river crashed head on against a cliff and was forced to turn back through ninety degrees or more until it found a way round.

The sandy lower slopes were covered with maquis consisting mainly of shrubs with small leathery leaves, notably *Pistacia weinmannifolia* in profusion, together with box, *Cinnamomum delavayi*, *Ligustrum lucidum*, *Viburnum cylindricum* and *Chionanthus retusus*. With its delicate fragrant white flowers, the last of these must have been a joy in early summer, and it now bore small fruits resembling plums. Among them grew a small hornbeam, *Carpinus monbeigiana* (a new species), and *Cornus*

capitata in great abundance, its ripening fruits emitting a scent somewhat reminiscent of raspberries. Perhaps even more extensive were the areas of garigue where most of the shrubs or undershrubs had white leaves (*Buddleia incompta*, though it had a somewhat rusty tinge) or felted silvery leaves (*Lespedeza floribunda*) or looked like besoms (*Excoecaria acerifolia*); conspicuous among them were *Ceratostigma minus* with spikes of azure blue flowers and calyces resembling those of *Statice*, and *Plectranthrus rugosiformis*. Scattered between them were several yellowish or brown wormwoods (*Artemisia sieversiana*, *A. annua*, *A. vestita*) with tufts of stiff stalks, and various steppe grasses. The trees, for the most part somewhat higher up, were *Pinus yunnanensis* and *Keteleeria davidiana*, as in similar situations on the Yunnan tableland.

Numerous small villages were scattered along the valley floor wherever level patches allowed cultivation, the first few being peopled by Bai, here known as Lama Ren, though further upstream their inhabitants were Naxi. There were also some larger villages, such as Louchang and Gangpu. The tall Naxi women wore heavy jewellery of silver and precious stones on the earlobes and the head. Dressed in long pleated skirts, singing and joking, they were at work everywhere in the fields. Even on the steepest slopes little patches of land had been planted with maize and buckwheat. Chinese settlers from the lowlands had left only the valley sides for the native Lisu tribespeople. Their villages were situated a few hundred metres above the valley floor, each consisting of two lines of log houses shaded by huge broad-leaved trees, chiefly walnuts. However, there were still a few Lisu families living by the right bank of the river above Gangpu, at a cramped site where access was difficult (Lopulo, Mahalo). Beginning just above the line of Lisu villages was a zone of sombre montane forest, covering the narrow spurs which jutted out between numerous lateral valleys. Only occasionally did we see the dark igneous rock of one of the higher peaks on the main crest or an unusually tall lateral ridge. Below the Gangpu monastery the track climbed up the hillside, and where it descended again to the valley bottom, opposite Maliping, the mouth of a lateral valley debouched through a limestone cliff. This valley, running westwards and splitting into several branches, was said to be the site of some large Lisu villages (Sololo). In this stretch the Lancang Jiang ran from the northeast and had not yet succeeded in smoothing out some steeply tilted beds of hard clay-slate. Hastened by the steeper gradient, its waters dashed against the rocks and recoiled from both banks to meet again in the middle, where they reared up, hurling spray into the air. Though not far above the river, the path was hidden in dense shrub cover and afforded only occasional glimpses of the rapids, but their thunderous roar tempted me to climb down to a spot from which I could see everything, and I took some successful photographs. A few kilometres further on the river reverted to its original direction from the northwest. At this sharp bend it widened

---

[97] Rock's map shows a rope bridge just below Xiao Weixi, but no path on the west side of the Lancang Jiang.

considerably and there was an island of stones and
gravel colonised by willows and tamarisks. They
were old trees and some of them, long dead, stretched their branches into the air like gigantic brooms.
The island extended almost to the corner of the rock
face which forced the stream to the right. The path,
hewn out of this rock and suspended above the
water, now entered the Yezhi basin. On the east
bank, which was not so steep, there was a series of
alluvial fans, terraced to make rice fields. Above
them we saw the rock crest of the Lancang Jiang —
Yangzi divide, this being almost the first glimpse of
either of the main ranges which we had so far
enjoyed. To the left of the path, not far above the
river, was the walled town of Yezhi, the seat of a
tusi whose authority ran as far as the Drung Jiang
(Jiu Jiang) [98]. High up on the right, crags and towers
marked the line of the crest, which came closer to
the valley as it ran northwards. Before we had gone
much further some huge black pinnacles came into
view on the right, high above the dark forests of the
Lancang Jiang — Nu Jiang divide. Down in the
valley, however, the terrain remained much the same
in appearance as far as Luoda, a long day's march
from Yezhi.

Luoda and Dashou were two hamlets of wooden
houses on terraces just above the river, which had
laid down sandbanks at this point. Here, where it
flowed out from the bowels of the mountains, it
began to deposit the products of its erosive action.
Emerging between vertical precipices on either side
of a ravine, the river now entered the open part of its
valley system. Two pale grey limestone crags, one
on each side of the gorge, made a background for
the village, while further upstream the steep sides of
the valley soared up to snow-flecked summits 2500m
above the water. This was the end of the good road,
and I therefore had to say goodbye to my honest
caravanmen from Lijiang, with whom I had never
had a moment's difficulty. Hewn out of the living
rock, often barely half a metre wide, the main
caravan route to Atendse led along the steep cliffs
above the river. The loads were lashed to the pack-
saddle itself, as high up as possible, with bulky
objects on the air side so as not to catch on the rock
face where it encroached on the path. If this happened the animal would not stand still, but would
press forwards, pushing itself out from the track, and
at one of the many exposed spots it might fall
straight down into the river. Along the narrowest
part of the defile, where it broke through vertically
tilted limestone strata running north and south, there
was a wooden bridge or gallery along the rock face;
it even had a parapet, but in both the years that I
passed that way half the parapet was missing. On the
opposite side, where the river dashed against the
rocks, large kettle holes like smooth black cauldrons
were visible when the water level was low (Fig.31).
As the river rose it resumed its erosive work within
them. On my side I saw the vestiges of similar kettle

holes above the path, dating from an era when the
gorge was not so deep. In the rock face beside the
gallery there were some small openings; when one
shouted into them the sound echoed through long
branching passages.

Here and further upstream and in a few places
lower down the arbor vitae tree (*Thuja orientalis*)
covered wide stretches of the dry rocky slopes. Its
roots found anchorage even on vertical rock faces,
and its longitudinally fissured grey bark almost
matched the colour of the rock; its branchlets, arbor-
izing freely in one plane only and clad with dusty-
looking grey-green scale leaves arranged vertically,
presented their narrow sides to the sun. This tree,
widely planted in Europe, is believed to have come
originally from north east China and Manchuria, but
this conjecture has never been substantiated. Many
travellers and even a few botanists must have seen it
growing here, but not one of them had noticed it and
I was privileged to be the first to find it in the
wild [99]. It also occurs under similar conditions in the
territory of the Yangzi Jiang, in the valley below
Shuba, north east of Yezhi. Among other plants
growing on the arid rocks, receiving a little shade
from the sclerophyllous shrubs above them, were
numerous orchids, now out of flower, and *Hoya
carnosa*, a creeper with thick fleshy leaves; *Sedum
drymarioides*, a little stonecrop with numerous
glands, and the large *S. indicum*; *Polypodium
nipponicum*, a fern with bluish creeping rootstocks,
and a few mosses.

At river level there was no level ground at all
and the sides of the gorge rose steeply to the peaks,
yet there were numerous tiny hamlets clinging to the
slopes. They were Tibetan settlements, most of the
houses having a flat-roofed penthouse in front; some
of them were topped by an upper storey in the form
of a gable roofed with wooden shingles. They were
ruinous and soot-blackened, and sticking up above
them were clusters of bamboo canes draped with
prayer flags. All of them had incense stoves, usually
three side by side, looking like small kitchen ovens,
in which pine needles, arbor vitae twigs and aromatic *Pistacia* leaves were burnt. The mouths of the
valleys on the west side were almost completely
barred by cliffs of dark slate. High up on the western
side was the village of Patong, two lines of houses
crammed closely together wherever space could be
found. A white building turned out to be the church:
we had arrived at one of the oldest missions in
Tibet. Behind Patong there was a valley coming
down from the mountains, but it was barred by a
ridge running parallel to the river, and we had to go
3 km further up the main valley before we reached
the mouth of the stream. The vertical strata running
parallel to the river caused several side valleys to
make a sharp bend upstream just before entering the
main channel. The path was very bad here, no more
than a narrow track across scree slopes, often completely covered by the downwards trickle of gravel,

[98] The eastern branch of the Nmai-hka — the upper
reaches of the Irrawaddy — where it flows through extreme NW
Yunnan (SGH).

[99] Handel-Mazzetti did not know that Forrest had found
it here before him, though all the material which Forrest collected
in 1905 was lost when he was pursued by Tibetans.

which had to be cleared away before proceeding; but such stretches would be followed by others where the path, trodden out by passing hoofs, ran over gently sloping rock ledges. The valley side sloped straight down to the eddying waters, ready to swallow up anything which rolled into them.

Beyond the mouth of the valley just mentioned were the scattered houses of Cigu. A ruined wall of white stone, the graves of the missionaries murdered by the lamas, and some Chinese burial mounds with names inscribed above them were all that remained of the mission burnt down in 1905. In that year George Forrest had spent several months botanizing on the Doker-la and above Cigu and was staying there as the missionaries' guest. On receiving warning of the lamas' approach he fled with the two missionaries, but they were overtaken by their pursuers; one was killed by their arrows and the other was tortured for three days before he died. Though cut off, Forrest was able to conceal himself and survived for nine days with very little to eat. In one encounter two poisoned arrows went through his hat. After sinking his boots in a stream to avoid leaving tracks, he escaped and found his way to some friendly Lisu tribesmen who hid him for four days and then guided him for nearly six days' journey southwards along the dividing range in rain and cold. During the descent he trod on a sharpened bamboo stake which went right through his foot. At Yezhi the tusi fed him and gave him clothes to replace his own tattered garments and finally, still disguised as a Tibetan, he reached safety at Xiao Weixi [100]. Only those who have themselves seen these immense and trackless ranges can fully appreciate what a feat of endurance that was.

Between the Cigu valley and the next major lateral valley a steep ridge formed a precipice above the Lancang Jiang. On it was a small green saddle, making hardly a break in the rock face as it soared up to the peaks. From below it seemed impossible that it could really be 1300m above the river, so difficult is it to estimate heights on such steep slopes. The route to the Nu Jiang led up and over the saddle. Some 4 km upstream of Cigu there was a narrow shelf, used for cultivating rice, above the right bank of the river. Upon it, in the village of Cizhong [101], a spot less exposed to surprise attack, the mission had been rebuilt.

Dusk was falling as I, unable to find any place large enough for the tent, unrolled my campbed at the rope bridge, put up the mosquito net above it and spread my sleeping bag over that to keep off the occasional showers. Lao Li sat on the path with a sour expression on his face at the prospect of what lay before him, and declared that there was no wood

for the cooking fire, but his cookboy Zhafa soon found some. In the morning the locals arrived, prostrated themselves on the ground, crossed themselves and then — after we had agreed on a price very much in their favour — transported my baggage across the river. Lao Li said, *"Moi pas connais passer la corde"* and pretended to walk away, but I shouted fiercely at him and his fears vanished. I waited until his baggage had reached the other side and then crossed over with the intention of calling on the missionary, to whom I had already sent the bishop's recommendation card. The bamboo rope was a thick as a man's fist and on it was placed a wooden slider (*"wata"*) with straps fastened to it. Two of them went under the thighs and another under the back of the neck; then they were tied tight. Holding on with both hands to the slider above, or with one on the knotted straps below, the passenger sails over the gurgling river, about 200m broad, in 15 seconds, the wind whistling in his ears. The crossing is perfectly safe unless the rope breaks, a mishap which does sometimes occur if the bridge has been neglected. If the rope is dry the first man to cross pours on oil or water, or squirts it from his mouth, for the friction is enormous. Clouds of smoke rising from the wata are clearly visible in a photograph of a horse crossing the bridge (Fig.30). Heavy passengers, such as I, are checked by a cord fixed at right angles to the rope so as to catch the wata, but lightweights have to haul themselves up the last stretch hand over hand, though it is of course forbidden to touch it during the transit. For the first time it is somewhat hair-raising, but later it becomes quite enjoyable. As it was raining and the rope was wet, the horses would have slid across too fast, arriving at the far side with a bump, and we therefore had to wait there for them. Moreover the next day was a Sunday and porters would be more easily found. This meant a further day's delay and, as funds were running low, I had to curtail my plans.

Cizhong was almost entirely pagan; the spacious mission building and the large basilica with its squat tower looked strangely out of place among the Ommani-padme prayer flags of the Tibetans, the outward manifestations of two religions so different in essence and yet so alike in externals. Monastic life, bells, music and chanting, incense, rosaries, blessings and consecrations and the exorcising of evil spirits are common to both. Crucifixes, statues and inscriptions have their counterparts in idols, mani stones and prayer flags. Be one a believer or not, one has to admit that the missionaries are utterly wholehearted in their endeavours to persuade the people to throw off the yoke of the lamas and turn to Christianity. In so doing they inevitably tend to diminish the lamas' influence in this world too, and though under the protection of the State they all too often forfeit their lives. Yet there are always successors ready to step joyfully into their shoes. They humble themselves to the level of their flock, living in the same conditions of dirt and discomfort instead of trying to teach them the fundamental rules of human dignity. Not many pure-blooded Tibetans lived in Cizhong and Cigu; most of the people were Chinese-Tibetan or Naxi-Tibetan crossbreeds, and there were also a few Sichuan Chinese, descendants of soldiers'

[100] Gardeners' Chronicle (1910) 3rd series, 47, 325 and 344 (Handel-Mazzetti 's note).

[101] Chinese — Tz'u-chung. "A scattered Tibetan village of about 30 houses, with a few Na-khi families who have settled there...and a few leper huts. The most imposing building is the Catholic church...built here after the destruction of the mission at Tz'u-ku in 1905, by Père Ouvrard, who also built the church at Ta-chien-lu" (Rock, p. 315).

families who had settled there long ago. The usual language, however, was Tibetan. Although the people were said to be a thievish lot, none of my property went astray during my several visits. The climate is unhealthy, malaria is not uncommon and there are numerous lepers. However, provided the traveller does not make any purchases from their houses and does not let them enter his own, he has nothing to fear. Naxi people were said to live in their own villages close to those of the Tibetans up the Lancang Jiang as far as Yerkalo, but Patong on the valleyside downstream from Cigu was a purely Tibetan village.

Père Valentin most obligingly found me the twelve porters required for the journey to the Doker-la and the Nu Jiang. My primary aim was to repeat the work done by Forrest on the sacred mountain — a place of pilgrimage — since his collections, which he described in glowing terms, had been lost when he had to flee from the lamas in 1905. All unnecessary equipment such as the camp table, chair and paraffin lamp was left behind. Lao Li had stepped on a *Prinsepia* thorn which had gone through his straw sandal into his heel. He had stopped the bleeding with salt, but told me nothing about it until it had become seriously infected. The whole foot was inflamed and foul-smelling black fluid was exuding from the wound. There was no question of his taking part in the next stage of the journey. I took a boy in his place and hired a pony so as to give my own a badly needed rest, but it proved to be one of those which would not go forwards without a man leading it by the nose. Before setting out on 13th September I had to deal with a quarrel among the men; the porters who arrived first had picked up the smallest possible loads and started off at once, leaving large amounts of baggage behind. This meant that I had to send after them and divide the loads fairly. Not far above Cizhong the Lancang Jiang makes a sharp double bend, less than 1 km in length. Having crossed the river at Cizhong, I continued upstream along the west bank. The path crossed two lateral streams and then ascended steadily to cut off a large loop caused by a ridge which projected at right angles to the valley. The higher we climbed, the more splendid was the scenery. The sides of the valley swept up steeply without any break. At the bottom there was cultivation, with picturesque clusters of dilapidated houses. Then came a zone of luxuriant mixed forest; above it were dark fir woods, and finally the rocky towers of the crest itself. Across the valley was a superb array of spires, yellow grey in the evening light. Far below the river slid past in its narrow bed, its waters reddish brown in the rainy season, swinging round in sharp curves for no visible reason. The village of Tola was particularly charming, its houses in two groups on terraces across the valley, looking as if they had been glued to the steep slope. The track climbed steeply to Serä, a village more than 400m above the valley floor; it was one of the biggest in the district,

consisting of three large groups of mainly stone-built houses. I slept there on a flat roof. Wu Suolong was looking closely at a box as a possible place to sleep.

"Look, there are fleas here, in broad daylight!", he exclaimed.

"Fleas? Yes, masses of them!", replied the householder soothingly.

The track went on, gradually climbing above a ravine which the river had excavated in a limestone wall projecting from the east, and then downhill again. From the top of the rise we looked upstream into a landscape of simple outlines and almost melancholy splendour. The arid sides of the river gorge, over 2000m in height, sloped down at a constant angle, uniformly furrowed and a monotonous brown in colour. Down at the bottom, near the river, their profile became slightly convex and then fell even more steeply, leaving not even the minutest level spot near the water. From Guta, a village down a the valley bottom, we had a view downstream into the limestone ravine we had just passed. Topped by rounded shoulders, the bare vertical cliffs, curling inwards slightly as they neared the water, dropped down to the river, running quietly in its bed some 150m across. The spine-chilling illustration in Cooper's book [102] is probably based on his recollections of this gorge, which he named Hogg's Gorge. From Guta the track continued along the river. It was bordered by huge cypresses (*Cupressus duclouxiana*), gigantic sombre pyramids towering into the air, as regular and uniform as an avenue of poplars. Throughout the rainy season, when the river is in flood, their tall trunks are partially immersed, and the water eats away the soil at their roots and even damages their bark. This tree was common here, growing on the steep rocky slopes together with *Thuja orientalis*, yet it generally prefers dry conditions, and I never again saw it in such a place, though its occurrence on the banks of the canals in the Kunming plain is in some degree comparable. A small patch of turf invited us to pitch the tent. Running across it was a briskly flowing clear blue stream, tumbling down from a wild rocky gorge, and on both sides cliffs of red clay-slate soared up towards the sky, their covering of scrub vegetation untouched by man.

---

[102] Setting out in January 1868, Cooper travelled up the Yangtse to Chungking and overland via Tatsienlu (Kangding) and Bathang (Paan) to Atenze. He continued down the valley of the Mekong, passing through the gorge on 14 June. He named it after his friend James Hogg of Hogg Bros., Shanghai. His frontispiece shows a ravine apparently 7-15m wide and 70-100m deep with a wooden gallery along its left side, and he says this was the worst part of the gorge. After crossing the river to Tz-coo (Tzeku) he reached Weisee-foo (Weihsi), but there he was arrested and forced to retrace his route. Cooper, Thomas Thorneville, *Travels of a pioneer of commerce in pigtail and petticoats; or, an overland journey from China towards India.* London,1871.

Chapter 19. The Doker-La

The Londjre valley — the pilgrims' route — mountain rain-forest — troublesome porters — on the pass at 4600m
— late summer flowers

This little nook gave some inkling of the un-tamed splendours of nature to be found further on — splendours to which the Doker-La owes its reputation as a holy place. It was located at the mouth of the Londjre valley, through which ran the pilgrims' route to Tibet and, branching off to the left, the main road to the Ju Jiang, laid out by the Chinese. The track was hewn out of the rock high up on the opposite side. A wooden bridge of the Tibetan kind I had encountered at Muli led over the stream; it was rotten and alarmingly unsteady. As it de-scended, the track passed across a sloping rock slab where it had been built up by human hands. The valley then broadened and the path crossed the stream several times, passing through luxuriant woodland of sclerophyllous trees and shrubs: *Pistacia weinmannifolia*, *Quercus parvifolia* and *Viburnum schneiderianum* — both the latter were new species — the conifers already mentioned, and an understorey of box. After travelling for some two hours we emerged into a small basin at Londjre, where the valley forked. Its flat-roofed houses, about twenty in number and similar in appearance to those already described, were scattered here and there under the shelter of old walnut trees. The people were pure-blooded Tibetans. Woods of arbor vitae, unmixed with any other tree, covered the arid slopes in the vicinity up to an altitude of 3000m. Old trees of the same species, with thick trunks and spheroidal crowns, grew in the rock debris of the stream.

The pilgrimage route came from Yangdsa below Dêqên (Adunzi), climbed up the side of the Lancang Jiang valley and curved round high up over a corner of the mountain to enter our valley. From Londjre there was a steep zigzag track leading up to it across granite soil. A narrow rickety bridge crossed the stream, but it was fit only for men on foot, and we had to bring the horses across by fastening their bridles to a long rope, so as to hold them if they slipped, and leading them through the fast-flowing water. The pilgrims' way, very narrow but well maintained, continued along the steep valleyside. Had we been in Europe there would have been a notice reading *"Unsuitable for persons subject to giddiness"*, but in China the sensation of giddiness seems to be entirely unknown to even the most faint-hearted Chinese, of whom Lao Li was an example. Fortunately, I am tolerably immune from such terrors, though I cannot claim to be absolutely proof against giddiness. In any case one is more likely to suffer from giddiness on horseback, when riding with one leg hanging over the abyss and unable to see any solid ground beneath, since the horses, especially those used as pack animals, have a habit of walking on the outermost edge, even when the track is quite broad. The edge, often consisting of little more than tufts of grass, is soon worn away by their hoofs and on one occasion I very nearly fell into the river at Weixi, horse and all. Most of the riding horses which I had in China were impeccably safe, but the packhorses were much less satisfactory in this respect; mules were far more trustworthy.

Certain years are especially propitious for the pilgrimage over the Doker-la, a circuit round the snow-capped Kakerbo [103] range. 1915 was such a year and during the five days which I spent on the pilgrims' way I met three or four parties of pilgrims, most of them on foot, but one consisting of lamas and laymen with a mule, two cows and a sheep. They camped under trees, beneath overhanging rocks or on the scanty level spots on the hillsides. We found such a spot, just large enough for the tent, beside a rushing brook. The valley grew narrower and narrower; the track descended some 200m and turned into a side branch with a tributary which we soon reached. The main branch of the valley to the south was totally pathless: not even the faintest track led up through its dark woods to the gloomy granite peaks which towered up, flecked here and there with snow, into the clouds. A conifer growing by the wayside caught my eye. Its trunk — not very stout — and its slender branches, arising in regular whorls, were covered with bark which was almost black in colour. Its needles, projecting in two lines from its twigs, made sparse overhead cover, and among them I could see its upright cones, like larch cones but much bigger and stouter. It proved to be *Pseudotsuga wilsoniana*, an Asiatic representative of an American genus (Fig.32). In some stretches it formed unmixed woodland, and everywhere else its rounded crowns stood out among the firs, spruces, maples, cherries, birches, oaks (*Quercus oxyodon*) and other trees. Low cloud hid the mountains and rain fell unceas-ingly; anything which was not drenched by the rain was soaked by contact with the shrubs and herba-ceous plants which jutted across the path. Wherever a torrent, a landslide or a gale had torn a gap in the primeval forest, it was promptly filled by masses of perennial herbs, almost twice the height of a man and already flowering though only in their second year. Among them were aromatic wormwoods (*Artemisia*), balsams (*Impatiens*), *Cimicifuga foetida*, and, covering large patches, a knotweed with bulky panicles of relatively large white flowers (*Polygonum polystachyum*). Half buried in the soil beneath the clumps I found its young sprouts with thick succulent folded reddish-pink leaves. Somewhat higher up there was open woodland of cherries and maples with an understorey of semiligneous *Strobilanthes*, which formed an almost unbroken canopy about 2m above the ground. A familiar lichen from the European Alps, *Trentepohlia iolithus*, was present here, in blood-red patches on granite boul-ders.

The track crossed the stream several times, and at a minor bend in the valley the bamboo thickets had been cleared to make a yak pasture. Waterfalls tumbled down from glacial cirques above, and in the background, peeping out over the screes, was the snout of a glacier. No wonder the Tibetans have

---

[103] Also written Ka-gwr-pu. The Chinese name for the main peak is Meili Xue Shan (6740m) (SGH).

peopled this land, so lonely and melancholy, with their spirits. Yonder, on the colossal mountain which bears his name, lives Kakerbo, the good spirit to whom the pilgrimage is dedicated. Unfortunately I could not see anything of the mountains, and it was not until 1916 that I ascertained that the main summit, some 6000m in height, does not slope down directly to the Londjre valley, but is located at the head of the next lateral valley up the Lancang Jiang, on the ridge between it and a valley still further on. Only the lesser summit is situated in the range bounding the Doker-la valley, some distance below its head. The porters wanted to pitch camp early, and to escape their importunities I rode on to a suitable camp site in the depths of the forest. The men followed, grumbling. A short distance further on the pilgrimage route quitted the main valley, which became somewhat flatter here, and climbed up to the left into a cirque. A cattle shed gave the pilgrims some shelter from the rain. Early next morning my porters threatened to strike: it was so cold up here, they said; further on was Tibet, and they were uneasy at the prospect of going there, although they had previously declared that we could complete the round trip via Aben and Bonga to Qunatong on the Nu Jiang long before the Tibetan border guards would hear any report of our movements, and although the journey over the Doker-la as far as the camping ground at Tsesuton was part of their agreement with me. I picked out the man who opened his mouth widest and who had the most crosses hung round his neck, and after I had conducted him to his load, somewhat ungently, the rest of them set off once more. At midday I pitched the tent in the cirque, just below the tree line, in a spot sheltered from the cold wind by huge boulders. I let the porters spend the night lower down, as it was really cold there.

A prattling brook ran down from a snowfield below a pointed summit, and further to the left there was a small green col on the ridge, which curved round to the south, rising up towards a cluster of peaks about 5200m high. When the mist cleared I had a good view of the col, and could see the bamboos waving in the wind. It was the Doker-la, and beyond lay Tibet, the forbidden land. The rain ceased for a while. *"Never put off till tomorrow what you can do today"*, I thought. Shouldering my rucksack and camera I set off by myself — the men were busily occupied and it was so late in the day as to rule out any risk of an encounter with ill-disposed lamas — to climb the last 400m to the pass. In the cirque the stream branched. Along its banks was *Aconitum pulchellum*, its dark flowers in ones and twos, and our own *Lomatogonium carinthiacum*. A large broad-leaved edelweiss (*Leontopodium stracheyi*) spread in mats among the rocks, and although most of the other plants had finished flowering I found some treasures growing in fine scree on a little crest, up which the path wound in zigzags. Among them were *Moehringia roseiflora* with large red pendent bell-shaped flowers; *Tanacetum mutellina*, resembling our alpine wormwood; *Delphinium beesianum*, a low-growing species with large deep-blue flowers; *Corydalis adrieni* with stout underground winter buds, and *C. trachycarpa*, *Crepis*

hookeriana and the new *Cremanthodium crassum*. Up on the pass itself at 4600m I collected the pink-flowered *Cremanthodium rhodocephalum*, *Allium forrestii* with large dark flowers and the tiny *Gentiana cyananthiflora*. On the Tibetan side, growing in fine consolidated granite scree, I found a new species of *Delphinium* (*D. tsarongense*), a low-growing, mat-forming plant with solitary flowers, the largest in the genus. They were a watery bluish-violet and looked as if they had been cut out of paper and blown up. A biting northwesterly wind tugged at the prayer flags dangling from the clusters of bamboo, the rain began again and the mist came down, blotting out everything except a few glimpses of the steep slopes on the opposite side. I wanted to photograph the delphinium, and I set the shutter to instantaneous and the diaphragm wide open, but the wind caught the lens cap as it dangled on its cord and the latter fouled the shutter release just as I was operating it. The result was a spoilt plate — one of the few that I had left. The path led down in steep zigzags to the uppermost bowl of a valley which debouched into the Nu Jiang at Lakonra below Mengong. I had neither time nor inclination to descend into it, especially as there would soon have been a renewed ascent, and contented myself with collecting a small specimen of Tibetan soil. Because the porters had travelled so slowly there was now no time to shift my camp up to the pass, as I had planned, and to go down into the forests of which Bacot speaks so highly. In any case I wanted to return to Londjre and visit the Nu Jiang from there, and I felt sure that the forests in that district must be the same as these. So I returned speedily to my tent and sat up late into the cold night putting plants into the press.

Next morning I collected the lichens and mosses which covered every boulder and filled every rivulet. It was nearly noon before the porters finally crawled up to my tent, and during the descent I had to check them from dashing on past the yak hut without me, for on the next day, if the weather was passable, I hoped to go back to the glacier at the head of the valley. In the event, however, it was far too inclement for a trip across such trackless terrain. The yakherd at the hut, a young Tibetan from Londjre, was surly and ill tempered, and demanded crazy prices for milk and butter, though in the end I bought some to provide a change of diet. When I scraped off the dirty rancid rind which covered the butter he picked it up and immediately smeared it over his hair, as is the custom in Tibet. He would not permit my men to dry out the plant paper over the fire in his hut, though it must be said that the hut was extremely small. As we went down I felt impelled to take another photograph of the *Pseudotsuga*. Carrying a good crop of cones, the trees stood high up on the hillside and certainly made a fine subject, but the only way to reach them was up a watercourse which came splashing down over the rocks. I was already too wet to get any wetter, so I climbed up undismayed, though with great caution as the boulders were slippery with algae, and took a successful picture. We then descended speedily to Londjre. For the ascent on the other side I would gladly have mounted my horse, but the young man who was leading it was disinclined to wait for me.

I shouted after him until I was hoarse, but all he wanted was to get out of the rain and down into the valley as fast as he could, as did we all.

I spent a day in Londjre drying out my kit. The people were most hospitable, and I found accommodation in a large partly open room, though I had some trouble with an old man whose snoring and groaning would have been annoying. In the end I persuaded him to clamber down from his chest and find somewhere else for the next two nights. Each evening the people invited me to take my place on the carpet by the fire and offered me tea, while two lamas made their prayer wheels whirr incessantly.

Chapter 20. On Foot to the Nu Jiang

The Chinese road over the Shenzu-la — frost — epiphytic shrubs on the Doyon-lumba — bracken — a view across the Nu Jiang — triangulation at Bahan — the missionaries — back to the Lancang Jiang over Nisselaka and the Xi-la — a wild valley — giant firs

As the routes to the Nu Jiang (Salween) were unrideable and Lao Li's fondness for opium had made him unfit for long journeys on foot, I had give my hired pony a rest and fall back on the scraps of Chinese which I had picked up on my travels. Zhafa was capable of doing the cooking by himself. The porter who had been so troublesome up on the mountain said he was sick and I therefore handed over the plants from the Doker-la to him and another and sent them back to Cizhong together with Lao Li. I engaged another man in Londjre, a sturdy Tibetan in high boots of multicoloured felt. He was a cheerful energetic fellow with unkempt locks hanging over his face. He had recently become a Christian and later, to my great delight, sold me his prayer-wheel. His better half did not want to let him go, but with a few words he wrested himself from her; curiously enough, Davies had a similar experience here [104].

On 21st September I buckled on my rucksack and my camera — I never entrusted it to anyone else — picked up my iceaxe and set off once more into the mountains, this time up the south branch of the valley, along its left side, which was at first barren and arid. At 2750m we entered woodland consisting of pines and prickly-leaved oaks, soon augmented by other conifers and deciduous trees including hazels. The track then went steeply downhill for a short distance to the stream, which was bordered by luxuriant mixed woodland. Clinging closely to the trunks of the giant firs and spruces and dangling down from their tops were huge climbers such as the vine *Tetrastigma obtectum*, *Euonymus aculeatus* and ivy. Close to our overnight camp in the densest woodland I found the violet-flowered twining *Crawfurdia trinervis*, a gentian relative with red fruits like paprikas. The valley bottom became flatter and moister, and the vegetation correspondingly more lush. Large-leaved knotgrasses were abundant and the dried up seed-bearing spikes of *Lilium giganteum* rose up above the *Strobilanthes* canopy. The soft woolly heads of *Cirsium bolocephalum* var. *ramosum* were not much lower, but nearly all of them had been nibbled off by deer or yak, and it was not easy to find good specimens. At a spot where the valley forked and broadened the track crossed the stream by a bridge. Indeed, although it had originally been well constructed, large parts of the track consisted of suspension bridges made of round logs as thick as a man's arm, with gaps of the same width between them. They ran along rock faces and between boulders, and I could hardly believe that it was possible to bring such heavy animals as yaks over them. All the rocks were thickly coated with mosses and filmy ferns (*Hymenophyllum corrugatum* and *H. paniculiflorum*). Before long we encountered *Rhododendron semnum* growing in profusion especially along the stream; it is probably one of the largest of the genus and has thick leathery leaves 40cm long, their undersides at first copper-coloured and later shimmering and silvery. The average gradient along the valley was quite gentle, but higher up the track left the valley floor and climbed in steep muddy slippery zigzags for over 300m. At the tree line and even more abundantly in the shallow cirque above it there were two species of small *Gaultheria* creeping between the bushes, one (*G. suborbicularis*) with red fruits and the other (*G. trichophylla*) with skyblue fruits like bilberries or cranberries, but differing in that they are made up of five fleshy lobules separated at their tips and exposing the small dry brown capsule in the middle. Sharp edged crests loomed through the mists on our left, and as we advanced the pinnacles which came into view seemed to rise higher and higher. The rain made them all look dark although they were of limestone, a thick bed of which outcropped here, folded between mica schist; just below the top of the Shenzu la [105] it contained some coal. The dark violet *Swertia atroviolacea* (a new species) was flowering there, and growing on the boulders were little ferns (*Polystichum duthiei*) and *Androsace graceae* with thick circular leaves. The yaks had already departed from the pastures on the pass at 4000m. I pitched my tent in light rain, while the porters tried to make the hut waterproof — half its roof was missing — with their goat-hair blankets.

---

[104] Davies tried to cross the pass to the Nu Jiang (Salween) in April 1900, but was forced to turn back by soft snow three feet deep (Davies, H.R., *Yunnan*, Cambridge,1909, p.261).

[105] Kingdon Ward calls this pass the Chun-tsung-la (*The Land of the Blue Poppy*, Cambridge, 1913, p.80).

A cold wind blew that night. Next morning there was frost on the ground and a thin layer of snow covered the tops, reaching down almost to the camp. It had also sprinkled the Maya-tra [106], the mountain which soared up boldly to the south and to which belonged the peaks indistinctly seen on the day before. This is the mountain which the Prince d'Orleans quite superfluously christened "Pic François Garnier". The distant views were equally splendid: to the north the range on which we were standing sloped up to the Doker-la; on the opposite side was another mountain, of about the same altitude as our viewpoint though decreasing considerably towards the left, and separating the Doyon-lumba [107], the valley where my destination Bahan was situated, from the Nu Jiang (Salween); and in the distance beyond it were some of the peaks of the Ju Jiang — Irrawaddy divide. Below me stretched the primeval forests of the Ludse Jiang, immense and unspoilt. This name is applied to the whole of the upper Chinese territory along the Nu Jiang as far as the river. It soon became clear that I had entered a floristic region totally different from any other part of Yunnan.

The track curved to the right and then ran steeply downhill, entering stands of bamboo where every plant had died. From a distance they looked as if they had been burnt, but on coming closer I saw that there was no trace of fire, and indeed the ground beneath the dried up culms — they were about 3m in height and some had already fallen — was thickly covered with bright green seedlings about 20cm high. It was a new species — *Arundinaria melanostachys*. As I later heard, 1914 had been an exceptionally dry year [108] in those parts, and it was this that had induced mass flowering among the bamboos, not only in more easterly districts, where we had indeed seen it, but also and more particularly here; and after flowering the bamboos die. A golden green moss (*Campylopus gracilis*) was growing in great abundance near the edges of the bamboo thickets; perhaps the sudden ingress of light had stimulated its growth.

Before long we plunged into the woods. Everything was soft and yielding. The track was a bottomless morass consisting of holes in the leaf mould between the roots of giant rhododendrons, the trunks of which were fully equal in size to those of the largest maples. Another substantial tree, one of the largest members of its family (*Araliaceae*), was *Acanthopanax evodiaefolia*. Spreading in the soft mossy soil were some tiny species of *Rubus*, notably *R. potentilloides*, but most interesting of all were the many epiphytic shrubs high up on the tree trunks: *Ribes acuminatum*, *Sorbus harrowianus* with leaves like a rowan and grey-white roots entirely covering

one side of the trunk which supported it, *Rhododendron tapeinum* and *Vaccinium dendrocharis*. Some of them, in particular the last-named, which is not unlike our cowberry (*Vaccinium vitis-idaea*), enveloped whole tree trunks in a dense mantle spreading up the very top. Growing on it were numerous ferns and a few herbaceous plants, though the latter had probably found their way there more or less by chance. Further down I found *Pentapanax truncicolus* growing as an epiphytic shrub. At 3150m the path, much of which had fallen away, crossed the little stream which ran straight down from the pass. A broad zone beside the stream had been kept clear of trees by repeated avalanches, and was occupied by willow scrub and tall herbaceous plants such as *Artemisia*, *Rodgersia* and balsams. Only at such opportunities as the midday halt does the traveller have time turn his attention to such things as a tiny *Myxomycetes*, attached to rotting leaves by a foot looking like a piece of coral and developing its spores in a narrow net a few centimetres in length. From here the track led gradually downhill along the side of the Doyon-lumba valley. The further we descended into this dank humid gorge, the more luxuriant was the vegetation. Broad-leaved trees predominated, evergreen and deciduous in roughly equal proportions: hollies (*Ilex dipyrena*), cherries, birches, tree-hazels, oaks and their relatives, maples, the fragrant *Enkianthus deflexus*, *Rhododendron sinogrande*, *Tetracentron sinense*, *Pterocarya forrestii* and the new *Corylopsis glaucescens*. The shrubs had much the same pattern: spindletrees, shrub hazels, redcurrants, *Sarcococca* and the yellow panicles of *Senecio densiflora*. Most striking of all, though not common, was *Gilibertia myriantha* (a new species of *Araliaceae*). It was in fruit, and its dainty umbels, grouped into clusters, covered the entire bush as if with a veil. The path wound its way through a dense understorey of lush *Strobilanthes* with lilies, knotgrasses, nettles and balsams.

After occupying this territory the Chinese had laid out a broad and well made track, but it had of course been allowed to fall into disrepair and in many places was now no more than a stairway or even a ladder made up of small holes serving as footholds up and down the steep gradients. Fortunately, bamboo culms grew nearly everywhere for the traveller to grasp. The lowest storey, perhaps more lush and sappy than any of the others, consisted of various species of *Elatostema*, *Pilea* and *Lecanthus*, all members of the nettle family; some had small fleshy inflorescences on stalks or sessile in the leaf axils while others had loose panicles of small green flowers. Also growing there was *Sarcopyramis nepalensis* (*Melastomataceae*) with juicy stems and calyces and four diamond-shaped pink petals drawn out to a slender tip at one corner. Ferns grew in large masses, one resembling our hard fern and the other (*Plagiogyra glauca*) having fronds of a beautiful bluish white colour on their lower surfaces. After going down the valley for some distance we reached a place where a mountain torrent had hurled down boulders as big as houses and piled up a bank of talus. A bridge built of two slender beams crossed the water and late that evening I pitched my tent on

---

[106] The Tibetan word tra means precipice or rock face (Handel-Mazzetti's note).

[107] The Tibetan word lumba means valley (Handel-Mazzetti's note).

[108] According to Forrest, 1914 was an exceptionally wet year in Western China. J. Macqueen Cowan *"George Forrest; Journeys and Plant Introductions"* London, 1952, p.30.

the bank. Although autumn was far advanced, the day's spoils had been so rich that I sat up long past midnight sorting out the plants.

Bahan was located high above the left bank of the stream, but first of all we had to ascend steeply for 600m along the right bank and then gradually climbed out of the valley on to the ridge which ran to the east of the Nu Jiang. During the ascent we passed a grove of wild walnut trees in the forest. The men were familiar with them, but their thick shells were difficult to break and the kernels were very small. Beneath the trees I found a large fern with long-stalked pedately divided fronds and narrow leaflets; it was the new *Pteris tomentella*. There was a tall magnolia tree (*M. rostrata*) with large, almost circular leaves 40cm long. High up and out of reach, I could see its bright red fruits. I tried to shoot one down with the Browning, but the attempt was even less successful than my previous endeavours higher up the mountain, when I managed to procure a bunch of leaves from *Sorbus harrowianus*, and I had to be content with some old dried up fruits. The Tibetan youth whom I had engaged as a plant collector in place of Lao Li caused some annoyance during this trip; he was seldom at hand when I needed him, and spent too much time fussing about the transport of his provisions. A few enormous trees of *Torreya fargesii* together with some spruce of a species I had not previously encountered (*Picea ascendens*) were standing on the Alülaka ridge, at an altitude of only 2900m. Also growing there was the Indian *Pinus insularis* with the usual *Quercus dentata*, and, as most of the forest had been felled, bracken was spreading in a most unwelcome manner. Its fronds formed a dense tangle, not easily penetrated, about a metre above the ground, though flourishing among it was hemp agrimony (*Eupatorium wallichii*) and, in more open spots, *Osmunda japonica*, a *Silene*, a pink-flowered orchid (*Bletilla yunnanensis*), *Leontopodium sinense* and *Carex cruciata* with golden brown panicles. Tangled amongst the last was *Apios delavayi*, a climber with upright racemes of conspicuous pale violet flowers and soft twining stems, and in the shade beneath grew *Houttuynia cordata*, the upright *Hydrocotyle javanica*, small green orchids, the prostrate *Pedicularis macrosiphon* with long tubular flowers and, in considerable numbers, a fern closely resembling if not the same as our own *Nephrodium thelypteris*.

The weather was splendid, and the whole of the Nu Jiang — Drung Jian (Salween — Irrawaddy) divide was visible. The tree cover permitted only occasional glimpses of the Nu Jiang winding 1200m below, but upstream I saw the level patch where Gongshan (Tschamutong) was situated on an old flat alluvial fan, deeply dissected by two streams. Behind it two pillars of crystalline limestone hemmed in the river. Towering up above this serene landscape was the Gomba-la [109], the snow peak of Gongshan, a pyramid with three broad glaciers side by side, their brilliant

white gleaming against the deep blue sky. Another summit peeping out behind it, a coronet of jagged spikes above a cirque, lay beyond the border in Tibet. Opposite us to the west, were dark serrated mountain peaks of granite and slate, intersected by numerous valleys. Dark green coniferous forest climbed high up the slopes, wherever the trees could find a foothold, but all the lower slopes were clothed with luxuriant broad-leaved woodland. The rounded treetops, in varied nuances of colour, formed a continuous canopy which hugged the folds of the terrain, though broken here and there by strips of bright green meadow and on dry crests giving way to sparse pine wood. This was the green land of the peaceful Nu (Ludse), and their villages were scattered along the less steep parts of the valleyside. Its superb clarity made it one of the most entrancing mountain vistas I have ever seen, and I sacrificed a plate to record it; it was my last but one, since the supply which I had ordered by telegram from Zhongdian had not yet arrived. The zone of pine and oak forest seemed to extend down as far as the river, and, feeling that I had already got to know it well enough, I thought it unnecessary to climb down to it, especially as the next descent into the Bhan valley was nearly as great. I spent the night at Meradon [110], the first village of the "small" Nu, lying half under the shelter of a maize drying rack and forgetting that the night sky was exceptionally cloudless. Next morning half my bed was wet with dew. Most of the wooden houses had one side raised on piles, as level ground is a rarity in their territory.

At midday on 25th September I reached the mission at Bahan (Beixia Luo in Chinese) after a steep ascent. It was 450m above Meradon and its white perimeter wall was visible from afar. The missionary was absent in Cizhong, so here too there was no choice but to speak Chinese. The mission house and its outbuildings were laid out round a courtyard, and on the side facing the mountain was a spacious church built of wood in the Chinese style and painted in bright colours. The caretaker offered me a room, having first enquired whether I was by any chance German, for he was forbidden to admit nationals of that country; however, he had never heard of Austria. He set milk and honey before me, but it would be wrong to suppose that this was a land flowing with milk and honey; indeed the Nu subsisted almost exclusively on maize and in 1914 there had been famine, caused — in the opinion of Père Genestier, a man well versed in natural history — by "mountain rats", which, feeding on the abounding crops of bamboo seed produced in 1914, had multiplied inordinately and had then consumed most of the maize before it had ripened. I had planned to take a rest day in Bahan and spent it in measuring a baseline and triangulating the valley system. In order to find a more or less level stretch of ground, 300m long and free from forest, and take bearings on the church, about one and a half kilometres distant, I

---

[109] According to Rock (footnote, page 337) this is not the name of the peak but of a pass to the south of it.

[110] Mu-la-t'ong (Kingdon Ward).

had to crawl for an hour through a deep ravine. I came back the same way and in the afternoon I extended the triangulation above the mission so as to include the Gomba-la. The labour was certainly worthwhile, since the depiction of the Nu Jiang on the existing maps was extremely sketchy and incorrect. Huge trees of *Manglietia insignis*, a genus not greatly dissimilar from *Magnolia*, were frequent here. I employed two men to climb them and bring down their fruit. *Rubus lineatus*, an exceptionally large bramble with long silky glistening silvery leaflets, was another prize collected on that unrestful "rest day".

On 27th September I left Bahan for the last high alpine trip of the season, the crossing of the Xi-la (Si-la) pass [111] back to the Lancang Jiang (Mekong). Offering splendid vistas, the path climbed steeply up a long meadow, the lower part of which was overgrown with willows with long silver grey leaves (*Salix salwinensis*, a new species). A few of the porters took advantage of the ponies grazing on the meadow. Seizing their tails, they made the ponies tow them up the steep path, quite oblivious of the fact that they were driving them beyond the boundary of the enclosed meadow. These were Tibetan ponies, extremely stocky long-haired beasts with pendulous bellies. Though they have often been described, this was the only time I saw them, or at least the only occasion on which their features were sufficiently distinctive to enable me to recognise them for what they were. The large handsome ponies which I saw in Zhongdian and Yongning did not belong to the same stock.

That evening it poured with rain again, and the task of pitching the tent at the top of the meadow took a long time, as my Tibetan youth had disappeared and despite all my shouting was nowhere to be found. There was frost that night and on awakening next morning I found the men tightly curled up in the nooks they had chosen to sleep in; it was so cold that even the Tibetans began to cough. The track went on through a strip of fir trees. The porters panted as they struggled over the slippery ground, led by their headman Li Tere, who marked each upwards heave by a mumbled complaint, which was mockingly imitated by Wu Suolong. Zhafa carried my raincoat, or rather hung it over his shoulders, and managed to lose a canvas hat cover which was in the pocket. This had been part of my kit in Mesopotamia, and at lower altitudes I used to wear it in place of a topee. On reaching the first pass, Nisselaka at 4200m, I took the opportunity of completing my triangulation. Before us lay the main divide between the Lancang Jiang (Mekong) and the Nu Jiang (Salween), a narrow crest covered with snow, separated from us by the Saoa-lumba valley which here ran parallel with the Doyon-lumba and debouched into the latter below Bahan. We paused to eat a little further down, beside a bog pool where I collected a fine haul of mosses and a cherry with deeply cut

leaves growing in tangled thickets. Though they looked most tempting, its fruits made us screw up our mouths. It was *Cerasus crataegifolia*, a new species.

Before long we met the two missionaries on their return journey from the Lancang Jiang (Mekong) to the Nu Jiang (Ludsedjiang). Père Genestier from Qunatong, a diminutive figure with a large grey beard, was famed as the best walker in the district though in his late fifties. Père Ouvrard from Bahan was a younger man, who had been my perhaps somewhat reluctant host during my stay there. They brought me some mail, including a letter from home and a few dozen photographic plates which had arrived in my absence. We sat down and chatted for a while until it was time for us all to move on. Of all Europeans living in the wilds, these two were perhaps the most isolated. For many months every winter the passes to the Lancang Jiang were blocked by huge masses of snow, so that visits to their parishioners entailed all the problems of mountain travel. They were completely cut off from the world. To the north of them were the fanatical Tibetans of Tsarong, who had swiftly expelled them from their first settlement at Bonga, while any attempt to travel downstream would have brought them up against the independent Lisu. A journey to the west would have been impracticable, as they had no idea where it would take them. Genestier's faithful Nu tribesmen recognized him as their true chieftain and on two occasions he had taken up arms and led them to drive out the Tibetans. In one incident the mission at Bahan had been burnt down and he had lost his collection of one thousand two hundred plants from the neighbourhood, though some specimens, evidently still unidentified, are believed to have found their way to Paris. Ouvrard was still unable to speak a word of the Nu language and could not bear the taste of maize, the only available food, even though he must have encountered it often enough in his native country. He and his confreres on the Lancang Jiang were diligent collectors of butterflies. It was most pleasing to find that many of the Catholic missionaries busied themselves in collecting material for the advancement of science. In so doing they were certainly not motivated by any desire to supplement their meagre stipends, but by genuine enthusiasm for their subjects, of which they often had considerable knowledge. They differed from their Protestant competitors, hardly any of whom were collectors, in not being completely wrapped up in their somewhat fruitless missionary activities.

We had another steep descent through bamboo thickets to the stream in the Saoa-lumba valley, where the fathers had built a hut at 3450m, though travelling tribesmen had soon used its roof for their campfires. When I came to put the new plates in the cassettes I found to my dismay that they were not of the size which had been stated in the telegram from the suppliers and for which I had already made inserts so that they would fit into my 9 x 12cm cassettes. Fortunately they were too large rather than too small, and I spent some time on that cold moonlit night cutting and filing the inserts to the right

---

[111] A photograph of the Si-la taken by Joseph Rock is reproduced in the book by Peter A. Cox, *The Larger Species of Rhododendron,* London, 1979, p.96.

sizes; next day I was able to set out with my cassettes loaded and ready to take farewell photographs of the beauties of the Nu Jiang.

The track at first ran for some distance along the valley bottom, which was filled with willow thickets, and then climbed steeply eastwards up the hillside into a little cirque. To one side, beyond the stream, we saw a tiny circular lake in the valley, between the canebrake and the last of the trees. Autumn was spreading over the landscape, but still in flower under the bushes was *Jurinea picridifolia*, a new species, and higher up I found *Aconitum pulchellum*, the yellow *Gentiana otophora* and a few other latecomers. The narrow path climbed steeply once more, past the last stunted windswept bushes of scaly-leaved juniper (*Juniperus wallichiana*) to the sharp crest of the Xi-la at 4400m which marks the watershed. The name simply means "bare mountain". The nearby peaks did not exceed 5000m, and as the more distant ranges were shrouded in mist and time was pressing, I remained no longer than was necessary to complete the triangulation and then began to descend the rocky mountainside, after the high range to the north of the Doker-la had revealed some of its snow covered flanks, as if in farewell.

Up there in the snow patches in the folds of the mica-schist which ran parallel with the crest there were still a few solitary blue gentians in flower (*Gentiana decorata, G. phyllocalyx* and the new *G. oreodoxa*), together with *Saussurea obvallata*, a plant with a stout stalk and numerous flower-heads in a nest of papery leaves, and *Polygonum forrestii*, which had kidney-shaped leaves and sizeable white flowers in pseudoumbels. In the chilly streamlets *Pegaephyton sinense* spread its greasy-looking leaves and lax stalks with their broad flat seedpods. In the scree lower down I collected *Aconitum euryanthe*, a new species with large deep blue flowers later becoming even darker violet. The path ran down into the bottom of a high walled rock bowl, then through thickets of rhododendron along a stream, which was so much enlarged by the influx of another from a small ravine to the southwest that the next time we crossed it we had a foot bath. All distant views were hidden, and the valley, here a U-shaped glacial trough, continued eastwards with only minor deviations. On the crest to the left we saw a few conical or diamond-shaped spikes.

All the ground was covered with forest or canebrake, but on every side there were scenes of savage devastation caused by the natural forces of water and snow: there were avalanche corridors with snapped off tree-trunks, bushes half buried in rubble, masses of earth carried down from above, landslides and piles of debris. Where the valley broadened the stream had spread out leaving behind a chaos of gravel and boulders mingled with roots and splint-

ered trees. The porters hurried on towards the warmth of the campfire and I loitered behind, still collecting plants and taking photographs. It was quite dark before I finally reached our dry and tolerably warm campsite below a pasture called Rüshatong. Once they had settled in the men became more cheerful. Wu Suolong tried to memorise a few words of Tibetan starting with the numerals, but like all Chinese he was unable to pronounce the glottal R. Up on the mountain I had told him to ask a porter the name of the pass. "Silarungu" was the reply ("rungu" is roughly equivalent to "pass"), but he reported it to me as "lungu", and Lao Li subsequently distorted the name "Ururu", also given to him in response to an enquiry, into "Ululu". Map-makers cannot be too careful in seeking to avoid such errors[112].

Next morning my porters took with them a bull which the yakherds had overlooked when departing from the pasture on the day before. The track went more steeply down through the valley for a considerable distance. Down here *Abies chensiensis* predominated, in contrast to *A. forrestii* higher up, and some were of gigantic size. One had a trunk no less than 6.5m in circumference. Its height was difficult to judge, but 60m would certainly not be an overestimate, and in many instances the lowest branches hung down in S-shaped curves spreading out for a distance of 10m from the trunk. From the clearings one saw their remarkably narrow tops soaring up above the rest of the forest to heights at least twice as great as the other trees. The valley curved to the left, but the track climbed up its right side for 250m to reach a col named Chranalake at an altitude of 3300m on the sharp crest which ran parallel to the valley, and then plunged in steep zigzags down the arid hillside, which was covered mainly with pines, though there were also some solitary *Pseudotsuga* trees. After passing Niapaton — no more than a few houses — we came to Cigu, where the mission had previously been stationed. An hour's journey up the river brought me once more to my lodgings at Cizhong, where I arrived on 30th September with a splendid haul of plants, a slight cold, grazed hands, three pairs of worn out boots, a tattered coat, tentpoles with all their points broken off and much of my kit soaking wet; I was short of cash but in the best of spirits, insofar as the unforeseeable news of the war permitted any such state of mind. I soon set to work on my boots with thread and penknife, and I also bought a pair of beautiful Tibetan boots, admittedly more as a souvenir than for use.

---

[112] Handel-Mazzetti clearly did make many errors, however, neither his Tibetan nor his Chinese evidently being very fluent (SGH).

Chapter 21. Via Weixi, Shigu and Dali to Kunming

The Lidiping ridge — an encounter with a caravan — government orders — fossil plants — a police search for opium

In Cizhong I packed up my collections as best I could, using sticking plaster to seal the lids of the tin linings inside the crates, and hired ten pack animals and an extra riding horse — the latter to carry Lao Li to Weixi, as his foot was still not completely healed despite the missionaries' care. As there were no professional mafus here I had to scour the whole of Cizhong and Cigu before I found a man who had one horse and another with two or three; and when it came to settling the accounts it was not easy to explain the calculations to them. After three days I at last set off, crossed the rope bridge at Cigu and travelled downstream along the road which I had taken on my outward journey. Growing on rocks among the maquis, in spots where there was not much shade, a pretty orchid (*Coelogyne ovalis*) had opened its pendent fimbriate brown flowers, most of them solitary, but here too the arrival of autumn had brought an end to most flowers and had tinged the foliage with new colours. Down in the valley *Excoecaria acerifolia* was robed in scarlet, and in the mixed woodland on the higher slopes various deciduous trees had assumed brilliant hues of yellow and orange, while the maples had turned dark red. The conifers and broad-leaved evergreens seemed even darker in contrast. After five days on the road I reached Xiao Weixi at noon, and wishing to learn something of the Lisu people I visited one of their villages an hour's journey up the side of the valley (Fig.33). On advice from Père Lesgourgues I took a few photographs in my pocket, as the people were at first very shy and timid, and I wanted to make them understand what I planned to do. When I reached their village they had all fled into the maize fields; all I could do was to take surreptitious snapshots of them between the piles on which their log houses were built. One of the pictures shows a tribesman peering nervously at a photo held out to him by my guide. Most of them wore grey garments of hemp fibre, and men and women alike had puttees round their legs, a few of them having strips of blue and red fabric in them. The men wore a headdress of similar material wound into a short cylindrical tube. In the stretch from Kakatang to Weixi the valley was not so deep and the vegetation was the same as that growing at the same altitude on the Yunnan tableland. Here I found *Cephalotaxus fortunei* again, though at one place only, which must be its most westerly site.

After arriving at Weixi at midday on 10th October I called on the official, who was on friendly terms with the missionaries. I made no protest when he asked me to accept an escort of two armed police as far as Jianchuan, as there had been several robberies on that road and if a traveller had no escort the authorities would disclaim all responsibility. For the journey from there to Dali I found a Chinese caravan willing to take me at a reasonable price, for they would otherwise have had to travel back unloaded, and we set off the very next morning. As money was

running short I was unable to insist on their taking the straight route to Dali, though it would have been of greater interest. In fact the caravanmen said that they were not willing to travel on any but the major road, though this was probably at Lao Li's instigation; he did not want to hear anything more about "little" roads. So we travelled due east up on to the Lidiping (3500m) road, which though it climbed higher was more direct than the road formerly in general use, shown on Davies' map. Gently sloping pastures covered the broad ridge, and between them were extensive forests. The only conifers were spruces, grey with beard lichens, but among them were various broad-leaved trees in brightly coloured autumn garb. The rivulets from the abundant springs on these pastures converged in a shallow trough running northwest along the ridge and forming the uppermost part of the valley which continued past Shogo and joined the Jinsha Jiang at Jizong. Gentians (*Gentiana picta* and others) were the only flowers still open. Situated on a knoll was the police post, a building of some size, as Lidiping was notorious for its bandits; indeed robberies still go on there, and I was informed that the police themselves take part in them. There were splendid vistas over the whole of the bowl-shaped Weixi valley, and eastwards over the small basin of Ludian and down the narrow valley below it as far as the Jinsha Jiang. Photographs enabled me to make important additions and corrections to the map. This part of the broad divide between the Lancang Jiang and the Yangzi has all the characteristics of a secondary range, and though deeply furrowed by valleys it presents a few prominent mountain groups. Owing to the predominance of sandstones and clay-slates the soil, visible everywhere through the sparse woodlands, was red-brown in colour. For a short stretch where it skirted the Ludian basin the watershed formed a narrow crest, and the track led down its steep declivity. On the next day I reached Labikou, where I made an addition to my small ethnological collection — a Naxi Buddha painted on a rough board in the shape of a shovel. The housewife was reluctant to sell it, but the tinkle of dollars assuaged her heartache. Another hour's march brought us to the Jinsha Jiang at Judian.

The track now continued along its valley as far as the bend at Shigu. Alluvial fans from the side valleys alternated with sandy river terraces, and the valley floor was dotted with Naxi villages. Only in a few places was it so narrow that the path had had to be hewn out of the rock, as it was where the limestone snout of Heshiya projected at right angles into the valley. A further bed of limestone, steeply positioned between slates, its top forming the border of the Zhongdian tableland, curved to the west here across the valley, though remaining horizontal. On the road I encountered a seemingly endless Tibetan caravan coming from Batang. When the leading Tibetan and his beasts failed to give way quickly enough, my mafu rushed at him. In his anxiety the Tibetan drew his cleaver, and the mafu threatened to attack him with the iron spit used to hang the cooking pots on, but by yelling at them I managed to separate them in time. No wonder the Tibetans were nervous: not long before, some Tibetan caravanmen had chopped some wood from a tree in a village. Thereupon the villagers had charged at them and shoved forty two of their mules into the river, where they had drowned. The Tibetans then went to the magistrate at Lijiang and demanded that the villagers should pay for the mules, but he decided that, as they had started the quarrel by their thieving, what had happened served them right.

"Wherever they go they cause trouble", declared the Chinese mafu, yet the very next day he himself entered a field beside the road and dug up enough turnips to last for a week or more. I spent the night of 15/16th October at Shigu, at the place where the Jinsha Jiang, surrounded by lesser mountains only 1000m in height, suddenly swings round, almost reversing its direction, and flows on to cut right through the middle of the Lijiang snow range. The weather was cloudy and overcast, and it rained all next day during the crossing to Guanshan.

In Jianchuan I told the soldiers to report to the magistrate; from here on the roads were safe and I would not need them any more. However, two of them came back in great haste and told Lao Li that an order had arrived by telegram directing that I was to be escorted by soldiers to Kunming and at all costs to be prevented from travelling to the Nu Jiang. All this arose from a journey made by a fellow countryman to the southern border of the province, arousing the suspicions of the French and British authorities, who thought he was politically motivated and alerted the Chinese government. Some of their attention spilt over in my direction, though luckily they were two months too late; even today the recollection still gives me a certain mischievous satisfaction.

On 20th October I arrived at Dali and halted for a few days. A servant from the yamen came to ask when I intended to resume my journey; I had not requested an escort, and I had therefore departed without one. The dishonest mafu whom Schneider and I had dismissed in 1914 because of his large-scale frauds, though we retained his horses in partial recompense, was still prowling around Dali, running up debts and telling anyone foolish enough to listen to him that I still owed him $400. Lao Li was scared of him and, before going out one evening, secretly borrowed the Browning automatic which I kept under my bed. I thought I must have mislaid it one night while visiting Père Guilbaud, but when I found it back in its place just after Lao Li had been in my room attending to some minor task, I immediately taxed him with the matter. At this he turned as white as a sheet; he had obviously supposed that his attempted deception had been successful. In Dali I drew out some cash and bought a few Chinese souvenirs, notably some beautifully made teacups and silk embroideries, and a collection of 270 Chinese drugs of plant origin; as an aid to their identification I also bought for 30 cents a three volume book with illustrations. I sent Lao Li back to his home in Lijiang with a note to Kok asking him to send the standard barometer by post to me in

Kunming. He was still very anxious about his foot and uncertain whether it would ever recover completely.

On 27th October I hired a boat to go fishing for plankton in Lake Erhai and learn something of the flowering plants: besides various inconspicuous underwater species I found *Xystrolobos yunnanensis*, *Boottia yunnanensis*, *Nymphoides peltata* and *Polygonum amphibium* growing there. I sailed on to Xiaguan before joining the new caravan, which had completed only half a day's march. Next day, because of this delay, we were overtaken by nightfall during the descent to Hongya and had to unpack the paraffin lamp from its box so as to find the ill-marked path; fortunately nothing got lost. Hongya is situated to the south of the main watershed of the Yunnan tableland in the territory of the Red River, and the pass which we had to cross, some 2600m in altitude, is the highest and most prominent on the road from Dali to Kunming. After the traveller has climbed up again on to the plateau there are only minor ups and downs from then on. As we were crossing the hilly limestone country between Xiangyun and Yunnanyi, the last terrain of its kind until just before the capital, a wolf ran across the road, at exactly the same spot as in the previous year. From there on limestone was replaced by sand, sandstones and marls. Between Nanhua and Lühe and also just after the latter village we again saw carbonized and silicified tree-stumps and portions of fallen tree-trunks embedded in seams of coal which were lying at a remarkably steep angle. A little digging with the plant trowel in the marls above the coal seam soon yielded some well preserved impressions of dicotyledonous leaves, though only in fragments. But I was not really equipped for such brittle specimens — how was I to transport them? A solution was soon found. I took off the waistcoat which I used to wear on those cool mornings and evenings, wrapped the pieces individually in it and put the whole package in a saddlebag. The village official in Lühe was a cousin of my servant and that evening I had an opportunity of observing an incident typical of the conditions existing in China. The police entered the hostelry in a routine search for opium smokers; but when, squinting through a crack in the door, they recognized Lao Li engrossed in his favourite pastime, they hastily withdrew.

Having arrived in Chuxiong I soaked the fossils in paraffin and went to bed early, as I had no plants to put in the press. Late that night, when all honest men were asleep, the lijin official appeared. He wanted to see my caravan pass and asked how it was that I had arrived there without an official escort — "like a thief", as the xianzhang (town clerk) had allegedly said. Lao Li replied that I was asleep and sent him away, telling him he could come back in daylight if there was anything he wanted. I left the official in no doubt of my attitude, namely that I was unwilling to waste any time on the matter. On departing I was provided with a messenger from the yamen carrying a letter. Whether because of this or because of an independent initiative on the part of the official in Guangtong, a large party of police entered the inn while I was there; in any event, their commander suspected that I had opium in my boxes and wanted to open them with his Chinese keys. Though small in stature, Lao Li was extremely useful in such crises; he argued with him for some time, then began to revile him in the most frightful language, and finally seized the fellow by his collar, though he was much taller than himself, whereupon the policeman withdrew apologetically with his entire party. Having caught two French missionaries smuggling opium — and I know of others for whom it was almost a regular occupation — it is not surprising that the Chinese had begun to suspect every European traveller of smuggling. If a report that I was under suspicion were to have reached Kunming ahead of me, my entry into that city might have been held up or might have attracted undue notice — complications which would have been doubly disagreeable because of the political tensions between ourselves and the French and English, who were on the lookout for any pretext to harm our good name.

On arriving at Shezi, the next overnight stop, I was glad to find that I was still in time to despatch an express letter to the German consul in Kunming informing him of the situation — the only other way would have been to send a special messenger — and it was an easy matter for him to arrange for an order to be issued to the guard on the city gate instructing them to let me and my caravan pass in without hindrance. For the greater part of the next two days I had a succession of "soldiers" as escorts. Most of them were ridiculous figures with little in the way of effective weapons: one man had a gigantic rifle with a broken butt and another had a pike three and a half metres long. The nearer we came to Kunming the worse were the inns along the road. There were still a few pretty spots near Lüfeng: an ancient bridge with several arches across the stream coming from Dazhuangkou, and then a fine view of the little river coming from Luozi and winding through a S-shaped ravine. This I saw standing on a crest which was clothed with steppe grassland, still green although it was early November, interspersed with a few subtropical shrubs. From there on the landscape was barren, though at the sides of the valleys there were patches of colour created by thinly laminated, gently sloping layers of marl and beds of red sandstone above them. Laoyaguan was a sizeable place, though not shown on the maps, situated just before the ascent to the watershed above the river Pudu He. Above the town I found the interesting *Eriolaena malvacea* growing in a hedge. Living in holes in the earth by the wayside were lepers, eerie and repellent figures who lived by begging from passers-by. In front of us we saw the Xi Shan range and on the left, after we had passed Anning, the mountain separating us from Fumin rose straight up from the edge of the track. Between them, slightly to the left, the Biqiguan saddle cut through the ridge, and on 8th November I re-entered Kunming, where my friend Stiebritz once more gave me accommodation.

PART III 1916

To the Frontier of Upper Burma

Chapter 22. To Lijiang with a Visit to Mount Cang Shan

Yunnan's war against Beijing — attempts to obstruct my departure — cook and caravan — fossil plants in a coal seam at Lühe — Dali marble — Mohammedans — on Mount Cang Shan — a trip on the lake

It was a conjuncture of circumstances — fortunate for me though unfortunate for others — that made possible the realisation of my wildest dreams in the summer of 1916. The leisurely calm of the little city of Kunming lasted for less than a month after my return. At the beginning of December we attended the funeral of our fellow countryman Maiwald. Typhoid fever carried him off before his time, the immoderate eating and drinking so prevalent in the East having enveloped his body in a thick layer of fat which proved impermeable to injections. He was laid to rest on the slopes of Mount Changchong Shan in a burial ground for Chinese Protestants. Otherwise little of note happened in our little community. However, various excursions including all-day rides into the country gave me an opportunity of adding to my collections, and I joined the German consul on a three day hunting trip to Zhongduilong near Yanglin from 4th to 6th February.

In December 1915 President Yuan Shikai, hoping to become Emperor of China, sought support from the Allies by offering to declare war on Germany. He needed to have himself formally elected as Emperor, and for that purpose he issued orders to the provinces. These secret orders were subsequently published in Yunnan: his supporters were to receive liberal handouts of cash and government jobs, and the opposition were to be locked up without delay. Titles of nobility were to be reintroduced, new medals and coins had already been struck and the coronation festivities had been arranged. We Germans would certainly have been in an unenviable situation, for Yuan Shikai was a militarist who detested foreigners. Then General Cai E, a man from South China well known as leader of the revolution against the monarchy, journeyed unobtrusively to Yunnan. At the end of 1915 he persuaded Tang Rirao, the dujun, to deliver an ultimatum to Yuan Shikai calling on him to declare his intentions, and to back it by ordering his troops to march to the northeast. As this brought no response, he then declared war on Beijing, claiming that his object was to save the republic. The English government, through their consul general, offered him three million dollars if he would abandon his plans, but he rejected the offer with feigned indignation. Moving more swiftly than anyone expected, his troops marched out of Yunnan and occupied Yibin, its garrison and local governor having fled on receiving word of their approach, and other towns in Sichuan. Before long all the south had rallied to his support. Unrest and disorder spread throughout China. In Kunming the streets were bedecked with flags every time a senior officer marched out with a few soldiers, but elsewhere in the province, although it had

previously had the reputation of being one of the safest, bands of deserters began to roam the country robbing travellers and interfering with the flow of traffic. Prices also rose considerably. However, Cai E's activities delayed China's entry into the European war for many months and he thus unknowingly rendered valuable service in enabling me to continue my scientific work in China. A huge obelisk has been erected in his memory on Mount Yuelu Shan near Changsha in Hunan, and we too should remember him gratefully.

The flora of the Nu Jiang region had proved so rich and unusual, although the flowers had been past their best at the time of my visit, that even before leaving I had resolved to spend the next summer there, or if this were impossible, to send two competent plant collectors to work there. As the authorities even in 1915 had looked askance on my travels, though admittedly for understandable reasons, I realised that they would now do all they could to prevent me from even approaching my goal, and I had to keep my plans secret. However, so as not to attract suspicion at the very outset, my departure from Kunming had to be open and above-board. Weiss, the consul, procured a pass for the two collectors valid for the territory ruled by the tusi of Yezhi, and gave it to me to hand to them if I was obliged to send them out on their own. The authorities at first boggled at the idea of issuing even this document, and then drafted it in most equivocal terms: it stated that they were not to be permitted to enter the district where the frontier between China and Burma had not been demarcated, and that if they engaged in any activity other than botanising they were to be reported to the aliens control office. I wrote to all the missionaries with whom I was acquainted telling them in some detail of the tasks which my collectors were to perform and asking them to remind them of their duties from time to time and to do what they could to assist them in their work. I therefore felt that I could expect some results from this project, provided the collectors succeeded in reaching the Nu Jiang territory ruled by the tusi of Yezhi. However, from the experience of Forrest and especially Schneider, I realised that the results achieved by collectors would fall short of what I could accomplish if I were on the spot myself.

I had already met the new commissioner for aliens — on his visit to the consulate I had watched him picking his nose and flicking the bits at the walls until it started to bleed so briskly that he had to use the wastepaper basket to catch the drips — and I had told him I might perhaps go to Lijiang for the summer, to which proposal he had raised no objection. As it was now clear that there was no prospect of my returning to Europe in the near future, the consul informed him of my planned departure date and asked for the usual letter of safe conduct. The authorities then declared that they could not now allow me to travel, as Lijiang was too near the border of Sichuan, with which Yunnan was at war, and the Burmese frontier, and naively pointed out that plants did not grow along major routes but near minor tracks, in places inhabited by "ill-disposed barbarians". Such reasoning carried no more weight with Weiss than with me, and he even suggested that if necessary I should simply travel without a permit; I asked him to tell them that my sponsors would hold me responsible if I failed to make good use of the money [113] which had recently been remitted to me, and that I could not postpone my departure even for a short time, for the results would then fall short of what such an expenditure might be expected to produce and, as human life in Europe was now so cheap, it would be cowardly not to accept slightly greater risks than usual in order to attain my lofty aims. The authorities then acquiesced, and I felt relieved that all my costly preparations had not been in vain. In reality nothing could have been more favourable for the execution of my plans than the state of disorder of the province, for under the prevailing conditions many officials paid little heed to the government's decrees.

Footgear, clothing and equipment had to be renewed. European products such as canned food — I needed at least one month's supply as iron rations — had soared to enormous prices; I had to pay 2.50 dollars a dozen for ordinary 8 x 10½ cm Ilford photographic plates, and quinine, which Dr Vadon, the French doctor, willingly supplied, cost four times as much as the year before. Pawelka provided me with a cook who had given him satisfactory service on his travels. Though he could not act as interpreter he was resourceful and energetic. I now knew something of the country and the people along my route. If I needed help in a difficult conversation I could turn to one of the numerous missionaries with whom J was already acquainted, but for the ordinary needs of the journey my grasp of Chinese was by now sufficient, and what I chiefly required was a man who could travel with me through the mountains on foot. Unfortunately, as later transpired, this fellow cared more for the bottle than for my cuisine. He finished all his work with amazing speed simply because he wanted to get back to his brandy. The chickens which he placed before me were half raw and still red with blood, the potatoes were green and the meat was impossibly tough. His bread began to stink after two days and turned ropy, and his cakes, which he baked himself to save money, were still worse. He lacked the first inklings of cleanliness, always a difficult matter to bring home to Chinese domestics; his habit of packing the grooming brush among the crockery was the least of his offences against hygiene. He had a high-pitched voice and whenever any other Chinese were present he showed off the few words of French which he knew, though he usually got them wrong. His favourite phrase was

"il-y-en-a-pas", by which he meant: "one cannot, I don't want to, I don't know" and other negatives of the same kind. These were not his only imbecilities: on the second morning of the journey he bought four hens at a low price but tied them to one of the loads so clumsily that by noon three of them were dead. Pawelka had sold me a horse cheaply for him, and for my own use I had bought from the consul one of his splendid Sichuan ponies, which proved an excellent mount. When I was recruiting the necessary caravan of ten pack animals it counted strongly in my favour that unlike other Europeans I always treated my men well, provided they did their jobs properly. My headman from the previous year's caravan rushed to join me and, although prices were now much higher, allowed me to beat him down to an increase of only five cents. He agreed to take me "to Lijiang, then for ten days further on main routes". As plant collector I initially took on an exceptionally dull-witted and idiotic fellow, since I expected to find Jin Jinwen in Guangtong and engage him. Wu Suoling was unwilling to go on any more journeys because his father was now too old; besides he had a travelling cookshop and probably felt content with his memories of the Nu Jiang trip; at any rate, he told everyone that in Beixailue the price of maize was one Sichuan rupee.

On the afternoon of 27th April 1916 the policeman on duty at the west gate bowed deeply, though without removing his cap, and asked, "Where to?". "If you only knew!" I thought to myself, but I had no good wishes to spare for him or the dujun as I set off on that hot and arid day. For most of the time I had two "soldiers" attached to me as an escort, but so far as I could see no special measures had been taken to check my movements. The fragrant *Symplocos paniculata* was in flower everywhere, as were *Dichotomanthes tristaniaecarpa* (the only representative of its genus), *Diospyros mollifolia* with greenish flowers, *Phoebe neurantha*, *Picrasma quassioides* and, further on, the low growing *Jasminum beesianum* with red flowers. I met a troop of local militia marching without weapons, their only military insignia being a label sewn on their clothing; their officer was asleep in his carrying chair. As Jin Jiangwen was no longer in Guangtong I sent a telegram from Chuxiong to Kok asking him to send Lao Li to meet me in Dali.

Lithocarpus dealbata, *Quercus franchetii* and other oaks were now putting forth their new shoots, which were arranged almost in whorled patterns, and in the little woods where they grew the ground was coloured yellow brown by a layer of young leaves which had dropped from them. Here and there were trees of *Castanopsis delavayi* in full bloom, looking just like sweet chestnuts. In the dry weather now prevailing I noticed that many of the shrubs, in particular *Osteomeles schwerinae*, growing on this soft friable marly soil stood on little hillocks held together by their roots, while all the earth around them had been swept away by wind and water — a phenomenon commonly seen in desert regions. I spent May 5th and 6th in Lühe studying the fossil flora of the coal seam where I had discovered it in 1915 but had then lacked the time to collect more than a few specimens. This year, forty metres below the coal seam containing the dicotyledon leaves, I found another marl stratum with older remains, among them a twig probably belonging to the genus

---

[113]The Academy of Sciences in Vienna sent him 6000 crowns on 24th February 1916.

Palissya, closely related to *Taiwania*. It was not exactly a pleasure to toil for two days in dust and burning sun, scraping and hammering, and the yield of usable pieces was meagre, as the marl was extremely brittle. I was glad to quit my lodgings — a hot, stuffy hole pervaded by an atrocious stench from the pigsty. However, the local people and passing travellers — the place was directly adjacent to the main road — were most friendly and in no way troublesome. I collected a few more carbonized plants from an outcrop of coal to the west of Lühe. As regards living plants, there were hardly any that I had not seen before. The weather was hot, often windy and dusty, and only once was there a shower of rain. I encountered some fair-sized parties of recruits wearing clean new uniforms. They had no rifles, first because there were not enough to go round and secondly because the authorities were afraid they would sell them. Although I had instructed my cook to tell anyone in authority that I was simply going to Lijiang for the summer, he was all too eager to boast of our projected trip to Weixi and Zhongdian, and I repeatedly had to remind him to be discreet.

I reached Dali on 12th May and was immediately visited by the official who had held the corresponding post in Zhongdian in 1915. He walked in smoking a cigarette and wearing a dandified European suit with an unbelievably high stand-up collar. Our conversation proceeded somewhat lamely as my servant had chosen that moment to absent himself. While in Dali I received a letter from Bishop de Gorostarzu of Kunming, to whom I had written a farewell letter expressing the hope that his missionaries would give me as friendly a reception as I had enjoyed in 1915 — thanks to his letter of recommendation — especially as I was now acquainted with them. His letter now advised me to resort to them only in emergencies, for he suspected that their Christian charity might in some cases have suffered from the effects of the war. However, in the districts where I hoped to work I was totally dependent of their help as go-betweens, and I must say that in the prevailing conditions I could not have wished for greater helpfulness; but for their fear of the civil authorities, they would even have offered me hospitality.

On 15th May I set out to climb Cang Shan, a long range rising steeply to the west of the town and running parallel to the lake. It was a sombre-coloured mountain, its core built of mica-schist and gneiss; between them, halfway up, the famous Dali marble was quarried. Polishing reveals multicoloured veining and mottling, resembling sections cut through bracken roots, though chiefly in reddish-brown and green, and without much strain on the imagination it is possible to make out figures of men and animals, trees, lakes, clouds and so forth. The Chinese give each piece a label saying what the figures are supposed to represent, and often embellish them with a few strokes of the paint brush, though pieces which have been touched up are less valuable. Several pieces are usually mounted together in a wooden frame for hanging on the wall; alternatively, single slabs are used as tabletops, or fitted together to make flower vases or similar objects. At the foot of the mountain, less than half an hour distant from the town, we came to one of the gently sloping alluvial fans which spread out from its short steep parallel gulleys as far as the lake. Stretching far into the distance were graves dating from the Mohammedan uprisings which took

place in the second half of the nineteenth century and depopulated the country for many years. They were finally put down by General Ma, who based his operations on Dali and was now worshipped as a god in a temple in the town. At the time of my visit the Mohammedans were once more very numerous, but they were entirely peaceable; they seldom put up signboards in Arabic (I saw some at the railway station in Kaiyuan) and only once — a few days previously in Xiaguan — did I meet one of them wearing a red fez. The slopes of the Cang Shan had been deforested to a considerable altitude and the ascent in the hot sun was not enjoyable. Some 600m above the town was a gleaming white temple, visible from afar. I rode up to it, sent my coolie back with the pony and continued the climb on foot with a bendi-boy [114] from the mountain woodcutters as my guide. There was in fact no proper path, and I had to use a timber slide or chute which had cut through the scrub and the humus layer down to the stratified rock beneath and ran in a straight line steeply upwards. The mountainside was dotted with a small sulphur-yellow rhododendron (*R. trichocladum*) and a larger one with fiery red blooms (*R. neriiflorum*). Everywhere between them were light green bamboos, willows with inconspicuous flowers, *Benzoin sikkimensis*, *Ilex delavayi*, *Viburnum cordifolium* and the white bells of *Vaccinium* and *Pieris* species. Immediately to the right there was a splendid view into the ravine, with the deep yellow *Rhododendron sulphureum* growing on the rocks at its top. As there were only a few trickles of water, the day's booty — not very large — was somewhat dried up by the time we got home. Though fir forest extended down the slopes of the ravine to about 3500m, on the spur the track ran upwards in its shade and then turned down to the left towards a spring, becoming fainter and fainter. However, I was obliged to climb straight upwards along the rounded crest of the spur, making my way through the forest which was here quite without a path of any kind. This meant a tortuous scramble through dense rhododendron undergrowth, slipping on hidden roots or sinking into deep cushions of moss (*Plagiochila* spp., *Herberta delavayi*, *Lepidozia pinnata*, *Anastrophyllum donianum*, *Dicranum perfalcatum*, *Rhacomitrium javanicum*, *Breutelia yunnanensis*) and then dragging myself up again over the slippery unstable earth by grasping the gnarled branches of the deep purple *Rhododendron haematodes*. The upper part of the spur was relatively sharp and rather dry, and here the undergrowth was formed by large cushions of *Diapensia bulleyana*, now opening its sessile yellow flowers. Noon had passed before I reached a minor summit at about 4050m, from which the route at first descended a little and then climbed again very steeply to the main crest some 250m higher (Fig.34). Rhododendrons and willows covered it thickly, extending to the very top beyond the firs. It was hardly feasible to reach it in a one day trip, and as I was not equipped to spend the night out-of-doors I turned back, having gained my chief objective — a general impression of the plant communities. Up on top, although no more than a small snowpatch still persisted, not even the rhododendrons were in flower. As I approached the town wall the mafu

---

[114]"Bendi" is a Chinese expression for "native", free from derogatory overtones. The boy was probably a Bai. (Handel-Mazzetti's note). "Bendi" simply means "of (or from) this place." (SGH).

came to meet me with my pony. I was surprised and pleased at his unexpected thoughtfulness, the more so as my new climbing boots were too tight and pressed uncomfortably, though that problem did not last long: they got so much use that they were soon broken in.

Because of a lame dog which kept falling into the cesspit and then running about the yard, the whole house stank abominably, and after a rest day spent in putting my plants in the press I was glad to depart. For the first day of my onward journey to Lijiang I went by boat, as I wanted to collect the deep water plankton of Lake Erhai. I planned to sail northeast across the deepest part of the lake, reaching the opposite shore at the foot of a steep mountainside, while the caravan went ahead to Shangguan. However, the wind got up and raised quite big waves. The boatman was unwilling to venture into open water and I had to be content with trawling at a depth of a few metres and collecting the surface plankton. The latter was obviously much better developed than in the previous autumn. The same green *Desmidiaceae* (in particular *Closterium aciculare*) made the water look quite turbid when viewed in the right light, and in every handful which I scooped up the slender, sickle-shaped unicellular plants were visible to the naked eye — indeed they almost clogged the net after a minute's trawling. Among the day's finds was a new genus of microscopic crayfish (*Handeliella paradoxa*); its nearest relatives are marine. Waiting for me at the landing place at Shangguan was the deputy commander of the local police. Without saying a word, he accompanied me to the inn, where my servant told me that during the journey two men from a caravan which had been overtaking ours had pushed our pack animals to the side of the track, and one of our loads had rolled down the hillside. He had at once had the men arrested, and now they were brought before me. As there was probably just as much blame on our side as theirs, I felt that all I could do was to tell them what I thought about the matter, and let them go. They thanked me on bended knee, glad to escape a flogging. The policeman fetched a carpenter and ordered him to repair the crates by next morning; they were quite badly split, but by fortunate chance their fragile contents were undamaged.

Once again I encountered numerous recruits, not yet in uniform; exceptionally large numbers had been levied from the Lijiang district, as the authorities knew that the Naxi were not seriously opposed to conscription. Next day I was met by Lao Li, who had reached Dali before me and stupidly departed again. With him was another quite young boy, who had joined him partly because every Chinese and, so it seemed, every native tribesman always had a companion with him, and also because he wanted to offer his services, though this was contrary to the wishes of Kok, who had already selected the best of Forrest's collectors for me. With the latter thought in mind, and also because I noticed that he had an eye infection, I did not even consider taking him. I chose the main route via Heqing, which crossed the Heishanmen range by the Sanshishao pass at 3275m, running through limestone and sandstone and passing to the north of Mount Ma'an Shan, outside the zone of volcanic rock from which the latter is built.

On 29th May there were still very few plants in flower, among them some willows, a white-flowered climber (*Schizandra grandiflora*) and, on the limestone rocks of the descent the opulent *Primula rufa* with egg-yolk yellow blooms and sticky glands which gave it an aromatic odour.

I arrived in Lijiang on 21st May and avoided any contact with the new magistrate, an old-style Chinese of somewhat fanatical religious outlook. Since he was in dispute with Kok over the erection of a mission building and as everyone knew that I was a friend of Kok, it can hardly have surprised him that I failed to pay him a call. I let it be known that I was spending the summer in Nguluke, but was retaining my caravan since I thought I might have to return to Kunming at short notice. I then got rid of the wretched fellow who had supposedly been a plant collector; I dismissed him with a generous reward and sent him back to Kunming. However, my cook claimed to be his friend and wanted to go back with him; it took all Kok's powers of persuasion to induce him to stay.

Chapter 23. Up the Yangzi and Over the Lenago Pass to the Lancang Jiang

Plant collectors — a clandestine departure — the upper Yangzi valley — orchids — through the Ronsha side valley — a clash with the Lisu in Shuba — flowers and vistas on the Lenago pass — in the Lisu village of Aoalo — adverse impressions

To lull the authorities into a feeling of security I remained at Nguluko — known to them as a village favoured by botanists — for four days, a time which passed swiftly in further preparations for my journey. Beside Lao Li I employed the two other collectors whom Kok had provided, together with my landlord He and the local headman Lü, in the task of folding the plant paper which I had just bought. They were both sedate elderly men, experts on the plants of the Yulong Shan, but they understood only a little Chinese, they were somewhat slow on the uptake and He was obviously shortsighted. Lü was the only one of my men who could write Chinese at all. Though my servant could read

Chinese a little — and even notices in French — he was unable to paint Chinese characters. Forrest's best collector was Rao, an extremely good-natured fellow whom I commissioned to make a collection of the rare plants of the Yulong Shan over the next three months.

Although I did not wish to devote my own time to this already well botanized mountain, it was now clear that Schneider's collections from the area were unlikely to reach any botanical institute in our own country. The material gathered by Rao later proved most useful, since water had got into one of the crates packed in 1914 and had spoilt a large proportion of my own collection from the mountain. Plenty of men offered their services, among them a ne'er-do-well who assumed a false name, realising that I knew the names of all the men in the village who were of any use. Another fellow volunteered to feed my horses, a task which he, like all his compatriots, obviously thought of as the be-all and end-all of a groom's duties. However, my three collectors were quite enough. One of them could easily attend to the drying of the plants and look after the horses while I was absent with the other two for long periods. During this stay in Nguluke I did not get even a glimpse of the snow peak.

When I departed on 28th May I gave Bede as my destination, so that if the authorities received orders not to let me travel any further, their soldiers would waste two days on a wild goose chase through uninhabited country before realising that they were on a false scent, and I would have the start which I required. I left Nguluke by the road to Baishui, but once outside the village I said I had decided not to take that road after all, as there might be bandits there. Then I said I wanted to go via Ganhaizi, and finally, as there might be bandits there too, that I was going via Axi. All the people, wherever they were, hence believed that I had gone in some other direction. Lao Li understood my intentions, but my servant soon forgot what information he was supposed to give out, or thought he knew better, but as he had only the vaguest idea of my real destinations he caused very little harm — and in fact no one bothered about me. Soldiers with the red cap-bands of the revolutionary army were guarding the Muxie [115] pass (2875 m) between Lashi ba and Axi, but they did not even ask where I was going. The pines growing here were once again coloured red by the parasitic *Loranthus caloreas*, but this time it was not the flowers but the previous year's berries which gave them their colour. Axi stretched to the right (down the valley) along an old river terrace some distance above the water. The ferry, situated at its lower end, took me across to the left bank of the Jinsha Jiang, along which I planned to travel upstream, for had I taken the main route to Weixi I might have been given away by one of the officials, soldiers or postmen travelling on that road. At the ferry I tried to give the impression that I was travelling downstream, but my attempts at deception were frustrated by the curiosity of the ferrymen and the stupidity of my own. From then on I gave the name of another, far distant place as my destination, but happily all these precautions proved unnecessary.

The water was low and had exposed broad sandbanks along the river banks, notably near Judian, where its bed widened to two kilometres and it split into several winding channels. Earlier in the journey the mountainous country to the southwest had risen steeply from the river towards the high mountain group known as Labako or Luotui Shan, but near Judian it became lower and less rugged, though on this side (to the northeast) the rim of the Zhongdian plateau gained height steadily. The weather was hot and dry, with brief downpours now and then, and once there was a dust storm which blotted out the entire valley. The vegetation was somewhat dreary, and most of the more interesting drought-loving plants seemed to be absent. Just above Judian the straight segment of the river ended and it continued in zigzag bends. Above Keluan, at the starting point of a steep track over the Kosiso pass to Xiao Zhongdian, there was an enormous crag of mica schist [116] lying on the inside of a sharp bend in the river, the waters surging round its foot and its crest crowned by a little temple. This scene was made even more picturesque by the pendent racemes of the subtropical orchid *Dendrobium clavatum*, which sprinkled the rocks with flecks of egg-yolk yellow. The last of the Naxi villages were small, and in Meka one of the elders, a man with a huge goitre, had to intervene to quell the chatter of two hideous old hags before I was able to find lodging in the least uncomfortable house in the place; apart from them the people were extraordinarily friendly. The valley became more romantic in appearance; on the right, in some stretches the steep edge of the Zhongdian plateau plunged straight down to the river, while on the left a rock bluff seemed to bar its course. Behind that, glittering in the distance, was the lamasery of Xianshendong, situated on a sharp spur which I clearly remembered from the previous year. This spur, located just above Jizong, projected between the Jinsha Jiang and the tributary coming from Xialapu. It dominated the valley, though it was small in comparison with the mountains in the background. At this point we entered Tibetan territory, insofar as Tadsa, a large Tibetan village, was situated on the opposite side of the valley, though our route climbed up the uninhabited valleyside, bypassed the narrow defile where the river twice broke through a vertical limestone bed, and led down a narrow, steep and exceedingly exposed path zigzagging between rock bands, to reach the river again some distance below the Jizong ferry, opposite the rock bluff mentioned above [117]. The water was now shallow and calm, and our crossing proceeded smoothly and without delay. That afternoon, after five days on the road from Lijiang, I was once again given accommodation by the Tibetan "prince". I now learned that he was a tusi and that the Tibetan, Pumi, Naxi and Lisu tribesmen living in an area five days' journey in circumference were his subjects. Together with my servant I heard him talking about a telegram which had come from Kunming to Zhongdian, but so as to avoid arousing suspicion that it might concern me I took care not to ask any questions. He would probably have said that it applied to someone else.

As the route from here onwards did not simply follow the river but climbed over a spur jutting out from the mountain on which the temple stood, the tusi gave me a guide for the next stage. He made no attempt to dissuade me from travelling on to my destination, which I now truthfully admitted — Shuba

---

[115] Mbo-shi on Rock's map.

[116] "a triangular rock islet about 150 feet high and crowned by a temple". Rock, p.291.

[117] See Rock, Plate 156, "The Yangtze at Ch'i-tsung".

on the crossing to the Lancang Jiang. However, he must have sent a message to Weixi, for, as Père Monbeig later told me, news of my passing through Jizong reached Weixi in an incredibly short time. Above Jizong the valley of the Jinsha Jiang, here known by its Tibetan name Dre Qu, becomes an extremely narrow gorge, and after the sharp bend below Meti it is almost straight, though the slightest bends are enough to block the view of the river where it runs between convex slopes, even when surveyed from elevated spots from which the intersecting ridges can be traced far into the distance. For a stretch of some 25 km the only habitations along the valley floor were isolated houses, occupied here and there by Lisu; the villages were situated higher up on the slopes, where they were less steep. The track, built of slabs of mica schist, led up and down the rock faces, sometimes climbing to a considerable height, and though it was of ample breadth my caravanmen had their work cut out, especially by one horse which repeatedly threatened to stagger over the edge and was rescued only by seizing its tail and dragging it back to the middle again. For long stretches, where bushes shaded the rocks, the same yellow-flowered orchid (*Dendrobium clavatum*) was growing in dense clumps. Scattered among them were solitary plants of *Vanda rupestris*, a new species of orchid with white and pink flowers and subulate leaves, its spongy white anchoring roots clasping the rock like tentacles. As on the Lancang Jiang, there was a well developed maquis of trees and shrubs with small leathery leaves. It extended far up the side valley which debouched near a village called Totyü. At this point the Yangzi emerges from a trackless limestone ravine which continues for some 10 km to the northeast. The high mountain range to the northwest of Zhongdian plunges down into this gorge in an exceedingly steep slope for about 2400 m. Beyond the gorge the main road to Benzilan and Dêqên led through the side valley and I at first followed it. The river was about the same size as the one at Xialapu, but above Ronsha it flowed from the opposite direction (from the north).

Gebauer was the only Westerner who had previously traversed and surveyed the Jinsha Jiang valley up to this point, including the lower stretch of its lateral valley, and as I was uncertain what had become of his records I repeated the survey. The Tibetan villages consisted of large houses similar to those near Zhongdian. Ronsha was quite a sizeable place, but the people were not very hospitable and communication was difficult. A Tibetan beggar and ballad singer gave a little help as an interpreter, but he was not really of much use. Then along came a Chinese pedlar who said that I would be able to take my caravan to Yezhi on the Lancang Jiang as the track had been repaired this year at the orders of the magistrate at Weixi — *"by the Chinese, you see Sir, so it must be good"*, my servant assured me. However, I did not expect much from their work for I was well aware that the Tibetans do not let their paths get as dilapidated as the Chinese do. From the

same source I learnt that Shuba, a place whose position I knew, was a Lisu village and no caravan animals would be available there.

This news had two aspects. It meant that I would reach the Lancang Jiang sooner and would easily be able to find a Tibetan caravan there, though that would have been difficult here. I could have taken a caravan from here as far as Cizhong without changing, but orders to prevent me from going any further might well have reached the Lancang Jiang, and on their return journey from here my men would very soon give away my presence. Accordingly I decided in favour of speed and on 6th June resumed my journey without halting, soon turning into a minor valley coming from the west. Here too trees grew on the rocks and *Pseudotsuga wilsoniana* was not uncommon. For the first time I found *Actinidia callosa* in flower; it is a climber belonging to the tropical family *Dilleniaceae* with pendent red and white-edged flowers like small roses. My pony began to limp and I found that one hind leg was affected by malanders, an inflammatory condition caused by the negligence of Chinese grooms; because of it I had to walk much of the way. After taking the wrong path we arrived at the little village of Shuba, high up on the steep hillside at 3000m, just as dusk was coming on. My servant came to meet me with a Lisu tribesman who kindly offered to show me the next part of the route. However, I had to spend the night there as there were no houses further on. The people cheerfully moved the beam of a treadmill and I unrolled my bed under their projecting roof. The interiors of their houses were extremely cramped and black with soot, and, having had enough of the hot weather at lower altitudes, I did not feel inclined to sleep next to their perpetually burning fire. My men lodged with the owner of the first house and I engaged him as my guide for the following day. He spoke a few words of the Naxi language, but it was not easy to communicate with the other villagers, and there was not nearly enough forage or other supplies for sale.

Later that night, when I was in bed, my men came to me and complained that a man belonging to a group of seven or eight Lisu armed with long swords and crossbows had struck He on the arm with a piece of wood; they were hence afraid to take the horses through the village to the water. They were plainly at fault in two respects: during a friendly conversation they must have clapped one of the Lisu on the shoulder or plucked at his sleeve; the Lisu regard such contracts as serious misdemeanours, and touching a chief is an insult punishable by death. Secondly, why was it that the mafu had only now remembered his beasts, long after attending to his own needs? As they had previously drunk from the stream below the village I told him to leave them till the morning. I saw no need to get involved in nocturnal adventures and I must admit that, remembering the evil reputation which the Lisu have had since the murder of Brunhuber and Schmitz[118], I lay awake much of that night thinking of the situations which might arise and how to deal with them, and listening to various noises. The reception which the villagers gave me was perfectly friendly; indeed I was impressed by the fact that they did not flock round and stare at me, perhaps because of their better manners. The men wore grey felt hats in a great variety of shapes, some of them just like our loden hats.

It was late before we got away, and just outside the village, for no apparent reason, one of the mules slipped off the track. The tin boxes bounced down the cultivated hillside in mighty leaps for a good sixty metres and the mule itself rolled only a little less far. The wooden saddle broke and one of the boxes disappeared further down where the slope steepened. I expected to find it lying shattered in the stream, but it had caught in some trees. All this caused nearly an hour's delay, and when we came to another steep place the men had to shoulder the heavier loads. At first the route led through mixed woodland, then uphill across humus-rich turf and through fir woods. It was 2 o'clock before we halted for lunch, a little below the crest of the divide, which reached 4050 m. Rising somewhat towards the north and falling a little towards the south, the crest on this side spread out in broad spurs and was abundantly wooded. Two branch valleys, one from the north and the other from the south, began not far away and united just below the village to form the main Shuba valley. Up on top a cold wind was blowing, and although it was June 7th there was still no vegetation bordering the rivulets; the succulent grey rootstocks of a roseroot, as thick as a man's arm and about a metre long, lay exposed on the ground. A few plants had put out flowers before their leaves, among them *Rhododendron beesianum, R. aischro-peplum, R. pholidotum, R. chaetomallum, Primula brevifolia* and, growing in the moss, the dainty creeping *Hemiphragma heterophyllum.*

The track now led southwards for a considerable distance along the ridge, traversing a strip of limestone at the actual crossing, which Gebauer called "Lenago". At this spot *Meconopsis pseudointegrifolia, Fritillaria cirrhosa, Dipoma iberideum* and *Gentiana bella* were in flower. Growing in dense colonies, *Primula calliantha* tinted the floor of the fir forest carmine red for long stretches. The divide sloped steeply down towards the Lancang Jiang valley, with rock precipices in places, and for the most part the spurs which separated the short lateral valleys of the Lancang Jiang did not emerge until we

had descended for some distance. Frequent downpours allowed only a brief glimpse upstream towards the multiple peaks of the range which was to be my next area of work. Opposite us, the Lancang Jiang—Nu Jiang (Mekong—Salween) divide formed an enormous wall not far short of 5000 m in height, crowned with dark pyramids and spires, but there was apparently a broad, less rugged plateau above the sources of the Sololo valley. The route now led straight down for well over 1000 m, the track descending in short zigzags only a few paces from one turn to the next, so steep and stony that it was hard to keep one's footing. At first it ran beneath trees of *Juniperus recurva* and then across the humus-rich leaf-mould turf of a gully surrounded by woodland interspersed with bamboo. Once again there was delay: where the path ran between boulders the gap was too narrow and the leading man had to hack down the bamboo culms to make a new path round the obstacle. However, I had a rich haul including *Tupistra aurantiaca (T. fimbriata),* an inconspicuous shade-loving member of the lily family with broad wavy leaves and short-stalked spikes or clubs of fleshy dull orange flowers, *Gaultheria griffithiana* with two kinds of flowers — its bisexual flowers are green and spheroidal while the other kind, female only, are narrower and reddish green — and lastly *Rhododendron praestans,* a tree with white undersides to its leaves.

At last the track reached a little valley coming from the left, crossed it and led along its side to a large Lisu village called Aoalo (Fig.35). By now it was dark, but I was most hospitably received and selected the "veranda" of an unoccupied house as the place to put my bed. There was plenty of forage for the horses and all the other supplies we needed; one of the women spoke Chinese quite well. I left the task of putting the plants in the press until next morning, having sorted them into lots designated by diary numbers which indicated their distribution and habitat. By summarising all the plants from each place under the same number (later discarded), instead of numbering each individual species, the botanist can save much time and labour in the field, though at the expense of some extra work after returning to base — where more time can usually be found. This task kept me busy until midday, and I had an audience who watched me humbly from a distance — mostly women and girls, the men having gone to work. The women wore fairly short grey pleated skirts and head-dresses which covered the whole of the nape of the neck, embroidered with rows of close-set cowrie shells and adorned with little silver plates. They all had tobacco pipes made from a long bamboo root with a small lathe-turned bowl, and carried them upside down in the necks of their garments. By taking them unawares I was able to get a successful photograph, but I had no luck in my attempt to buy one of their head-dresses; just as one of the girls had indicated to my servant that she would permit him to lift it off her head, an old

---

[118]The German travellers Brunhuber and Schmitz left Bhamo in Burma on 12th November 1908 with the intention of exploring the Salween valley. On 5th January 1909, while they were encamped on a sandbank at the side of the river just north of O-ma-ti (20km south of Latsa), they were attacked and murdered by Nu (Lutzu) villagers armed with spears. The account of their journey (Brunhuber, Robert, *An Hinterindiens Riesenströmen,* Berlin 1912) was based on Brunhuber's diaries and letters and on the report by the German consul in Rangoon.

woman chased her away with a vigorous prod in the ribs.

It was a gorgeous day on June 8th as I descended to the Lancang Jiang itself, and the bright sunlight heightened the yellow and brown tints of the arid slopes. Just before leaving the spur which juts out from Aoalo towards the Lancang Jiang — at 2525 m it is at the same level as the village — I glimpsed a colossal snow spire gleaming in the sun far away, projecting towards the river beyond and above the countless minor peaks into which the Lancang Jiang - Nu Jiang divide is fissured. It was Kakerbo on the Doker-la opposite Dêqên, a mountain certainly the equal of Satseto. In case I had to retouch my photograph I made a sketch of the mountain in my notebook. I joined the caravan route along the Lancang Jiang valley at Düku, not far from Yezhi, and immediately turned upstream so as not to risk a confrontation with the tusi. However, as my guide went down the valley to Yezhi, he cannot have long remained in ignorance of my journey, and in any case I soon met the mafu who had provided transport from here to Cizhong in 1915. I now had to buy rice for my men and hire pack animals with Tibetan saddles for the stage from Luota to Cizhong. On the way I met a mafu from Luota and arranged with him that he would be at my service from June 11th. Rice was not to be found in any of the villages and I finally had to send Lü to Yezhi to buy some. I instructed him and the mafu to say only that I was going to Dêqên and luckily they had enough sense to be discreet.

Certain incidents on 9th June left disagreeable impressions. That evening there was a bright glow in the sky, caused by a conflagration at Jitin, a village where I had spent the night in 1915. When I passed through next morning half the village had been burnt down; the mud walls of some of the houses had collapsed into the street and the posts which had supported them were still blazing merrily. However, no one bothered to extinguish them; some of the people were in the fields, while others were busy putting back the boards which they had previously

removed from their own roofs. Carried down in the waters of the Lancang Jiang, swollen by the melting snow, was a corpse, white and bloated, revolving slowly in the eddies. It was one of the dead bodies which the Tibetans throw into the river "to feed the fish". Yet such practices are idyllic in comparison with the orgies of slaughter engendered by the militarism of "civilised" countries!   I spent two nights at Dashan near Luota, though my repose was at first spoilt by the senseless howling of two large dogs on a flat roof just outside my window; I had to bombard them with roof tiles to make them stop. I then resumed my journey as agreed with the mafu, travelled on unchecked and crossed the rope bridge on the way to Cizhong. The people greeted me cheerily as I passed.

"Look, that must be a Frenchman", cried my servant in amazement, pointing to a man with a large beard; from my secretive behaviour he had obviously concluded that I had political projects as well as botanical. It was Père Valentin and he was just as friendly and helpful as he had been in 1915. He even postponed a journey to Weixi which he had planned to start on the following day so as to let me have the porters that I required to cross the Xi-la on the route to Bahan. He was quite talkative, yet after more than two hours' conversation we had got no nearer to the subject that was on my mind. Finally I explained to him, openly and without reserve, the reasons why I was anxious to travel from here to the Nu Jiang as quickly as possible, and he assured me that I could once again count on whole-hearted co-operation from his colleagues over there. The men whom I had sent to Yezhi brought back two pack animal loads of rice and also a most friendly letter from the tusi inviting me to stay with him on my return journey. Obviously, no orders directed against me had yet reached the district, but I had to be prepared for the arrival of such instructions and I therefore made every effort to get away from the Lancang Jiang into territory where the Chinese would not so easily be able to find me — or where they could be bribed.

Chapter 24. Over the Xi-la to Bahan on the Nu Jiang

Floral splendours in the forests and tanglewood — a frosty camp — over the Xi-la in snow — midge bites in the Saoa-lumba — over the Nisselaka — warm temperate rain forest — the Nu

After three days spent in preparations I set out on 15th June with my men and twenty five porters, though four pairs of the latter had been transformed into pack animals and one was represented by a woman. The track was so steep that the beasts were unable to carry more than the smallest crates, and at the price demanded — double a porter's wage (two rupees daily) — they did not give good value. Most of the porters were Chinese-Tibetan halfbreeds, several of whom had come on the Doker-la trip in 1915, but others, including the woman, were Nu who happened to be returning home, and one was a Lisu. They carried loads of up to 50 kg, either in a basket as used in the Alps, partly supported on the

head, or with the assistance of a band or strap across the forehead. My ponies came too, for I thought they might be of use during the ascent or later on the Nu Jiang, when I wanted to return to my base after a trip to the floor of the valley. In this district the people took great pains to prevent the horses from eating a grass that grew in stiff tufts along the path (probably *Calamagrostis arundinacea*), as it was allegedly poisonous. My pony, now restored to health by application of aluminium acetate, carried my heavy frame (83 kg) up the steep path to the col at Chranalaka with enviable agility, though dripping with sweat and panting — an ascent of 1300m, broken by a lunch halt at Niapaton. In the valley we had just left mist had enveloped us almost before we had vanished into the primaeval forest, and from then on the rain ceased only briefly.

The profuse herbaceous understorey of the moisture-loving mixed forests, of which I had seen no more than remnants in September 1915, was now at the peak of its development, and amazed even my Naxi plant collectors by its luxuriance. Flowers of all kinds were massed together above and among the lush green foliage, some owing their splendour simply to their colour, height and bulk, while others were of fantastic shapes and melancholy hues. Conspicuous among the latter were three species of *Arisaema*, a genus related to our lords-and-ladies, which grew one above the other or even side-by-side: *A. biauriculatum*, a tall plant with neatly curved outlines pencilled on its leaves and deep violet spots on its stems and spathes, *A. elephas*, distinguished by the dark purple interior of its spathe, and a third, probably *A. wilsonii*. Besides these there was *Diphylleia cymosa* with its remarkable umbrella-like leaves, *Cardamine griffithii* with deep pink flowers, the dainty *Senecio euosmus*, *Smilacina wardii* with white bell-flowers, and the tallest and perhaps the finest of all lilies, growing by preference in small clearings, *Cardiocrinum (Lilium) giganteum* (Fig.37). Its robust stem, as thick as a man's wrist at ground level, rises to a height of over 2.5 m and bears large light green heart-shaped leaves. At its top is a spike of several waxy snow-white flowers, each 12 cm long, their interiors striped with purple, emitting a delightful though perhaps somewhat cloying perfume, detectable at some distance. Its bulbs are eaten and its hollow stalks used for making musical instruments. A Chinese pedlar, the first to have attempted the crossing to the Nu Jiang that year, had already arrived with his goods — chiefly kitchen utensils — at Doshiracho, the lowest of the huts on the mountain pastures. I took shelter there, though its roof gave little protection from the rain, while waiting for my tent, part of which, as luck would have it, was in the last load to arrive. The elderly Lu was troubled by pain in the thighs and doubted whether he would be able to continue, but soon cheered up.

During the gradual ascent next day we encountered more and more species of rhododendron in flower, though the large tree rhododendrons along the stream had already gone over. Through the work of the missionaries Soulié and Monbeig alone, twenty three different species are known to occur in that valley. When we came to cross the stream I felt somewhat apprehensive, because it was such a raging torrent that we had to use the melting remnants of an avalanche as a bridge. It formed a huge arch, but the layer of snow on top was not very thick and I was seriously alarmed that the horses might break through; in the event, however, it was still strong enough. *Primula yargongensis*, *P. muscarioides* and *P. silaënsis* were in flower, diffusing wonderfully sweet perfumes. Beneath the tanglewood of rhododendrons and willows was *Berneuxia tibetica*, a member of the *Diapensiaceae* (Fig.36). It resembles our soldanellas, though it is not the fringed petals that give it this resemblance, but the white stamens alternating with the narrow pointed petal tips of its pendent flowers, grouped together in small inflorescences. Steeply tilted strata of clay-slate, their strike

parallel with the line of the mountain chain, formed thin sheets lying at right angles to the path, which led up in steep steps to the uppermost basin below the Xi-la. It was still full of snow, and I pitched the tent not far from its edge, at 3900 m. The porters went back to find a warmer spot to spend the night and better grazing for the horses. Up where I was the mist drifted to and fro, while the wind whistled through the last straggling stunted firs and drove the rain against the canvas. Water from the melting snow trickled and splashed down from the surrounding corries. The solitude of that frosty camp might have seemed eerie and forbidding to someone who had not grown up with such a love of mountains as I had.

Mirrored in the bog pools was the strangest of all primulas, now split off into a genus of its own under the name *Omphalogramma souliei*, with solitary hairy pendent flowers 6 cm long in various shades from violet to purple, most of them with six petals, the lowermost projecting obliquely (Fig.42, 43). The air was perfumed by the flowering of the willows. *Rhododendron saluenense* had opened its large flat purple flowers; *R. sanguineum* was covered with thick-petalled bells in shades ranging from dark purple to orange-yellow or orange-red, and *R. repens*, a small-leaved creeping shrub with large solitary bright red flowers, scrambled over the boulders. Between the stones were dense cushions of *Diapensia purpurea*, now sprinkled with purple flowers, and the new *D. acutifolia* with white flowers. The small white bells of *Cassiope* had opened in enormous numbers; besides the two more widely distributed species, *C. pectinata* and *C. selaginoides* and a hybrid between them, there was a third species, *C. palpebrata*, small and dainty. *Pinguicula alpina* and the tiny *Ranunculus hyperboreus* were growing beneath the rhododendrons.

Next morning the porters were in no hurry to leave their camp lower down, and I climbed onwards in the rain to the Xi-la, 500 m higher up. Its eastern side was still an almost unbroken snowfield, and at its lower edge only the little *Primula bella* was in flower. I do not know how the laden pack animals and my horses managed to surmount the steep snow slopes, the rock ledges and the unstable screes without mishap. I could certainly have been of no help to them, and I therefore left it to the Tibetans; they were quite capable of coping with the situation. At the steepest pitches the men had to carry the loads on their shoulders. Little rivulets trickled everywhere and most of the stones were more or less submerged, with the result that the lichens growing on them were washed so clean that their vivid hues were conspicuous from some distance. Nearly all of them were new: *Verrucaria cupreocervina*, *Ionaspis alpina*, *I. handelii*, *Staurothele sinensis*, *Lecanora cinereopolita*, *Lecidea caloplacodes*, *L. chondrospora* and *L. macrocarpa*. I pitched our third camp lower down, in the Saoa-lumba, near a bridge made from a single beam. The subalpine meadow plants were now so tall that they hid not only the ponies but even men standing upright. *Eutrema lancifolium*, *Draba surculosa* and *Cardamine polyphylla* represented the *Cruciatae*; among others were *Ranunculus stevenii*, *Meconopsis pseudointegrifolia* and *Heracleum* sp. However, among them lurked millions of biting flies, tiny creatures less than a millimetre long, probably species of *Simulium*. One was black all over and the other had transverse black and white stripes on the wings. Their bites were more painful than those of ordinary midges, and raised equally large papules. Despite every effort to seal the tent they found their way inside, and the flysheet was black with them. During the next day's march I passed through large areas of cherry tanglewood, especially on the Nisselaka pass. It had masses of dainty white bell-shaped flowers, each with a red calyx, usually arranged in rows along its horizontal or gently sloping twigs. Their bark was brown and their leaves, still small, were bright green and deeply serrated [119]. Flowering beneath the tanglewood, the small white *Primula vernicosa*, the large *P. calliantha* (Fig.40) and numerous other plants tempted me to take photographs, which came out well despite the rain. Arriving in Bahan that afternoon (June 18th), I had a cordial welcome from Pater Ouvrard and the elderly Pater Genestier, who had just come over from Qunatong on a visit. They were just as friendly as they had been in 1915, and it was good to know that there were still some people to whom humanity and science meant more than the rivalries between nations which still plague us today.

They arranged accommodation for me in the village headman's house, barely 20 metres below the mission building. After a rest day I set out to explore the gorge near the village by having myself lowered from a path in the upper part of the gorge leading to the village mills. Scrambling, crawling and sliding down, I suddenly found myself at the upper edge of a cliff overgrown by vegetation, and had to go back some distance to find a way down. Despite persistent drizzle I gathered a fine haul especially of shade-loving herbaceous plants — the same kinds as in the wet forests of the Doyonlumba, but now in flower — together with several ferns and *Eria graminifolia*, an inconspicuous white-flowered epiphytic orchid of tropical type. My collectors climbed trees to gather flowers and fruit, notably from the new *Corylopsis glaucescens*, a very large, almost tree-like shrub growing at the edge of the forest, and numerous climbers, among them a small pepper vine (*Piper aurantiacum*) which covered the treetrunks with a cushion-like mass of foliage. Finally I came to the brook and wading through it reached a little clearing in which I found the path which had led me back to my base the year before. Leaning at an oblique angle was an alder, apparently about to topple over. Its lower part had been denuded of branches, or perhaps had never had any. Instead, its trunk was enveloped up to the very top by the twining stems of a bramble. Round its lower part it formed a dense sack-like covering, but at the top I spotted some large round leaves belonging to a soft-stemmed epiphytic shrublet with large corymbs of white flowers, perhaps somewhat unattractive when viewed individually. It was *Schizophragma crassum*, a new species, and it and the bramble provided employment for one of the tree climbers. I got back at midday, wringing wet.

The people of Bahan were Nu, but there were also a few Tibetan families from the Lancang Jiang who had settled there. Besides cattle they had brought walnut trees with them, and I was interested to hear that the trees round their houses — already carrying a rich crop — were not derived from the wild walnuts of the Nu Jiang valley, but had been introduced from elsewhere. The Nu do not practice

alpine cattle farming: hence the well preserved state of their forests and the tracklessness of their mountains. They are a Burmese people and according to their handed-down traditions they migrated from the Drong Jiang. Most of them are short and somewhat unprepossessing in appearance, but absolutely honest. They are at a very low level of civilisation. They have no writing and their language is extremely poor in its vocabulary, being without any means of expressing abstract ideas; for example, they had no word for "colour". They do not lock up their houses when they go out, they leave their few cattle unattended on the pastures, they wash as seldom as the other peoples living in these parts, and they are very easily converted to Christianity. They are said to be immune to smallpox: when they contract the disease they walk around with only a few pustules and hardly any fever, whereas the Tibetans suffer from smallpox even more seriously than we do, and from dysentery also. A large breach in the wall of my room provided all the necessary ventilation, but moist air and gentle rain from the low clouds entered freely through it and the window, which though small could not be closed, and although the temperature was quite reasonable considering the altitude (2580 m), I was soon obliged to retire to bed with a feverish chill. From time to time a gust of wind drew aside the veils of mist and there, peeping over the forested Alülaka ridge opposite, were a few tall pinnacles of dark rock belonging to the Nu Jiang-Irrawaddy divide, with patches of snow still gleaming on them. That was the range which I had dreamt of though I had hardly dared hope of reaching it, and yet Genestier had encouraged me to think of going even further by remarking that a journey to the upper reaches of the Irrawaddy itself would be entirely feasible. There must surely be rich spoils to be collected over there; the territory was entirely unexplored, and the plant cover was said to consist of jungle and palm forest — quite different from that of the Nu Jiang valley. Genestier himself, together with Grillières, had at that time attempted the overland crossing to India by a route further to the south, but had been defeated by the climate and by food shortage and, gravely ill, had been forced to turn back after reaching the Drong Jiang, the eastern branch of the upper Irrawaddy. The only traveller who had succeeded in getting through to India was the Prince d'Orléans. He encountered serious difficulties and seems to have brought back hardly any botanical collections from this journey [120]. The call of the unknown — the country over the mountains was another blank on the map — was so strong that nothing would have deflected me from making the attempt. Happily I soon recovered from my fever, for there was no time to be lost: had the Chinese official in Gongshan got wind of my plans he would certainly have been able to bar my journey to this prohibited frontier territory; all he had to do was to command the ferrymen not to take me across the river.

---

[119] A new species later named *Prunus crataegifolia*.

[120] D'Orleans' book does in fact contain a five page list of plants collected during the expedition. Compiled by the botanist M.A.Franchet, it comprises over two hundred species, twenty two of them new. (**d'Orleans, Prince Henri**, *Du Tonkin aux Indes, Janvier 1895 - Janvier 1896*. Paris, C.Levy, 1898. English edition - *From Tonkin to India, by the Sources of the Irawadi*, translated by Hamilton Bent, London, Methuen, 1898).

Chapter 25. To the Upper Irrawaddy

The Lisu — a dugout canoe as ferry — climbs in the Tjiontson-lumba — discovery of *Taiwania* — slow progress — bridge construction — over the Chiangshel — a steep descent — a hazardous ropebridge — among the Drung in the Irrawaddy gorge — I fall sick and return over five passes — distant vistas — Gomba-la and Tsukue — subtropical flora on the Nu Jiang (Salween)

There were two routes from Gongshan to the Drung Jiang, neither yet trodden by a European. For the outward journey I chose the first, which did not actually pass through Gongshan, for the return the second. Five of my men from the Lancang Jiang (Mekong) remained with me, and the other ten porters were Tibetans and Nu tribesmen from the Bahan district. The guide whom I ultimately found was a somewhat suspect character of sinister appearance with the euphonious and meaningful name of Kru (donkey); he had fled to the Drung Jiang because he owed money to the missionary, and had only recently ventured back after hearing that the latter had been transferred. To make the journey with fewer porters would have been impracticable since the men had to carry enough food to last them for a fortnight; I had already left the paraffin lamp, the camp table and chair and other nonessential items at Cizhong. Père Ouvrard kindly undertook to record barometer and thermometer readings as a baseline for calculating altitudes on my journey.

After setting off on the morning of 26th June, I sent Lu back from the Alulaka ridge with the horses, for no one could possibly have ridden down the 1200 m descent to the river itself, and there was no question of taking them any further. He had the task of changing the paper between which I had pressed the plants I had already gathered, and of looking after the larger collections which I hoped to send back in the next two or three days. A few Lisu families from the Lancang Jiang and the lower Nu Jiang had recently settled on the ridge. They were the best hunters in the region; they would track a deer or a bear all day until they caught up with it, and in their own country they shot their poisoned arrows from the bushes at caravans and at any stranger who ventured there without a safe conduct. They were spreading resolutely northwards along the Nu Jiang and seemed likely to displace, exterminate or swallow up the feeble Nu. The village chief and his henchmen had recently absconded, having murdered and robbed four Tibetans on the path to Londjre the year before. Their houses consisted of a single low-roofed room, the floor covered with springy bamboo mats. I bartered salt in exchange for potatoes from them.

Flowering in the remnants of forest along the path was the bizarre *Arisaema speciosum*, its spadix drawn out into a thread a metre long dangling over the leaves; creeping over rotting stumps was the yellow *Lysionotus sulphureus* (a new species). Tjionra [121] on the east and Tjiontson on the west side of the Nu Jiang (Salween) were united by a ferry. Two dugout canoes, each carrying four men and four loads and propelled by two paddlers, took my caravan across. They were so narrow that one could sit with an elbow on each gunwale (Fig.38). The river was nearly at its highest level; its dark brown waters swirled round the boat and made it rock alarmingly. Not long before one of the boats had been swept away by the flood waters. Everything was green. The sandbanks were colonised by grasses spreading by stolons, and the rocks at the banks were covered as far as the highwater mark by pale green liverworts (*Marchantia cuneiloba*) and maidenhair fern (*Adiantum capillus-veneris*). One of the houses in Tjiontson offered good accommodation. Some built of stone with timber framing and others of wood alone with a gently sloping gabled roof, the Nu houses of this village were quite imposing.

Debouching at Tjiontson was a major lateral valley from the west-southwest; its Tibetan name was Tjiontson-lumbá. My route to the Jiu Jiang passed along it. First we climbed 700 m steeply up the arid hillside to a Nu village named Xuelamenkou; numerous tribesmen had already moved up there for the summer. It was situated on a flat shoulder, one of the few level places in the whole valley. Here I bought a few small musical instruments of a kind common to all the native tribes, among them three carved bamboo plectra in neat bamboo cases, also carved and painted. My servant indignantly showed me an opium poppy he had discovered there.

"Well, so it is, but there's only one", said I dismissively.

"But there are three seed pods on it!" he exclaimed.

It was in fact the Chinese official in Gongshan who had induced the natives to cultivate opium for his own use. But when an opium commissioner came along he of course left them in the lurch and allowed them to be punished. We crossed a side valley where wild walnut trees grew in large numbers and stopped for the night in an empty house. On the opposite side was a stratum of marble which extended along the entire valley-side, in some places forming tall cliffs and elsewhere a narrow vertical edge. Wild bees nested in holes in the marble. Beeswax obtained from them was one of the few taxes which the Nu had to pay to the Naxi tusi in Yezhi. Up to this point the path had been quite tolerable. On the next day, however, we rounded a corner to find that it consisted of steps barely half the width of a man's foot leading along the side of a precipitous slope. To traverse it called for a good head for heights, complete surefootedness and extreme caution, especially as continuous rain had made the clay soil slippery and it was covered with bracken and other tall vegetation. Though carrying loads of 40 kg, the natives walked along barefoot

---

[121] Kingdon Ward calls it Cho-la. (*The Land of the Blue Poppy*, p. 189).

with complete confidence, and my servant found it best to follow their example.

After several steep descents we reached the valley bottom, which contained mixed woodland drenched with moisture and similar to the forest in the Doyon-lumba. On the slopes there were numerous fallen tree trunks which we had to clamber over, a task made easier by notched poles placed where the branches joined the trunk or fitted into small manmade recesses. In many places we had to climb over steep rock shelves, most of them dripping with water, and we had to traverse old rockfalls, crossing boulders as big as houses consisting of extremely coarse-grained granite by balancing on sharp-angled edges or wriggling across a fallen tree trunk with a yawning black space on either side. In some spots there were ladders made from notched logs set almost vertically, but the footholds were too small to give a safe grip for climbing boots. A slip would have meant a long drop and a hard landing.

Twice I came across small trees, quite young and in appearance like the juvenile forms of a scale-leaved juniper, but having three lines on their needles, which were keeled and diverged from the stem in their upper halves only. In these respects they resembled *Cryptomeria*, and I was inclined to assign them to that genus. Growing nearby was a small conifer with dark pendent branches and fruits at first glance like those of a cypress; it seemed so unusual that I thought it worth struggling up through brambles and boulders to take a photograph, and I sent Lao Li up the tree. To my disappointment he brought me twigs of a spruce *Picea complanata* (now *P.brachytyla*) widely grown in Europe, bearing the well known *Adelges* galls. Before long, however, I saw some enormous fully grown trees undoubtedly belonging to the juvenile form of the first species [122]. In their habit of growth they were reminiscent of the American sequoias. Their pale grey trunks, well over 6 m in girth, had smooth bark, though on older trees there was some longitudinal fissuring. They soared arrow-straight into the sky, certainly reaching heights of 70 m, and were comparable in size to the largest pines of the region, though their lower branches spread out horizontally and were so large that any one of them could have stood comparison with a fair-sized tree. In some instances the trunk forked high above the ground and the separate branches towered up like a candelabrum into the mist which hung above these woods nearly all day, saturating the deep humus and the bulky moss cushions on the forest floor. However, I was still unable to identify the trees; they were so tall that I could not reach or even see their flowers or fruits, and no tree climber could have scaled a smooth trunk of such dimensions; nor were there any climbable trees nearby from which the necessary specimens might have been secured.

I pitched camp for the night among thickets of bamboo. Next day we were held up by a stream swollen by incessant rain. As there were no bridges I looked for a spot where the stream divided, waded knee-deep through the first part and crossed the second by balancing on a tree trunk, the usual expedient for bridging small watercourses. The porters were not so lucky: at another spot they tried to find a better way of crossing, but one of them flopped into the water with the blankets belonging to the rest of the men and another managed to slip down, bruising and lacerating his shin quite severely. As I was able to disinfect it at once, the wound healed quite well. Towards evening we reached another stream in spate. This one was so swollen and turbulent that any attempt to cross it was out of the question. We had to go back, pitch camp at 3000 m and wait. However, next day the rain continued relentlessly and the water did not subside at all. The main stream was a raging torrent, surging round whole groups of trees and tumbling down in roaring cascades. Only in a few stretches did the path come close to the edge of the deep vertical-sided trench which the stream had cut for itself; standing on the edge, one glimpsed the water between bamboos and moss-hung branches, but the view was obscured by swirling clouds of spray.

At this altitude the broad-leaved trees thinned out somewhat — among them were *Euonymus tingens*, its white flowers veined with purple, *Malus ombrophila* (a new species), *Rhododendron sinonuttallii* and *Styrax shweliensis* — and conifers began to appear in the woods, notably the new *Tsuga intermedia*, together with larches and firs, though the pines dwindled and disappeared. *Lilium giganteum* flourished in large numbers in the patches of tall herbaceous vegetation, and besides its bulbs we found another useful addition to our diet: the young sprouts of a tall bamboo with stout culms, which was common here and at similar spots in the forests of the Nu Jiang. In Kunming they fetched high prices as a delicacy. They tasted delicious and made a welcome change to my diet, as even my cook, inept as he was, could not spoil them.

Nearly all the time we were soaked to the skin; if the rain ceased for a while the vegetation — two and a half metres tall and dripping wet — drenched us from every side. To avoid catching cold I had to strip to the skin every evening as soon as the tent had been pitched and have my clothes and boots dried in front of the fire. This maltreatment reduced my boots — which were now for the most part of Yunnanese fabrication — to an indescribable state. I should have preferred to throw away the whole lot if replacements had been available, but I could not yet resign myself to going barefoot. The plant papers had to be dried sheet by sheet in front of the fire, beneath the tattered pieces of cloth which the Tibetans spread out between the trees for shelter, and all too often the rain fell on them from above while the fire scorched them from below. For kindling the men used splinters of resinous pine which they carried up from the valley with their baggage. They were wonderfully well adapted to the hardships of life in their mountains and the rigours of their weather; they could make themselves comfortable anywhere and they never grumbled. Even when the rain was pouring down they sang songs and called out jokes

---

[122] It was *Taiwania cryptomerioides* (Handel-Mazzetti, Symbolae Sinicae, Vol.7, 717).

from one shelter to the next. They soon picked up my servant's favourite expression, a word which was constantly on his lips instead of the usual indescribably filthy Chinese oaths. It sounded like "lungtent-io",[123] but I was never able to find out what it meant. They repeated it from dawn till dusk, and it echoed back and forth between them, and he very soon stopped using it. However, they were sometimes careless in handling unfamiliar European objects, and one of the porters continually leant on my pith helmet, which in cloudy weather was placed on top of his load, and soon squashed it into a shapeless mass.

The valley had the U-shaped profile typical of glaciated terrain; its floor was covered by vegetation and its sides were almost vertical, in some places extending upwards in a staircase of rock slabs — mostly dark in hue, but here and there sparkling with water from rain or melting snow — and culminating on the south side in Shatsakon, a summit apparently 5000 m in altitude. We had to wait until 2 July before the stream, which splashed down the valley side in splendid waterfalls, was low enough to cross. *Gleadovia ruborum*, a short-stalked, branching plant of the broomrape family previously found only in the northwest Himalaya, peeped out from beneath a rotting tree trunk, forming clusters which looked like birds' nests. Otherwise the number of new plants was not yet sufficient to be worth sending back a load. Towards noon we had to cross the main stream. An uprooted spruce lengthened with a sapling bridged it almost completely, and we continued up the south side of the valley. *Magnolia tsarongensis*, its long narrow leaves covered with brown felt on the undersides, formed what amounted almost to a tanglewood. Its broad-cupped snow-white flowers were opening among the rhododendrons of the forest floor, some of which were quite sizeable little trees, in particular *R. ixeuticum*, whose leaves, also covered with tawny felt beneath, gave large stretches of the forest a brownish tint. Beneath them grew the tall *Arisaema verrucosum* with warty hairy stems and leaf stalks. A lateral stream gushing out through a rock cleft proved too deep to wade. A young fir was felled, split in half and laid across at a narrow spot; my rope was stretched out to make a handrail, and in a quarter of an hour we had all reached the further bank. There were leeches here, and as we had no chance of choosing our footholds and handholds some of the men were bitten. Yet again the stream was impassable, so I called it a day, pitched the tent on a boggy patch, collected the liverworts growing in profusion on the boulders and tried to work out how long it would take the men, working with their small cleavers, to fell a fir big enough to reach across the stream. The tree which they cut down that day fell on to a trunk lying in the water, broke into pieces and was lost. Next morning, however, after an hour's work a second fir was felled and made a splendid bridge. Using my rope as a handrail once

more, we were soon across, and having struggled over fallen tree trunks and through thick vegetation, in which I found the tall *Cathcartia smithiana* (a new species) and *Corydalis pterygopetala*, we found that the stream was now so calm and shallow that we could easily have waded it at that spot on the day before. Further on there was a delightful waterfall, past which we climbed steeply, using a rivulet in the cane-brake as our path. Beneath a boulder lay the body of a man — not yet completely reduced to a skeleton — who had frozen to death here in the winter, his pack beside him and his dog lying at his head. Every year a few people die from cold and exposure in these mountains, and even more bleed to death after stepping on the razor-sharp end of a bamboo culm, chopped off obliquely near the ground.

Soon we came to the first of the high alpine plants in a grass-grown avalanche channel: there were primulas (*P. dickieana* and *Omphalogramma elegans*), orchids (*Pogonia yunnanensis* and *Pleione scopulorum*), edelweiss (*Leontopodium jacotianum*), the tiny pink *Utricularia salwinensis*, *Vaccinium modestum* with solitary pendent flowers on long stalks, gentians and others; they made a pleasant change. In this stretch the south side of the valley was less steep, and its lateral valleys entered it between rounded forest-covered spurs, descending at a gentle slope and evidently beginning a long way off. At its last or more correctly first fork we crossed the northern tributary of the main stream and camped on the tongue of land between them — the last camp on this side of the divide, reached after eight days' travel averaging barely over 6 km a day. There was not a patch of level ground anywhere, and the tent looked lopsided and askew, although the men had hacked away the earth on the uphill side and built up the downhill side with stones and brushwood. There were some thick roots which defied their efforts and made the campbed tilt even further.

On 4th July it was still raining as I at last went up along the southern tributary towards the pass. The little valley was a veritable garden of flowers. *Nomocharis aperta, Doronicum altaicum* and many other species already known to science grew in colourful throngs above the fresh green of the grasses and sedges on the banks of the stream, which is some stretches offered the only practicable route. *Primula agleniana*, its large bell-shaped pale crimson flowers emitting a delightful perfume of vanilla (Fig.41), flourished in profusion beneath the tanglewood, which here consisted of a cherry, the new *Cerasus mugus* (*Prunus mugus*), together with *Sorbus poteriifolia, Rhododendron saluenense* and the yellow *R. chryseum*. The sky was gloomy and overcast; clouds drifted between the mica-schist towers of the crest which still separated me from the goal I had dreamt of so long, and hung above the snowfields, along which we ascended through gulleys and corries. Flowering at the end of the snow were the first-comers of spring at that altitude: the new *Corydalis polyphylla, Caltha scaposa*, some splendid louseworts and *Omphalogramma minus* (apparently a dwarf form of *O. souliei*). On compact turf I found the small *Primula valentiniana* (also a

---

[123]Perhaps (allowing for dialect pronunciation and errors of transcription) *"longtan huxue"* meaning "dragon's pool and tiger's cave" — a dangerous place. A Chinese would have found the Nu Jiang area unfamiliar and threatening (S.G.Haw).

new species) with bell-shaped flowers of deepest purple-red, together with *Rhododendron campylogynum*, a dwarf creeping shrublet with solitary long-stalked pendent flowers of a colour which can only be described as black. New for China was another discovery — *Diapensia himalaica*, growing on boulders in small cushions with flowers only 8 mm in diameter. Though the Chiangshel pass was only 4075 m high it was noticeably above the treeline and on its western side there were other finds to keep me busy, such as the dainty *Meconopsis lyrata* and the dwarf shrub *Diplarche multiflora*. The porters had gone ahead, and in the mist my collectors and I wandered from the track and started to go straight downhill. Fortunately the absence of any trace of a path soon aroused my suspicions and vigorous blasts on my whistle brought the guide back to us; otherwise we would have strayed into trackless primeval forests. In fact the path curved sharply to the right and led further uphill on to a crest largely covered with dwarf cherries and *Viburnum cordifolium* var. *hypsophilum*, though it soon descended again to the uppermost firs. Between them were patches of turf and creeping among the grasses was a rhododendron — probably *R. repens* once more; sitting there on the ground, its flowers seemed quite extraordinary: they looked almost like purple gentians. We went on for some distance, continually clambering up and down between piles of granite rubble but not losing or gaining much height, and finally pitched camp beside a pool at the western extremity of the crest.

Next morning we began the craziest part of the whole journey — a dead straight descent for more than 1600 m down a natural stairway of rock steps, roots, tree stumps and mud holes through a jungle of bamboo. Except in one short stretch where it ran obliquely, the track led straight down the mountainside. In many places we had to face inwards and though there was usually a curved root or a bamboo culm to cling to there was sometimes no handhold at all. In some spots we gazed almost vertically down from the top of a rock face, through the gaps between the roots and boulders on which we had to place our feet, on to the tree-tops below. From 3400 m downwards there was a larch forest with only a few firs, and lower down mixed forest similar to that in the Nu Jiang. The tree-trunks were covered with epiphytes; besides the shrubs we had previously seen I found *Gaultheria nummularioides* forming large woody clumps on trunks and boulders, and several orchids, including the new *Coelogyne taronensis* with small numbers of large green flowers marked with rust-coloured spots which made them look as if they had been singed. All these were growing high up in the branches among the lichens and golden-green mosses (notably *Plagiochila* species and *Pseudospiridentopsis horrida*) which formed thick mats over every piece of wood and dangled down in long strands even from the leaves themselves. At last we came out into a small clearing and saw that we had nearly reached the valley bottom. However, it was only a lateral valley coming down from the north and curving round to the west. Its name was Naiwanglong. At the edge of the clearing was an unusual pine, the Indian *Pinus excelsa*, a huge tree

with exceptionally slender needles hanging down as if in mourning and narrow cones over 20 cm long, resembling those of the Weymouth pine. Its rounded, bluish green crowns stood out conspicuously from the surrounding forest. We clambered down another steep descent into the gorge itself. Two large ferns grew there, looking oddly out of place. One was *Gleichenia glauca* with arching fronds several metres in length, branching and forking several times before terminating in finely pinnate arborizations. The other, *Dipteria conjugata*, was erect and looked like an enormously enlarged *Ginkgo* leaf with its blade deeply cleft in the midline, and tiny heaped-up sporangia thinly scattered on its back. Both species would normally be regarded as tropical rather than subtropical.

Rope bridge at Naiwanglong
[Handel-Mazzetti's sketch]

The porters had hurried on ahead, and suddenly I found myself standing among them on a rock platform above the raging torrent. If anyone says that he does not know the meaning of fear I should like to despatch him to that very spot to learn what it is, under the same conditions as those which I encountered. It was a gloomy ravine, filled with spray from the waterfall which crashed down it. Dangling straight across the water were three bamboo ropes, each no thicker than a man's finger, some distance above one another. We had to rely on them to get across. There was no means of telling whether they were rotten, and for extra safety I added my rope to them. The natives launched themselves across without an instant's hesitation; as evening was drawing near they used the opportunity, the mission caretaker at their head, to extort a few rupees for expediting the task. My men, however, gazed apprehensively at the ropes and at me. Not until the weight of the wata (the wooden slider) was applied to them did the ropes come together into a reasonably compact strand or cable. As my own rope was somewhat shorter than the others it was impossible to secure it without tying a knot and all it did was to impede us on starting. Resting one foot on the stump of a small tree, one pushed off from the bank and slid across on the wata as far as the halfway point, but from there on one had to haul oneself up hand over hand. However, the men pulled me up faster than I could manage and my hands sustained a few grazes. The trees to which the bridge was fastened had to be supported by men pulling on short ropes, otherwise the weight would have uprooted them and the entire bridge would have collapsed into the water. The scene will always remain imprinted on my memory and I was sorry not to be able to photograph it; however, the ravine was far too dark for a snapshot and the movements of the branches and the ropes were too lively for a time exposure; in any case the view was obscured by twigs and foliage in the foreground. At a drier season the scene might have been less daunting and the river might have been easily waded, but such considerations did nothing to alter the situation as we faced it on that day. As we had only one wata — and that only by lucky chance — the work proceeded very slowly, and communication was hindered by the roaring of the torrent, which drowned our voices although the banks were only 25 metres apart.

After a short but extremely slippery and exposed scramble I pitched the tent on a small spur projecting from the mountainside. I spent the next morning there, putting the collections in order, and that afternoon proceeded along the stream almost as far as the Drung Jiang. On the mountainside there were patches of bracken, and once again I found birches (*Betula cylindrostachya*) and *Pinus excelsa*, their twigs and needles festooned with orchids (*Bulbophyllum?*) which twined among them like a tropical *Tillandsia*. Unfortunately nearly all of them, like the many other orchids which grew there, had already finished flowering. The only species still unfaded was *Galeola lindleyana*, an orchid devoid of leaves and chlorophyll. Its eggyolk yellow flowers, never more than half open, projected above the decaying undergrowth, through which rambled *Rubus chrysobotrys*, a new species of bramble with golden berries. Not until we had dug up the orchid did it disclose its full height of 2½ m, not to mention its creeping stolons a metre long. Beside the river there was an ancient rockfall where the incessant rise and fall of the water had precluded any accumulation of small debris, and there was nothing except a little sand between the granite boulders, some of them as large as houses. We squeezed along pitchblack passages between and beneath them. Scrambling up them was *Rhaphidophora decursiva*, an aroid with thick creeping stems and dark green leathery leaves cleft into irregular pinnate divisions.

When I arrived, the iceaxe in my hand, at the first Drung house in the little hamlet of Nicheluang the people were at first so timid that they hid from me, but the mission servant, who had previously made friends with them, managed to calm their fears. Was there anything for sale?

"They've just barred the chicken coops with crisscross sticks", said my cook, showing me what

he meant, "but otherwise they're all right. They haven't any weapons or even any clothes on."

That night was marked by the onset of an illness which seriously hindered my work. Whether it was due to the water from the forest streams which I had drunk unboiled, the Japanese canned meat acting directly on the intestine, or simply a chill from exposure to rain and wind, the diarrhoea which I had already experienced now became unbearable. Furthermore, the house was so densely populated with fleas that a good night's rest was out of the question, and lack of sleep added to my feelings of weakness. The three kilometre stage to the next village upstream, Shuche, was almost a day's march, so severe were the ascents and descents. There is probably nowhere else in the world where the tracks which link neighbouring villages are such miserable breakneck scrambles. As Burrard says in the notes to his new map of Tibet, of all the parts of the Irrawaddy district surveyed by his men, it was here on the Drung Jiang that the difficulties of the route were at their worst. From a corner 275 m above Nicheluang there was a good view of the valley. Its walls were even steeper and less dissected than those of the Nu Jiang valley. As its channel was more or less straight, one could see a long distance upstream to the north west and downstream to the south. The river itself was about half the size of the Nu Jiang, with numerous rapids and some minor bends round small projecting spurs. According to the Prince d'Orléans, who travelled to it from Yuragan, it makes a major bend to the west at Turong 30 km to the south. However, as my view down the valley extended for a distance which, at my estimate, must have been almost 50 km, I felt obliged to ask whether — contrary to all appearances — a major west-east channel might not really constitute the river valley. However, this has been categorically denied and was in fact subsequently disproved by a better view from the mountain. According to the map drawn by Roux (d'Orléans' topographer), the Prince's further route passed close to that channel and when I was drafting my survey I formed the impression that the error which undoubtedly exists in his map arose from the circumstance that he never got a view of the course of the river as a whole and sketched the bend as too small. Remembering that Burrard's map of Tibet, which is notoriously inexact and, where it covers the adjacent parts of Yunnan to the east of the boundary, is extremely sketchy and full of errors, shows the bend as extending very much more broadly, it seems to me highly probable that the river actually makes a complete reversal, in the form of a huge S-shaped loop. The terrain being what it is, such an assumption is by no means absurd, and on the relevant sheet of the latest Indian survey (not for sale) there are indications of just such a bend[124]. The mountain range on the opposite side reached an average

---

[124]In fact the Irrawaddy — this part is now known as the Drung Jiang — does not continue in a straight line for as far as Handel-Mazzetti believed. After running south for some 20 km it curves to the west and crosses the Burmese frontier (see Operational Navigation Chart [ONC] H-10).

altitude of 4000 m, and an impressive peak further upstream, between the fifth and sixth lateral valleys, was considerably higher, though even that was devoid of glaciers. The whole range consisted of dark igneous rock. Below a crest across the valley a detached portion of blue sky peeped through an enormous hole in the rock.

We now came to a deep ravine where the men who had been sent ahead had bridged the tributary stream with branches and bamboos. Here I hoped to learn something of the plants growing down at river level at 1650 m. *Gleichenia glauca* hung down over the rocks and there was a *Brassaiopsis* (probably *B. hookeri*) with inflorescences at least a metre in length, but once again it was out of reach. Then we climbed up almost vertical ladders made from notched logs for a distance of some 50 m to the village of Shuche, which consisted of two groups of houses, the upper group at an altitude of 2025 m. There was no longer any trace of the woods of Yunnan pine and of oak which exist on the Nu Jiang or of the maquis of sclerophyllous shrubs; this valley was much wetter than the Nu Jiang. Nor was there any sign of the palm woods which Génestier had seen further down the valley. Yet I found trees and shrubs belonging to the subtropical flora of the Sikkim Himalaya, among them *Bucklandia populnea, Neillia thyrsiflora, Pentapyxis stipulata* and the twining *Trichosanthes palmata*, all of which were new to the flora of China. As defined by the frontier line, though it was totally unnatural and had not yet been substantiated by any treaty, this part of the Irrawaddy valley belonged to China, and the people paid taxes in kind to the tusi of Yezhi. They told me that beyond the mountains there was English territory, and there was a good track. From time to time a minor official, who though Chinese was subordinate to the Yezhi tusi, was sent here to collect taxes, but the year before he had arrived too late; the Tibetans from Tsarong, who were alleged to carry their raids for booty and slaves much further down the valley, had appropriated them. Burrard depicts the entire valley including Ridong, a Tibetan settlement much further upstream, as part of Burma.

I had my bed set up under the projecting roof of a house in the upper part of Shuche, on a platform just over a metre in width, and decided to take a rest day. The men had carelessly neglected to bring enough provisions and on the previous day had sent Kru to another village to buy meal. The delay was not unwelcome, for besides the diarrhoea I was troubled by soreness in the thigh muscles after the long descent. Kru came back that evening without having bought any corn; that had probably not been his intention at all — he simply wanted to visit some old friends and give the others a rest day. I therefore consulted the village headman, who sold us millet and a pig — at a price! Two men dressed only in loin cloths of loosely woven fabric rolled up into a narrow strip pounded the grain with a wooden pestle made from a piece of tree trunk in a hollow tree-stump set up on the "veranda" of the house; while engaged in this strenuous labour they chattered continuously, repeating over and over again two scraps of Chinese which they had just picked up

from my men. The Drung people were at a far lower level of civilisation even than the Nu. They had dark hair hanging thickly over their foreheads. By no means all of them were of short stature, and they displayed a wide range of facial shapes, from high and narrow to low and round. The women wore somewhat more clothing than the men and dressed their hair in exactly the same style. Their faces were tattooed with blue squares covering the area between the eye and the corner of the mouth, and also on the forehead and chin. Their speech was allegedly a dialect of the Nu language, and not greatly different from it[125]. Their houses were small, built of wood on low piles and covered with a gable roof thatched with reeds. The single room had a small door at one end opening on to a narrow platform in front, and an even smaller window at the other end. Ox and yak skulls were hung up round the doors, although the tribesmen did not themselves keep cattle of any kind, and in the interior were numerous skulls of smaller animals killed by their hunters. Maize, buckwheat, beans, yams, millet, a little wheat, and tobacco were their crops. They tilled their fields with a wooden implement like an axe but without any blade or point of iron; it was simply a forked branch. They hunted with crossbows and arrows like all the indigenous peoples of the region. The weather now cleared, and I was able to measure out a baseline, survey the features and take photographs. As is clear from Burrard's reports, the terrain had previously been surveyed as far as a village named Naktai some distance further north. However, if his map represents the entire outcome of these labours, it seems fair to say that my efforts were by no means superfluous.

On 9th July I set off along a somewhat better track on the side of the next lateral valley where the men had built me a bridge beforehand, and then northwards up the valley itself. In the mixed forests there were three new woody plants, *Ficus filicauda* with a long drip-tip, *Pentapterygium interdictum*, an epiphyte related to our bilberry, and *Hydrangea taronensis*, a low growing subshrub with blue flowers. On the steep slope below the track there were pure stands of sombre *Tsuga*. We pitched camp by the stream and next morning we had to wade it immediately after starting; but for this we might have stayed dry all day. A steep ascent up to the right brought us to the pass, which had the typical Nu name of Pangblanglong. From there I had a good view south westwards beyond the Drung Jiang to a range which displayed broad rounded ridges above the headstreams of a fair-sized lateral valley. Then, joining it to the north, on a bearing of 228°, I saw dark spires with little glaciers between them. I was granted only a brief glimpse of these, just long enough to take bearings on the district as a whole, before they were again hidden in cloud. Beyond

---

[125] There are great differences between different dialects of the Nu language; its exact affinities are still unclear. But the Nu dialect of the Gongshan region is close to the Drung language. The two are almost mutually intelligible. Many Nu can also speak the Lisu language (S.Haw).

Pangblanglong the route ran down a side valley of the Naiwanglong, deep down in which the remnants of avalanches were still lying. We had to stay high up and reached the crest itself once more near a nodal point between the valley in which we had ascended, the Naiwanglong valley with its numerous branches, and another valley which ran northwards and then bent sharply westwards towards the Irrawaddy. The structure of this part of the range is extremely confusing, and erosion by the abundant rainfall has obscured its original simplicity. The river Naiwanglong has cut into the main range, which runs almost exactly northwest to southeast, and it was not entirely clear why the whole group now appears to be made up of several chains running due north and south, terminating 8 km northeast of Pangblanglong in a transverse block which forms part of the watershed between the Nu Jiang and the Irrawaddy.

It was a stiff climb up to the ridge, and no less steep on the west side beneath its crest up to a third col, which shared the name Bushao with the one before it. We then proceeded on flatter ground across a broad cirque situated at the foot of a chain of rock towers, becoming taller as they continued northwards to the watershed. We marched steadily at an altitude of 4100 m above the firwoods, which, grievously furrowed by avalanche tracks, covered the upper slopes of the valleys. The white-flowered *Potentilla brachystemon* (*Sibbaldia perpusilloides*), a most peculiar plant, probably the smallest of its genus, formed low mats on the boulders, as did *Leontopodium muscoides*, an edelweiss with very narrow stellate bracts. *Draba granitica* was slender and had small flowers; *Primula genesteriana*, like all these a new species, is related to our birds-eye primrose but was several times smaller, and the eggyolk yellow *Draba involucrata* grew in masses on the scree slopes. At the point where the transverse ridge joined the jagged crest we crossed the latter by a pass named Shualuo, the fourth of that day's march, and then went along the top of the crest towards the Gomba-la. Late that evening we pitched the tent on a small patch of level ground above the valley which ran northwards to the Nu Jiang. Fearing that he would not be able to find us, I had to send some of the men back in the dark with my lantern to look for one of the porters who, feeling unwell, had sat down beside the track. Up there, above the treeline, we were able to cover greater distances in each day's march than on the outward journey. The track and the weather were also better.

Next morning was wonderful. Mount Gomba-la, an enormous dome with a small glacier in a dark ravine, towered above us into the deep blue sky. Crowned by serrated peaks, the chain to which it belonged plunged down in vertical precipices on our right into the valley running northwards and debouching into the Nu Jiang in an inaccessible gorge near the Tibetan frontier. To the left there was another rugged rock peak, but straight ahead, above the intersections of the valley, was a line of gigantic snow peaks gleaming in the sunshine far beyond the Nu Jiang — the summits of the Lancang Jiang-Nu Jiang divide to the north of the Doker-la. They were

mantled in fresh snow extending far down their lower slopes, and silhouetted against it were dark fir trees looking like tiny dots. The peaks themselves, incredibly steep pyramids and towers, each one of them a colossus, towered up to heights certainly over 6000 m [126]. Kakerbo projects towards the Lancang Jiang and was not visible from there, but I consider that it is only an outlying peak of these huge mountains, the highest I have ever seen. This interpretation is supported by Gebauer's observations and photographs taken from the mountains near Dêqên (Atendse). A foreground to this superb alpine scene was provided by *Pegaeophyton sinense*, a plant with solitary bluish white flowers growing here and there in patches of sandy mud and among flat pieces of slate in spring-fed bogs (Fig.43). It is one of the largest of its family (*Cruciatae*) and its clumps, sprouting from carrot-shaped roots, covered considerable stretches. By stopping down the diaphragm to a barely visible pinpoint, I took a photograph which showed the plant and the distant peaks, both in sharp focus. The fifth pass, Tsukue, at 4175 m the highest in this part of the route, led over the Gomba-la crest just to the east of its junction with the main ridge on the same side of the Naiwanglong that we had skirted on the day before, and then turned southwards into a side valley leading down to the Nu Jiang. From the top of the pass one can trace several narrow vertical bands of light grey marble which run exactly north westwards through the bedrock. They bear witness to the original structure of the mountain, though the present line of the highest crests does not correspond to it at all. In front of us, below the treeline, was a lake bordered on the right by a green meadow, and to our left the screes of the Gomba-la, intersected by strips of turf and bands of rock, plunged steeply down from the windgap below its twin summits. The gap would probably have been within reach and the high level circuit would certainly have been uncommonly rewarding, but I could only have tackled it if I had been in good health; furthermore, supplies were running short and my boots were worn out.

I therefore felt obliged to drop down to the lake, and in its meadow found some plants of the daisy family not yet in flower, including the stemless *Jurinea salwinensis* (a new species), *Lactuca amoena*, similar but with blue flowers, and *Leontopodium himalayanum*. We went on into the main valley which led northeast for some 18 km to the Nu Jiang. Down to the right we saw the gleaming water of some small bog pools among the forest on a flat shoulder. They were arranged in a pattern which I often encountered and which reminded me of the sinter basins at Bede, although they were certainly not formed in the same way. The track led to the left over a spur on the valleyside; from the top it offered

---

[126]Handel-Mazzetti's map shows Kakerbo (ca. 6000 m) to the east of the main line of the Mekong-Salween divide. The higher peak further north is not shown, but according to ONC H-10 it reaches 6810 m. The main peak is called Meili Xueshan in Chinese, and its height is given on Chinese maps as 6740 m (SGH).

brief glimpses through the trees of the tangle of
summits in the direction of the Doker-la, without
giving a satisfactory panorama. There were some
more scrambles, and though they were not very long,
in my weakened state I found them quite exhausting.
After crossing rock slabs scoured by avalanches, the
path finally reached the valley bottom at a point
where the entire valleyside on the left, formed from
slabs of dark granite, was completely denuded.
Elsewhere the slabs were clothed with trees, but here
their cover consisted only of shrubs pliant enough to
survive the unceasing onslaught of snow and ice
which sweeps down every winter from the glaciers
gleaming high above us on the Gomba-la. That
evening there was no place large enough for the tent,
and I had to set up my camp bed under the shelter of
a huge boulder in the forest. However, the rain soon
began again, and it offered scant protection against
the water which ran down its face and the overhanging roots and dripped on to the bed. In the forest I
noticed a bright red toadstool. Because of the difficulty of preserving such fungi I did not usually
trouble to collect them, but on this occasion I told
my collector to fetch it, remarking that it would not
have any roots. However, he found that it actually
had a large and troublesome root, and on looking
more closely I recognised it as *Balanophora involucrata*, a parasitic flowering plant, which I later
encountered quite frequently in similar places in the
forests of the Nu Jiang. The valley curved gradually
to the right, remaining narrow and steep walled.
Again and again we thought its end was in sight, but
what we saw was only the crests of the lateral
slopes, while new bends came into view further
ahead. The puzzling conifer which I had seen on the
ascent from Tjiontson reappeared here, at the same
altitude as before. Once again the trees were gigantic
and inaccessible, and I could not make out any detail
at their tops. Evening was coming on and we had no
time for any serious attempt to climb them. But I
had decided on my plan. I was not going to depart
without identifiable material from those conifers. As
the high alpine flora on the Nu Jiang-Irrawaddy
divide was still in its vernal condition, I should in
any case have to send my plant collectors back there
in late summer, and then they would have time to
get some cones for me. That evening I reached
Niualo — as its name indicates, a Lisu village, and
indeed the most northerly of them — and enjoyed a
hospitable reception.

From there it was not much further to the Nu
Jiang. As we descended we entered subtropical rain
forest just below 2200 m. One of its commonest
trees was *Sloanea forrestii*, which resembles our
beech in its foliage and the bristly spines on its fruit.
Another huge tree was *Schima khasiana*. Hanging
from the tips of the highest twigs were the long
racemes of *Dendrobium devonianum* with deep
yellow flowers 8 cm in diameter. Once again there
was shrub vegetation with *Saurania napaulensis* and
the tall *Rhamnus henryi* with soft foliage. Then a
stretch on bare rock brought us to the slopes of the
Nu Jiang valley itself. After a short descent through
arid terrain with a few pines we reached Xiqitong, a

scattered village 3 km north of Gongshan. The Nu
Jiang flows down from Wuli in the northeast,
breaking through a bed of crystalline limestone. A
short distance further on, in the Gongshan gorge, it
turns to the east, but very soon corrects this devia-
tion and resumes its general trend from NNE to
SSW. This hard rock formed a steep precipice
everywhere, and in the lower gorge it rose up into
huge pillars 600 m high, one of which had necessi-
tated the building of a high wall or causeway in the
river itself to carry the path. When the river rises,
however, it floods this stretch and the only route to
Gongshan is high up, over the ridge. Although there
were still a few xerophytes on the sandbank deposited along the river below Xiqitong, among them
Schefflera delavayi, here with a dense layer of
brownish felt, the gorge itself was filled with luxuriant subtropical vegetation. Enormous lianas, the new
Mucuna coriocarpa with thick trunks and seedpods
50 cm long, climbed high up into the *Sloanea* trees,
the soft *Rhaphidophora peepla* moulded its juicy
green stems closely against the treetrunks, bearing
flower spikes sheathed in white high up among its
elliptical leaves. *Agapetes lacei* had produced its
strange swollen woody stem bases, and among them
flourished the unmistakably tropical *Asplenium
nidus*, a fern which forms large nests of tongue-
shaped fronds 70 cm in length. Among essentially
xerophilic plants were numerous small epiphytic
orchids, though unfortunately they had all finished
flowering, and the palm *Trachycarpus martiana*, on
the rock faces across the river, where it was almost
inaccessible, it had grown into trees with substantial
trunks. Gongshan is situated on a flat talus fan
which forces the Nu Jiang to make a smooth curve
round the eastern side of the mountain. I took a
shortcut across it below the main village, as I was in
haste and felt no need to call on the resident official;
at the time I did not know that he had previously
gone mad and died from overindulgence in opium
and schnapps, which he drank in quantities of eight
to ten rice bowlfuls daily. I stopped for the night at
Dara, a village up on the hillside, populated mainly
by Tibetans. I received maize cobs as a gift from my
hosts, but my porters did not have much success in
their search for provisions. When I was mustering
them next morning my servant suggested that I
should blow my whistle, because there was so much
shouting in the village. Before I could stop him he
seized the whistle, which was hanging round my
neck, and put it into his mouth — yet another example of Chinese disregard for hygiene! At Tjionra,
where I crossed to the east bank, there was a soldier
who had just arrived from Dêqên. I was afraid that
the authorities might be looking for me, but it
transpired that he had been sent there because of the
death of the official, and that he was in fact a good
friend of my men from the Lijiang district. My horse
had been sent there to meet me on my return. After
that long march I was so delighted to see it that I
could gladly have hugged it, shaggy and filthy as it
was. On 14th July I was back at Bahan, and was at
last able to concentrate on restoring my inside to
health.

Chapter 26. Along the Lancang Jiang - Nu Jiang Divide towards the Tibetan Border

Units of distance — a limestone peak (Maya, 4575 m) — structure of the mountain — through trackless wilderness — dead stands of bamboo — Kakerbo — Tibetans preparing tsamba — a moonlit night by a mountain tarn — Yigeru, Shidsaru and Gondonrungu (4475 m) — the path to Qunatong

By dosing myself with opium, bismuth and mint tea I strove to bring the diarrhoea under control, but the condition was slow to respond, probably because I also drank milk, which in my case tends to counteract such remedies. The Nu houses were ill-equipped for an illness of that kind, and to have to keep going out into the maize fields in the rain was unpleasant even in daylight, and far worse at night. The fleas in my room were gaining the upper hand and there were bugs as well; streamers of soot from the ceiling fell on to the bed, on to my head, into the food and on to the paper when I was writing. The flowering season was ebbing away and the material which my plant collectors gathered in the neighbourhood of the village contained little of note. Before long I yearned to be up in the mountains again; camping has its drawbacks, especially in wet weather, but all the trouble and toil brings its reward and would have been far better than doing nothing down there — which was not the purpose for which I had come to China.

By 31st July I was at last well enough to undertake another major journey into the mountains. My aim was to study the summer flowers of the Lancang Jiang - Nu Jiang (Mekong - Salween) divide near the Tibetan border, to visit one of the limestone peaks in that area, and to explore the depths of the Nu Jiang valley more thoroughly than had been possible on the return journey from the Drong Jiang. Setting out with fourteen porters, I at first followed the main track which I had used on my journey from Londjre to Bahan and reached the Shenzu La[127] on the third day. In the Doyon-lumba the men pointed out two wild bees' nests on a cliff high up on the opposite side of the valley. From that distance they looked like gigantic wasp nests and must have been at least 1.5 m in diameter. More plants were in flower in the forests than in the previous year, notably the rough, hairy *Begonia asperifolia* (a new species) on disturbed soil at the sides of the track, and *Rhododendron bullatum* hanging down over the rocks. The Maya[128] peak was free from cloud and I took the opportunity of sketching a clearly visible route, running between its rock towers, by which it could be climbed, as I foresaw that I might have to find the way in mist. My cook-servant went ahead, having been told by the head porter that it was still "liangge bei" (carry twice) to the next campsite, i.e., that the porters would have to lay down their loads once more before reaching it. This was an even more inexact measure than the Chinese "li", a unit not

favoured among the Tibetans. However, when they do calculate in li, theirs are longer than Chinese li, and the latter call them man-li ("savages' li"). It is quite wrong to regard the li as a measure of distance travelled; it is merely a measure of time taken, a fact clearly proved by the answer which I once received when I enquired how far it was to my destination: "Six li - but no, you're on horseback, so you can get there in four li!"[129] I pitched my tent on the same spot as in the year before, and found the cook awaiting me with a large lump of butter. The alpine pastures were now occupied. The senior herdsman weighed out his butter with great precision and took care not to let the Chinese cheat him. He had two strapping lads to assist him in his labours, there being numerous animals to look after — sheep, ponies, ordinary oxen, yaks and several bulls including one gigantic yak whose curly head and massive neck made him look like a bison. In the morning they applied themselves diligently to the propagation of their kind. The old herdsman had a black eye, apparently sustained when he had intervened between two bulls while one was trying to push the other off a cow.

The Maya looked splendid in the evening light; its grey limestone towers cast long shadows on the emerald green pastures and clouds drifted through its ravines. It was my prime objective, and I devoted August 3rd to the climb. I had not gone far beyond the pass at the foot of the first rocks when the summit of Kakerbo came into view — a narrow wedge of snow above the ridge to the north of the Shenzi La — as if heralding fine weather, favourable for geographical observations. Yet by the time I had reached the open stretches of turf above the first broad gully it had vanished. The clouds sank lower and lower and my earlier joy gave way to bitter disappointment. Botanically, too, the mountain, though a limestone inclusion in an otherwise igneous range, yielded less than I had hoped for. *Corydalis adrieni* had opened its fine blue flowers in the scree and the little orchid *Amitostigma forrestii (Orchis forrestii)* went right up to the summit. *Primula limbata* was in fruit on the rocks. *Ligularia cremanthodioides* was new, but *Sedum oreades, Pedicularis elwesii, Allium forrestii* and others were already known. I climbed steeply up grass slopes, over a scree and finally along the crest to the summit at 4575 m, but no sooner had I reached it than the clouds began to gather, permitting only brief glimpses of the forest-filled valleys at its skirts — views which though of great beauty were of little use for topographical purposes. The Gomba-la, a huge glaciated massif visible in its entirety during the

---

[127] Zhi-dzom La on Rock's map (3750 m), Shentse-la on Gregory's map.

[128] According to Rock (p. 327, 340) its name is Drachhen. The French christened it "Pic François Garnier". Rock gives its height as about 5180 m; Handel-Mazzetti's figure is 4575 m. Gregory's map gives 4506 m.

[129] Though officially a unit of distance, the "li" was indeed often calculated in this way (and sometimes still is). Thus, in mountainous areas, a downhill li might be much longer in distance than an uphill one (SGH).

ascent, had now vanished. Only to the north-north-east, towards Dêqên, did the view remain unobscured. Situated in that direction was Beimachang, a dark mountain with small glaciers. Using the treeline and the glaciation as indicators, I was able to estimate its altitude, and that of the other ranges, with reasonable confidence as 5300 m. Between Dêqên and the Yangzi was a limestone range of roughly the same altitude, its multiple peaks reminiscent of the Piepen group, and further north lay another even higher mountain, an enormous rugged massif with little glaciers. I lingered on the summit in the hope that Kakerbo and the taller snowpeaks of the Lancang - Nu Jiang divide might yet show themselves, but in vain; even the mountain group — about 5200 m high — on the near side of the Doker-la was cut off by a cloud bank. Below me stretched the buttresses and towers between which I had ascended. Beyond them I saw the hut and the tent, people and yaks looking like dots, and to the northeast on the treeline were some dark bog pools grouped on a level patch of ground. On the east side of the Saoa-lumba a limestone inclusion, dipping almost vertically to the west, formed the impressive sharp smooth crest of the Tratje-tra, but it ended before reaching the track from the Xi-la pass to Nisselaka and did not continue northwards over the Shenzu La. The watershed, however, bent eastward immediately to the south of Mount Maya, separating the catchment area of the Saoa-lumba from that of the river running down from Londjre; its highest peak was apparently not far north of the Xi-la. Another crest branched off at almost the same altitude to join a mountain group projecting towards the Lancang Jiang, situated more or less above Sere. However, the highest peak in the Lancang - Nu divide to the south of the origin of the Doyon-lumba was evidently Nange-la, [130] an obelisk probably reaching 5000 m located to the southeast of Bahan. The whole range has many similarities to our Central Alps in the shapes of its peaks, its terraces, cirques, avalanche corridors and other features. I took bearings and photographs as best I could and then started the descent, having spent more time in waiting than I liked.

To travel from Shenzu La to Qunatong on the Nu Jiang I now had to make a high level circuit round the heads of all five tributary valleys which ran down into the Doyon-lumba; at lower levels the forests were pathless and impenetrable. First there was a path across the east side of the Pongatong massif, which rises to 4600 m at a nodal point where a transverse chain joins the longitudinal mountain chain of the Maya. The track passed a mountain lake a few metres deep, which I netted for plankton. Filling the snowdrift hollows around it were *Draba jucunda, D.oreades, Potentilla microphylla* and *Polygonum nummularifolium.* The rest of the high alpine vegetation was extremely luxuriant. Among the plants were *Polygonum calostachyum, Aconitum* spp., numerous cruciates, *Meconopsis impedita, Veratrilla baillonii,* a gentian relative with green

flowers, *Gentiana subtilis,* a new species almost vanishingly small, a tall sage of the *Salvia campanulata* group, *Streptopus simplex, Ligularia yunnanensis, Nomocharis aperta, Nephrodium barbatum* and the dull red *Pedicularis tzekouensis,* but the most remarkable was a thistle, the new *Cirsium bolocephalum,* which I had previously seen in immature state on Mount Chiangshel in the Nu Jiang - Drung Jiang divide, a fiercely prickly plant with thick leaves and at the top of each spike a mass of white wool as big as a man's head, in which the large purple inflorescences appeared to be sunken. Climbing gradually, we reached the crest at 4375 m; going down the west side we entered the zone of dwarf rhododendrons above the tree line, where the bushes formed a continuous cover. The path faded out, and we trudged on laboriously to the north along the steep hillside, not losing or gaining much height, plodding across a low tanglewood of dwarf rhododendrons which yielded beneath the tread. In some places the pressure of my boots stripped off the bark, exposing the bare, slippery surfaces of the rhododendron branches. Punctuated by rock outcrops, small cirques and boulder fields, the mountainside stretched in a curve round the head of the valley, and though it was barely 3 km as the crow flies, the trek before us seemed endless when we turned to compare the stretch we had just traversed with such toil with the stretch which our guide — once again it was Kru — pointed out in front of us. At this juncture it seemed better to strike across the next branch valley; although that meant dropping down some 800 m and climbing up again, we did not have to plunge into the forest. We therefore steered straight ahead down a grassy gully. Then the slope grew steeper and steeper. Sliding rather than walking, catching hold of the bamboos and branches of larger rhododendrons, we finally reached the stream, after negotiating the rock ledges of the glaciated valleyside and an avalanche corridor. At the edges of the thickets I found yet another new edelweiss, the twelfth species I had gathered; it was *Leontopodium forrestianum,* which represents a link with the genus *Gnaphalium.* A little further down, on the salient between this and the next lateral stream, I found a place for the tent, among bog pools in a grove of large tree rhododendrons with brown leaves.

Next day we went up the lateral streams to reach the opposite crest higher up. The bamboos on the valleyside — probably all of them were *Arundinaria melanostachys* — had flowered a few years earlier and were now dead and fallen. To struggle through the tangle of canes, more than knee-high above the ground, either by wriggling through them or scrambling over them, was no easy task, especially as each man had believed that his chosen route was the best, with the result that no one had trodden out a path. After two hours we had made little progress, but then we realised that the stream itself was the best route, not merely here but also for the steep ascent further on. We clambered up over boulders with water running over them just as mountaineers in our own Alps sometimes have to use watercourses as routes up the steep sides of glacial valleys to avoid impenetrable thickets of alder. In a glacial hollow all

---

[130]Rock calls it Nam-la-shu-ga peak (p. 333). ONC H-10 gives its height as 5052 m.

the rivulets were filled with glistening bronze cushions of *Bryum handelii*, a new species of moss. Having passed through a cirque situated above the vertical step in the valleyside, I climbed up to a point where the watershed ran east and west, forming a broad flat ridge at 4425 m. To the north-northeast some movement was visible in the clouds and after a long wait I enjoyed a few brief glimpses of the summit of Kakerbo, gleaming in the sun. It emerged somewhat to the east, separated from another range consisting of countless little peaks rising up along the east side of the valley which ran down from the highest snow peaks to the north of the Doker-la and afforded access to the latter from the east. Another branch of this valley, perhaps almost as large as the northern branch, ran down from my viewpoint and joined it five kilometres above Londjre. Once again we followed the valley-side southwards along the high part of the Doker-la range which terminated here. In some places we had to make our way round the spurs which projected between each tributary stream. A few of the porters made a detour round the foot of each rock salient while others scrambled over them. I always went with the latter, for I knew that it was on the rocks that I would find the flowers that interested me most. Progress was slow and toilsome, especially as the porters kept stopping to collect stones for their fire-making equipment and roots of pemo [131] (*Nomocharis souliei*), a valued medicinal herb, or just to rest. It was in any case a strange experience to be journeying through these trackless mountains in the company of "savages" who ate with their hands. They prepared their tsamba in a stout bamboo or a hollow wooden cylinder. First they made the tea, then they threw in the butter and pounded and mixed them with a beater made of a perforated disc fastened to a long rod. The mixture was then poured into a simple wooden dish or a more valuable bowl turned from one of the galls which occur on various conifers. It was then filled with meal, and the mixture was kneaded by hand and eaten with the fingers.

We pitched camp beside a clear glacial tarn, bounded on one side by a moraine bank on which a few stunted firs struggled to survive. It was a gorgeous night. The full moon shone forth behind a huge rock pinnacle which was reflected on the smooth surface of the little lake. The moonbeams made a cone of light in the water and illuminated the screes plunging down from the upper crests of the Doker-la towards the tarn. Lost in admiration, I walked up and down on the shingle and the carpets of moss (*Polytrichum*) in front of the tent in the silence of that alpine night until the setting moon was replaced by the feebler but equally idyllic light cast by the stars and my Tibetans' campfires.

On 6th August a short march brought us to the Yigeru pass at 4315 m, which led from the fifth and most southerly branch of the Doyon-lumba into the high valley of Shidsaru. This turned in the opposite

direction and ran northwest via Bonga to Aben, where it joined the valley coming down from the Doker-la and debouched into the Nu Jiang a little further down, at Lakonra in Tsarong in Tibet. In its upper part the valley floor was flat; its forested slopes ascended gradually and the splendid peaks around it seemed to recede a little. I should have liked to climb one of the five thousand metre summits to the north, but after that clear night the weather had changed again and was not to be relied on. I collected a good haul of plants in the upper-most valley basin, where I again found *Cirsium bolocephalum*, though as was to be expected at that altitude of only 3950 m, it was taller (1 metre) and laxer in habit with up to forty flower heads. At midday, while we were surrounded by tall meadow vegetation, there was a violent hailstorm with loud peals of thunder and we had to crawl under the tent covers and awning until it had passed. A Nu tribes-man who had built a cattle shed on the opposite side exchanged a few shouted words with my men. He too was engaged in botany, though his interests were confined to medicinal roots; he was the only soul we met between the Shenzu La and Qunatong. The valley grew narrower and was completely filled with forest and jungle grass. Once again we had to use the stream as our route, and we camped in the undergrowth at the mouth of a short side valley on the right called Sandu. Viewed from the ascent next morning, it formed a bowl filled with forest and jungle grass, flanked by sombre mountain crags. The next valley beyond this lateral mountain chain was known as Lungdja; it belonged to a Nu community under Chinese sovereignty and not to Tibet. In this part of the forest there was no understorey of flowering plants except along the stream, where I found *Aconitum souliei* with green flowers and *Myricaria rosea* climbing up the willow trunks, but toadstools had already sprung up everywhere, and I filled my alcohol jar with them.

Next day we followed a narrow track leading steeply upwards through the forest on the south side of the Shidsaru valley. The treeline ran along the rounded glaciated rocks at the sides of the valley, and above it there was a narrow stretch of level ground, as everywhere in this valley. It was really an elongated corrie, and among its boulders grew *Cryptogramma crispa*, a little fern common in the Central Alps. We then climbed steeply up once more to Gondonrungu, a col in the sharp rock crest which separates the valley system of the Doker-la from the Nu Jiang gorge.

The col was at 4475 m and did not yield many plants, but on the descent, first over rocks then across boulders and loose scree, I found the beautiful *Pedicularis insignis* and a new *Meconopsis* (Fig.44) with blue flowers emitting a gorgeous scent of vanilla (*M. ouvrardiana*). [132] Unfortunately the distant views were obscured, and although I kept a watchful eye at all times, even during the midday rest, on the treeline of the short trench or rift valley which led

---

[131] Probably derived from "beimu", a term usually applied to Fritillaria bulbs when used as medicine (SGH).

[132] Handel-Mazzetti subsequently assigned it to *M.speciosa*.

steeply down to the Nu Jiang, only once or twice did I get a brief glimpse of the dense unbroken canopy of the dark broad-leaved forests lower down on this and the opposite side of the narrow Nu Jiang valley. Crossing grassy slopes with an abundance of flowers, we came out along the right side of the rift valley and at last found a place to camp, where the ground was made tolerably level by hacking away the tussocks of sedge, *Potentilla* and fern, though it was inconveniently far from the water. On the crest of Tongong itself we discovered a little path which, sloping gently at first and then very steeply, led down along the ridge in a descent of 2200 m. Below 3000 m we entered the warm temperate zone, and here we came to a Nu village named Punka, situated on the steep hillside and used in the summer only. Here I had to find another porter, for one of mine had just collapsed at the side of the track with a severe stomach upset and was unable to proceed at

more than a crawl. A second fairly large side valley sloped down much less steeply from the north-northwest into the Nu Jiang, and at the bottom both rivers ran for a short distance side by side in a small hollow, separated only by a narrow reef of mica schist. After descending a further 550 m on hard steep paths, somewhat punishing to the feet, I reached Qunatong [133] on 8th August. This village, lying at an altitude of 2025 m, consisted of a few houses and the mission building scattered amid maize fields on an old talus bank deposited above the northern stream.

----

[133] Chhu-na-thang on Rock's map, Kionatong on Gregory's map.

Chapter 27. Exploration on the Nu Jiang; Back to Cigu

The plant collectors depart for the Gomba-la — the great gorge of the Nu Jiang — renewing a rope-bridge — Gongshan — wild rumours — the collectors return — over the Xi-la — a robbery — famine on the Lancang Jiang — extortion

Although the Qunatong district might have been expected to offer a foretaste of the arid Tsarong and to be much drier than Gongshan and its surroundings, that was not my experience, even though it was true of the talus bank beside the stream, on which *Lycoris aurea* was flourishing, its large yellow flowers appearing before the leaves. Père Genestier found lodgings for me in a Nu house and we exchanged gifts as guest and host customarily do in China; he gave me fresh meat and I gave him canned foods. He was a man of wide experience, free from prejudice of any kind, and a good naturalist. I spent many a pleasant hour in his company, enjoying a never-failing supply of sweet Spanish altar wine. But the best thing he offered me was a set of herbarium sheets of spring-flowering plants, eleven in number, which I chose from his collection, most of which had been sadly damaged by insects. I used his help as interpreter when I wanted to give Lao Li and He instructions for collecting material from the giant conifer, which still puzzled me, and the late summer flora of the Nu Jiang - Irrawaddy divide round the lake and on the slopes of the Gomba-la above it. I could not blame the men for being reluctant to go back there; the reasons which deterred me from another high alpine expedition to that district applied with equal force to them. We had all had enough of those scrambles. He, who was already somewhat disgruntled, declared that he was going straight back to Lijiang. Lao Li burst into tears and said that he would do the journey with me, but was not willing to travel into the mountains without He, accompanied only by Tibetans and Nu tribesmen as porters; the sum of money which I offered left them both unmoved.

"In that case you won't get the big gratuity; that was promised only if you carry out my plans exactly as I wish," said I.

"We would rather go back home as beggars than go up there yet again," was He's rejoinder, delivered with the assurance of a man who was the owner of several houses.

It seemed that I had no option but to execute my plan myself, the main consideration which held me back being the lamentable state of my boots. I ordered the cook to get everything ready for the trip, and the faithful Lao Li declared that he would not desert me. But now the cook in his turn was greatly upset, for he too shared the emotions which we all felt. The cook then managed to persuade He to carry out the original project in conjunction with Lao Li, as he wanted to avoid the journey and to save himself the trouble of doing the cooking — not an easy task on the Nu Jiang. Next day, however, they actually set off. I had promised them a few dollars extra for flowers or cones from the mysterious conifer.

Near Qunatong there were rocks of crystalline limestone jutting out of the forest on this side of the river as well as the other, and according to Kingdon Ward there are large stretches of limestone further

north in the Doker-la [134] valley in Tsarong. I staked out a baseline on the horizontal ridge between the two streams and on 12th August, in order to obtain a third azimuth, I visited the corner at the exit from the great gorge through which the Nu Jiang flows down from Tibet. From these I was able to take cross-bearings on points which I had surveyed from the baseline at Bahan the year before, and hence establish the position of the new baseline in relation to the old. Opening upstream before me was one of the most impressive vistas I have ever beheld, not a far-ranging and diversified prospect, but an almost too narrow and confined spectacle of sombre magnificence, a picture of nature herself totally unspoiled by the hand of man, for the river gorge was without a path of any kind; only when the water level was exceptionally low was it possible to walk along the sand of the river bed itself, and the track from Qunatong ran high up over the mountains [135]. On that day the brown waters of the Nu Jiang came roaring, foaming and swirling down the gorge, crammed between vertical cliffs of brown rock. Continuing immediately above them, the sides of the valley sloped upwards at an angle of 60°, on the right for over 2000 m and on the left, though out of sight, to an even greater height. The slopes were covered by dark forest, broken only by rock outcrops. The view extended north-westwards up the gorge to a point 8 km distant where it was blocked by the huge rock massif which guards the Tibetan frontier. Its jagged summit, 4500 m above sea level, rose 2700 m above the river. Opening at its foot, in a re-entrant behind the Gomba-la, at a point concealed by projecting cliffs, was the lateral valley the headwaters of which I had seen on my return journey from the Irrawaddy.

The crate which I had ordered to be sent from Bahan now arrived after two days' delay, as the porter had been afraid to use the ropebridge and had taken a roundabout route along this side of the Nu Jiang. On 14th August I left Qunatong with Lü as my plant collector instead of the other men whom I had sent off to the Gomba-la. Acting on Genestier's advice, I had sent a message to the new official at Gongshan asking him to have the ropebridge renewed as the old one was too dangerous; here on the

---

[134] F. Kingdon Ward travelled up the Salween in June 1911 and refers to "a wonderful limestone gorge" above Aben on the ascent to the Doker-la. (*The Land of the Blue Poppy*, Cambridge, 1913, p. 101). He revisited Qunatong (Kienuatong) in November 1913 (*Mystery Rivers of Tibet*, London, 1923, p. 186)

[135] There was in fact a path through the granite gorge upstream from Qunatong (Tjionatong). Kingdon Ward travelled it in January 1914 and describes a perilous journey: *"For a couple of miles the path, through scrub forest, soon two or three hundred feet above the river, was easy enough, but presently we came to a series of terrific granite precipices ... Smooth walls of rock 20 and 30 feet high faced us, and to negotiate them long thin tree trunks, with notches for steps, led from ledge to ledge..... No wonder the natives prefer crossing the mountain to going through the granite gorge!"* (*Mystery Rivers of Tibet*, London, 1923, p. 258-9).

Nu Jiang they did not last long, and on one occasion two out of a party of four travellers had been drowned. He replied that the bridge would be open on 13th August. On reaching the bridge located between Qunatong and Wuli we found that its ropes, though not new, did not look unduly old, and we began cautiously to cross, though it creaked most alarmingly. When nearly all of us had crossed, a large party of Nu tribesmen arrived bringing the new ropes, which appeared to have been insufficiently twisted and badly knotted. They offered a good opportunity for group photographs, but otherwise were of no use to me. They set to work at once. Most of them crossed over, wound one end of the new rope round the old for some distance and lashed them together at several points. The old rope was then cut free, and a large gang, hauling with all their might, pulled the heavy load out of the water, which seemed reluctant to let it go, wound the rope round the post on the far side and tied it securely in place. To tighten a rope which has slackened needs six men, and is no light task. Down by the river the air was humid and sultry, and the plant life was of a kind to be expected under such conditions. Woodland of maquis type as in the Lancang valley is found in only a few places on the Nu Jiang; for the most part it was subtropical rainforest, with a profusion of orchids (*Cymbidium giganteum*) on the treetrunks, though their flowers were alas over, and I found a new Gesnerad with purple flowers (*Lysionotus sessilifolius*) creeping over the rocks. I stopped for the night in Sitjijong [136] so as to be able to collect plants at leisure, but made no new discoveries of any great interest.

Having arrived in Gongshan [137] I paid my visit to the official and spent the night in his office. Formerly there was a large lamasery [138] in Gongshan, but the monks had dispersed and become peasants and the flow of novices had dried up. The temple walls and the statues of the gods were now crumbling beneath the collapsing roofs. At one time the Chinese had established a military post there, but a few years ago, alarmed by rumours that the Tibetans were approaching from Tsarong, the soldiers hastily fled, and Gongshan had lost any importance it may once have had [139]. The official was of junior rank and had only two soldiers under him. That autumn, however, I heard stories that a town was to be built there as base for trade with Tsarong. As I had now completed what I had set out to do, I could afford to disregard the expressions of dismay and concern which crossed the face of the official as he listened

to my servant's hurried account of my journey to the Drung Jiang, and his description of the savages who did not wear any clothes; it was now too late for him to interfere. The flat alluvial fan of Gongshan was covered by moist meadows in which *Hypericum hookerianum* and *Pieris ovalifolia* were numerous. Because of some legal objection raised by the Chinese the people were not allowed to grow rice there, although the terrain would have been ideal with it. There were two deep, steep-walled trench-like valleys — one carrying the tributary from the Gumbälo valley and the other, much shorter, lying immediately to the north. Near the foot of the mountain they approached closely to one another, cutting channels through the alluvial fan, and from some viewpoints creating an impressive effect by their sheer simplicity of form. In the afternoon I walked downstream along the bank of the Nu Jiang, where I collected a creeping and climbing Gesnerad with scarlet flowers (*Aeschynanthus chorisepalus*) and some lichens and mosses living on leaves. After crossing the Nu Jiang I slept at Tjionra and on the evening of 18th August arrived once more in Bahan, riding on my horse which had been fetched for me by a porter sent on in advance.

In Bahan I received letters from home — the first to have reached the Nu Jiang — and reports of unrest on the Tibetan border to the north; there were fears for the safety of the mission at Yerkalo (Dsakalo) [140]. The Chinese also asserted that serious disturbances were imminent in Dali and perhaps throughout Yunnan. Lü, the headman and landowner of Nguluke, was said to be extremely anxious. The men who brought these reports had come there to purchase native herbal medicines and were obviously trying to depress prices — an instance of market-rigging on the borders of Tibet! I climbed up once again into the forest behind the mission to look for an unusual tree which Genestier had described to me. It proved to be *Magnolia rostrata*. As my guide I had taken with me my host in Bahan, who was also the local headman and landowner. With his hatchet he chopped out notches in two tree-trunks, put them together and climbed up barefoot to procure some of the old infrutescences, as I had not previously been able to reach any.

On 22nd August my collectors returned with a splendid haul amounting to seventy-five botanical specimens. They also brought plenty of ripe cones from the conifers which had aroused my interest. The branches were closely covered with small scale-like leaves and divided into numerous twigs, the cones being located at their tips. They had had to fell one of the trees and charged me an extra 20 cents for the hire of a small hatchet borrowed from a Tibetan. Considering the long hours of work which this must have cost them, I paid it gladly. I immediately sent a specimen to Camillo Schneider at the Arnold Arboretum, and in the following winter received his identification: it was *Taiwania cryptomerioides*, a genus discovered on Formosa in 1905 and first described in 1906. Some of the porters failed to arrive in Bahan until late that evening and one tent

---

[136] Ssu-chi t'ung on Rock's map.

[137] Ch'ang-p'u-t'ung on Rock's map. Tra-mu-tang in Kingdon Ward's books — also T'sam-p'u-t'ong (*The Land of the Blue Poppy*, Cambridge, 1913, p.84).

[138] The lamasery, built in 1765, was burnt down in 1905 by Chinese soldiers sent to avenge the murder of the Catholic priest and the destruction of the mission at Bahang. (Rock, page 336 and Plate 193).

[139] It is now the administrative centre of the Gongshan Drung and Nu Autonomous County, established in 1956 (SGH).

[140] Yanjing (Tsha-kha-lo) on the Lancang Jiang.

load was missing. At noon next day a man from Meradon brought it up and said that the porter responsible for it had absconded. I withheld payment, and was then confronted by about a dozen men, mostly Chinese, who wanted me to pay the debts owed to them by the porter who had run off. One of them had lent him $1, another $3; their claims totalled about $20, all at good rates of interest, while my liability to the missing porter amounted to only $5. I gave them that sum to share out, laughed scornfully at them for having lent money so indiscreetly, and threw them out. If they caught him they would certainly give him a sound thrashing and that, according to the ideas of justice in that remote spot, would wipe out the debts as effectively as if they had been repaid. In addition the silly ass would be forced, amid general merriment, to distribute his wages to all and sundry and would have been beaten for good measure.

I let the men rest for two days and then set off once more along the track to Cizhong, taking with me as porters some of the numerous people who had come from there to Bahan as soon as they heard of my impending departure. Père Ouvrard once more took charge of my barometer so that I could ascertain the altitude difference between Cizhong and Bahan from a short series of observations. The gallant fellow, to whom I am deeply indebted, stood there waving long after I had departed. I crossed the Xi-la, halting at the same places as in 1915 though I lost my bearings because of poor visibility, and reached the crest at a point somewhat to the south. I sent ahead all the things I had finished with and took shelter in a hut not far from my highest campsite on the outward journey (Dotitong) in the hope, weather permitting, of climbing the highest peak in the vicinity. As I had just confirmed, this was located near the origin of the first lateral valley to the west and was accessible through it. However, mist and drizzle persisted until midday, and I finally struck camp, reaching Cizhong in the evening of 29th August.

Here I was presented with a collection of some two thousand butterflies which the people had assembled at my request. Unfortunately — despite the good training which the missionaries had given the collectors — barely one quarter of them were in

usable condition. On 31st August I sent a messenger to Bahan to fetch my barometer on the following day. However, on the same afternoon he came back, greatly excited, with the news that there were "two hundred" Lisu tribesmen in the Saoa-lumba; they were robbing all the buyers of medicinal herbs and assaulting anyone who opposed them. These reports were confirmed by several other people coming from the mountain. Yet a second messenger, sent off soon afterwards, got through without any trouble and found no remaining traces of the Lisus' presence. Probably their raid was, as usual, aimed at the flocks guarded by the shepherds on the mountain pastures, but conceivably they were looking for me; whatever the truth of the matter, it was indeed fortunate that my journey along that route had been completed some days earlier, at a time when there was not the slightest hint of any trouble. I now spent some time in purchasing objects of ethnographic interest. Here again I was lucky: on the Lancang Jiang the weather had been exceptionally dry; the maize bore small deformed cobs or none at all, and in the buckwheat fields there was no more than a little red patch in the middle. Famine compelled the people to sell everything they possessed and buy rice in Weixi. Some families had already emigrated and banditry began to flare up again in the Lancang Jiang valley, where it had long been almost unknown. I was accordingly able to purchase religious objects which their owners would normally have been reluctant to part with. In these negotiations Li Tere and a man from Sichuan acted as middlemen; chaffering beneath my window, the latter shamelessly extorted his own rake-off from each of the vendors and would not let them come up and see me until I intervened to enforce fair play; even then, however, he found other excuses — the owner of the object was on the other side of the river, and so on. Li Tere swindled a poor old lama out of two thirds of the price of his prayer wheel. When his misdeeds came to light he broke down in tears, but both of them had lost face with the villagers. On 6th September I went up the Lancang Jiang valley to Sere, where I photographed a few important subjects omitted in 1915 because of lack of plates, and then said farewell to that land for ever.

Chapter 28   Via Weixi to Jianchuan and Lijiang

Surveying in the Lancang Jiang valley — the Weixi valley — distrustful soldiers — over eight passes through unknown country — escorted by Lisu guards — honey — Luotui Shan and Lanchouba — geological formations — over the Yenaping pass south of Laojun Shan

I reappointed Li Tere, now somewhat humbled and contrite, as caravan leader and he assembled the muleteers from Cizhong and Cigu. On 8th September we crossed the ropebridge at Cigu, that being the one I knew best. The men would gladly have renewed it at my expense, but I declined, having already spent quite enough money in their villages. They enquired tentatively whether I would hold them responsible if any of the baggage they were carrying rolled into the river. One of them, having lost some property belonging to a Chinese from Dêqên, had had the unhappy experience of

being sued for compensation, and although he had been cleared by the court in Weixi, the case had cost him good money. I was willing to absolve them from responsibility only if they stayed beside their mules and not if they walked at the rear of the caravan chatting to one another. However, I was not seriously concerned, as I knew that any mishap would cost a Tibetan his beast as well as its load, while a Chinese muleteer is more or less indifferent to the loss of his employer's property, carried as it is on a pack frame on which it rests loose and unsecured.

The natural vegetation was as parched as the field crops and I was therefore free, without fear of missing anything of botanical interest, to devote my attention to a detailed survey of the river valley, its slopes and lateral valleys as far as I could see along them; the results enabled me to make useful revisions to the existing maps, especially as regards the lengths and directions of the side valleys. Having reliable guides, I was able to verify the distribution of each tribe and the place names by repeated cross-checks, and to ascertain the names of the numerous Lisu villages on the sides of the valley. On reaching Yezhi I took good care to lodge with the tusi, who was on friendly terms with the missionaries. Near Maliping was a spot formerly dreaded by travellers, where bandits used to lie in wait among stone walls and maize fields, in the bushes or in the fir woods. On that very day there seemed to have been some incident of that kind. Standing at the side of the forest path was a Chinese trader with a wound in his temple; two Tibetans from his caravan were carrying sacks on their backs and higher up in the forest I saw his packhorses. I never found out what had happened, but it seems likely that he had been ambushed. The tusi of Gangpu [141] invited me to a meal, but I declined with thanks, as I had plenty to do. He nevertheless sent me a few delicacies, including a dish of roast grasshoppers. Their flavour was not at all bad, but after trying two or three my gorge rose and I could not stomach any more. The revolting dishes which my cook set before me had totally spoilt my appetite for Chinese titbits.

I spent 15th and 16th September in Weixi and persuaded my muleteers to extend our contract as far as Lijiang. They were at first reluctant to go as they had heard that horses were being requisitioned there, but in Weixi they evidently received reassuring reports. My servant said he could not understand why I wanted to keep the "natives", when Chinese mafus were available at low rates. For my part, I wanted nothing to do with obstinate Chinese caravan-men and horses with running sores on their backs; I had Tibetans who responded with anxious exclamations of concern — their word was "alee" — to the least sign of undue pressure on their horses' backs, though their mode of loading tended to put the main weight on the shoulders, and they even asked me for medicine to treat them. I knew that the official was an intelligent man, well disposed towards foreigners, and I gave notice that I would call on him at 3 pm, but although I waited for a considerable time he did not appear. He had probably heard where I had been and wanted to avoid any conversation on matters that could only have been disagreeable to him. A policeman asked to see my passport; as I did not at once understand the word, and as my servant perhaps did not know that I possessed any such thing, he had to be content with a visiting card. I was more than pleased that the xianzhang [142] provided without demur an escort of

two soldiers for the straight road to Jianchuan, for on this occasion I had no desire to deviate from the route. During the following winter he was murdered with boiling oil during a rebellion against taxes.

On 17th September the cook had gone shopping, a task which he had evidently not had time to complete during my two day stay. I waited until 9 am but he did not return, and Lao Li was unable to find him in the town. He was presumably holed up somewhere with a bottle of schnapps and must have forgotten all about our departure. I waited quite long enough for him at the lunch halt, and he finally turned up at Jingutang that evening, an hour after I had got in, riding on a pony dripping with sweat and accompanied by two more soldiers whom he had engaged for his personal protection — and for whom I made him pay — and immediately threw himself down on a bed beside me.

The road followed the stream beneath the gravel plain, here 4 km wide, which filled the Weixi basin; it had a few low terraces and was furrowed by tributaries. At a Naxi village called Toju the main branch of the valley ran up through a somewhat deeper basin to the east; there were said to be iron mines higher up. We turned south-eastwards along a narrow little valley in which Jingutang was situated. This village and the others nearby, occupied by Chinese and Lisu, consisted of only a few houses. Among their fields of maize and buckwheat were patches of cockscomb (*Amaranthus hypochondriacus*), its deep bloodred flowers making a brilliant picture. Hemp, used by Lisu and Pumi for making clothes, was also widely cultivated. The stems, tied into bundles, had been hung up to dry from the branches of the trees bordering the fields. The soldiers slept in the cramped and crowded house where I was accommodated, and that evening, as I was sitting at the camp table making a fair copy of my route survey, one of them suddenly appeared and gazed down at my work. What was I to do? He had approached unexpectedly out of the darkness and probably understood what I was engaged in. In my alarm my first impulse was to turn the sheet upside down or lay it aside, but such an action would certainly not have saved the situation. I therefore went on with my sketching as if I were completely unconcerned. I often heard the soldiers talking about my map-making, an activity which was strictly prohibited, especially in those border areas, but whenever the situation seemed to look threatening my servant slipped them a dollar and I was able to pretend that I was doing it with a clear conscience. Every time he gave them a bribe they asked: "What's that for?" and he simply replied: "To buy rice." At the end of the journey I handed them a generous tip as well. I felt they were unlikely to give me away, since they had never tried to tell me that map-making was forbidden and if they had informed on me at that late stage they would have found themselves in trouble for not stopping me much earlier. This resourcefulness was one of my servant's good points and because of it I was willing to overlook his drinking. In many a crisis he managed on his own initiative to find a way of dealing with the situation. He never confined himself to mere obedi-

---

[141] Kangpu on Handel-Mazzetti's map.

[142] County magistrate. A popular term, not an official title (SGH).

ence to the letter of my orders, but on the other hand it was difficult to induce him to obey commands — for instance those concerned with cleanliness — when he did not understand their purpose. At the last overnight halt before reaching Kunming he had been sweeping out the room at the hostelry and had collected a substantial pile of rubbish. When I told him to get rid of it he replied: "I'll just sweep it under the bed!" However, I later heard that this reluctance on the part of the Chinese to sweep anything out of a room apparently has some religious basis.

Leaving the Weixi valley system, the track then climbed over a steep ridge at 3025m and entered another valley running down in the opposite direction. All the tops were clothed with dense mixed forest, but the sides of the valley were under cultivation everywhere and there were numerous large Lisu villages. The next part of the valley was a narrow gorge leading southwest; after some 7 km it curved southwards past a fairly low range of mountains consisting of several wooded domes lying on this side (east) of the Lancang Jiang. The track did not follow this valley, but ran southwards across it and continued for two and a half days some distance from its eastern side. To the left (east) we now saw the limestone crest of Baiyazi [143] rising abruptly to a height of some 3800 m. On the right of the track, between it and the main valley, was a more or less vertical limestone wall running in a straight line to the south-southeast, though visible only here and there among the forest. Its existence was the reason for the peculiar configuration of the landscape. Between it and the high mountains to the east a channel running north-northwest to east-southeast had been scooped out in the soft sandstone; it consisted of a series of cols, all at much the same altitude (2850 to 3020 m), arranged in a straight line and cutting to differing depths into the ridges, which rose up again to higher altitudes to the right of this limestone wall. Between these east-west ridges ran six side valleys, coming together exactly along the line of the route, which led over all these cols. In some places several headwaters united in a small basin and then broke through a narrow spot in the limestone wall to reach the west. In Muguazuo, our second night's halt, we heard that a robber band some twenty strong had been roaming about on the next col for the last few days; they had already shot at and wounded several travellers and relieved them of their property. In response to our request the Lisu headman gave us an escort of twelve of his men armed with swords, crossbows and poisoned arrows, so that we were at least as numerous as the bandits and were equipped with weapons which would certainly command more respect from them than the soldiers' rifles could have done. Apart from a few baskets and scraps of paper scattered on the ground beyond the pass leading to Basulo we saw no trace of them.

---

[143] Pengaitse on Handel-Mazzetti 's map.

The view from the next col was most instructive. It was a gracious, undramatic landscape of gentle rounded hills and ridges in every shade of green, covered by forests — chiefly pine, but also some fir and spruce — and meadows as far as the eye could see. Growing along the brooks were *Pterocarya forrestii* and an elm. The straight channel formed by the four cols which we still had to traverse continued in front of us along the narrow plain of Lanchouba, which stretched out in exactly the same direction along the left branch of the river, now flowing towards us. Here I made a discovery which gave me great pleasure. In the rotting leafmould of the mixed woodland, I found for the first time *Neottia listeroides*, a slender grey-brown orchid previously reported only from India. It was present in considerable numbers, and among it were a few specimens of another saprophytic orchid without any leaves, *Epipogium aphyllum*, suffused with a pinkish violet tinge, also a new record for China. It brought back memories of home; as a fourteen year old boy its discovery at a new location in Tirol had been the first major botanical triumph of my early years. Lisu villages were scattered here and there, and as we descended we came to Yisitsa, a large Pumi village where the Chinese had established a police post. Here I dismissed my Lisu escort, not because of the police, but simply because the road from there on was safe. The sturdy Pumi people, here quite tidily dressed in simple garments of grey hempen cloth, were perhaps of better physique than any of the other tribesmen in Yunnan. Their dwellings, and those of the Lisu people, were built in exactly the same style as the Naxi houses. Remembering the bread with butter and honey which I had enjoyed on the journey from Weixi onwards the year before, I instructed my servant to ask whether honey was available in this district; butter I had brought with me from Cigu. He came back and said, "There is honey here, but it looks so strange that I'd better show it to you first, so you can see if you can eat it." It was in fact pure clear golden-yellow honey fresh from the comb, as fine as any I had ever seen at home, but being familiar only with the opaque fermented honey which the Chinese always adulterated with cheap sugar, he hardly recognised it for what it was.

In Jinkou, the next village, all the school children, wearing brick-red caps of military style, were marching in a line along the road. At their teacher's command they bowed deeply to me; in response I graciously raised my right hand to my hat while using my left to hold together a large rent in my coat. The teacher ran after me and tried to start a conversation, but I felt disinclined to stop. A short distance further on we saw on the left a substantial group of mountains, known as Luotui Shan, Labako or Tapiso in the Pumi language, called Laba Shan by the Chinese. I had often seen it from high vantage points near Lijiang, but had never been certain of its exact location. It was built of dark sandstone in sharply demarcated bands. The main summit was a steep, almost horizontally stratified block reaching an altitude of about 4300 m. Around it were a few lower crags, their strata tilted at various angles, disposed along a broad high ridge. As I came to each of the valleys coursing down from the left I could see that they all debouched into a main channel which ran north and south, diverging further and further from the line of my route. This channel apparently ran parallel with the Lancang Jiang, separated from it by the aforementioned range, which was clothed with broad-leaved forest. I never viewed this range in its entirety, but having seen several portions of it at various times, I found when I came to draft the map that they fitted together in continuity. As there was no sign of any transverse valley or water gap breaking through the range down to the Lancang Jiang, I concluded that this longitudinal channel must be the one which debouches into the Lancang Jiang at Yingpanjie, despite information later given to me when I was in Shadian, namely that the river at that place, which quite obviously belongs to the same valley system, allegedly debouched into the Lancang Jiang at Xiaodian, i.e., at the same latitude as Muguazuo. When one gets to know the heedlessness and irresponsibility of the Chinese in such matters, one learns to trust one's own eyes in preference to their stories, though in Yunnan there actually are deeply cut channels and water gaps which can easily escape the distant observer, and I therefore regard the above conclusions as falling some way short of certainty. Nevertheless, the survey of the route from Weixi to Jianchuan and the adjacent territory was one of the most valuable results of my travels in China, as there had previously been no satisfactory map of the broad tract of country between the Lancang Jiang and Yangzi (Yangbi Jiang) rivers from Weixi to Dali.

From the last col, at 2850 m, between Daizidian and Shadian we now saw the Lanchouba itself. It was an extended plain, a little over 1 km broad, covered by meadows through which the river meandered. The slopes on either side were at first quite low and gentle, with small rounded shoulders projecting here and there. Along the sides of the plain there were several villages and in the middle, where it began to merge into the horizon, we saw the gleaming white walls of Dongdian, a town of some size. On the left (east) were two conspicuous peaks forming a double summit, and to the right, looking over a broad high forested crest, we saw Yelu Shan, a flat treeless pyramid probably reaching 4000 m. Continuing without alteration in breadth, the Lanchouba formed its own horizon, rising at first imperceptibly and then sloping down in the same configuration to a tributary of the Yangbi Jiang. Shadien, where we spent the night, was situated at a considerably greater altitude than the entry to the gorge through which the little river curved down to the west. I followed the plain for another full day's march, keeping always along its eastern margin. The inhabitants were Bai and were subject to the authorities in the salt mining town of Lanping Xian or Ladjimin, lying further to the west. The watershed marking the transition to the next river drainage area was almost imperceptible, and was situated at 2775 m. A rivulet coming from the west flowed down only a short way before reaching the middle of the

plain and turning southwards in a deeply incised trench, while further streams, coming down from the mountains on both sides and uniting at Fengjia and Huangzhuchang, still adopted a northerly course.

As we came down from the col the scenery gradually changed. First there were rounded headlands of hard limestone which brought some diversity into the sandstone landscape. On the right side of the valley they were arranged in a straight line, but as they ran south they gradually diverged from the route. They emerged from beneath the talus of the plain and the mountain range to the east, extending only a short distance on the mountains to the west, and terminated there in steep stratified bluffs above the core of the mountain, which consisted of crystalline rocks or sandstone. Above the smooth arid rock slabs the hillsides were covered with brownish holly-leaved oak scrub interspersed with pines; the bluffs were capped by luxuriant forest and the rocks of the mountain core were also wooded. The valley broadened into a triangle, the stream being pushed to its left (east) side by talus fans which ran down from Yelu Shan on the left (west) and formed a sloping area, parts of it under cultivation. Emerging from this slope, apparently disposed at random, were more bluffs or headlands, both large and small, all evidently of limestone, some coalescing into large islands while others formed peninsulas or spurs connected to the foot of the mountain. These wonderful geological formations await investigation by a specialist. The valley seemed to continue for some 20 km, bending a little towards the east, before it was once again narrowed by the encroachment of the mountain range on the west. Bai villages were scattered throughout its length, some of considerable size such as Xianshengyi [144], through which we passed, and Majiping further downstream across the river on an enormous alluvial fan. We stopped for the night at Dajingtou, at the confluence with the main river, which rose about 25 km away to the northeast in the Laojun Shan, a mountain range whose steep walls extended even down to this level. Here I again took bearings and photographs in every direction, as I now had to quit the valley.

The track now turned eastwards through a small side valley about 10 km long and climbed to the Yenaping pass situated at 3250 m on the crest to the south of the Laojun Shan, a mountain at that time not shown on any map. It lies 25 km northwest of Jianchuan, reaching roughly 4200 m — a broad, seemingly arid limestone bastion above the sandstone, with steep precipices on this side. The track had been washed away by a cloudburst and recently rebuilt — which was lucky for me, as the sections of the old track which I saw were in a frightful state of disrepair, although it was the main road between Jianchuan and Ladjimin. The roadmender had to beg his wages from passing travellers, a state of affairs I had more than once encountered among the Chinese; yet after all, they were his customers. As in many parts of the Yunnan highlands, red sandstone in gently dipping strata, here and there forming steep

---

144 Schiensendyi on Handel-Mazzetti 's map.

escarpments, made the floor of the basin, which was uncultivated and filled with light green pine forest. After a short stretch along the crest, which sent off broad spurs to the south and gradually diminished in altitude, the track descended into the basin. It then followed a brook running southeast, which like its tributaries, most of which came from the north, had cut itself a narrow trench. Late that evening, having passed only a few poverty-stricken dwellings, we arrived at Liping. Here the valley floor grew broader and cultivation appeared. The stream continued in the same direction past some fair-sized villages, but my route led due east over a ridge 450 m higher running between the basin and the Yangbi Jiang. If the views from the Yenaping and Balashu passes had not been so clear, my survey of the basin, made simply while passing across it, would certainly not have been a success, but in fact the results were highly satisfactory, although the fine weather now broke. Descending from the Balashu pass I reached Jianchuan exactly one week after leaving Weixi; there I was once more in known territory.

For the last stage of the journey I had an escort of four soldiers, one of whom craned his neck with curiosity every time I pulled out my notebook. However, they all slunk to the rear of the caravan as we climbed up to the pass where bandits sometimes lurked. Retracing the route of my return journey in 1914, I arrived in Nguluke on 26th September after three days on the road.

Chapter 29. Autumn in the Lijiang District

Fungi — the American zoologists — views of the Yulong Shan from Lozhatso — an ascent through snow — autumn flowers — the Jinsha Jiang gorge and its cataracts

There were still plenty of tasks to be done, but the fine weather needed for them was a long time in coming. Rain fell from dawn to dusk, changing to snow 200 m above the village, and it was cold, misty and abominably dark. What made it even more annoying was that most of the nights were beautifully clear. Gleaming in the bright moonlight, the snow-capped peaks soared into the dark sky, while the main summit, peeping over the col between Hosayigo and Ünlüpe, seemed to look straight down into the house where I lodged. Under such conditions there was an abundant crop of fungi sprouting in the woods round the village, but it was so wet that I felt disinclined to go hunting for them. One of the natives brought me a basketful every day — over a hundred species of toadstools in all. I had them dried on a bamboo mat over a charcoal fire, made notes of their colour and form, and then, when they were hard and dry, left them in the room until they softened sufficiently to be pressed between paper into a somewhat flatter shape. There were others which seemed unlikely to respond well to drying, and these I pickled in alcohol. Although much of this labour and money was spent in vain, the identification of toadstools from preserved specimens being very difficult, part of the material yielded results of some value, more especially as no one had previously studied the fungi of the Chinese mountains. The inconspicuous mosses of the heavy meadows and fallow fields round Lijiang proved of special interest: one of them, *Brachymeniopsis gymnostoma*, constitutes a new genus, *Aongstroemiopsis julacea* was previously known only from the high mountains of Java, and *Astomiopsis sinensis* belongs to a genus otherwise represented only by two species from the Andes. Zhao had collected 450 specimens of flowering plants for me and dried them very neatly, an operation which was easily performed in his house. He could no longer remember what wage I had agreed to pay him or how much of it he had already received through Kok, but he said that I would certainly know how much it was. I sent all the collections to Lijiang and had them soldered up in tin boxes. I had to ride there twice in the foulest weather, for all this work had to be carefully supervised to make sure that none of the joints were left open. An imperfectly soldered tin box is worse than none at all. I invariably nailed down the wooden crates myself, as the Chinese would certainly have driven the nails into the tin lining.

On 8th October the skies at last brightened. The fine weather of autumn began and I was able to set to work. On the next day I was expecting the American Zoological expedition — Mr and Mrs Andrews and Mr Heller from the Zoological Museum in New York — having already heard of their arrival in Lijiang. They were lodging in the temple and as I arrived there to call on them I was astonished to be greeted with the words:

"Do you have clean hands?".

The next sentence made the situation clear:

"You've arrived just in time to deal with a case of blood poisoning".

I helped Mrs Andrews to open a whitlow on her husband's finger, possibly caused by handling arsenic, and in a few days it had healed. They were experienced hunters; Mrs Andrews travelled on horseback wearing men's clothing, and she describes in their book[145] the amazement and delight with which the ladies of the Pentecostal Mission in Lijiang greeted her sudden appearance, despite her unconventional dress. Our conversation turned first to the question of good hunting grounds, but I was unable to give them much advice as I had never taken any interest in such matters and could offer nothing more than hearsay and my inexpert appraisal of the terrain through which I had travelled. Contrary to all expectations, Andrews and Heller caught a rich assortment of mammals in their traps on the Yulong Shan.

In order to complete my map I decided to climb a minor summit which promised a good view of the snow peaks and the mountains to the east of them.

---

[145] Roy Chapman Andrews and Yvette Borup Andrews, *"Camps and Trails in China"*, New York, 1918.

Its name was Lozhatso [146] and it was situated in the range on the east of the Dagu road, directly opposite the enormous Luoqu gorge. Seen from Nuguluke, it had the appearance of a low pyramid of white scree. My first visit was unsuccessful. Although the morning was enticingly fine, by midday the range was hidden by a bank of cloud through which individual peaks emerged fleetingly here and there, and though I took compass bearings, photography was impossible. Two days later, on 12th October, I set out again and this time, luckily, I had glorious weather all day. We took the main Lijiang-Dagu road, which we reached at the edge of the forest, but soon branched off to the right over a narrow transverse ridge covered with bushes and perforated by sinkholes. This was one of a number of such ridges which, though only a few paces from top to bottom, carved up the gorge into several separate ravines. The gorge itself, perhaps originating in earlier times from the Gaba glacial lake, debouched into the Lijiang plain.

Riding through pine forest and across turf, we soon came to the foot of the mountain, and I was actually able to ride halfway to the top along a kind of timber chute. For the rest of the way I climbed through holly-leaved oak scrub, reaching the rounded summit at 3625 m, just north of the white scree pyramid, after a three hour journey from the village. The Yulong Shan [147] range was now revealed in its entirety just opposite. The gigantic snow peaks towered into the blue sky, flanked by knife-edged ridges of ice; very few rock faces were visible, and they were powdered with recent snow. To the north and slightly to the west of Satseto was the second main peak, Dyinaloko, evidently its equal in height (5450 m). Like a recumbent giant, the mountain range, slightly indented by the headstreams of the Baishui torrent, sloped down to gently undulating forest and the broad meadow known as Gaba, at one time a lake. On the south side of Satseto was the colossal Luoqu gorge, its mouth opening directly opposite us. During former ice ages its glacier had pushed huge moraines far out into the lowlands. The whole vista, though by no means the largest, is perhaps the most perfect and most beautiful example of glacial scenery to be seen anywhere in the world. The largest of the present-day glaciers on this side was fed by a snowfield high up on Satseto, and its fissured snout hung down the slope to an altitude of 4075 m. Starting from the névé basin, a high snow-covered rock wall led up to the crest, and the latter itself had a vertical overhang. Having at last had this clear view, I realised that I had to give up any thought of climbing the main summit, even though it might be attainable by really capable mountaineers. To the north the chain of rock pinnacles, foreshortened from my viewpoint, seemed to merge into a continuous wall, and vanished behind one of the lower heights, a rounded dome above the Heishui torrent known as Konsago. All round me were mountains, the ranges between Yongsheng and

Yongning, and those round Muli and Dagu. In the clear autumnal air all the snow-capped tops were so distinct that I could even see, far away to the south southeast, the ranges of the Yunnan tableland. But at that moment I was more interested in the less distant scenery, the mountainous terrain on either side of the Yangzi to the northeast of Lijiang. All of it was lower than my viewpoint on Lozhatso, but several peaks stood out distinctly, notably Tomanyo, a pointed cone projecting near the river with a gleaming white temple on its top. However, I was unable to make any sense of the tangled confusion of valleys; there were evidently several blind-ended channels similar to one to the south of my viewpoint, in which the Yi settlement of Gwube was located.

Ünlüpe, a summit roughly 5000 m in altitude in the southern part of the Yulong Shan, had previously struck me as being not too difficult a climb, and what I saw of it on that day strengthened that impression. Rain fell in the night and next morning the mountains were shrouded in cloud, but on 14th October I was able to tackle the ascent. Starting from the Pelchua cirque, familiar to me from the expedition made in June 1915 with Kok and the Chinese official, I had to climb up to a broad, steeply sloping ledge which led on to a lateral ridge. This was not very steep and looked as if it should offer a climbable route to the top. Taking the last remaining nails I drove them two at a time into my climbing boots, choosing the points where they would give the best grip. Indeed, I had no others, since the boots made in Kunming had given up the ghost in the Nu Jiang, but as an extra precaution I took crampons as well. The American party had pitched their tents on Ndwolo, the great meadow, and their local hunters and muleteers had found shelter under trees and boulders; now that frost had banished the leeches and the brook, swollen by the snow, came further down the slope, it made a good campsite.

At 8.45 am, just as I was dismounting from my horse, I met the Americans above the huge crag below which the spring emerged. They had put out traps overnight and had had a rich haul; all their pouches were filled with mice, moles and other such creatures. I went on uphill in the mist which had just gathered, but bore too far to the left, missed the cirque and found myself on the screes, now thickly covered with snow, sloping down from the ridge. The mist lifted again, giving me a view of the route before me. My objective, a three-pointed rock pinnacle, stood out pale grey against the blue sky, and Satseto itself emerged for a moment from the mists enshrouding it. The snow had already slid off the avalanche slopes and was piled up below them less than two metres deep. As the sun had not come out, I was able to cross the mountainside without serious danger, deviating round the avalanche slopes either below them or above their uppermost extensions. However, I often broke through the snow crust to a depth well above the knee.

On starting the climb up to the ledge I wanted to send Lao Li back and take the rucksack myself as he was wearing thin shoes and was getting very cold, but he said he would go with me wherever I went. The route continued up an extremely steep snow-

---

[146] Lu-zher-dsu on Rock's map (12,200 ft = 3719 m)

[147] Yulong Shan was climbed on 8th May 1987 by an American party led by Eric S. Perlman. American Alpine Journal, 1988, **30**, 265.

slope with rocks projecting here and there. The crossing of the avalanche slopes had already cost precious time, and now we were plodding even more slowly forwards; every step had to be stamped out or chopped out with the ice axe. We were fatigued by constantly breaking through the snow crust, and at such altitudes, especially when breathing air above the snow, one has to pause after every few steps with pounding heart and aching head. An easier, less steep pitch led on to a little sharp-edged ridge which gave us a view of the next part of the ledge; seen in profile it looked exceedingly steep, and the rock crest, now we were close to it, proved extremely slippery. We were at 4750 m. Vestiges of flowering plants were still to be found, but it was already 1.30 pm. The peak, and indeed the whole of the mountain above the spot we had reached, were again hidden in cloud. To reach the summit would have taken another 1½ hours at least. At 6 pm it would be dark, and in any case I had accepted an invitation from the Americans to dine at 5 pm. I therefore gave up any hope of reaching the summit, photographed the view to the east, though even in that direction it was not entirely free from cloud, and started to descend. At the beginning of the steep pitch Lao Li was seized by an attack of dizziness. He turned round so as to face the mountainside; and in some stretches I did the same so as to get a secure foothold in the steps kicked out with the toes of my boots, but proceeding cautiously in front of me and obeying my detailed instructions he managed the descent successfully. [148] Once below the ledge we sat down and glissaded through the snow, to his great amusement. We then walked down through the cirque a good deal faster than we had ascended.

Although the snow had been lying for some time a few flowering plants were still undamaged, notably *Delphinium forrestii*, its papery pale blue flowers with their conspicuous veins well preserved under their caps of ice. There were also deep blue gentians and *Lomatogonium*, and somewhat lower down the azure blue *Allium beesianum*. I spent an enjoyable evening with the Americans in their heated tent, finally descending late that night to the village by the light of a lantern. In 1918, when they had returned to China for a further expedition to Mongolia and I was in Hunan, we resumed a friendly correspondence despite wartime conditions.

On 16th October I told the men to assemble the kit for a short excursion and load it on three pack animals. The cook of course thought that two animals would be sufficient, but after causing an hour's delay by his endeavours to pack everything into two loads he at last agreed that I was right. I set out westwards over the pass from Ganhaizi to Yuluo with the object of mapping the Yangzi gorge where

it breaks through the mountains. The police hut on the pass, though built only one year previously with funds provided by traders having an interest in the security of the route, was already falling into ruins; however, a strip of woodland had been cleared along the side of the track so as to deter bandits from mounting ambushes.

From Yuluo I made a halfday trip on foot up to a viewpoint above the bend in the great gorge. It was situated on the slopes of a high forested dome called Lamidyi which jutted out in front of the main crest of the Yulong Shan. As I reached a minor ridge the view suddenly opened out, revealing the narrow stretch of the gorge as far as the Dagu basin. The vista was magnificent in its scale and equally splendid in its colouring. On the right was a uniform grey wall of rock with a few snow-filled recesses. It was Atsako, a line of pinnacles lying to the west of the northern part of the Lijiang range, foreshortened and apparently merging into one. On the left was an arid yellow mountainside sloping steeply up to Mount Chata Shan. Its summit, probably over 5300 m high, located straight in the line of the ridge, was concealed by the higher part of the latter, but gradually came into view as we climbed higher up the slope. Far below us was the white water of the rapids where the river surged between the vertical walls of the gorge. Gaunt pine trees blocked parts of the view, and I had to shift from place to place to find a spot from which to take a photograph. We wasted some time in trying to pull down a pine tree which was in the way, but although it was already half chopped through and withered it resisted our efforts. The next viewpoint was not so satisfactory, but we improved it by snapping off the top of a young oak.

On the way back I visited Labazi, a hamlet occupied by Buyi, a people who had migrated from Guizhou [149] but whose condition had degenerated. They lived in low houses built of earth with shingle roofs. The men, always clothed in black, were in the fields, but the women were friendly and offered me chewing tobacco.

That afternoon I took the ferry and rode up to Qiaotou at the beginning of the Xiao Zhongdian valley. Ladsagu was situated somewhat above the river, opposite the entrance to the gorge. The water, seemingly almost stationary, pressed straight towards the slopes of Dyinaloko. Just above the river was the subtropical zone — steep slopes, grey or yellow in colour, with scattered scrub; next came the warm temperate zone — red steppe dotted with pale green pines; above this were the temperate zone mixed forests in their multicoloured autumnal garb, then the dark green subalpine fir forests, above them the high alpine zone, here certainly very barren, grey and windswept, and finally the snow-capped spires. It would have made a superb colour photograph. The summit of Dyinaloko was still just clear, so I swiftly set up the camera, but then, like a Mohammedan woman, the mountain hurriedly veiled her snowy countenance. I waited for half an hour, but she did not reappear. I was peculiarly unlucky in that, although I passed the spot several times, I was never able to photograph the whole view.

[148] Handel-Mazzetti was an experienced mountaineer, and though he makes no mention of a rope, Lao Li would have been roped to him. Andrews describes their meeting: "While we were far up on the mountainside, Baron Haendel-Mazzetti appeared armed with ropes and an alpine snow axe. He was about to attempt to climb the highest peak which had never been ascended but the drifts turned him back several hundred free from the summit. He dined at our camp and as all of us carefully refrained from "war talk" we spent a very pleasant evening." (*Camps and Trails in China*, p.123)

[149] Most Buyi still live in Guizhou today (S.G.H.).

The next day was devoted to a journey on foot into the gorge itself, on the very path along which I had mistakenly set out the year before. Now, in the rainy season, the xerophytes of the subtropical zone had spread out their leaves. *Nouelia insignis* formed quite large thickets, though in its present state of development I completely failed to recognise it at first, and even the gnarled bushes of *Randia lichiangensis* had put out their dark green leaves. One of the herbaceous perennials was *Aconitum coriophyllum*, a new species which mimicked our native wolfsbane. After two hours we came to a village called Luoyu, beyond which the track climbed up in zigzags to get round a steep rock ridge sloping down to the bend in the river. As we reached the top the roaring of the water, over 800 m vertically below, thundered in our ears. On this side the river abruptly broke into a stretch of tumultuous rapids, practically amounting to a cataract. Squeezed between the pillars of a stratum of hard rock, a vertical bed of limestone running north and south between the phyllite, its waters crashed down in a torrent, forming a clearly discernible arch, though from above it was impossible to estimate the height of the fall. From there downstream the river was white with foam, one rapid following another in the depths of the gorge which the water had cut through the yellow rock. This gorge splits the Lijiang range into two parts, the Yulong Shan with its peaks Ünlüpe, Satseto and Djinaloko to the southwest, and the Haba Shan to the northeast. The range as a whole is set at an angle to the lie of the geological strata. The track ran along the gorge at about one third of its height. I searched for a place from which to photograph the entire vista, from the cataract at the bottom to the snow peaks at the top. An awesomely steep gorge, filled with rock-strewn primaeval forest, led up to the screes, above which were colossal precipices crowned by the snow-topped pyramid of Djinaloko. Mere words cannot express the immensity of this almost vertical face, over 3500 m in height. Perhaps I can give some idea of its scale when I say that I needed two plates, one above the other, to photograph it — and I still feared there might be a gap between them. Once again, unfortunately, the summit was partially obscured by cloud. The snow mountains in the southern part of the range were indeed superb, yet the rock peaks of the northern part, gradually diminishing to heights 500 to 1000 m below them, were hardly less splendid. From that viewpoint they did not merge together: each had a character of its own — here a narrow pinnacle, there a sharp crest sloping down more steeply on one side than the other, then a massif built of numerous towers which seemed to have been bent upwards, the niches between them scoured smooth by the winds, and lastly a gigantic snow-capped obelisk. If you picture the Drei Zinnen [150] of the Rosengarten in the Dolomites and enlarge them to twice their actual size, you may get some impression of what the mountain really looks like, although it lacks any such narrow towers.

High up the mountainside small black patches of fir forest clung to the steep slabs. The most northerly part plunged down to the river in an unbroken vertical rock face over 2000 m in height, and on this side a triple peak, hardly less steep, soared up to the same height. This was Shuchamba, an outlier of the Haba Shan massif. Opposite us, on a steep turfy slope in the depths of the gorge, a few Lisu families had built their huts at a spot called Dahosa. The only access to these isolated dwellings can have been by ladders up the rocks. The track, here negotiable by pack animals loaded in Tibetan style, continued through the gorge at the same height. Further along it we saw Dyipalo, a Naxi hamlet of a few houses; still further on there was said to be another called Bundua. The old pine trees growing here had flattened asymmetrical tops drawn out towards the northeast: the result of the persistent wind which swept round the crest from the opposite side of the gorge. Down below there was said to be a route along the river, consisting of notched logs "like the one on the Drung Jiang". As I had not time to explore it I turned back along the original track to Qiaotou. Next day I followed the unsurveyed part of the Jinsha Jiang along a beautiful valley to Axi, the river — very broad and perfectly smooth — flowing down towards me. Two days' brisk marching then brought me to Lijiang.

There I found enough to keep me busy for three days. In my absence Zhao, who claimed to understand farriery, had attempted to shoe my nice little horse, and had botched the job. The consequences did not become apparent until I had set out again. For the last two days of the journey I had to let the horse travel without a load, and on reaching Lijiang I had to leave it under Kok's care until it recovered. I tried a motley collection of mules, as the Lijiang ponies were far too small and quite worthless. The prices asked for mules were very high — up to $300 — and none of them was suitable. Many of them were intractable, and most of them could not tolerate the crupper; it slipped up over the tail and allowed the saddle to ride up on to the neck. This of course made the mule furious and if I had not managed to jump down at the right moment, the mule and the unsecured saddle would, between them, have given me a nasty fall. When riding mules, the Chinese did not use a crupper; instead they had a rod which lay across the backs of the animal's knees and which was connected to the sides of the saddle so as to hold it in place. This device never remained clean and I therefore wished to avoid using it.

---

[150] The Tre Cime di Lavaredo

Fig.33 Lisu people in their village
above Xiao Weixi. Chapter 21.

Fig.34 *Rhododendron
rarosquameum*
(*R. caeruleum)*
on the Ji Shan crest

Fig.35 The Lisu village of Aoalo. Chapter 23.

Fig.36 *Berneuxia tibetica*
beneath *Rhododendron sanguineum*
at the tree-line (3900m) on the alpine pastures
of Dotitong above Tseku. Chapter 24.

Fig.37 *Cardiocrinum
giganteum* in the forest
below Doshiracho (3100m)
on the ascent to the Xi La.
Below it: *Paris polyphylla,
Polygonum alatum,
Elatostemma sessile;*
behind: ferns and
Cornus montbeigii.
Chapter 24.

Fig.38 Crossing the Nu Jiang (Salween)
at Tjionra in a dugout canoe. Chapter 25.

Fig.39
Subalpine woodland
in the Saoa-lumba (3450m).
Eutrema lancifolium,
Cardamine polyphylla;
left: *Ribes* sp.,
Prunus cornuta,
Betula utilis
with *Usnea longissima.*
Chapter 24.

Fig.40 *Primula calliantha* beneath *Rhododendron beesianum*
at 4200m near the Nisselaka pass. Chapter 24.

Fig.41
Primula agleniana
beneath
cherry tanglewood
(*Prunus mugus)*
on the Nu Jiang
(Salween)-Irrawaddy
divide. Chapter 25.

Fig.42
Temperate zone
rain forest with
Strobilanthes understorey
at 2700m near Gongshan
(Tschamutong).
Acer caudatum,
Ilex dipyrena,
Sorbaria sp.
Chapter 25.

Fig.43 *Pegaeophyton sinense* in alpine springwater flushes
beyond the Tsukue pass on the Nu Jiang (Salween)-Irrawaddy divide
to the west of Gongshan (Tschamutong). On mica-schist soil at 4100m. Chapter 25

Fig.44
Meconopsis speciosa
on mica-schist
on the Xi La.
Chapter 26.

Fig.45 *Omphalogramma souliei* beneath *Salix* sp.
at 3900m on the Xi La. *Potentilla leuconota* in front. Chapter 27.

Fig.46 *Didymocarpus eburneus* near Anshun. Chapter 33.

Fig.47 The Jinsha Jiang
gorge below
the Yulong Shan.

Fig.48 A cataract on the Jinsha Jiang in its gorge
below the Yulong Shan. Detail from Fig.47.

Chapter 30. Via Yongsheng and the Jinsha Jiang to Kunming

Mount Shizi Shan — rocks and fossils in the Jinsha Jiang gorge — a stemless palm — poor people — wild cotton — frontier guards — opium — winter in Kunming

So as to avoid travelling yet again over the same uninteresting tract of the Yunnan highlands, I decided to return via Yongsheng and the Jinsha Jiang basin from Machang. On 24th October, having despatched the caravan — the same men as I had had for my journey to the mountains in the previous year — along the main road, I set off on a detour, riding my servant's horse, with the aim of visiting Shizi Shan, a mountain in the range which forms the eastern rim of the Lijiang basin. The upper part of the mountain (3350 m in altitude) is built of limestone conglomerate, weathered into rounded shapes, and this also forms the crest over which the route passes. Beneath the conglomerate are sandstone and bands of hard limestone. Though quite good, the track was obstructed by fallen trees, not all of which the pony could jump and, contrary to my expectations, there was no track down the mountain leading directly to Duinaoke.

There was a splendid view from the little temple on the summit, and having taken the observations needed to complete the map, I turned back and found to my dismay — and my pony's — that I had to ride down all the way to the foot of the mountain again. Then, after ascending 600 m along the caravan route, I finally reached the pass as darkness was falling. Growing there on the rocks and on the conglomerate at the foot of the moraines were dense cushions of the white *Sedum primuloides*. Escorted by men carrying pine torches, I at last entered Duinaoke, where I found my servant in a state of total drunkenness. I upbraided him with some vehemence and am glad to say that he did not offend again. Besides the autumn flora of these low altitude zones, I was particularly interested in the geological structure of the terrain. Just below the village I found blocks of limestone formed entirely from brachiopod shells (*Rhynchonella* species and a new species of *Dayia* from the Upper Silurian or Devonian) though otherwise I did not have much luck with fossils. Limestone conglomerate, sandstone and carboniferous marl with a gentle westerly to almost vertical dip were exposed on the scarp.

En route, as I looked downstream, a fascinating picture came into view. The river had gnawed into a steep rock face until a large piece had broken off and fallen down without shattering. The river, presumably dammed back for a time, had forced its way through the cleft, which it had then adopted as its new bed, and the broken off piece was now left on the other side of the river (the east bank). The whole picture was as clear as if the events had happened only the day before. At Guanyilang there was a thick bed of grey sandstone, sharply cut off and dipping gently to the west. Still overlain by limestone, it continued beyond the Jinsha Jiang. From there I could see its valley — here once again a smooth-walled gorge — coming down in a straight line from the north. Its sides were dark green, as the subtropical flora was then at the peak of its development. At noon on the fourth day I reached Yongsheng, where I spent a few agreeable hours with Père

Monbeig, a man with whom one could discuss any subject. I also had the opportunity of buying a handsome mule, a female, which I rode from then on. She proved entirely satisfactory and I kept her until was in Hunan, where I sold her for the price I had originally given.

There I left the route which I had travelled in 1914 and continued eastwards, though first deviating towards the south. On that and the following three days my attention was attracted by a small stemless palm which occurred in large numbers among various oak communities in this sparsely populated terrain. I had previously seen solitary specimens beside the main road to Dali near Shezi, but although they were in flower I had taken them to be escapes from cultivation, dwarfed examples of *Trachycarpa excelsa*, a palm planted in every village. Here it was so plentiful and was fruiting so abundantly that I discarded that notion. It turned out to be *Trachycarpus nana*, a palm originally collected by Delavay though first described, from his material, in 1910. Travelling onwards, we met a few more strata of sandstone, set almost vertically though dipping towards the west. They caused the little stream which we were following to make numerous small meanders. Then we came to limestones and sandstones, marls and clay slate, only slightly disturbed, especially on either side of the valley leading south-southeast, and another valley leading eastwards, which we reached after a short march on the third day. On the northern side these rocks formed gentle east-facing slopes which were inhabited and cultivated, though deeply cut by the lateral streams. If these topographical features had been more clearly delineated, the depiction of this stretch, surveyed by Ryder, would have been one of the best sections of Davies' map. Although the geological picture is one of more or less undisturbed stratification in a basin which was filled up possibly much later, the surface configuration of the landscape is closely similar to that of the intensely folded Yunnan plateau — a resemblance heightened by their having the same plant cover of pine and oak forest. High up in the valley which we had just reached the track led through a beautiful gorge filled with *Lithocarpus* forest and even having a little waterfall. Growing in the gorge, the tall shrubby *Edgeworthia gardneri*, resembling a daphne, was now putting forth its pretty white flowers.

Down on the valley bottom the subtropical vegetation and the ancient tufa formations on the limestone rocks reminded me of the valley of Shiwanhe [151] in the Yalong territory between Huili and Yanyuan. Growing abundantly in niches and fissures in the rock was *Remusatia vivipara*, an aroid previously found only in the Himalaya; it does not produce any fruits, but multiplies by means of bristly golden brown multi-pointed vegetative buds or bulbils on its elongated twisted spadix. A short stone

---

[151] Chapter 9.

bridge led over the deep ravine of one of the lateral streams, so deep that one could not see its bottom; it was just like the *ponte alto* at Ampezzo. From here the usual route left the stream and led straight over a saddle to the little town of Huaping, formerly known as Jiuyaping.

On 31st October, while staying in a hostelry outside the town wall, I was visited by the local official. He and his numerous retinue waited patiently for an hour and a half for my cook-interpreter to return from the town — a wait which lasted late into the evening and put my patience to the test, too. Then he engaged me in conversation for a further hour before I could at last settle down to my work. From there on I again encountered a medley of stratified rocks including beds of massive sandstone up to at least 150 m thick, while in some stretches the valley side was formed by the laminar surfaces of the red arkose sandstone itself. Flourishing in small pools beside the rivulets which trickled over the rock, cutting only slightly into it, were two species of *Utricularia*, the pink *U. racemosa* and the yellow *U. bifida*. Unlike our own species they are not totally immersed; at flowering time they put up erect spikes from their withered leaf rosettes.

Some distance before we reached Machang the Jinsha Jiang came flowing down from the south, and the track continued eastwards in its rather unattractive valley. Once again there were conglomerates and other strata lying vertically; above them was limestone, lying unconformably, together with the sedimentary deposits previously encountered at high altitudes. On reaching Machang I felt impelled to visit Père Salvat, who had remained on friendly terms with Schneider and myself. He was now clean-shaven, and at first I hardly recognised him, being quite unaccustomed to seeing a French missionary without a beard. Coal was dug in large amounts on the far bank of the river and carried downstream in boats, though certainly no further than Longjie. The valley was fairly broad and extremely arid. The houses did not need gable roofs, and even flat roofs seemed superfluous, to judge from the number which had been allowed to collapse. The climate was warm enough to make clothing superfluous too, and people of both sexes — adults as well as young children — were not infrequently to be seen in a state of total nakedness.

"Now what about the wild men who don't wear any clothes?" said I to my servant, who still loved talking about the sights he had seen in the Drung Jiang in 1915. My own thoughts turned longingly towards the comfortable and convenient loft rooms of the Naxi houses, so much more habitable than the wretched Chinese huts which I was now obliged to use. In a village near Xinzhuang I was amazed to find *Carica papaya* in cultivation. This tropical fruit seemed quite out of place in that climate. Manhao on the Red River was the only other place in Yunnan where I had seen it, though it does grow in one other non-tropical site, namely Baiyanjing, where Simeon Ten collected it. Another interesting find was a cotton, *Gossypium obtusifolium*, a fair-sized shrub, unquestionably wild, growing among rocks near the hostelry halfway between Xinzhuang and

Geliping (Luoluoping) and on grassy slopes further on. It had previously been recorded from India only. At midday on 3rd November I crossed the Jinsha Jiang by the ferry at Geliping, a crossing considered dangerous because of the fierce currents. A mule, tired of being kept waiting, leapt out of the boat into the water and swam right across the river.

At Yong Xing (Renhejie), situated in a lateral valley leading southwards, I met Père Durieu, who had come from the next market town and brought the latest news of the war. All the missionaries were now much less partisan than they had been earlier, when they had been influenced by wild rumours in the newspapers, and we found that our opinions on the causes of the war were in close agreement. Further up the valley I stopped at a little wooden bridge. Looking backwards through the bushes, I saw the men rescuing a load which had fallen into the water and hurriedly reloading it. They were greatly disconcerted to find that I had seen them, for they would have preferred to cover up the mishap. Had they succeeded, all the undeveloped plates from that summer, packed as they were in an unsoldered tin box, would probably have been ruined. As it was, the cardboard boxes containing the plates were only slightly damp and I was able to dry them that evening.

I met several parties of soldiers, mostly militia or young lads with enormously long antiquated matchlocks, lances and swords. They had been sent to guard the Sichuan frontier, where renewed trouble was expected. Some of them, under the command of an officer, were busy pulling up young opium poppy plants which a peasant had been shamelessly cultivating beside the main road[152]. During the midday halt by the stream my men came up to me with their hands full of sand, shouting "Jin duo, Jin duo!" ("lots of gold!"). They were sadly disappointed when I explained that the bright particles were merely mica, washed out of the soft granite by the stream.

Next day, from a spot at 2350 m on the pass above Dadianjie, I had an immense vista in the clear autumn air, extending over the Yunnan highlands and northwards as far as the mountains near Dechang and Yanyuan. From Yongren (Zhujue) onwards the terrain was monotonous. The basin was filled with conglomerates which formed a bare treeless high-altitude plain covered with steppe grasses and deeply incised by streams. Here I was once again struck by the loose fluffy wool which covered the tussocks of steppe grasses in such dense balls that later they broke off and rolled along the ground. *Ischaemum angustifolium* has white wool, and *Pollinia phaeothrix* dark brown. It consists solely of the hairs from the sheaths and leaves, but they contain so much silica that they can survive several fires. Because of the wide rings of dead sheaths, these and other steppe grasses are so firmly embed-

---

[152] Since that time the cultivation of opium seems to have been legalised again; at any rate, Rock, in his account of his travels in 1923, prints a photograph of opium poppy fields near Lijiang (National Geographic Magazine *46*, p. 474) (Handel-Mazzetti's footnote).

ded in the sward that it is almost impossible to divide them with a trowel or to dig out the freshly flowering parts from the armour plating which surrounds them. Not until we were approaching Majie did we pass any villages. We crossed the Longchuan Jiang in a leaky ferry boat, pushed by a few stark naked coolies wading across the river.

From Majie the track went up into the hills, without entering Yuanmou. The mountains in the Jianchang were still visible and the familiar triple summit of Longzhu Shan near Huili seemed so close that one could almost grasp it. Two photographs, taken from different points, would have been enough for a photogrammetric survey of the entire Huang-zhen valley, but alas I had not one plate left, and for the same reason I was unable to photograph the *Trachycarpus* palms, though they were of great interest. For the next few days we had long marches on tracks which in some stretches were in appalling condition in consequence of rain. The animals sank in above their knees, and their riders were plastered with mud. As there were said to be numerous bandits, I was always provided with two soldiers, but only once, between Wuding and Chebei, did they trouble to go ahead with loaded rifles to inspect possible hiding-places beside the track; elsewhere

they plodded dumbly along among the pack animals. Outside the town gate of Fumin a man had been hanged. Women were sitting around on the grass, chatting and drinking tea; yet another instance of Chinese callousness!

On 13th November I arrived safe and sound in Kunming. The police were on the lookout for opium and eyed my tin boxes with great suspicion, but I refused to let them be opened. Later they came to my house, but finding only the empty pack saddles in the yard they went away disconsolately.

I moved into lodgings with Herr Pawelka in the lower part of Kunming, since Herr Andersen and Herr Schoch and his family had left the town some time before. Here too I fixed up a dark room; the drain was a rat hole. Many of the plates brought back from the distant west had been damaged by moisture. Before long we had company in the house — two German technicians sent from Japan for the electricity works. During that winter I took my meals as the guest of Herr Weiss, the consul, and am greatly indebted to him; despite our wide differences in outlook we never had any of the disputes so frequent among fellow countrymen in the Far East.

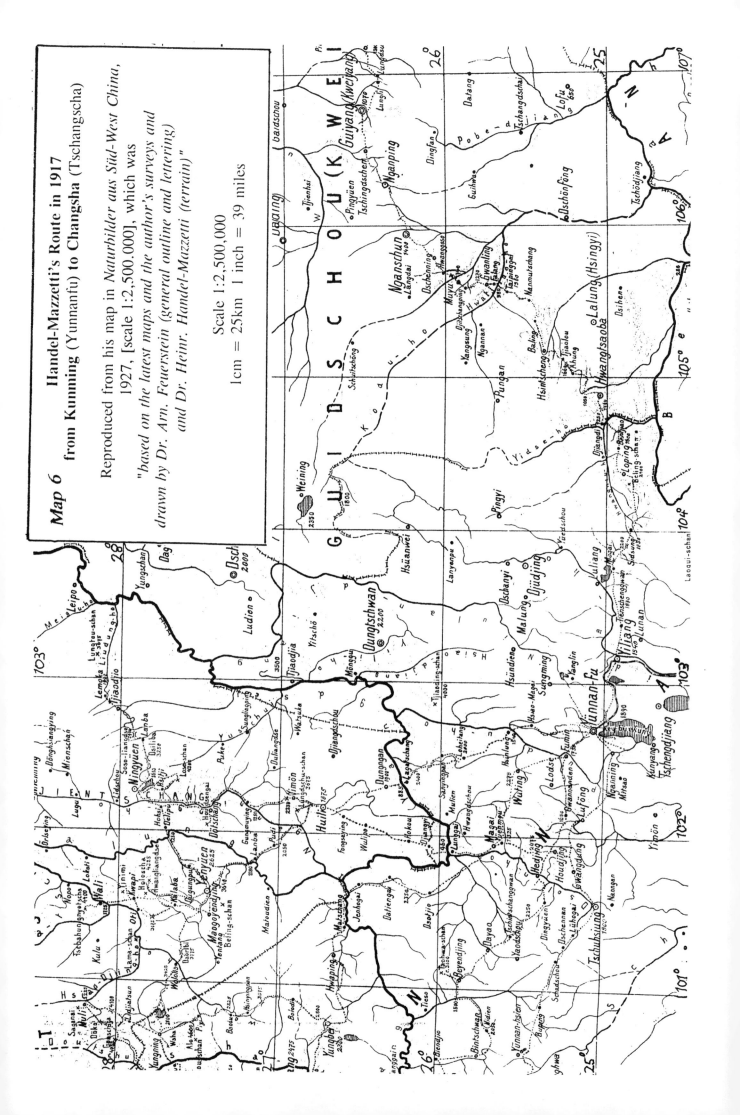

Map 6

Handel-Mazzetti's Route in 1917
from Kunming (Yunnanfu) to Changsha (Tschangscha)

Reproduced from his map in *Naturbilder aus Süd-West China,*
1927, [scale 1:2.500.000], which was

*"based on the latest maps and the author's surveys and
drawn by Dr. Arn. Feuerstein (general outline and lettering)
and Dr. Heinr. Handel-Mazzetti (terrain)"*

Scale 1:2,500,000

1cm = 25km   1 inch = 39 miles

PART IV 1917

Through Guizhou to Hunan

Chapter 31. Across East Yunnan

China breaks off relations with Germany — barren karst — buffalo carts — my survey resumed — the mountain range of Majie and Shizong — a guard of honour — Bailing Shan — the cone hill terrain of Luoping — the central Chinese floral region — hill forests

The task of sorting out and repacking my collections lasted well into 1917, and the uncertainty of the political situation also made me hesitate before undertaking any major enterprise. On 13th March the government and parliament in Beijing decided to break off diplomatic relations with Germany in conformity with the example set by the Americans — a decision reached after the majority originally opposed to this course had been induced to change their minds by a payment of 16 million dollars. Tang Rirao, the dujun of Yunnan, was a tolerably honest man, even though he engaged in opium smuggling as a sideline and financed counterfeit coiners.

"I would actually go along with the government, if I could see any advantage in it for us," he said to the German consul, when the latter urged him to protest against the decision.

I visited him on the following day to show him my plant collections and with the unstated purpose of stiffening his half-voiced resolve to go against the government's decision. In the meantime, however, he had reconsidered the matter, and on 21st March Herr Weiss, the German consul, with his wife and young children, was compelled to set out on the arduous overland journey to Yibin on the Jinsha Jiang. Weiss chose that route after steadfastly resisting the blandishments of the Aliens Commissioner Zhang Yizhu, who wanted him to travel via Tonkin, a route which would have delivered him into the hands of the French authorities, who were intensely hostile towards him. German nationals were deprived of extraterritorial status and forbidden to travel outside the district, though apart from perfunctory house searches and confiscation of firearms they were not otherwise molested. Pawelka having departed with Weiss, I went to live in the consulate and took my meals with Stiebritz and his family, who were now living in a somewhat cramped house in the lower part of the town. In giving Stiebritz notice to quit his former residence, the bishop had acted under pressure from the French consul, but the conditions on which he terminated the lease were commendably generous. Being an Austrian citizen, I was still more or less free to travel, but the breaking off of relations with Germany was just a foretaste of what was to come. Nevertheless I knew that — once I had got safely away into remote country districts — there would be ways of eluding any restrictions which might arise from the progress of hostilities and I would thus be able to continue my work as long as possible, and it was perfectly clear that I had nothing to fear from the Chinese people themselves.

My aim was to undertake something new, and to see as much of China as possible, especially those parts still unknown to the western world. As my final destination I chose Shanghai and planned to journey there via Guizhou, Hunan, Jiangxi and Zhejiang. At that time I did not realise that a great deal of material had already been collected by the missionaries in Guizhou and studied by Léveillé — though unfortunately published in quite unusable form — otherwise I would have chosen a route further south through Guangxi, a province still entirely unknown even today. I also wanted to keep to the main mountain chain, because there were still forests to be found there — and hence the flora would be of greater interest — and because it would give me an opportunity of escaping, from time to time at least, from the worst effects of the climate. When I paid my farewell visit to the dujun I was highly amused at what he had to say. He asked whether he should provide me with an escort; if so, it would have to be a troop of at least twenty soldiers — any fewer, and their rifles would be stolen! I declined, on the grounds that as a European I had nothing to fear from any party of bandits fewer than twenty in number, and against a larger band even twenty soldiers would be useless. The Aliens Commissioner advised me that the southern route from Yiliang via Xingyi was safer, and I gladly followed his recommendation, because it diverged from the Yunnan highlands — of which I had seen quite enough — much sooner than the northern route via Qujing, and because it passed through lower lying territory. In Yunnan my interest had been focused on the mountains, but now, if I was to make new discoveries, I had to concentrate on subtropical areas at low altitudes.

I again took Lao Li as my servant, for I knew that I would have to cope with difficult discussions and might need to communicate in writing in other dialects. I also hoped, sometimes at least, to enjoy tolerably well cooked meals. The caravan was provided by the same mafu as in 1916. Unfortunately he did not have the same men and came with the caravan himself; more than once I had to show him who was master. When the appointed day came the caravan, of course, failed to turn up; the men were still away in Houyanjing collecting salt. I was not willing to wait, so I told him to assemble another caravan and catch me up. I needed only eight pack animals, for I had cut down my baggage to the bare essentials, and expected to be able to despatch crates of specimens as I filled them. I had had the tent made into waterproof bags for the herbarium sheets; I knew I would not need it for this journey, and the old bags were worn out. Kok had long since returned my dark brown Sichuan pony after treating it successfully, and I told Li to ride the mule, although the little chap found it alarmingly high off the ground. Unfortunately the only coolies he could find as plant collectors were Yafcha, of whose work in 1914 I had unhappy memories, and another fellow — equally tiresome, and shortsighted into the bargain; I sent him home after three weeks.

After a warm farewell from the German community, I departed from Kunming on 5th June, feeling somewhat uneasy at having to leave behind all the specimens I had collected — material of inestimable value to me — together with the remainder of Schneider's collections. Packed in fifty-one carefully soldered tin-lined crates, they were deposited in the storeroom at the German consulate. Fire, water and war were constant perils, and no one could foretell how the political situation would unfold or what ill effects it might have on my material. When war was declared the authorities actually had several of the tin boxes opened, and it was only through Stiebritz's efforts that they survived intact — indeed, in 1918 he arrived barely in time to rescue the whole roomful of crates from a flood.

I took the old caravan road, which must have been heavily used in the days before the railway was opened, for in some places it had been worn down through the marl to a depth of five metres. On the second evening I reached Yiliang and there, barely an hour's journey from the railway, I received a reminder of the joys of travel in the rainy season in China. Arriving at the Nanpan Jiang, I found that the latest flood had deposited a broad strip of glutinous slippery mud on the meadows to a level of two metres above the top of the river bank. I had to dismount into the mud and jump into the wretched ferry boat. The route continued due east above an arid lateral valley having the appearance of a graben. Growing on its slopes was *Ziziphus sativa*, a thorny shrub bearing fruits not unlike dates; indeed, Europeans called them "Chinese dates" and used them to make preserves [153]. The valley led up to a marl ridge at 2000 m. This ridge ran parallel to the Nanpan Jiang valley, where the river had cut a gorge running east and west. Near the village of Dashao a broad offshoot branched off northwards from the ridge. The ridge was covered with forest consisting of *Keteleeria*, *Quercus variabilis* and *Pinus armandii*, and was still typical of the Yunnan highlands, though the view to the southeast revealed something quite different. Stretching away before me was a gently undulating expanse; in the distance beyond it was a low, uniformly jagged range of mountains, disappearing into the blue at each end, and still further way to the southeast was a broad massif of greater altitude which the people called Laogui Shan. All these mountains had a remarkably uniform southwesterly trend or strike. In the foreground was a shallow channel extending southwestwards to Mile. Projecting from its floor — not, as more usually seen

in mountainous country, from the crests on either side — were rock outcrops cleft into rectangular shapes by the processes of karst formation. Their limestone towers and walls looked like crenellated castles, or the distant ruins of an Oriental city excavated by archaeologists, and had been shaped by the action of the weather on the hard underlying stratum after erosion had stripped off the soft marl above it. A few of these rocky hills were wooded, as was one situated directly in the centre line of the valley and crowned by a temple called Shifeng Si. It was here that we crossed the uppermost stretch of the valley.

We stopped for the night at Tianshengguan, a village on arid level terrain beyond the valley. The only available drinking water was coloured red by the clay which it contained, just as had been the case in the closely similar karst territory to the west of Yanyuan in Sichuan. Here there was another reminder of that district — the buffalo cart which served as a means of transport as far as Banqiao, something which I saw nowhere else in South China, except in the towns of Kunming and Mengzi. The creaking emitted as its imperfectly circular wheels rotated on its single ungreased axle resounded far and wide over the waterless plains, and the low growing thornbushes did nothing to damp the resonance; it was a counterpart of the melancholy sounds of the Illyrian karst. The rock formations resulting from the action of the weather were reproduced on a smaller scale in the bottoms of the erosion channels. There the red earth had been washed away and pointed grey limestone cones, as tall as a man, stood exposed. Their smooth rounded sides were irregularly grooved, the rock having been leached away by downpours of rain. Some of them were grotesquely sculptured and even perforated, while others had been so deeply undercut that they had toppled over. Agriculture and food preparation were extremely primitive. Besides hand mills there was a stone roller; turned in circles by a buffalo, it ran on an almost flat conical bed and ground the corn. *Dendrobium clavatum*, an orchid which I had seen on the rocks in the upper Jinsha Jiang valley, was flowering on the walls of the farmyards and the rooftops. At one spot the route approached the river valley, but it then turned aside on to the flat tableland beside it, giving me a vista of the pine-clad mountain range north of the river, a landscape of the kind I had so often seen in the Yunnan highlands. Some distance further on, having passed the karst terrain of Muji Shan, we descended to Majie, a town situated in the broad valley plain of Luliang, itself largely occupied by karst. A considerable part of the plain, from the town as far as the foot of the steep hill on the eastern side of the valley, was taken up by a lake. This is not shown on Davies' map, though it seems to be indicated in Stieler's Hand Atlas [154]. However, the only permanent part of the lake seemed to be the deeper, roughly circular, area about 5 km in diameter at the foot of the hill; the rest consisted of a lagoon which bordered on the tongues

---

[153] The wild ones are sour; the fruits usually eaten are cultivated (SGH).

[154] No lake is shown on modern Chinese maps; perhaps it fills in the wet season only (SGH).

of land at the mouths of minor streams and was perhaps occasionally fed by an overflow from the river which normally ran past it. Round the lagoon were rice fields on fertile alluvial soil with an underground water supply. That evening I found my mafu sitting in the yard sewing up an old wound in his foot with coarse black thread, an operation which caused some merriment among the Chinese bystanders.

Next day I left surveyed country behind me and set foot on virgin ground. Though Leclère had visited parts of the district, his exploration had been confined to the country south of my route and had been purely geological. Davies' conscientiously drafted map shows the district as a blank; the distances marked on the dotted line representing the road are far from the truth, and the features shown on other maps are pure conjecture. Despite the political unrest I felt under an obligation to recommence my route survey, having until now merely made a few additions to the map. I simply took the precaution of sketching the survey in one of my own notebooks so that none of the men who watched me putting plants in the press would see anything of it. Next morning I therefore rode up on to the mountain range which we now had to cross. I photographed the lake from above and that single plate enabled me to map its exact outline as it existed on that day. The massif, which reaches about 2500 m at its highest point north of the pass, extends northeastwards and hence belongs to the Chinese strike line, the general trend of strata found everywhere in Central and South China. Up there at Dongshan was a sulphur mine; I met one of the packhorse caravans taking the sulphur away. From that spot I had a view of the Nanpan Jiang valley — a wide, green and apparently cultivated channel extending as far as Qujing. The slopes of the mountain consisted mainly of limestone, with some bands of coal dipping southeast in their lower parts. Growing there in surprisingly large numbers were little juniper trees, slender and pyramidal in outline; this species, *Juniperus formosana*, is even more prickly than our own. After a long wait for the caravan I realised that they must have taken another route and rode on by myself. The track descended slightly into a hollow where there were more limestone knolls outcropping in rows. At a teahouse I found a guide who showed me the way to the next ridge. It had a thick covering of evergreen oak forest and was built of sandstone with outcrops of coal. Not far beyond it I found my caravan just finishing their lunch break, and snatched a hasty meal. Once again we saw below us parallel ridges and channels, the ridges broken by many gaps and the channels partly filled by knolls and hillocks where stratified rocks outcropped. All this obscured any clear picture of the structure; all one could see were alternating strata of limestone, sandstone and marl. Far away to the east I saw Mount Bailing Shan, the emblem of Luoping and the whole of that district, towering up to a comparatively high altitude at the end of a short range of jagged peaks. From the first ridge onwards the track led along a contour line, the streams running in the contrary direction from northeast to southwest, and finally descended into a

hollow where it crossed a stream flowing down from the right.

Shizong was a little town on a river which likewise came down from the southwest. Traced downstream, its valley, bounded on the left by the range we had just crossed and on the right by broad gentle ridges of no great altitude, became wider and wider. Rising out of the plain in front of us were a few small limestone hills, some if not all consisting of vertically set strata, and on the right were a few tributary streams flowing between spurs projecting from a tract of hummocky sandstone hills covered by pine forest. The military commander, a major, came to visit me and explained that he had received a letter from the dujun instructing him to give me an escort of soldiers, and that the authorities in Guiyang had been commanded to replace them when I got to the border. I protested indignantly, but when I saw that resistance was of no avail I tried to negotiate a reduction in their number.

"But why so few," he asked, "surely an important man is always glad to have a large retinue?" However, servility and bootlicking have always been detestable to me, and why should I, a humble private citizen, be bothered with a party of soldiers? But my objections left him unmoved. The dujun would hold him responsible, he said, an argument which I could not deny, and in putting my own case, I had to remain polite despite my annoyance. My escort accordingly turned up next morning — a lieutenant with a detachment of twenty regular soldiers equipped in full marching order. Despite my fears, their behaviour was impeccable and wholly discreet. Indeed, I formed the impression that the dujun might have had second thoughts about letting me depart with such a beggarly caravan, and really intended them as a guard of honour rather than a means of supervising my activities. It hardly needs adding that I did not allow their presence to interfere in any way with the work of surveying the route, which, though carried on quite unobtrusively, was now producing results.

The dominant species in the steppe which filled the valley basin was *Imperata cylindrica*, a grass with silver-white flower spikes. Beyond the basin the route ascended towards Mount Bailing Shan, crossing a stream at its foot. There was no bridge, for only in short stretches did the stream run on the surface, having cut its bed into the conglomerate. In at least two places and, judging from the configuration of the landscape, in other spots further on, it ran through natural tunnels, and the route led over one of these. We climbed through sparse woodland, *Lithocarpus spicata* var. *collettii* alternating with *Pinus yunnanensis*, on to a ridge. On the right it sloped down to a stream flowing towards us, and on the left deep, steep walled channels descended northwestwards in line with the strike of the strata towards the valley — from here no longer visible — of the little river which ran through Shizong. The crest itself soared up in front of us towards a line of conical summits, the furthest being the main peak of Bailing Shan (ca. 2400m). The track passed to the right of it, reaching only 2110 m. *Lilium delavayi* had opened its splendid red flowers in the pine forest; there was also a peculiar dry-habitat form of

Dracocephalum urticifolium resembling a large sage, together with the little *Iris collettii* and a remarkable low-growing bamboo, *Indocalamus andropogonoides* (a new species), with soft, almost non-woody culms. Growing on fertile red earth among the grass was the multi-stemmed red-flowered *Pedicularis henryi*, which kept us company all the way through Hunan and turned up again on the border of Guangdong, and the tall, deep yellow *P. lopingensis* (a new species). The people of this mountain range were Miao [155]. Dressed in grey hempen clothing, they were tilling their meagre fields, but none of their villages was situated near the main road. Flowering among the limestone rocks was *Smilax herbacea*, an erect herbaceous plant with olive green flowers — belonging to a genus which otherwise consists mainly of woody climbers — and *Bletilla yunnanensis*, a pink orchid with grass-like leaves. *Magnolia delavayi* was still frequent there. The district yielded such rich spoils, and seemed to promise still more further on, that I was unwilling to hurry and stopped for the night in a little Chinese village called Cha'er, still in the mountains at 2050 m. The people lived in wretched mudhuts thatched with straw, each having three rooms, one in the middle for human occupation, and two others, one on each side, without doors of their own, for buffaloes, cattle and pigs. As accommodation for the party of twenty soldiers they were far from satisfactory, and the officer in command was most displeased, but that had been one of the reasons why I had not wanted an escort. For my own lodgings I found an empty house, which at least enjoyed good ventilation, as half its roof had fallen in.

The clear weather on that day, coupled with the sight of a few little summits peeping over the next ridge, tempted me to walk forwards a short way to the edge of the mountainside. There, revealed before me, was one of the most striking views I have ever seen, one of those startling vistas which remain unforgettably imprinted on the mind of a traveller unexpectedly confronted with a new landscape of a kind he has never even dreamt of before. I was totally unprepared for the journey across Guizhou, and there, lying before me, was the distinctive scenery of the province, a landscape with which I was destined to become thoroughly familiar, but here suddenly unveiled in its most characteristic form, finer and closer to perfection than I ever saw it afterwards. Yet what first rose into my mind were not the earnest thoughts befitting a scientist: I simply burst out laughing at the sight. It looked as if the forces of nature had gone crazy and in their play had flung down a pile of spinning tops which lay there with their points upwards, though some were tilted sideways and a few had longitudinal instead of horizontal grooves. Or was it really a petrified fir forest, spread out there beyond the subsidence area of Luoping? There were certainly at least a thousand, if not several thousand, of these conical hills arranged side by side in irregular rows, each from 50 to 100 m in height, becoming somewhat taller as

they receded into the distance south-eastwards. Everywhere between them were funnel-shaped potholes, looking as if they were the moulds in which the cones had been cast. The cones themselves were girdled and banded by the horizontal strata; the more even the stratification, the more regular were their shapes. Here and there, however, were a few in which the strata ran obliquely or even vertically up to their apices, the separate layers of rock standing out distinctly because of the absence of vegetation [156]. Because it lay so much lower than my viewpoint, the whole scene could be taken in at a single glance; the slope of Mount Bailing Shan leading up towards us was formed mainly from the flat surfaces of the strata; either it had been raised up, or the ground beyond it had sunk.

Situated among the cones was a large polje of typical form and appearance, deepening somewhat all round its edges, which were under cultivation. The mountainside itself also consisted of karst. There was a deep, steep walled doline on the left at the foot of the huge summit cone, and a broad shallower one to the right of the track. We had in fact passed several others on the previous day. The Luoping basin lies at an altitude of 1600 m, and on the descent into it there was a noticeable change in the plant cover, visible on the slopes only 300 m above it. This point evidently marked the end of the climatic aridity of the Yunnan highlands. This district was exposed to the southeast monsoon, and the abundant precipitation compensated for the edaphic dryness, in other words the waterless state of the freely draining karst soil. The lower altitude was equivalent to that of the subtropical zone even in open country in central Yunnan, and besides the greater warmth the more uniform distribution of rainfall throughout the year in that more maritime climate had a marked effect on the plants. Although the slope had been deforested and converted to pasture and although the Chinese were still trying to burn as much as they could, I was struck by the luxuriant growth of grasses, low shrubs, climbers and herbaceous plants, all of them vigorously asserting their right to live. We had entered a new floristic region, though it did not coincide with the political boundary; indeed we still had two days to go before leaving Yunnan. Flourishing there were two scramblers with large round leaves: *Actinidia chinensis* with shaggy brown hairs and a bramble, *Rubus clinocephalus*, with entire leaves and sessile flower clusters in the leaf axils. Tall grasses were just starting to sprout — probably *Saccharum arundinaceum* and *Themeda gigantea*. Amongst them, almost completely hidden, *Castanea seguinii*, a shrubby chestnut barely a metre tall, was coming into flower. *Lilium brownii*, its stems as tall as a man, with small leaves and a few very large perfumed flowers, brown externally, was also growing there. An alder (*Alnus nepalensis*), though a water-loving tree, was still frequent. Another woody plant was *Viburnum cylindricum*, which has larger leaves than most of its genus. Down at the bottom, by the village of Jinsuo-

[155] Possibly Buyi rather than genuine Miao (SGH.).

[156] Handel-Mazzetti's photograph (Fig. 128 in the first edition) is unfortunately too poor to be worth reproducing.

luo, was a grove of tall trees beside a spring, among them *Photinia, Eriobotyra* and a whitethorn of tree-like dimensions, the stiff pinnate thorns at the base of its trunk covered by white lichens pencilled with black. The lichen was *Graphis lopingensis* (a new species). On the dry plain itself *Cunninghamia lanceolata* was abundant, forming woods and alleys. Though it was perhaps not wild even there, further west it is exceedingly uncommon and its occurrence at that site testified to the change in climate.

Luoping, only two hours further on, was a little town much like Shizong, situated near the western border of the plain, which had no drainage outlet. I continued my journey next morning (12 June). Some of the hills were clothed with broad-leaved forest, and I climbed one of them near the village of Jinzhishan. The trees were remarkably uniform in height — about 10 m — and they formed a canopy of dark green foliage without any very large leaves. *Itea yunnanensis* was the dominant species, a tree which might be taken for a bird cherry with small green flowers and leathery leaves, but which really belongs to the saxifrage family. Others included *Platycarya strobilacea* with pinnate leaves, *Xanthoxylon alatum, Schoepfia jasminodora,* a large-leaved fig *(Ficus silhetensis),* the loquat or Japanese medlar *(Eriobotrya japonica)* and near the top *Photinia crassifolia,* another species with a felty covering. From the top of the conical hill I could see the next few. Here they were further apart and the strata dipped gently to the east; their sides hence ascended in remarkably regular steps, like the pyramid of Cheops. This part of the terrain had apparently subsided somewhat more than the rest; the dolines were hence filled in and cultivated tracts of fertile weathered friable soil stretched between them. How is it that the forces of the weather, acting on a geological formation (the Trias) which elsewhere presents totally different external appearances, can produce such strange manifestations as these conical hills? That realm of science is too far removed from my own for me to attempt to answer the question, but I have a feeling that the rainfall — almost tropical in its character — may have had something to do with it.

Further eastwards we came to a row of large shapeless hills extending to the left of the track, and in front of us we saw a plateau dipping gently to the north east; its lower strata seemed to extend outwards from beneath it and, bent upwards through an angle of 90°, projected vertically in jagged peaks reaching a somewhat higher altitude to the south of the plateau. After crossing a stream which squeezed out of the valley between two hills on the left and flowed on towards some larger mountains, we arrived at a little market town called Banqiao. The forest growing on a limestone hill there was somewhat different in its composition. *Lithocarpus dealbata, Pistacia chinensis, Carpinus turczaninowii* and *Xanthoxylon* were the dominant trees; *Cupressus funebris* was also frequent but may have been planted. That evening the caravan leader whom I had engaged in Kunming at last caught up with us. He had picked out the very worst of his beasts for our little stroll to Shanghai, and his only utterance was the unprintable oath which makes one word in three of the speech of some people of Yunnan. The stream from Banqiao, after uniting with the next, also flowed towards the line of hills on the left, but finding no breach it disappeared into a sinkhole at the foot of a cliff. Before long the track climbed up to the jagged peaks we had seen on the day before, reaching an altitude of 1920 m. The plants again provided a reminder that we were still in Yunnan: the reddish steppe consisted of *Andropogon delavayi* with the usual herbaceous species, while the trees were *Pinus armandii, P. yunnanensis* and *Keteleeria davidiana.* But we soon met something new. Beside a large stream which we crossed near Kougai at midday I found *Pterocarya stenoptera,* and further on, near a hamlet called Baigong, *Cinnamomum glanduliferum,* a close relative of the camphor tree. The track veered away from the mountains along which we had been travelling and turned at first partly and then fully to the north, affording a view of two deeply cut river valleys. The first river was the Huangni He, which rose to the west of Shizong and flowed towards us at the bottom of a smooth south-facing precipice crowned with jagged spires, and the second was the Kuaize He, which came from the north and flowed in a westerly curve round a bluff to join the first at Jiangdi [157]. Down to an altitude of 1250 m the forest, growing on sandstone, consisted of pines, *Keteleeria* and *Quercus variabilis.* The subtropical flora which I had expected, and for which I had planned a day's stay, was completely lacking.

---

[157] Handel-Mazzetti seems to have the names of the rivers the wrong way round, or to be misapplying the name Hwangni He (SGH.).

Chapter 32. Across Southwest Guizhou

The Huangni He — Xingyi — rock landscapes and underground rivers — maize cultivation in karst terrain — the gorge of the Beipan Jiang — Huajiang and Guanling — Miao tribesmen — waterfalls

The Huangni He[158]marked the boundary between Yunnan and Guizhou and the village of Jiangdi lay just beyond it. The river flowed on southwards to join the Nanpan Jiang at the border of Guangzi. As became apparent when I drafted my route survey, the village was situated some distance further east than the position shown on previous maps[159]. Sixteen soldiers from Guizhou were awaiting me; drawn up in a somewhat ragged line on the steps, they presented arms as I arrived. My lieutenant let one of his own men cross the river with the baggage, but took possession of his rifle so as to deter him from absconding. I found lodgings in the lijin house, which had been intended mainly for the salt trade. One hundred tjin (60 kg) of Yunnan salt paid a toll of $2. *Pterocarya stenoptera* was growing in large numbers by the river — tall trees with spreading branches, pinnate leaves and pendent catkins, some over 30 cm long, with widely spaced, winged seeds like those of a maple. Though often submerged by the river, various pliant shrubs flourished there, notably *Cornus paucinervis, Ficus piriformis* and *Distylium chinense*. The narrow river valley ran at first southeast, turning south-southwest after 10 km. However, the track soon quitted it and climbed eastwards. On the opposite side was a karst spring, its abundant waters splashing down for a distance of several metres into the river. The limestone, lying on top of sandstone and blue slate and dipping north-westwards, extended down as far as the river, and the plants growing on it were of somewhat greater interest. Here, for the last time, I found *Engelhardtia colebrookiana*, related to *Pterocarya*. The steep climb ended at 1600m and there, on flatter ground, were pines and alders — a dryland species and a wetland species growing side by side in some pleasant little woods. On the right, beyond a depression, was the edge of a plateau which extended, geologically undisturbed, far towards the south.

The track reached summit level at Gaocha (1760m), revealing a chain of jagged mountains of somewhat lower altitude. It then turned left and ran down through a valley filled with *Cunninghamia* trees. Here they were unquestionably wild, and they soon became the predominant conifer of the district. The next valley veered to the southeast and climbed up into a group of barren, pointed mountains rising up from arid steppe terrain; where the stream went was not clear, but perhaps it flowed round to the north of them. After passing the mouths of several valleys which coursed down between parallel rock spurs from the massif to the north — in which coal was mined — we soon reached the little town of Huangcasba, otherwise known as Xingyi-xiau[160], where all I could find was a most miserable hostelry. Nevertheless, I decided to spend a day there, as the shrubs growing on the rock spurs called for closer investigation.

The town spread over a sloping tract at 1300 m, and the walls surrounding its two separate parts extended up on to two hills where they were crowned by watchtowers offering picturesque views. The telegraph line from Anlong (or Xingyi-fu) to the east had recently been completed and, as I found on the next stage of my journey, a brand-new paved road had been constructed. Being accustomed to the ancient and dilapidated roads of Yunnan, I was amazed at the sight. On visiting the official — a most helpful and obliging man held in great affection by the people — I was able to get rid of my military escort, as the route was reputed to be perfectly safe, and one or two riflemen would be quite sufficient, as the official admitted with a smile. Here he was stationed in Guizhou and outside the authority of the dujun of Yunnan. Though someone in Jiangdi had told me that it was 60 li to the Nanpan Jiang, I heard here that the journey would take six or seven days on bad mountain roads and had to give up the idea of making a short detour to visit the low lying river valley, even though both my informants might have been equally far from the truth. On 15th June I visited one of the rocky spurs: in fact the first to the west of the town, as it seemed to be well clothed with vegetation. However, in its lower part there was nothing more than nut trees and maize; the natural shrub covering had been destroyed and survived only on the very top. There, however, the spoils were rich indeed: *Tirpitzia sinensis (Linaceae)*, a shrub with soft leaves and large flowers; *Alangium chinense* and *Sapium rotundifolium; Salacia sessiliflora*, a new species in a genus of tropical affinities: *Rhamnus paniculiflorus* and another species with equally inconspicuous flowers (*Rhamnella martinii*): *Ficus baileyi* scrambling over the rocks, and many more. Clambering about in the broiling sun, I worked off some of the fat which had been laid down by the generous diet provided by my kind hosts during the previous winter, and the sweat streamed down my cheeks. Down below by the brook I collected *Bischofia trifoliata*, a large tree with a spherical crown and trifoliate leaves; though it looks like a *Pistacia* it really belongs to the spurge family. Also growing there was an ash, *Fraxinus chinensis*.

On the hillside below the town there were little waterfalls where the streams splashed down over deposits of travertine. On the plain I saw the tea oil bush (*Thea oleifera*) in cultivation for the first time. *Cynanchum atratum* with brownish black flowers was frequent there, and the fern *Lygodium japonicum* was creeping about on steep roadside banks among *Gleichenia linearis*. At the edge of the plain

---

[158]Handel-Mazzetti has definitely confused the names of the rivers here (SGH).

[159]Handel-Mazzetti's own map also appears to be wildly inaccurate in this area (SGH).

---

[160] Now the preferred name (SGH).

a river had cut a ravine, and at a narrow spot, far to the left of the line which the road would otherwise have taken, it was crossed by a stone bridge [161] some 25 m above the water (1050 m above sea level). It made a marvellous picture: the gloomy ravine winding away into the unknown, the tufa deposits on its walls, the perpendicular rock towers on either side, and beneath them the bridge — a work of man and not of nature, yet by no means out of keeping with the scene. We went gradually uphill and the cone hills began again. From afar this stone forest at first seemed totally formless, but before long a pattern emerged, the cones apparently being arranged in rows along the approximately east-west strike of the strata, which were tilted almost vertically.

Soon after leaving Dingxiao, where we spent the night, we turned off the road to Anlong [162] and climbed in stages to the left up to a plateau. It had been raining since the previous day, but visibility was clear enough for me to make out the structure of the landscape. Small villages were scattered everywhere, and all low-lying areas were in use as rice fields. Up on top the strata were horizontal again, and the projecting rock cones were marked by regular bands. There was low-growing scrub consisting of *Myrsine africana* and *Pyracantha crenulata* as in Yunnan, while *Pinus yunnanensis* was still widespread. Up there on the plateau — further away it evidently sloped down to the southwest — we crossed a rivulet, probably the main affluent of the river which flowed under the Tianxin Qiao bridge, and near the village of Ahong we met it again, this time on our right. Raging in their channel below the road, its waters tossed spray high into the air between the bushes. Its main source was a spring which gushed out from a hollow in the rock, and the underground streams which fed it had been swollen by the rain. Higher up, above this spring, the stream was very much smaller. During the lunch halt I found some more fossils embedded in laminar limestone strata sandwiched between beds of solid rock; when subsequently identified, they proved that the formation belonged to the Carboniferous. In some stretches of its little valley the rivulet flowed underground. Its source was located near a col at 1600 m, traversed by the road. The surrounding terrain was somewhat barren, the plant cover consisting of sparse discontinuous sward, quite different from the Yunnanese steppe. Although *Drosera peltata* was still present in it, the dominant species was *Scleria hookeriana*, a sedge with black panicles. *Osmunda japonica*, *Lysimachia clethroides*, *Cirsium belingschanicum* and *Houttuynia cordata* bore witness to the moister conditions, while *Castanea seguinii*, *Indigofera esquirolii* and *I. dosua* were still the characteristic shrubs. As we went downhill the stream accompanying us once again ran underground in some stretches. The limestone formed a fold at right angles to the northeasterly course of the road, and the hollow in

which Qiaolou was located was a syncline, its drainage running eastwards.

Beyond the hollow was a quartzite ridge, rising up out of the rocky headlands in which the limestone terminated. Climbing the ridge next morning, we came to some bogs situated along little brooks. In places there were bogmosses and liverworts (*Nardia truncata*); *Osmunda cinnamomea* growing in tussocks; rushes, bulrushes and reeds; a large fern, resembling bracken, with rounded terminal pinnae (*Histiopteris incisa*); *Hydrangea yunnanensis*, upright shoots of bramble, and *Polygonum cuspidatum* at the margins of the surrounding shrub community. Flowering in profusion on a marshy meadow on the first saddle (1720m) was the snow white vanilla-scented orchid *Platanthera hologlottis*. The hillsides were covered with bracken interspersed with numerous hazel shrubs (*Corylus heterophylla)* and a few birches (*Betula luminifera)*. Leaving the next valley, where the stream splashed down in a series of little waterfalls, we climbed up yet again into another valley running in the same direction. Here we found coal, and beside it there were flat cones of reddish brown sinter deposited by the springs. The bushes seemed reluctant to colonise it, but it was thickly overgrown with luscious green liverworts and soft cushions of algae (*Ulothrix subtilis*) with moss (*Polytrichum commune*) in smaller amounts. At last we reached the edge of the quartzite ridge and found a little saddle which gave far reaching views. Below it were some inconspicuous limestone hills dipping slightly towards the northeast. However, this region does not form part of the "Chinese strike line", though its actual structure is not clear, even from a profile: to the north, some 20 km distant, I saw the border of a higher mountain tract, below which the streams ran from west-southwest to east-northeast; further on, like the river at Xingren at our feet, they turned east-southeast, indicating that the strike line evidently takes a new direction. Although the weather was now splendid, the atmospheric humidity was a hindrance to distant views.

Xingren was situated at an altitude of 1450 m. There was therefore a short ascent from the river to the town, but in general the district was uniformly elevated, the only higher ground being the Long Shan range far away to the right of the road, consisting of a variety of strata dipping gently away from where we stood. The little market town of Baling where we spent the night was situated on a stream which emerged from the mountain to the south and hurried on to join the Beipan Jiang. Here the telegraph line from Anlong rejoined our route. Continuing in this same direction, the road led over three minor hills, with a lake between the first two of them; two of the streams flowed to the right into a channel which extended eastwards below the Long Shan, but a third one disappeared into a sinkhole. This stream came from Nanmuchang, a place of some importance with a mercury mine. We passed through it at noon, and then turned northwards, soon descending along a valley. The baila trees (wax trees: *Ligustrum lucidum*) at the village of Qidun were larger than any I had ever seen; climbing up them was *Celastrus gemmatus*, while their trunks and branches were covered with *Drynaria fortunei*.

---

[161] Tianxin-Qiao — Handel-Mazzetti's Fig. 130, not reproduced in this edition.

[162] Hsingyi-fu (Xingyi fu), now Anlong, not Hsingyi-hsien (Xingyi Xian), now Xingyi (SGH).

One of them even had a little palm tree growing from a fork in its trunk; it must have sprung from a seed which had lodged there. Another remarkable species seen here — and indeed on the previous two days — was *Kalopanax*, a tree belonging to the ivy family. Its long shoots, carrying thorns and large deeply divided palmate leaves, shot straight up for several metres, while the older branches had smaller leaves lobed like those of a sycamore. Besides the *Catalpa* tree common in Yunnan (*C. duclouxii*), which was still present here and now bore pods almost a metre in length, there was another species, *C. ovata*, of similar appearance when in growth; it had large leaves and white flowers with brown spots and yellow streaks inside. The valley ended in a funnel-shaped depression and the road continued through rocky terrain with gently inclined strata, an alternating succession of knolls and scarps, dolines and karst pavements, though except at the sides of the road and around the sparse dwellings it was covered with scrub and forest. The houses in this stony district were built from stone slabs and the people lived on maize. Arable fields of any extent were rare, and were mainly confined to the bottoms of dolines; elsewhere maize was planted in the *terra rossa* which filled the hollows between the projecting rocks, often only a single plant in a little hole. The road traversed a shallow doline 1 km in breadth and then crossed another. This one was extremely narrow and elongated; it extended in the shape of a proper little valley 80 m deep — and even deeper on both sides — until it reached the transverse crest used by the road. Continuing along it, we soon came to the village of Taipingjie, which was situated on a ridge of marl.

Next morning the weather was superb. Just below the village, where the descent into the Beipan Jiang valley began, I once again set eyes on a tract of savage mountain scenery; even after the far loftier alpine landscapes which I had seen in Yunnan it was still quite dramatic. From that spot the river was not yet visible, but 200 m below us there was a broad terrace roughly 5 km wide. On it, sunk in the marl, was a basin under cultivation; beyond the latter was limestone, its strata dipping gently away from us and therefore lying above the marl. It had produced a strip of the distinctive conical hills, arranged in several rows. These ones were exceptionally steep-sided and of diverse shapes. Further away still, beyond the river and clearly higher than the conical hills, was a steep mountain wall, its top slit into numerous pinnacles like a gigantic saw placed at right angles to the direction of the road. Further left, to the northwest, the valley broadened into an open space, evidently at the confluence of the Kedu He, but to the right there was an inextricable tangle of mountains on both sides of the river, all of much of the same altitude and closely packed together, and I was unable to trace the windings of the river valley. The stream arising from the Shuigaoji basin turned off to the right, but the road went straight on through the tract of conical hills. The shrub vegetation was almost impenetrable and did not offer many novelties. However, there was a large *Rapanea*, a tree with inconspicuous flowers sprouting directly

from its branches beneath tufts of leaves; *Sapium rotundifolium*, a small tree with leathery circular leaves (*Euphorbiaceae*); and *Iodes vitiginea*, a climber with a dense canopy of rough-surfaced leaves and twining stems carrying bunches of fruit resembling cherries in colour and shape, though somewhat flattened and covered with short hairs. They looked so tempting that I tasted them, but mingled with their delicate flavour was a distinct aroma of prussic acid, so I left them alone; indeed I learnt later that no one ate them. *Nephrolepis cordifolia*, a light green fern with simple pinnate fronds, was common on the limestone pavements. It had conspicuous water-storage tubers, covered with brown scales, attached in rows along the rootstocks, some of which were lying free. Here again it was apparent that the wetness of the climate offset the natural aridity of the freely draining soil — not merely from the rampant profusion of the vegetation as a whole, but notably from the luxuriance of the mosses (*Papillaria nigrescens, Anomodon integerrimus, Hypnum leptothallum*) which swathed the rocks, and the large olive green algae (*Nostoc commune*) which swelled up and sprang into life in every little hollow after a rain shower. From the hamlet or, more correctly, the inns at the edge of the river gorge itself the road descended steeply by stone steps. At an altitude of 970 m I encountered some old friends from the subtropical flora of the hot, arid, deeply eroded river valleys of the Sichuan-Yunnan borderland: besides *Phyllanthus emblica, Alangium chinense* and *Ficus cuspidifera* there was *Oroxylon indicum*, a tree with giant seed pods which I had seen near Huili. Its evil-smelling flowers grouped into capitate inflorescences were now open; ants visited their calyces, but the fleshy, dull red corollas dropped off in succession immediately after they had bloomed. Among them was the tall *Mallotus barbatus* bearing hanging racemes of fruits with shaggy reddish hairs, the elegant fragrant *Dalbergia cavaleriei*, the twining *Argyreia wallichii*, the waxy white *Aganosma elegans* and a new species from the *Verbena* family, the climbing *Premna crassa*. Down by the river's edge there was a jungle of tall grasses (*Saccharum arundinaceum* and *Themeda gigantea*) and rising up almost like a palm from a steep rockface below the road was *Brassaiopsis papayoides*, a thorny shrub belonging to the ivy family, with dense tufts of leathery fan-shaped dark green leaves approaching 1 m in diameter. Also growing there was *Callicarpa macrophylla*, a small tree belonging to the *Verbena* family with panicles of pretty rose-red flowers arising from the axils of its large opposite leaves and aggregated towards the ends of the twigs.

An iron chain bridge crossed the Beipan Jiang some 10m above the mean water level, at an altitude of only 580m. Beyond the river, using a breach in the valley wall, the roadway ascended in steps which were so steep and unremitting that I had to dismount from my mule, after it had paused for a breather and was unable to get started again. Upstream (west-northwest) and downstream (east-northeast) the river had cut a gorge with almost vertical walls to a depth of 300m into the gently inclined limestone strata. At the top of this gorge was a narrow shelf which provided space for a village called Falang. A few surviving trees and shrubs of savannah woodland type showed that such woodland had once occupied the whole of that bare mountainside, and I spent the afternoon there (20th June) studying its affinities to the savannah known to me from similar sites in Yunnan. The great depth of the gorge coupled with the direction of the rain-bearing winds must cause greater aridity there, on the north side of the valley, and this was presumably responsible for the occurrence of savannah woodland — the last place at which I encountered it on my journey. Admittedly, my own observations did not provide direct evidence of undue aridity: that afternoon, under partial cloud, my wet and dry bulb hygrometer read 64% relative humidity, and at 8 pm, a wind having sprung up, it read 72%. On the rocky edge near the village I found *Nandina domestica*, a shrub related to *Berberis* and *Mahonia* but having panicles of white flowers and pinnate leaves; *Ficus caesia*, a new species of fig, robust and beautiful; *Premna anthopotamica*, also new, and various others.

The view was breath-taking. Vertically below me was the river, bordered by a narrow yellowish-white strip of pebbles and boulders within an outer green band of grasses and trees; on either side of the gorge was the track, a slender ribbon winding down the slopes; then the bridge and below it the tremendous chasm into which the river vanished. Obliquely opposite, some distance upstream, was a hamlet looking as if it were glued on to the mountainside, but I could not see how the people — here all of them were Chinese — were able to exist in such a wilderness. The ascent from Falang to the pass over the saw-edged mountain wall led across steppe which was almost devoid of trees or shrubs, but I found two interesting and beautiful herbaceous perennials: *Hibiscus sagittifolius* with a thick woody rootstock and large scarlet flowers, in no way inferior to the steppe plants of the Middle East, and *Phaius steppicola*, a tall orchid with white flowers (a new species).

The mountain chain consisted of two parallel ranks of peaks, overtopping the pass (1270m) by about 100m, though the clouds seemed to exaggerate their height. The strata had a steep westerly dip, quite different from their disposition at the bottom of the gorge. The ground now levelled out, and we came to the small town of Guanling, only 50m lower down. It was formerly known as Muyu or Muyusi and the next place to the north was then called Guanling, but now, in accordance with an official decree, they had exchanged their names — undoubtedly a somewhat unpractical procedure [163]. Extending northwards was a broad depression, a shallow saucer of marl exposed below tracts of limestone on either side. However, the road soon left it and turned to the right. *Cupressus funebris*, at that spot and frequently from there onward unquestionably wild, formed groves on the tops of some of the rock cones and also occurred mingled with *Cunning-*

hamia, but pines were absent; indeed, we had not seen any for some time. Before long we were once more in a wilderness of rock — or at least that was the impression it gave, since the shrubs and trees, though by no means sparse, were hidden among rock crests and ledges and in the fissures of the limestone pavements. At this spot there were short crests or spines of considerable dimensions, running from west-southwest to east-northeast, with deep narrow dolines sunk between them, arranged in parallel to the right of the road. Their shapes were a vivid reminder of those I had seen on the mountains between Mengzi and Manhao in Yunnan, and evidently the same geological formation extends from Guizhou to that district.

During the lunch stop at Jichangping I took the opportunity of climbing a wooded rock cone. It reminded me of those delightful highways on the Nu Jiang-Drung Jiang divide: the ascent from ledge to ledge called for gymnastic manoeuvres, and the resemblance was heightened by a brisk downpour. As was the case everywhere in those montane woods, *Itea yunnanensis* was the dominant shrub, recognizable from afar by the rows of green catkins 20 cm long hanging down from the horizontal twigs. Together with the erect inflorescences of *Platycarya strobilacea* they brought a vertical motif into the scene. Fruits of *Eriobotrya japonica* were now on sale everywhere at low prices, and the inhabitants declared that it was native. They said the same of *Trachycarpus excelsa*, a fan palm planted in every village, though where it was growing in the woods its tops remained hidden beneath the closed canopy. Other noteworthy trees included *Cinnamomum glanduliferum*, *Celtis biondii*, *Photinia* spp., *Albizzia julibrissin*, *Euonymus*, *Pittosporum*, *Helwingia* and the new *Andrachne attenuata*. The herbaceous understorey was very sparse, but I found *Liparis acuminata*, an orchid with brown flowers. My work completed, I hurried on to catch up with the caravan, crossing a few brooks which united further to the east. Here for the first time I saw the indigenous people, Hua Miao [164]. They were coming back from market in large numbers, each carrying his scales on his shoulder, for they had a well founded distrust of the scales employed by the Chinese, who kept one set for buying and another for selling. The women wore long pleated skirts which distinguished them at a glance from the Chinese. Dropping only a little, the road continued to Muyu.

Next morning we soon descended into a deeply incised, almost unpopulated valley, but its floor lay at a higher altitude than that of the Beipan He and its appearance was totally different. There were steep uniform slopes on both sides, but though they consisted of limestone it was only at the tops, where flat beds of harder rock had been laid down, that vertical cliffs outcropped. The slopes were completely covered by a green mantle of grass, and in the two lower thirds there was a proper jungle of tall grasses — *Saccharum arundinaceum*, *Themeda gigantea* and *Arundo donax*. Extending down around a temple at the same level was a wood with some of

---

[163] It seems that the original Guanling has now reverted to that name . Muyu is apparently now Huajiang (SGH).

[164] Probably Buyi, who are not true Miao (SGH).

the characters of the forests of the river gorges. Its main element was *Dalbergia hupeana,* a leguminous shrub with an abundance of sweetly scented pink flowers; *Ficus cuspidifera* was also plentiful. A masonry bridge with several large arches, the Baling Qiao, led over the river and the road climbed gradually northwards. Rainstorms in the night had swollen all the watercourses, and a stream tumbled merrily down the stone steps. It may be that such impressions caused me to overestimate the magnitude of the falls and other phenomena of that district, even though I strove to imagine them as they would be under average conditions. To the north the valley bottom was almost entirely obscured by huge clouds of spray. As we ascended the valley the Dishui Tan waterfall [165] slowly came into view. It would certainly be no exaggeration to compare it, in the state in which I saw it on that day, with the Krimmler falls. Its overall height — fully 300m — was the same, and it plunged in an unimpeded leap over the lowest step. Higher up the bed of the stream had cut into the rock for some depth and there were two further falls, not so clearly visible. The uppermost fall began at the edge of the Guanling plateau, into which it had cut only a shallow notch. The thunder of the waters was plainly audible, and yet, starting from a little col named Jigong bei situated at least 3 km to the north [166] I had to go quite some distance up the side valley before I was able to get a clear picture of all three waterfalls on one plate. Further downstream the valley became somewhat broader, and below its junction with the valley of the Baishui He which flowed down from Huangguoshu it formed a shallow basin where it collected all the streams which we had crossed before reaching Guanling, and then, some 15km distant from our route, swung round towards the east.

A narrow plateau with outcrops of coal — a continuation at the same altitude of the Guanling plateau — separated us from the Baishui He which ran in a less deeply cut valley. Along the route was deciduous woodland in which *Cunninghamia* and *Thea oleifera* were abundant, and *Gleichenia linearis* grew in profusion among the trees. The Baishui He ran in a U-shaped valley, bounded above by evenly bedded, reddish yellow limestone. Swollen by rain, its brown waters had risen well above its banks; they surged down the steep gradient, throwing up clouds of spray. Some distance further up I saw a cloud of vapour rising high into the air from the middle of an arid plain. I had already heard of the waterfall at Huangguoshu, but I had not expected it to be so immense and I approached the spot with interest [167]. Above the fall the riverbed had not cut deeply into the rock, but at the village the water crashed down for a height which I estimated at 50m [168] into a ravine which led away from it in an S-shaped curve completely invisible from a distance. One might have imagined that one was gazing at a section of the Niagara falls, so tremendous was the sight which it presented on that day. After a small horseshoe-shaped step only a few metres high, the broad sheet of water plunged down without a check into the seething cauldron below, shooting out wedge-shaped columns of water which broke up into clouds of spray. On that day this waterfall certainly exceeded the Dishui Tan in volume, but in the dry season it is apparently reduced to a few separate streams. The village of Huangguoshu, just above the fall, was situated at the junction between my route from the southwest and the main road from Yunnan via Qujing and Langdai, the route used by the telegraph line from Guiyang.

---

[165] Now usually called the Banling Bridge waterfall.. Modern Chinese sources give its height as over 100m (SGH).

[166] Handel-Mazzetti's map shows the col to the <u>east</u> of the waterfall (SGH).

---

[167] The Huangguoshu waterfall is the largest in China in terms of flow, though not of height (SGH). Colour photo in *"The Natural History of China"*, Collins, London, 1990, page 47.

[168] Chinese sources say over 60m (SGH).

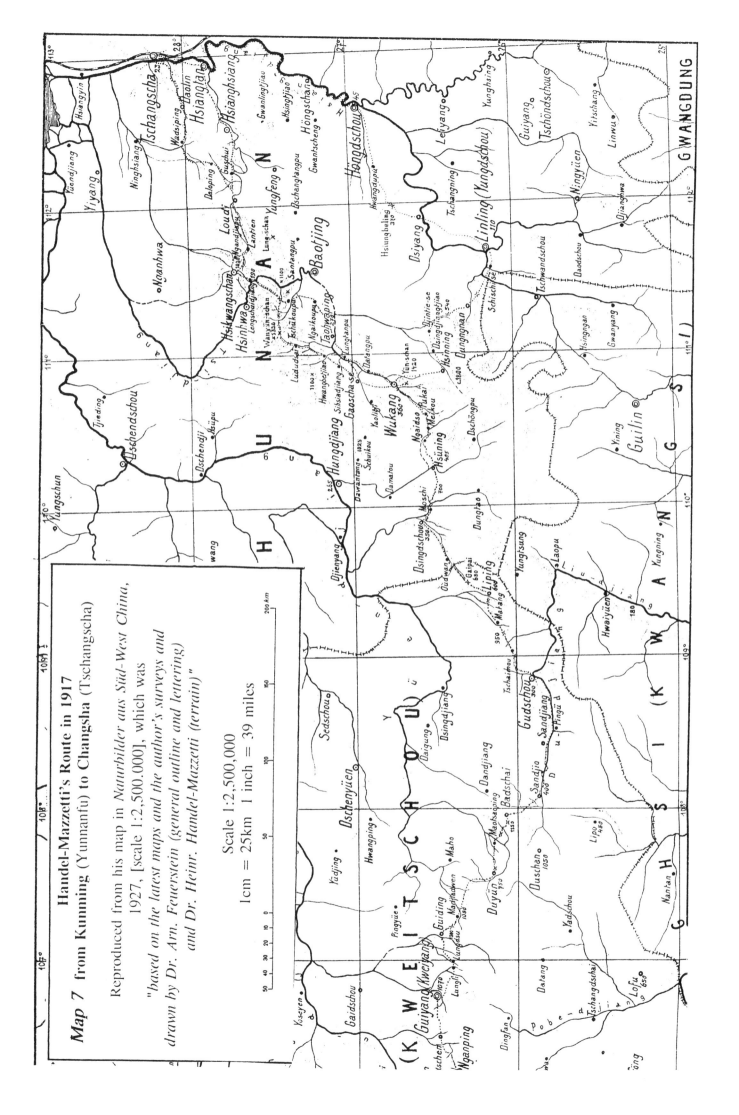

Handel-Mazzetti's Route in 1917

Map 7 from Kunming (Yunnanfu) to Changsha (Tschangscha)

Reproduced from his map in *Naturbilder aus Süd-West China*, 1927, [scale 1:2.500.000], which was

"based on the latest maps and the author's surveys and drawn by Dr. Arn. Feuerstein (general outline and lettering) and Dr. Heinr. Handel-Mazzetti (terrain)"

Scale 1:2,500,000

1cm = 25km   1 inch = 39 miles

200 km

HUNAN

KWEITSCHOU

KWANGSI

GWANGDUNG

SIKWAN

Tschangscha
Changsha
Linling (Yungdschou)
Hengdschou
Guilin
Guiyang (Kweiyang)
Oschenyüen
Gudschou
Wukang
Baojing
Hsünning
Hungdjiang
Djienyang

Chapter 33. Along the Main Road From Huangguoshu via Guiyang to Guiding

Anshun — shrub meadows — tea — the watershed — a noisy inn — a visit to the dujun — Qianling Shan, Dong Shan and Nanyue Shan — a mountain circle — meadow bogs — rest houses

The road, in much better condition than most of the main routes in Yunnan, led north-eastwards to Zhenning, passing over horizontally stratified ridges of coal-bearing marl above limestone, with quartzite on top. Conical rock formations were only a little less prominent than before and seemed to belong to the quartzite layer. Next day a short march, for the most part in a channel between rows of limestone cones, brought us to the large town of Anshun. Most of the inns were better than those in Yunnan; in one place the mafu was greatly alarmed when I found an inn that was perfectly clean.

"There can't have been any horses here for ages," he said, "and there could be evil spirits inside. I'll have to drive them out before I take my horses in there." So saying, he set light to a bundle of straw and waved it about under the manger.

On another occasion it was my turn to be annoyed. The local official had provided me with a watchman, and just as I was going to sleep he began to make an earsplitting clatter outside my open door by hammering on a large hollow bamboo, with the idea of keeping thieves away. The Chinese may be able to put up with such a racket, just as they will sleep under an electric light, sometimes even with their eyes open, but I rejected his well meant endeavours with unconcealed indignation. Along the road were the ruins of numerous stone-built houses belonging to deserted villages, the occupants having presumably fled to escape extortion and looting by passing soldiers from China's growing armies.

Anshun lies on a fair-sized river flowing south-eastwards. Previous measurements of its latitude were correct, but its longitude differs considerably from that shown in the atlases; according to my route survey it is 105° 58' 30" east of Greenwich [169], i.e., somewhat further west than the distance stated on the margin of Davies' map, "about 35 miles to Guiyang". In fact it is 80 km south west [170] of the provincial capital. The road continued more or less in a straight line along a similar channel to Pingba. My mafu was greatly amazed to see a horse harnessed to a plough, though certainly it was a pitiful sight and one that we met nowhere else. He was equally astonished at seeing horsemeat on sale — apparently it was sometimes eaten in that district. Broad-leaved trees of new and different kinds began to appear beside the characteristic species of the montane woods, some of them even in the short distance we had travelled since leaving the Guanling district. Among them were Paulownia tomentosa, Cercis chinensis and Firmiana simplex, all three now showing an abundance of brown shading among their dark foliage: in the first two it was produced by their closely packed fruits and in the third by the felty covering of its young inflorescences. Growing on the bare rocks were two splendid gesnerads,

Didymocarpus eburneus with thick fleshy leaves and large pendent violet flowers (Fig.46) and Lysionotus pauciflorus, the latter not yet fully developed; equally frequent was the small yellow-flowered Sedum drynarioides with abundant glands. Except in such places much of the ground was covered by shrub meadow [171], a community of plants all of which were under one metre in height. A few grasses were still flowering, as were the shrubs and subshrubs; there were various Leguminosae including several species of Lespedeza, Desmodium and Indigofera which formed besom-shaped or pyramidal bushes studded with pink flowers in various shades, those of Lespedeza formosa contrasting elegantly against its silvery foliage. There was Castanea seguinii with a profusion of yellowish flower spikes, Hypericum hookerianum with golden yellow flowers, Salix praticola (a new species) and other shrubs. Mingled with them were herbaceous plants with magnificent flowers, the finest of all being Osbeckia crinita with large dusky pink blooms, their calyces covered with long red bristly hairs, followed by Platycodon grandiflorus with deep blue saucer-shaped bells, Iris tectorum, Belamcanda sinensis with pink flowers, Anemone japonica and Senecio argunensis. Bracken — our native species — was abundant and there was a understorey of Nephrodium xylodes or some other fern resembling our native Thelypteris. The entire plant community showed unmistakable resemblances to those flourishing under similar climatic conditions in certain stretches of the Nu Jiang and Drung Jiang valleys, especially as small trees of Betula luminifera were growing here and there. Today for the first time I saw tea in cultivation, something I did not meet again until long afterwards. The bushes were planted at an altitude of 1300 m, in rows between maize, and looked somewhat windswept. Their twigs were blanketed with lichens; probably the damage done when the leaves were picked made the twigs prone to colonisation by them. I stopped at a tea-house where the local product was proudly set before me. I remembered then that I had seen a few tea bushes planted in the grounds of the Provincial Agricultural College at the foot of Changchong Shan near Kunming, but I do not know whether they survived [172].

Next day, beyond the southwards draining valley channel in which Pingba lay, there was yet again a change in the landscape. We came to a chain of limestone hills dipping south-westwards beneath the marl bluffs of a low mountain range. At their foot were some truly mesophilic meadows with an

---

[169] 105° 56' on Operational Navigation Chart H-11.

[170] Correctly only slightly south of west (SGH).

---

[171] "Buschwiese". Handel-Mazzetti defines this as *"lush mesophilic meadow with scattered shrubs, resembling broom in their habit of growth, spreading out at their tops, their twigs covered with lichens. The shrubs are for the most part the same as in mesophilic mixed forest, but also include several species of Berberis. Grasses are somewhat scanty."*

[172] Tea is nowadays grown as far north as Shandong province (SGH).

abundance of cocksfoot grass and familiar central European flowering plants such as *Daucus carota, Senecio argunensis, Agrimonia zeylanica, Prunella vulgaris, Hypericum perforatum* and *Lotus corniculatus*. On dry sandstone I again met the *Vaccinium* shrub communities I had seen in Yunnan (*V. camphorifolium* and *V. fragile*) together with the small fern *Gleichenia linearis*, but soon we were once more among conical limestone hills, though we followed the surface of the stratified rock across country which was gently folded towards the north west. In a little defile I found the last edelweiss of my travels in China (*Leontopodium artemisiifolium*), while the hedges and thickets became more interesting. *Torricellia tiliifolia*, a tall tree with leaves like our limes, was frequent. The streams were edged by deposits of tufa and growing on their banks were willows and dense colonies of *Mariscus chinensis*, a sedge. On crossing a river at an altitude of 1200 m I realised that we had traversed an inconspicuous but important watershed. The river flowed from the south and, to judge from its size, must have journeyed a considerable distance from its source. We had therefore crossed the watershed between the Yangzi Jiang and the Nanpan Jiang, the headstream of the West River of Canton. In this more or less uniformly elevated country there were hardly any vantage points giving far-ranging vistas, but from here there was a fine view to the north, across a green hollow to two mountains, one of which was wooded and carried a temple. The river emerged from between them after making a gentle curve to the east. Beyond the river, near the little town of Qingzhen, I once more encountered a few pine trees, clearly of a different species from those seen in Yunnan, though a close relative. Their needles were shorter and thinner and the trees were darker in hue than the Yunnan pines, differences which were immediately obvious to me, having as I did the appearance of the Yunnan species freshly imprinted on my memory. It was *Pinus massoniana*, a pine which extends into the tropics. Occurring with it was *Liquidambar formosana*, a stately tree resembling the planes, and indeed related to them. We met it here for the first time, and it accompanied us for some distance.

On 27th June we climbed slowly up a col at 1320 m and during the afternoon went steadily downhill, first into a little hollow and then eastwards along the stream which drained it. Before long we again came to limestone strata, dipping eastwards above the marls of the ridge. The new pine formed woods and *Abelia microphylla*, carrying a profusion of little pink bells, grew on the rocks. We hardly noticed the plain on to which we emerged on leaving the narrow valley. We soon caught sight of the city wall, hidden among the trees; another half hour and we were entering the west gate of the provincial capital, Guiyang. After searching for some time I found an upper room in a tolerably comfortable inn.

Guiyang (Kweiyang) was situated on level ground at 1070 m altitude; it extended over a larger area than Kunming and claimed seventy thousand inhabitants. Being provided with neatly covered drains, its streets made a favourable impression of cleanliness, but its trade was less prosperous than that of Kunming and it lacked any buildings substan-

tial enough to lend it an air of dignity. Late that evening and early next morning the police came and asked to see my passport; if I had none, they said, they would have to put a guard over me and my baggage. However, Lao Li entreated them to come back by daylight, and after they had finally inspected the passport, they withdrew satisfied. Later came a visit from a higher official, who apologised, though not directly, and said that they had indeed received excellent recommendations some time before my arrival, but they were surprised that I had sought lodging in an inn so crowded with Chinese. "But where else could I have gone", I thought, "there were no fellow countrymen of mine in the town; no Chinese citizen had offered me hospitality and I was certainly not going to ask for an invitation; moreover, as a guest in a private house it can be even more difficult to keep intrusive onlookers at a distance than it is in an inn." Schoch, my Swiss friend, had lodged in the same inn in 1916, when he travelled on foot from Kunming to Zhenyuan [173], and during the journey had diligently collected plants, a set of which he presented to me. The people here still remembered the large bundle of Chinese straw sandals which he used to carry on his back. Though a pair of these sandals would certainly not last a European more than a day, they cost only 15 cash (= 2½ heller) and on paved roads they were undoubtedly the best footgear; walking round Guiyang in my leather shoes I slipped and fell several times on paving stones worn smooth by constant use. The ponies also had a hard time on the paved roads. My pony — its hind hoofs unshod as was usual in Yunnan — had recently had several attacks of inflammation of the pasterns and I therefore let Lao Li ride it, as he was much smaller and lighter than I. However, I did not want to entrust it to him for long, for he was as bad a rider as any man in South China. An officer lodging in the inn helped me to treat it and with shoes on all four hoofs it trotted along merrily once more. He also offered his services as a guide to the temple groves in the vicinity, and told numerous untruths, for instance that he was going to Liping with a convoy carrying money and would meet me again there; he was evidently not a man fit for any serious enterprise. Another visitor was a highly intelligent youth who spoke English and was sometimes tiresomely persistent in his attentions when I was sitting at my work. I had to extend my stay in Guiyang to have shoes made in European style; a pair cost six Mexican dollars, but I cannot remember whether they lasted until the autumn. I also got a tailor to make me a raincoat out of raw silk coated with oil, a tolerably durable fabric, as my camel-hair cape was too heavy for that climate. However, the raincoat turned out to be atrociously ill-fitting; it stuck out some 20 cm beyond each shoulder and even though I had it re-oiled twice it did not remain waterproof for long.

Upstairs I was able to keep idle spectators at bay, but my stay was not really enjoyable. On a gallery a few metres across the street was a man suffering from a venereal disease. He lay there, stark

---

[173] 160 km east-northeast of Guiyang.

naked, wiping away the pus with scraps of paper which blew about all over the yard. After I had sent someone to complain, he hung up a sheet of paper, but soon forgot it once more. The episode casts a revealing light on Chinese perceptions of decency and antisepsis. Down below in the yard I watched the hotel guests dragging the bedsteads out of the rooms and pouring boiling water over the cracks to destroy lice and bedbugs. All night long there were outbursts of hellish din with loud voices and singing in a room diagonally below mine, but the innkeeper was unwilling to put a stop to the racket as he profited by selling tea to the party.

As Zhang Yizhou had given me a passport which was valid for Yunnan and Guizhou only, saying that when I reached Guiyang I would be able to get one for the provinces further east, I paid a visit to the dujun. The government in Guiyang had neither an aliens' officer nor an interpreter, and I had to take Lao Li with me for the latter purpose. Like many of our elderly generals in Austria, the dujun's knowledge of the world was strictly confined to military matters, and when Li told him that I had come to China for the purpose of collecting plants, his mouth dropped open in astonishment.

"What sort of plants?" he asked, with an expression on his face which said "Surely you don't expect me to believe that tale!" Li in his turn pretended to be amazed at such a stupid questions.

"Plants growing in the wild, of course", he replied. In the subsequent course of our interview I evidently failed to make him understand the real nature of my activities, for he kept a close watch on my trips out of town, and the policemen at the town gates always asked my men where I had been. He raised no objections to my proceeding along my chosen route across Guizhou and issued me with a new passport, but his authority did not extend to Hunan or Jiangxi and I therefore had to request our ambassador A. von Rosthorn to apply on my behalf to the government in Beijing, as I expected to encounter difficulties in those provinces. However, my fears proved groundless; the authorities there did not bother their heads about European travellers and did not even provide me with an escort.

To the south and east of the town there were cone hills, and to the north and west were tracts of more or less continuous mountainous terrain. For my first outing, on 1st July, I chose Qianling Shan, a hill some 200 m higher than the town, situated at the edge of the mountains just north of the route along which I had come. On the limestone which formed its lower part and on the sandstone overlying it were forests of tall broad-leaved trees including *Quercus acutissima* and *Myrica rubra*, a shrub remarkably similar to the strawberry tree (*Arbutus*) in the appearance of its leaves and its red fruits, which have a sharp resinous flavour but when cooked with sugar make excellent eating. There were also hornbeams (*Carpinus fargesiana*) together with smaller numbers of other broad-leaved trees, a few pines and *Cunninghamia* trees. The understorey consisted of camellias (*Thea oleifera*), *Vaccinium japonicum*, a shrub with angular winged shoots and white flowers like those of *Oxycoccus*, and *Gaultheria laxiflora*. Huge trees of *Meliosma henryi*, resembling privet but covered in blossom, stood among the *Liquidambar* trees around the temple which was situated in

the hollow between the two summits. Growing there in damp shady spots were a few plants which I had not previously met with in China, among them our familiar garden *Funckia (Hosta coerulea)* together with *Lysimachia trientaloides, L. capillipes* and various ferns, which also flourished on the rocks. Dong Shan, reached through the east gate, yielded fewer novelties but it offered a wide ranging prospect over the entire town and the surrounding countryside, now mantled in green: the calm blue river flowed from the mountains in the south-west and swerved eastwards round the southern end of the town, where it was spanned by a large bridge visible among the pale grey houses. Further afield, a few bare cones of whitish limestone and a yellowish brown band of marl lent colour and diversity to the landscape. At the foot of the mountain lime was quarried to be spread on the ricefields. The heath meadow communities established here furnished some interesting plants, among them *Potentilla chinensis* with finely cut leaves and yellow flowers.

Nanyue Shan, somewhat further away to the south, also gave a fine vista from its bare summit. The view was in fact most extraordinary. A little distance away from the mountain was a series of cone hills 200-300 m in height. Most of them tended to merge into one another, though here and there was one which stood out from the rest. They were arranged in a closed ring or oval, roughly 15 km from north to south and 5 km from east to west. From its shape it might have been taken for a gigantic crater were it not that its outer perimeter was so clearly demarcated from its surroundings and that its sedimentary structure was so obvious. The limestone strata of this mountain ring dipped radially towards the middle of the trough and above it were deposits of marl and two bands of harder rock with a softer band between them. Inside the limestone ring the two harder bands formed two low concentric walls, much more regular in shape than the outer ring. Far away to the south the slightly elevated ground in the middle of the trough hid part of the ring and I could not see whether it was completely closed. The entire triple ring stood in the middle of a plain which stretched far into the distance, especially towards the south. The trough had obviously been formed in the same way as a doline, by the sinking of its middle, but what were the forces that had cut off its outer perimeter and shaped it into such a smooth circle?

Platycarya, Itea, Cinnamomum, Xanthoxylon, Ligustrum lucidum, aspens and oaks were the main elements in the woods around the temple, but higher up I found *Schizophragma integrifolium*, usually an enormous climber, but here in the variety *S. integrifolium minus* spreading over the bare rock. Another find was *Pyracantha discolor*, a new species. On the way back I passed a spot where a cadet school or some similar body had been engaged in a surveying exercise. An immense number of plane tables had been set up at intervals of twenty paces or a little more. Chinese paper had been spread over the sketching paper to protect it and work had obviously come to a standstill. I knew that the Chinese had failed to produce any topographical survey of their country, but the sight made me regret even more keenly my decision to abandon any further surveying, a decision which I had taken because in that tangled and intricate terrain mapmaking would have diverted too much time from my botanical work, and as I descended to lower altitudes that work became more and more exacting.

When I left Guiyang on 6th July I had sacked my plant collector and took with me instead a young lad formerly employed by the mafu. He was called Xiao Zhu ("little pig") and I had had my eye on him for some time. He was lively and resourceful, and an excellent tree climber, and he proved quite satisfactory once I had given him and Yaftscha a good telling-off for shirking their work. I found out that they were changing the paper on only half the plants in the presses, and leaving the other half until the next day, simply to save themselves trouble. Knowing this, I was not surprised that the material collected on the journey at the height of the rainy season was less than perfectly preserved.

East of Guiyang the landscape was formed mainly of sandstone. The road crossed several rivers flowing northeast; the smaller channels were bordered by *Mariscus chinensis* and sometimes almost filled by it; pollarded willows and ash trees grew along their banks. On a hill in the little town of Longli I found *Poliothyrsis sinensis*, a large tree covered with panicles of small white honey-scented flowers; it belongs to the tropical family *Flacourtiaceae*. A little further on the road was bordered by boggy meadows where I gathered rich booty among the large colonies of reedmace (*Typha orientalis*), including our native moss *Acrocladium cuspidatum*. Twining among the spiny-leaved twigs of the *Cunninghamia* and spreading up to a considerable height over the low trees were the branching fronds of a clubmoss, *Lycopodium casuarinoides*, with curved leaves, hair-thin but remarkably stiff. Pines and deciduous oaks, with an understorey of shrubs consisting of *Clethra cavaleriei* and *Vaccinium iteophyllum*, made up the woods growing on the hillsides. During the midday halt in a village called Longzu I took the opportunity of exploring a gully filled with shrubs. Scrambling over them was the shaggy *Actinidia fulvicoma* var. *hirsuta* with narrow leaves and white flowers; down at the bottom I found *Nephrodium decursivopinnatum*, a slender fern with spreading tufts of soft fronds. Some of these

newcomers stayed with us constantly as we travelled along the road, while others such as *Macleaya cordata*, a herbaceous perennial well over 2 m tall with thick round seagreen leaves and bulky panicles of pink florets like meadow rue, turned up only in a few spots.

Each stage in the journey brought changes in the flora and in the customs of the people. The heat became more and more oppressive. I had bought a fan, and was obliged to ply it vigorously. In the hostels the porters and other travellers used to wash themselves — or at least their feet and their bodies above the waist — in hot water every evening, and in some places along the road there were resthouses, not hostels but stone buildings of solid construction, sometimes with a little temple adjoining, extending over half the width of the road. Water for the use of travellers was set out in earthenware jugs and in some of them there were traders offering food for sale. I had to forbid my men to buy beef, as rinderpest was rife among the cattle. Everywhere along the route we saw cows at their last gasp, and freshly flayed hides stretched out to dry. The ridge between Wangcheng Qiao and Guiding ("Kweiting") is an anticline in a stratum of limestone; the route led across it through a little ravine with miniature waterfalls and caves. Otherwise, however, the scenery was monotonous, and the scale of the landscape was much larger than it had been west of Guiyang, so that I soon regretted having given up my mapmaking; along this stretch it could have been done quite easily, without demanding much time or attention. But the link with what had gone before was already severed, and to start again somewhere in the middle would not have given reliable results. Guiding (1020 m) lies slightly lower than Guiyang. One of the "soldiers" sent to relieve my escort turned up there at noon on the third day of the journey, but the other, bringing the safe-conduct letter, did not arrive until some time later. The crowd of people who were gaping at me as I ate my lunch greeted this fellow with cheering and roars of laughter; he was evidently a popular figure, though one side of his mouth hung down almost as far as his chin.

Chapter 34. To Sandu in Southeast Guizhou

Quartzite mountains — the forest gorges of Majiadun — heath meadows — giant salamanders — Duyun, Maocaoping and Danzhai — Miao villages

A pass at 1300 m led south-eastwards over a mountain range built of quartzite. Its contours were much gentler than those of the terrain we had traversed before reaching Guiyang, but there were still plenty of deep, steep-sided valleys. The descent brought us into a valley running eastwards which belonged to the system of the Yuan Jiang, a river which debouches into Dongting Lake in Hunan. We had hence left the territory drained by the Wu Jiang, which ultimately discharged into the Yangzi in

Sichuan. Close to the steep downhill track was a little river gorge filled with woodland of a most unusual kind. *Schefflera delavayi*, a small tree belonging to the *Araliaceae*, was more or less dominant, and its almost unbranched trunks, topped by whorls of large thick grey-green palmate leaves, each segment almost threequarters of a metre in length, presented an extraordinary appearance, not unlike the crowns of a grove of palm trees. Hardly less strange were the thick shaggy, softly thorny fruit each segment almost threequarters of a metre in length, presented an extraordinary appearance, not unlike the crowns of a grove of palm trees. Hardly less strange were the thick shaggy, softly thorny fruit spikes of *Mallotus nepalensis*, a small tree belonging to the *Euphorbiaceae*. On the hilltops there were oak woods, with *Cunninghamia* on the slopes lower down, while the steep sides of the narrow cultivated valley and the lateral gorges were covered by bush and forest which was obviously of great diversity.

The hamlet of Majiadun, situated at 1080 m in the middle of this landscape, made an ideal centre for botanical exploration, and I spent 9th July there. Everywhere on the open hillsides the bushes were lit up by the dense umbels of *Hydrangea aspera* in various shades of blue and violet, sometimes with double flowers. My main goal was the little wooded ravine opposite the village. All the trees and bushes in it were entwined with small or medium-sized climbers, notably *Schizandra henryi*, *Jasminum lanceolarium* with white flowers, *Trachelospermum axillare* with small red flowers, even more cloyingly scented than the jasmine, and *Rubus swinhoei*, thickly hung with black fruits each backed by a purple calyx; they looked as tempting as our finest blackberries, but their flavour was tart and astringent. Hanging down over steep rock faces was *Gleichenia glauca*, a large fern with finely cut leaves. Growing in moist recesses in the rock was *Gymnotheca chinensis*, a herbaceous plant related to the pepper vine, with a powerful odour reminiscent of cow parsnip (*Heracleum*); it had stems extending as runners and rooting where they touched, and lax spikes of white flowers devoid of petals. The shrubs included *Acer fargesii* with reddish leaves and fruits, and *Dichroa febrifuga*, a small bush with soft pith-filled twigs and skyblue flowers. Towering above them were huge trees of *Castanopsis tibetana*, perhaps the finest oak (in the broadest sense of the word) that I have ever beheld; its rather narrow, leathery, evergreen leaves had a brown felty covering beneath and were up to 25 cm long, while its upright spikes of thorny fruit capsules were 15 cm in height. There was also a new species of bamboo (*Indocalamus longiauratus*); its lush shoots were putting forth leaves up to 10 cm broad with long auricles edged with bristles, and it occurred frequently from there onwards far into Hunan. Below Majiadun the valley diverged to the northeast. The road left it and followed a tributary south-eastwards. The steep slopes, beside the stream and above the road, were studded with the round golden-yellow flowers of *Caesalpinia nuga*, and its long slender shoots weighed down the bushes over which it scrambled.

At Gudong we crossed a stream flowing directly northeast, and next day, without any major ascents or descents, we finally reached the Duyun valley, which at first ran southwards. Once again the mountains were deeply dissected and showed some similarity to the conical hill formations we had seen earlier, though here they had evidently been modelled from quartzite by the action of the climate, but all the terrain was green and lacked any sharp-angled outlines. Near Wendun limestone hills reappeared beyond the little river, and the valley continued as far as Duyun between strata dipping eastwards at

45°. The river, bordered by the new *Rhododendron rivulare* and other plants, received a large tributary from the left and another from the right. The latter ran at the foot of an impressive forest-clad mountain, but because of my prolonged stay in Guiyang I could not spare even one day to explore it. Although I was no longer plotting a route survey, it was clear from the distances stated in li and from the time taken by my caravan that Duyun lies some 20 km east of its position as shown in Stieler's atlas. Very early next morning, before we were ready to start, the local official came to call, bringing with him gifts for which I had nothing to offer in return. Lao Li declared that there was no need for me to offer presents while I was travelling, but I doubt whether he was correct; more probably he just wanted to avoid extra work.

The river at first continued in the same direction, but my route turned eastwards here and climbed up to a saddle at 970 m. All the slopes were grass-covered; not a vestige of forest remained. Beyond the col, on flatter ground, there were small areas of dry meadowland with low-growing plants, in many respects comparable with our heath meadows. Their characteristic species included various herbaceous plants of low stature, notably *Oldenlandia uncinella* which resembles our woodruff, *Potentilla chinensis* with deeply cut leaves, the scarce *Burmannia disticha* with winged blue calyces, a few small orchids such as *Calanthe angusta* var. *laeta* and *Phyllompax galeandra*, and *Melastoma repens* which arises from a woody rootstock and spreads out into mats dotted with large flowers.

From a man coming from the opposite direction I bought two giant salamanders (*Megalobatrachus maximus*), creatures no less than 42 cm in length with a crest along the spine and a flattened head 6.5 cm broad. He said they had been caught in the river and that a medicine was extracted from them, but I pickled them in formalin. After we had passed through a little valley where we encountered sandstone once more, trees began to reappear. At first they were only pines, but as we descended into the next valley the woodland became more diverse. Among it was *Meliosma pannosa*, a small tree with brown hairs on its leaves and inflorescences. To judge from the steppe-like appearance of the grasslands, the whole of this district seemed to be somewhat drier than the rest, possibly because it was shut off between two chains of mountains. By the stream at the bottom, near the village of Duojie, was a small hill consisting of limestone strata overlying the sandstone and dipping steeply westwards. Though I had no time for more than a brief foray, I collected several novelties there, including *Sorbus folgneri*, its leaves white on their undersides, *Loropetalum sinense*, a shrub with small, rough-surfaced leaves, now in fruit, and among the bushes beside the stream *Apios fortunei* with green flowers. The wood on the hill above looked so enticing that I decided to break my journey for a day (13th July) at Maocaoping, a village half an hour further on.

Next morning I went back to Duojie and investigated the hill more closely. The gently sloping surface formed by flat beds of sedimentary rock was blanketed by a layer of humus soil carrying tall bamboos (*Phyllostachys puberula*). Towering above them were huge oaks and *Liquidambar* trees together with *Eriobotrya* and *Photinia davidsoniae*, and in the shade cast by the trees a small pink *Ardisia* was flowering, accompanied by *Rubus chaffanjoni*, a bramble with white spots and lyre-shaped leaves. On the crest, however, and the steep scarp beneath it there was maquis woodland of small-leaved trees, none of any great height yet gnarled and obviously ancient. There were hornbeams, *Quercus phyllireoides*, *Pittosporum floribundum* with small round fruits, the evergreen *Euonymus dielsiana* with vivid yellow flowers, and *Platycarya*. The most remarkable however, was a tree which resembled a *Lithocarpus*. Its erect flower spikes were clothed with golden brown hair, as were the 3-pinnate or less frequently 5-pinnate young leaves. It finally turned out to be *Engelhardtia chrysolepis*, a relative of the walnut. I spent the afternoon hardly less enjoyably in exploring a meadow bog situated on spring-watered gravel in a hollow in the ridge. Apart from *Mariscus chinensis* the main element was the tall *Schoenus sinensis*, a new species of sedge which formed exceedingly solid tussocks ultimately developing into rings.

Travelling on next morning, we soon reached the little river coming from Duyun, at an altitude of 660 m. The ferryboat took only a few strokes on the oars to carry us across, and we at once began the ascent up the 1200 m mountain. Twice we crossed strata of limestone sandwiched between the sandstones which made up the ridge. *Liquidambar* and *Cunninghamia*, the latter huge old trees, covered the hillside; *Callicarpa lyi* was less common. I met Miao tribes-people in festive attire, perhaps going to a wedding, but they were extremely timid. At the top of the ridge the strata were disposed vertically; it was presumably the persisting synclinal component of a fault, for further on the strata dipped in the opposite direction — to the west. On the short descent to the market town of Danzhai *Hydrangea paniculata*, a shrub which I had already seen more than once, was now blooming; its yellowish-white flowers, some of them enlarged and infertile, were aggregated into large panicles. The room which I found was tolerably clean, but after the sun went down I had to make a hurried move; clouds of mosquitoes came swarming out of a rat hole in such numbers as to make work impossible; though I could have crawled under my mosquito net to sleep I could not work inside it. The landscape to the east of Danzhai was in some respects similar to that of the Yunnan plateau; there

was a the same red earth derived from sandstone (or clay-slate?), and there were low ridges and gently sloping conical hills mantled with forests of oak and pine.

However, my route did not lead through that district. I turned southwards and went downhill, as I wished to explore the low-lying valley of the Du Jiang, my curiosity having been aroused by meeting numerous porters carrying huge, ponderous planks which must have come from gigantic trees — even though they were only pines. To the right of the little valley was the mountain chain which we had just crossed, and on its slopes were some large Miao villages. From a distance they resembled Naxi villages, and the buildings gave the same impression of loftiness, but here it was produced not by the grain-drying racks which jut up above the roofs of a Naxi village, but by the dark wooden houses themselves, which were taller and narrower than those of the Naxi. Here, as in the Naxi homelands, the Chinese had not yet encroached on tribal territories and the forests were still largely intact; dense stands of tall evergreen oaks covered the low hills above the Miao villages. The people here were certainly not accustomed to Europeans; that evening, as I was ransacking the bushes outside the village of Qiaoli, two women who had come to fetch water from the spring burst our screaming when they saw me standing there, rushed back into their house and bolted the door with a loud clatter, and next morning, only a few hundred metres further on, a peasant took to his heels on seeing me, even though I was quite alone.

Beneath the shrubs I found *Lysimachia paridiformis*, an unusual plant with a single whorl of four broad leaves, and *Mahonia léveilléana*, now putting forth splendid flowers. Growing wild in large numbers on the dry hillsides was the tallow tree (*Sapium sebiferum*), with small diamond-shaped leaves like those of a poplar. Here, at 500 m, we entered the subtropical zone and soon encountered cultivated orange trees (*Citrus aurantium*) together with another kind having larger fruits almost devoid of flesh — probably a new species. After passing through a tract of more or less barren country we were joined by another stream, and at midday we entered the small town of Sandu, situated on the Du Jiang. The river flowed from the west, and in the distance we had a clear view of the cone hill terrain which forms the entire southwest part of Guizhou. Looking as if it were a forest, it stretched far away towards the horizon.

Chapter 35. To Liping Via Rongjiang

On the Du Jiang river — tropical plants — river bank shrubs — an eventful boat trip — Rongjiang and Mount Baotie Shan — Central Chinese architecture — bandits — the Shui — buffalo breeding — Liping and Mount Nanjing Shan

T hough not of any great size, Sandu was quite an important reshipment town for trade with Guangxi. On the road leading to it we met several pack-animal caravans, but the traffic at that season did not seem to be very heavy. At Sandu all merchandise

was loaded on to boats on the Du Jiang[174], and as

---

[174] The lower reaches of the Du Jiang are called the Liu Jiang; the whole river is often known as the Du Liu Jiang (SGH).

the road along the river was barely passable even for unloaded horses, I had to hire two boats at 6 dollars each to convey my baggage to Rongjiang. This transaction, together with certain other tasks — sorting out my dried plants and having my campbed repaired — took all afternoon. Early next morning I mounted my mule intending to ride with the unloaded caravan, for I certainly did not wish to sit in a boat and sail past all sorts of glorious plants without being able to collect them. It was 90 li to Dujiang. The boat got there easily by midday, but the journey by road left little time to spare for botanical work if I was to reach the town by nightfall. We had to cross the river four times and although, after the first of the horses had been loaded into the ferryboat, the rest of them swam across without urging, the delays were always ample for my purpose. I paid each of the ferrymen the same amount — a handful of copper cents — and it was amusing to see how some of them accepted it with folded hands and deep obeisances as if they could not thank me sufficiently, while others glanced contemptuously at the money and muttered: "That's nothing like enough!"

The track was certainly very bad and narrow, and in parts there were flights of steps built from round boulders flung down at random. However, my mule was an agile beast and bounded up them four or five steps at a time; all I had to do was to keep my seat in the saddle. The head mafu, an idle fellow, had slipped away when my back was turned and had found a place on one of the boats. He had given me only two of his men — not enough to keep the animals on the steep track and prevent them from straying to right or left. That evening we came to a place where a landslide had blocked the track and we had to find a way round it. Then there was a bridge consisting of only one beam. Because of these delays it was dusk when I arrived at Shuixing, the boatmen's village on the river below Dujiang. My two collectors and I had been fully occupied all day, for the plant life, rich and luxuriant, was different from anything I had seen before; in its powers of regeneration, obviously encouraged by the sultry humid air of that shut-in valley, it resembled the vegetation of the tropics and seemed to bid defiance to man's efforts to destroy it. *Croton tiglium*, a little tree with light green leaves, was frequent and evidently wild. It is poisonous, and one of its small seeds is enough to produce a violent purgative effect. *Ficus hirta*, a fig with large leaves and golden bristles, was not uncommon. *Meliosma fordii*, a tree thickly covered with tiny reddish flowers, gave off a sweet scent of honey; *Erdysanthera rosea*, a climber with large panicles of quite showy pink flowers, was scrambling over the shrubs, but *Mussaenda wilsonii* and *M. puberula*, each of their deep yellow flowers flanked by a single enlarged calyx lobe, were less conspicuous. On the other bank of the river, unfortunately out of reach, I saw several examples of a small dark green palm, undoubtedly distinct from *Trachycarpus excelsa*. *Saccharum arundinaceum*, growing in separate clumps, covered extensive tracts of wind-blown sand beside the river.

Its leaves alone were tall enough to overtop a rider, and its silvery flowering panicles rose up higher still. Growing in large numbers beneath it was a fern (*Nephrodium proliferum*). The tips of its fronds curved down until they rooted in the ground and then, creeping further along, sent up more and more new fronds. The enormous *Crinum latifolium*, a new species with snow-white flowers and huge leaves 10 cm broad, was much less common.

The water was not high, but on the banks it had left clear marks of the level to which it rose and obviously remained for some long time every year. In narrow stretches of the valley this was as much as 7 m above the present low water level. Where the banks were lower this strip spread out over considerable distances, but it was far from barren. Growing on it was a wide variety of shrubs from different families, all of them having pliable branches which bent before the torrent and survived undamaged. In some places they formed thickets as tall as a man, with grass and leaves carried by the flood waters hanging from their upper branches. Willows, figs (*Ficus piriformis*), oleasters (*Elaeagnus lanceolata*), representatives of the myrtle and laurel families (*Syzygium odoratum, Machilus salicina* with juicy blue-black fruits), *Distylium chinense, Cornus paucinervis*, and the pretty *Adina globiflora* with dainty globular heads of pink and white flowers flourished here, and on the bare rock was a low growing box, *Buxus harlandii.* The only other plants in this zone were grasses, notably the new *Arundinella fluviatilis* which grew abundantly in sand-filled rock fissures, and lichens, including the black *Heppia applianata* and another species, white in colour, which in my haste I was unable to knock down from the rocks where it was growing. The task of putting all these treasures in the plant press kept me busy until late that night, more especially as I was delayed by a visit from an official who arrived with two policemen to shut down the gambling dens on the boats which were anchored there in large numbers, and then wanted me to visit him in the little town above the river.

I decided to spend the next day there so as to explore certain promising spots on the river and at the mouths of its lateral gorges. For this purpose I used the boats, and as river pirates were active, I was given an escort of four policemen. I took one with me on my boat and left three on the other. The boat slipped past the mouths of several steep-sided ravines filled with sombre woodland, but alas we found nowhere to land. On the previous day, as luck would have it, all the gorges had been on the opposite side of the valley, and the wild bananas — undoubtedly an interesting species, one of several which are known to occur in South China — the gigantic leaves of *Alocasia*, and heaven knows what other hidden treasures remained for ever beyond my grasp. The local banyan, *Ficus parvifolia*, grew in the depths of the gorges, its plant-like buttress roots exposed, but it was also planted in the villages for the sake of the shade cast by its huge dark crowns, and I had already obtained flowering branches. The water level was just right for our trip. In some places, where the river surged down over the pebbly bottom, the boat pitched and rolled and leapt, spray spattering across the deck. At other spots the stream was broad and level, but between the rock walls ahead there was a narrow opening towards which the boatmen had to steer. There the boat rode up over the torrent with its prow in the air, plunged down in an arc and dipped deep into the water again before levelling out. It was a delightful trip, and perfectly safe, for the Miao boatmen, whose speech with its numerous terminal A-sounds reminded me of the Bai language,[175] were fully equal to their task. They knew every little cranny in the rock where they could insert their long poles, and they used them to control the boat at sharp corners where it threatened to hurtle down against an overhang with sinister whirlpools eddying beneath it. Then they shoved will all their might until the danger of shipwreck was past and they could resume their cheerful singing. At last we came to a little cove at the opening of one of the side valleys on the right where I was able to land. The steep hillside was shaded by huge trees, among them *Liquidambar formosana, Castanopsis fissa, Myrica esculenta* and *Schima crenata*. Beneath them was a dense understorey of large ferns (*Gleichenia glauca*). I worked my way upwards, clinging to their tough stalks, and collected the mosses growing on the ground, notably the tropical *Bazzania tridens*. Along the lateral stream I found a few other items of interest, including *Ficus sordida* (a new species of fig), *Embelia parviflora* and *Polypodium coronans*. All told, however, the day's booty was not very large, and I searched in vain for another good place to land. From there onwards until we arrived at Tiantang the only sights which attracted my attention were the Miao villages, some of them on the green valley sides, steep but not very high, and others by the water's edge.

At Tiantang the valley was not so narrow and much sand had been deposited. Indeed, it was evidently so deep that the ordinary shrubs of the riverbank were unable to find a foothold in it, though *Pterocarya stenoptera* was established within the flood zone, where its straight robust trunks were a match for the water. The scenery was unattractive, though there was some diversity in geological structure: the almost horizontal greywacke which had accompanied us all the way from Sandu reappeared near Rongjiang dipping vertically at right angles to the river and was then overlaid by conglomerate with an eastwards dip — which formed bulging convex rock faces — with a layer of marl superimposed. A number of floating mills in the mouth of a tributary on the left heralded our approach to the town of Rongjiang, which our boats reached a few minutes later. Though my boat trip ended there at midday on 19th July I had to wait another day for the caravan, for the men had decided to take their time over the journey from Tiantang and enjoy the comforts of the boat trip. I was glad of the delay, for on a low hill just opposite the town was the grove of the Yanggu Miao temple; it consisted chiefly of *Quercus variabilis* but also yielded *Photinia subumbellata* and *P. davidsoniae, Pyracantha discolor* and

Porana sinensis, a climber with splendid blue flowers. To the southwest, on the steep hillside of the Baotie Shan, was a larger wood which I visited that afternoon (20th July). Climbing up through shrub meadowland, I found an orchid with yellow flowers (*Habenaria linguella*) together with *Striga lutea* and *Wikstroemia indica*, a relative of the daphnes. *Lycopodium cernuum* was creeping on the ground beneath the grass. In the wood itself was *Clerodendron mandarinorum*, a huge tree studded with large fragrant white flowers, together with *Firmiana simplex, Castanea henryi, Eriobotrya japonica, Liquidambar formosana, Myrica rubra, Aleurites fordii*, birches, poplars and other trees.

On departing next morning I passed through Rongjiang itself and was amazed to find a town quite different from any I had previously seen in China. Riding along the main street between houses several storeys high, richly carved, painted in gold and other colours and adorned with stone sculptures, one might have fancied that one was now among a new and different people, so striking was the impression of splendour which the buildings created, in a land where the traveller does not expect anything of the kind. Yet the town cannot have enjoyed any extraordinary prosperity; Rongjiang was certainly a trading centre, but it was located in territory occupied by native tribes known as "turen" or "bendi" and the architectural style can hardly have been of earlier date than that of the buildings erected by Chinese settlers over the border in Yunnan. Or could there be some indirect connection with the hot climate prevailing at that low altitude — only 300 m above sea level? Could that be the reason why the same architectural style predominated in the towns which I encountered as I travelled eastwards?

Against my wishes the authorities had given me an escort of sixteen soldiers and six policemen, since the country between Rongjiang and the boundary of the province was extremely unsafe. The road ran north-eastwards across the wide valley of the lateral stream. Cotton was grown there and also vines — the first I had seen in China — trained on espaliers or over pools, and apparently used only as fruit. We climbed through a small valley on to a sandstone ridge superimposed on the last of the marl. In two places the track was blocked by landslides and the men had to find a way round or carry the loads on their shoulders. Before long we heard that two hours earlier, on the saddle ahead of us, a caravan of Chinese traders some twenty strong had been ambushed and plundered by a robber band of roughly the same number. Several men had been wounded, and the robbers had swiftly vanished taking with them the most valuable goods, said to be worth $3000. At the midday halt numerous other travellers attached themselves to my party, anxious to share the protection of my escort. Before long we encountered two wounded men who were being brought down in makeshift carrying chairs, though their rescuers had not even bothered to wipe off the blood which they had lost. In a little eating house on the col was a third casualty with a stab wound through the lung, his mouth full of blood. There was not much I could do for him and in any case, even if I had started treatment with European remedies, the

---

[175] The languages are not generally thought to be related, but the affinities of the Bai language are disputed (SGH).

Chinese doctor who took over would not have been able to continue the treatment. A few hundred yards further on blood stains and scraps of paper marked the site of the ambush. The bandits had hidden in tall grass beside a sunken road. They were said to be men from Hunan who had crossed the border into Guizhou. The authorities' response was to say: "They are not from our area, and we can't pursue them across the border", while the authorities in Hunan declared: "They haven't committed any robberies here, and what they may have done in Guizhou is not our concern". Some of my soldiers climbed up the hillside but of course they did not find anyone. In Chaimou, the village where I spent the night, I saw two more Chinese who came to have their wounds dressed, one with a deep stab in the thigh and the other with a gash in the scalp. He said it had been caused by a stone but it looked more like a gunshot wound.

In general the terrain can be described as a table-land 950 m above sea level, though it is made up of innumerable ridges and valleys. For the most part its drainage runs to the south, but near Liping it drains to the northeast. It was agreeably green and well wooded, though large areas of the woods had been felled and the timber exported. Timber chutes made of hollowed out tree trunks had been erected in many of the valleys, some of them on tall supports like those in the Alps. The logs were carried down by this means until they reached a spot where the river was large enough to allow them to be floated down as rafts — apparently as far as Guangzhou.

The inhabitants were Dong and Shui tribesmen, though there was evidently little difference between the two. They were related to the Shan people of Burma and their costume was in sharp contrast to that of the Chinese. They dressed entirely in black, and the women wore pleated skirts down to the knees. The men had their black hair plaited into a small "bun" just behind the forehead. They were of low stature and comparatively clean, but allegedly a thievish lot. Their villages would have resembled those of the Miao people but for the numerous temples which gave them a totally different aspect and showed that their ancestors had come from India. Built of wood like the houses, these temples were tall structures with numerous narrow roofs one above the other; like some Indian pagodas, they seemed to consist almost entirely of roofs. Their storehouses and even their dwellings were built on piles above the water, perhaps to protect them from rats and other vermin. In the lowermost rooms, which were open to the weather, coffins were stacked everywhere, evidently waiting, as is the Chinese custom, for the arrival of a propitious date for the burial. Chinese traders lived in all these villages, their plain and unattractive houses being adorned, as everywhere in China, with wooden shutters and strips of red paper carrying painted or printed inscriptions. The district was a centre for the rearing of buffalos, and gigantic examples of that species were to be seen there. The stud bulls, which were not used for any other labour, were distinguished by metal caps on their horns. Horses, however, were totally unfamiliar; my caravan, its

arrival announced by the bell carried on the leading animal, brought the entire population running from the villages along the road and from farther afield. Sometimes people came with their children and pointed: "Look, that's a horse". However, this meant that there were no stables or courtyards; we always had to leave the animals in the village street, and had nothing to feed them on except rice and fresh grass. During the nights they sometimes knocked down the planks and beams which had been stacked up to confine them and wandered into the rice fields, an event always followed by strife, shouting and broken sleep.

Halfway to Liping was a military post where my escort was replaced by a troop of no fewer than 23 soldiers commanded by an officer attended by a man walking behind him to carry his sabre. This idle crew, whose looks filled me with repugnance, could not have been of use in any circumstances. They had already shown themselves incapable of tracking down any of the bandits responsible for the numerous robberies which had recently taken place — indeed we had just passed the grave of a trader murdered only three weeks earlier. The plant life offered plenty of novelties, and my collecting duties kept me busy en route, during the lunch halts and in camp until late at night. Among the plants I collected were *Antidesma japonicum, Randia yunnanensis, Quercus picta* (a new species), *Blastus spathulicalyx* and *Oldenlandia speciosa*. Ash trees grew along the streams, but perhaps the strangest plant of all was one which I encountered towards the end of the journey. A green island in the middle of a little brook proved to consist of *Pentasacme stauntonii*, a species belonging to the *Asclepiadaceae*, a family which does not contain any water plants except in this genus. It grew there with its lower third or half permanently submerged. Below the water line its stems were devoid of leaves, but above the surface it looked like a willow gentian, though smaller.

Despite the rain and the oppressive heat the journey from Rongjiang to Liping was one of the most memorable parts of my travels in China. At Matang, where we halted for the second night, there was an amusing incident. I had lodgings in a loft room open at the sides. Next door was the framework of a house under construction. Some of the villagers, full of curiosity and anxious to get a good view of me, climbed up on to the beams and sat there like sparrows on telegraph wires. Before long there was a creaking and a cracking like the noise of Chinese firecrackers; just as I looked up the framework collapsed and the spectators fell into the muddy water beneath. Those who clung on to the part which remained standing had some trouble in getting down, but they all burst out laughing except one lad who howled for a time, having landed heavily on his posterior.

After crossing the last low crest we entered the green vale of Liping, a broad channel stretching away to the southwest. The slopes had been clear felled and were furrowed by countless gullies. In some stretches there were patches of bracken which lent the shrub meadows a bluish lustre.

I stayed at Liping from 24th to 28th July, since I had a severe tropical cold with fever and nasal congestion. It was not much of a town, yet it had a few glass windows and better stocks of foreign merchandise on sale than I had seen in some far larger towns in Yunnan, for example condensed milk from Hong Kong at a low price — only 30 cents a can. I was very glad to buy it, and used it to mask the muddy flavour of the water with which Li made my tea. The recently appointed official was extremely sensible and friendly. However, on 25th July when I visited the woods around the temple on Nanjing Shan half an hour from the town, he wanted to send four of his servants to accompany me and was offended when I insisted that two of them should stay at home. There were always several of these garlic eaters standing round me which I worked, but it would never have occurred to any of them to bend down and pick up my pencil when I dropped it. A Chinese servant never considers it necessary to do anything which he has not been instructed to do. The temple woodland consisted of gigantic trees of great age which had been allowed to develop unchecked, but its understorey was disappointingly poor except at the margins, where *Symplocos confusa* had opened its fragrant blossoms; within the wood itself the dense canopy had presumably shaded it out. Among the herbs round a spring was the tall *Hydrocotyle nepalensis*.

Chapter 36. Through Southwest Hunan to Wugang

Jing Xian — news from a German missionary — forests of the Qu Shui gorge — mountains of Suining — opium smuggling — bamboo forests — varnish — Wugang — to Mount Yun Shan (1420m) — superstition — temple woodlands — mountain structure and distant views — pilgrims

Limestone reappeared in the valley below Liping, but the crags and pavements were cloaked by luxuriant vegetation; *Ficus pumila* spread over even the smoothest rock surfaces. Before long the road left the valley and turned north-eastwards over a low saddle into another valley which sloped gradually downwards in the same direction until it reached the Hunan boundary. This was the fourth province of China into which my travels had brought me and, despite my plans, it was to be the last, though I was destined to remain within it longer than I had expected. Once more I had an escort of ten soldiers, as there had been a robbery only the day before, and the official had arranged for them to be relieved at Jingxian. He had also had the road tidied up, though all that his men had done was to hack away the grasses and other vegetation which overhung it, an operation which was most displeasing as it might have destroyed some plants which I would gladly have collected.

The first part of the valley was quite narrow, and for long stretches its low slopes were covered with trees which looked like walnuts. The stands were so pure that they could not have been natural, and they had evidently been planted for the sake of the oil extracted from the fruits. Before reaching Liping I had seen a single specimen of this tree in one of the villages, but here it did in fact seem to be genuinely wild, being scattered through the mixed forests of the valley slopes. These forests were quite luxuriant, through oaks were not conspicuous. The pinnate leaves of the unfamiliar tree were smaller and narrower than those of a walnut, and its fruits were somewhat angular and had a brown felty covering, though their internal structure was the same. It was not a true walnut, but the Chinese hickory *Carya cathayensis*, a member of an otherwise purely American genus, first discovered in 1912 near Changhua in Zhejiang. [176] Further on the valley broadened and the lower parts of the higher slopes on either side were thickly covered with *Cunninghamia* trees, though for long stretches the road passed through plantations of tea oil shrubs, a species which also occurred abundantly in the wild state. The bedrock of the low mountains was entirely green clay-slate veined with quartz, gently inclined, but down at the valley bottom there was once more a thin stratum of limestone which had weathered into karst formations. The valley then became flat and sandy. The streams were bordered by large sweetly scented trees, *Viburnum odoratissimum* and *Xylosma racemosa*; the first had white and the second had yellow flowers, but most of them had faded. At one spot I found the scarlet flowered climber *Bignonia chinensis*, but the low hills on the approach to Jingxian were covered by sparse heath and steppe vegetation.

Jingxian, where I arrived at noon on 31st July, lay on a river crossed by a pontoon bridge. The houses along the bank were raised on tall piles, as was the inn where I sought accommodation. While I was busy making the largest and best ventilated room habitable by chucking out the straw mats and killing the enormous bugs that lived beneath them, someone told me that there was a German missionary living in the town. I already knew that there were some fellow countrymen in Hunan, but to meet one in the very first town was more than I had dreamt of. I dashed off to visit him at once, hoping to get the latest news of the war and the situation in China. He was Herr Arendt, a German of Russian extraction. He and his wife were astonished and delighted at the unexpected arrival of a compatriot and immediately invited me to be their guest.

[176] "This species was discovered by F.N.Meyer in 1915 in the province of Chekiang, China...." (Bean, W.J., *Trees and Shrubs Hardy in the British Isles*, 8th edition, 1970, Vol.1, Page 515).

Nothing could have given me greater pleasure than that stay in their spotlessly clean house. My only regret was that it was so brief, for next morning I had to set out once more. During my travels I had enjoyed clean accommodation in American households and in the home of an English missionary in Guiyang to whom I paid a short visit, but this was a *German* family, and it was a joy to converse in our mother tongue without needing to struggle with a foreign language. Riga had fallen, [177] and there was no prospect of any further worsening in the relations between China and Germany. The official who called on us voiced the same opinion. Could anything have done more to lighten my gloomy spirits? The official, a man from Southern China, was extremely pro-German and had nothing but harsh words for the Beijing government's decision to break off relations with Germany. He was wearing an embroidered coat of loosely woven black silk; from there onwards all the officials whom I visited wore similar coats — yet another difference between East and West China. Herr Arendt gave me some more tinned food and the latest newspapers from Hankou to take with me, and it was with a blithe heart that I mounted my steed next morning — not quite as early as I had planned — and rode off, he leading me for some distance, after a delightful but all too short stay in his house.

After crossing a small ridge the road soon came to the main river (the Qu Shui) and followed it for some distance upstream. Some fine woodland survived in the warm humid gorge, and during the lunch halt at a village called Moshi I investigated it more closely. It differed considerably from the forests on the Du Jiang. Besides certain widely distributed species such as *Castanopsis hystrix, Fraxinus retusa* and *Acer davidii*, there was a new species of *Hibiscus* of tree-like proportions (*H. saltuaria*) together with *Mallotus apelta* and *Elaeocarpus lanceifolia*, which belongs to the small family *Elaeocarpaceae* and has numerous spreading flower spikes which drop their pointed white petals and their stamens on the slightest knock. Among others was *Helicia cochinchinensis*, also having cylindrical spikes of scented white flowers with the tip of each petal rolled back in a spiral. *Pterostyrax corymbosa* was the most distinctive tree. *Alangium faberi*, the only semi-woody plant in an otherwise woody genus, was putting forth its greenish flowers. Spreading on wet rocks beneath the trees was *Saxifraga sarmentosa* with its threadlike runners; *Begonia lipingensis* was flowering and the fern *Trichomanes parvulum* formed dense low-growing cushions resembling those of certain mosses which grow near springs (*Philonotis*). *Mucomitrium quercicola*, a moss first found in Yunnan growing on oaks, flourished here on drier clay-slate rock faces where it formed large cushions. Their thicker central parts were fruiting and at their edges they were spreading outwards by means of tufted branching creeping shoots. The edge of the flood-water zone was mark-ed by a large fern (*Diplazium esculentum*) with deeply dissected bright green fronds broadly triangular in outline and over a metre tall. Flowering in a few places in the same zone was a beautiful shrub (*Lagerstroemia indica*). The most interesting, though perhaps not the most striking plant was a climber with perfumed flowers sulphur yellow in colour. It was *Mappianthus iodoides*, and represented a new genus.

In some places we had to clear the path with my ice axe, as the flood-waters had washed it away, causing landslides and covering the rice fields with mud. We crossed a bridge over the river and climbed up a mountain closely resembling the one between Rongjiang and Liping, and of the same height. It had a luxuriant mantle of forest and bushes consisting of rhododendrons, *Quercus variabilis* and, less abundantly, *Q. glandulifera* together with other broad-leaved trees and numerous pines. Not until the next day did we descend to the little town of Suining. On the third day, travelling through numerous tea oil plantations in intermittent rain, we reached Yazuo, a town situated near a larger river which debouched into the Yuan Jiang at the major commercial city of Hongjiang. I had just reminded Lao Li that his favourite vice of opium smoking was strictly forbidden in Hunan, and that some addicts had recently been beheaded. That evening, nevertheless, the sweetish fumes of opium came drifting up into my room in the loft, and through a crack in the floorboards I saw his lamp. As soon as I called out, demanding to know who was smoking opium just beneath me, it was immediately blown out. I did not want endless strife with Lao Li, yet I had no inkling that he and the head caravanman had conspired to exploit the journey for large-scale opium trading. After we arrived at Changsha the latter disappeared with all the profits. Having returned to Kunming, Lao Li confronted him and claimed his own share, but the authorities got wind of the business and put them both in prison.

The track, in some stretches extremely narrow and rocky, continued along the river, which was bordered here and there by splendid woodland. One of the pack animals crashed down into the bushes and was rescued only after some difficulty. Another put a hoof through the edge of the track and fell into a rice field several metres below; however, it remained upright with its load still on its back and walked out of the field quite unperturbed. At Shijiaping we crossed by a ferry. On the far side was a cliff, its picturesque appeal heightened by a little temple, but the track was so steep that the men had to carry the loads. The route then quitted the river valley and turned again to the east. We were now in a land where bamboo was used for every conceivable purpose. After being floated down the mountain streams, the bundles of culms were crudely fastened together and a little hut was built on top for the boatmen whose task it was to ferry them across the Dongting lake as far as Hankou. The hillsides were clothed by a bright green mantle made up of the abundantly branching crowns of bamboo up to 10 m tall, all bowing uniformly in the same direction, borne on stems about 15 cm in diameter. Though there can be little or no doubt that this species

---

[177] Handel-Mazzetti's memory appears to be at fault here. It was not until the beginning of September 1917 that the Germans captured Riga from the Russians by a surprise attack.

(*Phyllostachys puberula*) grows wild in that district, the stands in their present form owe their appearance to selection by human hands, if not to actual planting. The densely interlacing network of roots, intolerant of incursions by other plants, and the litter of fallen leaves and sheaths which blankets the ground also serve to ensure the maintenance of unmixed stands. After finding our way round a landslide, we had to hack a path through the bamboo, finally emerging on to a little saddle where we halted for lunch. Varnish was tapped from a sumach (*Rhus verniciflua*) which was grown there, though it also occurs in the wild. Every second year the woodmen made oblique cuts in the bark and collected the sap in mussel shells fixed beneath them. So as to enable them to climb up into the crowns they had lashed poles between them to bridge the trees together.[178]

Yet again there were new and interesting finds when we reached the same altitude as on the previous day. We were between the higher parts of a mountain ridge still composed of the same clay-slate, but here with a steep dip. *Clethra pinfaënsis*, a small slender tree, was common there; its flowers, coloured by a covering of ochre yellow felt, were borne on long, almost horizontal spikes spreading like fingers above the tufts of leaves at the ends of the twigs. Another find was *Sargentodoxa cuneata*, a large creeper like the wild vine with red bordered leaves in threes and hanging bunches of black berries with a blue bloom carried on swollen fleshy stalks suffused with purple. It belongs to the *Lardizabalaceae*, a family related to the barberries (*Berberis*). Owing to the delays en route I was unable to travel as far as I had hoped; dusk was falling as we reached the rim of the Wugang valley and halted for the night in Pukai. Next day we passed through a small group of limestone hills on which I found *Camptotheca acuminata* (*Rubiaceae*), a tree with conspicuous, glossy leaves and white and pink flowers in large spheroidal heads, finally reaching the valley floor and following it north-eastwards. Here and there were solitary *Liquidambar* trees, some of them as large as any in the country, with *Ficus pumila* climbing up to the very tips of their wide, spreading branches. The large figs, though they look appetising, are inedible, being filled with a dry woolly mass which is used as a medicine. On our right was the Yun Shan, a higher mountain than the hills we had just crossed. Arendt had told me that the Wugang missionaries had a summer residence in a splendid forest up there. This seemed to offer an excellent opportunity for studying the mountain flora of the district. Arriving late that evening in Wugang, I chanced to meet one of the missionaries, Herr R. Paul, who was down there as it was a Sunday.

Next morning we set off together, Herr Paul in a carrying chair as far as the foot of the mountain some 7 km distant, and I riding my mule. From the Banshan Miao temple the track ascended gradually at first along the western side of a small valley to the second temple, San Li An, and then ran almost horizontally along the slope until it reached the

stream. Large sulphur-yellow flowers, borne in rows on long trailing shoots, adorned the hillside. They belonged to *Momordica meloniflora*, a new species, and they had a remarkable structure. The male flowers, each enveloped within a pale papery bract, have large saccate nectaries covered by a lid, and short thick curved filaments, black and gleaming as if varnished; the female flowers are somewhat smaller, and the ovaries later develop into ovoid thorny fruits 15 cm long. The stream tumbled down in waterfalls which must have been quite impressive in wet weather, and the track climbed beside it, up steep slippery stone steps. The hillsides had been clear felled and the air confined between them was still and sultry. Not until we reached the Wu Li An temple at 850 m did virgin forest appear. It filled two steep-sided channels which united behind the temple, and it clothed the ridges between them. It consisted mainly of evergreen trees, and their dark circular crowns formed a closed canopy casting deep shade on the ground 15-20 m below them. Even the steepest slopes and crests were covered; indeed, there was not a single patch of level ground on the Yun Shan.

The track climbed in zigzags ever more steeply upwards, the stream leaping over the rocks beside it and plunging into the depths beneath. Rising out of its foam were the green sword-shaped leaves of a low growing sweet flag (*Acorus tatarinowii*), which rooted in the fissures and carpeted the rocks. Nearly all the trees had finished flowering, but most of them were species which I had not previously collected and I was glad to have them whatever their phase of development. At 1190 m, in a hollow partly deforested for growing beans, was the large temple of Guanyin Ge, a place of pilgrimage. Next to it was a small temple (Shengli Si) which had become deconsecrated in Chinese eyes owing to the death of a priest, and had been rented by the missionaries, who had built a wooden house with six rooms nearby. Ten adults and ten children spent the summer there, at an average temperature 8 C cooler than that of Wugang, the difference in altitude being 823 m.

That evening I visited the upper part of the forest. The trees were not so tall and there was much young growth with slender trunks. Many of them belonged to the *Cupuliferae*, including a beech (*Fagus longipetiolata*). Next day I went back to re-examine the stretch I had already traversed, and the results were so encouraging that I decided to prolong my stay by two days. The shrub meadows, which occupied all the terrain outside the forests, were in full flower. Most of the shrubs were *Leguminosae* with red blossoms. Rising above the grasses and sedges were tall herbaceous perennials; although not outstandingly beautiful, some of them were of striking colours. There were bellflowers in blue (*Adenophora*, *Platycodon*), *Eupatorium lindleyanum* in violet, thistles, louseworts and *Anemone japonica* in red, yellow lettuces, yellow and white valerians (*Patrinia scabiosifolia* and *P. villosa*), *Lysimachia clethroides* with broad white spikes, *Aster scaber*, *Artemisia anomala* with entire leaves, and others. In the hollows the grass grew so high that a man standing in it was completely hidden. The highest

---

[178] See Wilson, E.H. *A Naturalist in Western China*, Vol. II, p.68, and illustration opposite p.70.

summit (1420 m)[179] projected some distance south-eastwards. The mountain sloped down with equal steepness on all sides, and all its crests were narrow green knife edges. Towards the south was a basin 50km across, filled with low hummocky limestone hills, stretching as far as Xinning. The exposed edges of the stratified rocks sloped down into an almost continuous shallow trench which separated the basin from the distant mountain range. That range formed a semicircle facing northeast, like the rim of a dish, one end of it being the Yun Shan. The mountain on which we stood was built of clay-slate, and the range to the southwest probably consisted mainly of the same rock, though near Xinning I encountered granite derived from that on the Guangxi border. On the morning of my departure I made another brief visit to the mountain. The change of the moon had brought splendidly clear weather in place of the previous rain, and I enjoyed long-ranging views. Eastwards the prospect stretched over the basin as far as the Long Shan beyond Shaoyang, northwards to the mountains in the vicinity of Xinhua; to the northwest was the Wugang valley, apparently a geological fault which recapitulated the structure of the Yun Shan, and beyond the valley was a mountain range with a few distant peaks peeping over it. Far away to the west yet more mountains were visible, but I was unable to ascertain their position.

I made several other excursions, notably one along the eastern part of the valley up to the tree line. In many spots there were large stands of tall perennials up to 1.5 m in height, which brought back vivid memories of similar plant communities in the Yunnan mountains. Among them were *Saussurea cordifolia, Strobilanthes pentastemonoides, Asystasia chinensis, Cacalia leucanthema, Ligularia veitchiorum* with giant leaves like those of our butterbur, and *Eupatorium reevesi* with numerous branching stems. Growing at the margins of grassy clearings was *Boehmeria nivea*, known as ramie or China grass, a species of nettle with leaves snow white beneath, from which the Chinese produce a fibre which they call bai ma (white hemp). Another trip took me down through the eastern part of the ascending valley system. There I found *Sorbus caloneura* growing epiphytically high up on the trunk of a cherry tree. It formed a broad shrub with divergent branches, some almost hanging downwards, and had several thick roots running down the tree trunk and closely pressed against it. It reminded me of a similar species I had seen in the Nu Jiang valley. The descent through the steep-sided channel was totally pathless and somewhat troublesome. The slope grew steeper and steeper as I went down, and in some places I slid down on large masses of scree. The forest was so dense that I could see nothing outside it and the channel seemed to be leading me towards Wugang. Despite the advice of one of the missionaries who had attempted the descent, I had an uneasy feeling that I was going to emerge far from the spot at which I had aimed and would have to climb all the way up the mountain again. However,

the channel changed its direction and after scrambling up some slippery rocks beside a waterfall, I finally reached the temple track above Wu Li An.

One event during my stay was the birthday of Guanyin, the goddess of mercy, the principal feast day of the Yun Shan. Bands of pilgrims came from far and wide, wearing red smocks studded with little plates of gleaming golden colour, swords buckled round their waists, some carrying little footstools on which they knelt down after every few paces and bowed down to the ground. The missionaries used this as an opportunity to send out their Chinese converts to sell their literature, although the treaties are supposed to forbid religious propaganda at places of pilgrimage. However, on the mountain there was a place of sacrifice known as the Belvedere, the only spot at the level of the temple which offered distant views unobscured by the forest. The elderly Chinese priest who was in charge of the ceremonies said to the pilgrims:

"These books are evil. You ought not to read them; indeed, you must burn them. I have a fire ready here; throw them straight in".

When taken to task by the missionaries he was ready with an apt reply: "If we journeyed to Germany and ate your rice, you would certainly not allow us to lure away your people from their faith".

In fact, fanaticism is totally foreign to the Buddhist ideal, and the old priest was perfectly correct. What would be our reaction if a Buddhist priest were to preach his doctrines at one of our places of pilgrimage! The treaties which oblige the Chinese to tolerate the missionaries' activities were imposed by force of arms, and their object was not to spread Christianity but to further European influence. There are more missionaries in China than there are Europeans in all other occupations together. First comes the missionary, then the businessman, and then the consul. None of this does anything to raise the level of civilisation among the Chinese. Their ancient culture — which according to Richthofen is in no sense their own, but adopted from elsewhere [180] — tends to perpetuate conceit and obscurantism, and our modern civilisation seldom penetrates beneath the outer veneer. Not far from Wugang there was a good example. At spots where the road divided were large groups of stones, up to twenty-five of them side by side. Though apparently marking the route, that was not their real purpose. In fact there was a prophecy which foretold that a certain child was destined to live in danger from an arrow until reaching such and such an age. The worried father therefore erected stones at all the nearby forks in the road, each stone bearing the inscription: "This is the road to X. The arrow is respectfully requested to take the other road." Such thinking can persist only in a society where the concepts of science are totally alien. As late as 1917 Chinese newspapers were still carrying stories of dragons a kilometre long, telling how they killed people by their breath at a range of up to two kilometres.

---

[179] 4520 ft (1378 m) on ONC H-11.

[180] A totally discredited theory now (SGH).

On returning from the Yun Shan I found to my annoyance that my horse, which had had a splendid tail reaching down to the ground, had lost half of it. The grooms told me that a crowd of children had entered the temple courtyard where the horses were standing and had plucked out the hairs from his tail; yet they were such idiots that the idea of stopping the children had not entered their heads.

Chapter 37. To Changsha via Xinning and Yongzhou (Lingling)

Summer heat and its effects — filth — aquatic flora — China declares war and I break off my journey — attempted poisoning ? — Hengyang — a journey by river steamer — mishaps — outbreak of civil war — the captain murdered — baggage examination

On leaving Wugang I turned my steps towards Xinning, 40 km to the south-southeast. On the way I was overtaken by a messenger bringing a specimen tube of insects which I had left behind on the mountain. He also carried a letter from L. Jensen, one of the missionaries, with the news that the Beijing government had decided to declare war on Germany. I called on the Xinning missionaries at their country residence, but as it was near the town and at no great altitude its surroundings did not offer anything of botanical interest. They told me that the Guangzhou government had previously let it be known that if Beijing declared war on Germany they would declare war on Beijing. The uncertainty regarding the political situation and its consequences for me took the edge off my enthusiasm for work, and the heat was equally dispiriting. The sun blazed mercilessly down from a cloudless deep blue sky. There was not a breath of wind, nothing more than the heat haze shimmering above the rice fields, which now, as the grain was starting to ripen, emitted a peculiar odour resembling that of iodoform. The blue sky was mirrored in the rivers. Seen from slightly elevated spots the landscape presented a medley of colour. Every pond and stream was edged with vivid green turf; steep outcrops of red rock were dotted here and there, and between them were water meadows where the principal trees were weeping willows and *Pterocarya stenoptera* with its whitish trunks and broad light green crowns. White-washed farmsteads with coloured paintwork and carvings enlivened the scenery, and wooden houses contributed touches of brown. Small patches of woodland survived on the hilltops; though not extensive, they consisted mainly of tall trees, and stood out like tufts of hair on a man's head. Camphor trees were frequent among them, and it was in one of these little woods that I found a fine horn-beam, *Carpinus handelii* REHD., which was the first plant to be identified as a new species when my material from China came to be worked out at home.

The route now ran across limestone; the terrain once more became barren and stony, and the sun's heat seemed even more intense. Man and beast suffering alike, we trudged listlessly onwards, I supporting myself by holding on to my pony, which had developed sores in several places in consequence of the persistent wet weather and the subsequent heat. At one halt I told the mafu not to let the pony wallow in the mud, but he carried out my order by tying it to a tree with its head so high off the ground that it could not reach down to feed. That was the only occasion on my travels on which I was unable to refrain from violence. Once or twice a tiny cloud would cover the sun for half a minute, and the men would breathe with audible relief. The thermometer rose to 38°C. In Mesopotamia I had endured temperatures 10° higher without experiencing such exhaustion, but there the air had been dry, the relative humidity being only 8%, while here it was still 30%. The skin eruption known as "red dog" (prickly heat) — unpleasant though not dangerous — is caused by hindrance to the evaporation of sweat. The Chinese employ their barbers to pinch the skin of the forehead and back until it turns blue, presumably with the purpose of diverting excess of blood from the brain.

As we progressed the mountain on our right came closer to the Xinning river. After two days' march we turned away from the latter into a side valley and crossed a low pass over a line of sandstone hills, reaching the district centre of Dongan on the fourth day. That night there was a violent storm which filled the streams but brought little respite from the heat. The road continued across bare karst terrain, but here it was gay with brightly coloured blossoms. *Lycoris aurea* and *L. radiata* had put up leafless stems with umbels of flowers not unlike our Turk's cap lilies, the first being egg-yolk yellow and the second scarlet. The shrubs included *Lagerstroemia indica*, now studded with large pink blooms, and *Vitex negundo* carrying panicles of violet flowers. Separated from the karst ridge by a channel cut in the softer grey sandstone, a westward-facing line of limestone bluffs ran NNE to SSW, emerging from beneath layers of soft stratified rock worn smooth by erosion.

Shishi Si, the next place of any size, had been raided by bandits that spring and partially burnt down. Some of the larger villages in Hunan were built along streams, the houses carried out on piles above the water. This style of construction was also to be seen in Changsha. The latrines, always a major consideration to the Chinese, were placed above huge open wooden tubs arranged in lines at every exit from each village, so that whatever the direction of the wind the stench pervaded the whole place. Most of the rooms in the inns were fairly large, very dark and hence tolerably cool. Although the Hunanese people were personally clean — in summer even the coolies washed themselves all over in hot water every evening, large wooden basins being provided for that purpose — they found nothing objectionable in having a large wooden urine bucket in every room, and in leaving it unemptied for at least a week. When I told them to take it away, they were usually content to shift it from the middle of the room into a corner.

The next day's journey (18th August) provided a sample of Hunan's superb aquatic flora. Every pond was now a blaze of colour. Except in places where they were shaded by the large shield-shaped leaves of the lotus (*Nelumbo nucifera*), the waters were crowded with *Euryale ferox*, a water lily with puckered, spiny, dark reddish-green leaves almost as large as those of the lotus and carmine flowers which remained almost unopened within their thorny calyx and projected only just above the surface of the water. A small white water chestnut, *Trapa maximowiczii*, was extremely frequent, as was *Trapella chinensis*, similar in appearance but belonging to a different family (*Pedaliaceae*), a plant with splendid pink flowers held high on slender stalks. Equally common were *Nymphoides (Limnanthemum) peltata* with deep yellow flowers, *Utricularia* (more than one species), the white frogbit (*Hydrocharis morsus-ranae*) and *Elodea*; the tall *Jussiaea repens* carried its striking yellow flowers in rows along its long floating stems between tufts of white aerating roots. Much rarer were *Nuphar sinense* (a new species) and *Castalia tetragona* (small yellow and white waterlilies), and the dainty white *Nymphoides indica*, none of which I found until I was nearing Changsha. Other aquatic plants which I had previously met in the rice fields of Yunnan, notably *Azolla pinnata*, were also to be seen here. That afternoon I arrived at Yongzhou, a large town now known by its old name of Lingling. [181]

I wanted to halt there for a short rest and to despatch the plants which I had collected and dried. During my stay in Xinning — though at the time I had been visiting the missionaries outside the town — the district official and the military commander had wanted to call on me, and said that I had been specially recommended by the Beijing authorities. On arriving in Yongzhou I was therefore surprised not to find any message from the legation, and when the clerks in the telegraph office refused to accept telegrams from Germans or Austrians I at once scented trouble. Nevertheless, I showed no sign of my concern and made preparations for resuming my journey, the next objective being Chenzhou. However, a brisk attack of malaria obliged me to prolong my stay, and a day or two later an official of magistrate's rank came and told me, without giving any reasons, that I must depart immediately to Changsha. I had a pretty clear idea what it was all about, but said I was unwilling to accept that he could send me off wherever he wanted without stating the reason. However, further enquiries confirmed that China had declared war on Germany and Austria on 14th August. China? No, merely the prime minister and a small group of supporters, after parliament — which had been wholly opposed to the decision — had been dissolved by force. No one could have behaved more correctly than our ambassador, who pointed out to the President the illegality of his action and com-

mented that the declaration of war was the decision of a party and not that of a people, and that according to law it had to be confirmed by parliament. If only we in Austria had abided by such principles, the world would be a happier place today!

I accordingly departed from Lingling (Yongzhou) on the afternoon of 23rd August with an escort of eight soldiers. Barely a week later, in consequence of the dissolution of parliament by the militarists in Beijing, the town was destined to become the starting point of a new civil war, which during the next three and a half years was to bring untold misery to the prosperous province of Hunan. I followed the main road to Hengyang. At the first place where we stopped for the night I was served with tea which had been purchased at the inn, but I rejected it, suspecting that I smelt prussic acid. The Chinese are masters of the art of poisoning; while not wishing to claim that it was an attempt on my life, I believe that some of the men — my caravan leader for instance — would have been capable of such an attempt if they had believed that I was now, as an enemy alien, outside the protection of the law. The terrain became flatter and less interesting; far away to the right I saw the mountain ranges which I had intended to visit before my plans were disrupted. Beyond Qiyang we crossed the Xiongbei Ling, a chain of bamboo-covered hills some 300 m high. On the third evening the noncommissioned officer in command of the escort told me that ten li further on was the residence of a German missionary, and said that one week previously he (the NCO!) had ordered him to leave his house and move to Changsha, so that next day he would have to travel with us. The next morning I rode on ahead, met the missionary, Herr Riedel and his wife, at the village of Huangdupu, and gratefully accepted their kind invitation to spend the day with them, although their house was merely a wretched shack, since in the unremitting heat I was still feeling far from well. The NCO grumbled at the delay, but I took pleasure in his annoyance since the tale he had told me had proved to be sheer lies. On 27th August, after travelling through rice fields bearing the second crop of the year, I arrived at the large town of Hengyang.

As the German missionary was still on summer holiday on Mount Nanyue [182], another famous place of pilgrimage, I took a room in a somewhat better-class Chinese inn. The local official pressed me to travel on to Changsha, but I first sent a messenger there with a letter to the consulate, as I was vaguely considering the possibility of returning to Yunnan and wanted to know whether I should have to sell my horses here, where I could find accommodation in Changsha and, in general terms how the declaration of war was likely to affect me. As boat traffic on the river was already impeded by the low water level, my messenger's return was delayed, and the answer — explaining all the arrangements in the most detailed and helpful manner — failed to reach me. In the meantime the official himself came to visit me,

---

[181] Both names are still in use, Lingling as the name of the Xian [county], Yongzhou as the name of the shi [municipality] (SGH).

[182] This is Heng Shan, the Southern Sacred Peak (Nanyue) of China (SGH).

but his efforts to make me move on roused my annoyance and when Herr Breton returned from his summer holiday I moved into his residence, although the official had declared that I was under internment in the inn. I enjoyed a few agreeable days as Breton's guest, his house offering some shelter from the constant heat — the temperature was 40°.

Hengyang was the most impressive town which I had so far seen in China, the tall, richly decorated houses being especially striking. One amusing note was provided by a shoemaker's signboard, in English, hung up across the main street upside down. The roofs were made from bundles of bamboo with mats laid over them; although they shaded the streets from the sun, they also prevented noxious vapours from dispersing. Among the main sources of stench were the enormous urine buckets, standing uncovered in the middle of the streets and invariably leaky; a scientist is certainly not prudish, but anyone who sees this trade being carried on cannot but feel disgust. At that time of year all the coolies in the streets went naked to the waist, as did the shopkeepers in their shops.

Owing to the drought the water level in the river was sinking rapidly, and there were fears that steamship traffic would very soon be suspended. I felt disinclined for further overland travel in that climate, which I had already got to know all too well, and therefore hired one half of a junk, one of three being towed by a steamboat. For this I paid $16, of which $3 vanished into the pocket of an official of the steamship company and $1 was surreptitiously appropriated by the NCO in charge of the escort. We embarked on 3rd September and steamed down the Xiang Jiang with great difficulty, as the channel was almost blocked by sandbanks. Every few hours the ship ran aground, often remaining fast for many hours. The three junks which it had been towing were then cast off and waited further downstream, while the tiny steamer, after various pushing and pulling manoeuvres, was finally freed by the efforts of the crew, who jumped backwards and forwards on the roof. As we were usually unable to travel at night, the journey took three days instead of one and a half. On the first evening the captain wanted to stop and send for female company from a nearby village; only after loud shouts of indignation at the delay did he agree to proceed. At one point some soldiers approached us in a boat and fired two shots across our bows. They made the ship stop and wanted to send us back to Hengshan. This was apparently the first hint of the coming unrest, for we now heard that the southern province had lodged a protest against Fu Liangzuo, the dujun appointed by Beijing to govern Hunan, and that the Hunan troops had refused to obey his orders and had withdrawn into the interior. I sent the soldiers my card and explained that I was under orders from the authorities to proceed to Changsha. The soldiers then let the

ship pass, though not without compelling the captain to fork out a few dollars.

"You still don't understand the Chinese," said my servant, "all they want is to extort money."

Once again the ship ran aground. As the junks floated downstream, the captain declared that he could go no further; the engine had broken down and he, a native of Jiangxi, had never been here before and did not know the sandbanks. This provoked an outburst of rage from the passengers, who were already incensed at being charged five times the usual fare. For a few moments I saw a forest of clenched fists and heard their angry shouts; then the junk drifted round a bend and the grimy steamship was hidden from view. We landed and waited for a long time. I wanted the crew to row my junk down the river; in that way we could have reached Changsha sooner or later, and if the steamship did actually overtake us we could have picked up the tow rope again. However, the owner of the junk said that he had received only a small advance and that the captain would have to pay him in full before he could proceed. I therefore sent one of the soldiers from my escort to fetch the captain so that the matter could be settled. While we were waiting a small boat with three passengers came past. They told us that the captain had been killed because of his refusal to proceed, and the soldiers, returning shortly afterwards, confirmed their story. Nevertheless, the steamship soon reappeared and took us in tow once more. The rest of the journey to Changsha was completed without any long delays. A north wind had sprung up and the last night of the trip was quite cool. In the early morning mist the smoking chimneys of the factories on the southern outskirts seemed hostile and unwelcoming. After proceeding a little further the ship stopped before reaching the centre of the city and tied up opposite the villas on the willow-covered island of Nintou Zhou.

Knowing nothing of local circumstances I moved into a Chinese hotel, intending to call upon my compatriots and seek accommodation. This I found with the Wollheim family, in whose house I enjoyed the warmest hospitality. That afternoon my baggage was examined by officials of the "Supervisory Commission for Enemy Nationals". Though I expected to have to surrender my revolver, I managed to retain it. I placed it on a table, covered by my tropical helmet, and told the officer from the consulate, who was present during the baggage examination, that the weapon was there. At these words the English-speaking official from the supervisory commission seemed to cast curious glances in that direction but did not presume to ask questions or look under the helmet; subsequently I learned that he understood German quite well. For half a day's stay and a luncheon which I had not taken the hotel presented me with a bill for $6, including $1 for moving in and $1 for moving out, and I was unable to beat them down below half the sum demanded.

PART V 1918
Work and Travels in Hunan

Chapter 38. Changsha

Warfare and pillage — extortion — Yuelu Shan, its evergreen forest and its gorges — hills and laterite terrain — afforestation — spring flowers of the shrub steppe — friendliness towards foreigners

Chiefly because of lack of funds but also because of reassuring reports on the climate, I decided to remain in Changsha. Herr R. Janssen kindly offered me a pleasant apartment in the consulate building, near the Liuyangmen gate on the eastern side of the town. In Changsha there was a printer who produced quite decent labels for my plants, and I was fully occupied throughout the winter in sorting out my collections. The hot weather continued until the end of September, and from then on the winter was fine and dry. As in Kunming, snow lay for only a few days.

There was plenty of excitement in Changsha. The whole of the south had declared war on the north and Hunan was the scene of the fighting. Troops from the north passed continually through Changsha until suddenly the counterstroke came. In heavy fighting the northerners were defeated, first at Hengshan and finally at Xiangtan. Fu Liangzuo fled one night from Changsha, taking with him $540,000 which he should have used to pay his soldiers. They came streaming back in total disarray, in over-crowded trains and steamships, or on foot along the railway and on every road and path, abandoning their equipment as they went. The British kept a ship in reserve to evacuate neutrals and Allied personnel, as the soldiers had threatened to plunder Changsha if they were not paid. The southerners pressed on in hot pursuit, capturing a thousand prisoners at the southern end of the town; the estimate of ten thousand for the total number of prisoners taken during their advance is probably no exaggeration. From 20th November onwards the southern troops began to appear; most of them, like the northerners, came straggling along singly and entered the town just as they happened to arrive. They carried their booty with them; I saw some fellows with a dozen bayonets in their belts; one soldier walked through the streets without head covering or rifle but with a bayonet in one hand and its sheath in the other, while another man had a clock hung round his neck. Horses could be bought for as little as sixteen paper dollars. A few days later they fired off all their ammunition in a *feu de joie* in the town, though later they were to need it very badly. I felt somewhat uneasy on venturing out into the streets, but in fact there was no disorder and no damage to civilian property. The police, who had formerly been in the service of the northern government, decided at the last moment to demonstrate their new-found loyalty to the southern cause, which they did by shooting down northern soldiers who had surrendered their arms and were attempting to give themselves up. One policeman fired his entire reserve of fifty cartridges before finally hitting a single soldier, and then bore off the dead man's bayonet as a trophy. In Linguandu another man discharged a volley blindly along the street, killing several Chinese civilians just in front of the German residents' houses; not a single soldier had been present. However, such behaviour did not prevent the southerners from dismissing the entire police force and replacing them with soldiers. The southern troops advanced as far as Puqi on the Yangzi Jiang [183] and remained there for some time. Troops from Yunnan, reinforced by robber bands enlisted as mercenaries, fought their way as far as central Hubei ("Hupeh"). The people of the south — their soldiers and the general population alike — were bitterly hostile towards the northern invaders, though the latter claimed to have come to liberate Hunan. That the hearts and other organs of enemies slain in battle were roasted and eaten is a well attested fact, yet when the Chinese declared war on us they claimed that they did so "because of our contraventions of international law".

At the beginning of March 1918 came the counterattack. The soldiers had not been paid, and when the northerners beckoned them with bright shining dollars that was apparently sufficient to induce half the southern troops at Puqi to defect to them. Nevertheless, none of the southerners dared to go any further until the commander of one contingent, Colonel Chang Qinyao, promised to give them a free hand to loot the next town, Pingjiang. The town, including the American mission buildings, was then totally ransacked, and the Spanish Catholic priest wounded by a bullet. The southern troops poured back through Changsha, while the last of them — Changsha men themselves — reinforced by riffraff from the town spent an afternoon and the following night looting the shops and offices in the main streets of the town. The mint was thoroughly ransacked, its own officials allegedly sharing enthusiastically in the looting, and set on fire three times. The yamen was also set alight. The civil population left the town in long columns, well dressed people carrying their belongings on their shoulders while others conveyed them on wheelbarrows, a means of transport widely used in those parts. The fields were left untilled and the commercial quarter of the town was a scene of desolation. The shops were shut, and the streets were littered with shattered glass, broken shutters, scraps of paper and other debris thrown aside by the looters in their search for gold and silver, silk and other fabrics, and shoes. Here and there, hung up or stuck on a spike, was the severed head of a straggler who had been caught in the act of looting. Vigilantes from the town militia patrolled the streets in large detachments. A few days later the northern troops entered the town. Although they

---

[183] Puqi in Hubei province is actually just south of the Yangzi, on a tributary of the great river (SGH).

committed no major atrocities, the people suffered grievously at their hands. The towns of Zhuzhou and Liling fared even worse; they were completely burnt down and their people, apart from those who had already fled, were massacred.

Chang Qinyao now became dujun of Hunan. He was a master of the art of extortion and used his skill to suck the province dry. Slowly but steadily nearly all the silver coinage disappeared into his personal account in a foreign bank, and when the silver had gone he started on the copper. The paper currency dropped from 1400 cash to the dollar, falling as low as 16,000 cash. The details of how this was done fall outside the scope of a travel book, as perhaps do some of the events outlined above, but I have chosen to describe them because they governed the conditions under which I had to exist. I do not propose to recount the tactical manoeuvrings of the Chinese forces, as such matters are utterly repugnant to me. For the most part they engaged in flanking movements so as to avoid actual fighting as far as possible. Major battles, when they were eventually fought, usually resulted in one soldier wounded, a few civilians killed and several villages looted. The northern authorities were interested solely in empty successes of that kind, and did nothing to enforce effective rule. In Changsha, formerly reputed to be the cleanest city in China, piles of rubbish now spread right across the streets. The tall, well equipped buildings of the commercial district still presented an imposing exterior in the glare of the electric lighting, but it was some time before they were restocked and reopened. The streets swarmed with soldiers. Though their accoutrements were modern — some even had riot shields — they were dirty, slovenly and loutish in their behaviour. The mood and atmosphere of wartime prevailed throughout the city.

None of this hindered my botanical collecting. Changsha proved to be an excellent place for the purpose, not because its flora was unusually rich — it was of a type widely distributed in Eastern China with numerous admixtures from the south — but because it was totally different from those of the areas which I had previously traversed and hence provided an almost entirely new assortment of plants, and because hardly any botanical collectors had previously worked in Hunan. The richest locale was the Yuelu Shan, a 300 m hill opposite the city. Growing on it was the only natural woodland in the district, a temple forest which covered a surprisingly large area and which had evidently enjoyed total protection from time immemorial. During the winter, even under the short-lived cover of hoar frost and snow, there were three species of *Symplocos* in flower, together with the evergreen trees (*Quercus glauca, Castanopsis tibetana* and *C. sclerophylla*) which made up the bulk of the forest. All their trunks were clothed with mosses closely pressed against the bark (*Homalia targioniania, Hypnum yokohamae*) together with innumerable lichens. They provided plenty of work for me, even in winter, and it was time well spent, for among the mosses on that mountain there were no fewer than seven new species. Herbaceous plants began to flower in March

and April, and though there were only a few in the evergreen forest I found more in the gulleys, which were filled with *Liquidambar* and a few other species of thin-leaved deciduous trees. Rivulets splashed down over the sandstone; ferns and liverworts clothed every damp rock-face and lined every niche with vivid green. Among the first to open their flowers with the coming of spring were a small *Chloranthus* with white spikes (*C. fortunei*), two violets, a larkspur, *Arisaema ambiguum, Mazus saltuarius* (a new species) and *Thea fraterna*, a small bush with scented white blossoms tinged with pink. The Yuelu Shan was at its finest in March, when its slopes were coloured by the purple blossoms of *Rhododendron simsii*, although this is merely a forest undershrub and only exceptionally grows into a small tree 4 m in height. At the same time the dainty white racemes of *Symplocos caudata* diffused their delightful scent through the air, together with contributions from the green and yellowish flowers of other species of the same genus of trees. In early autumn the low-growing *Hemiboea subacaulis* (a new species) opened its large flowers on the rocks, which were covered with other herbs and grasses. Further away, roughly two hours' brisk march, was Gu Shan, about 400 m high; though covered only by bushes it yielded a few interesting plants.

Both these hills offered wide vistas over the country. To the northeast the high mountains of the Pingjiang district were visible in clear weather. To the southwest was a disjointed tangle of shorter and longer mountain ranges, only in the far distance attaining heights substantially greater than my present viewpoint. Far away to the east and southeast were several long low ranges, the nearest of them comprising the pointed Zhao Shan and sloping down to the Xiang Jiang at its bend below Xiangtan. The slowly flowing river was well over one kilometre wide and carried a brisk traffic of steam boats and countless sailing junks. Low water level at Changsha was only 23 m above sea level; when the Yangzi Jiang was in flood its waters filled the Dongting lake, which was of considerable size, and the water level in the Xiang Jiang between there and Changsha sometimes rose so high that the low lying parts of the city were inundated. The low ground — apart from the rock outcrops, which throughout Hunan had a southwest to northeasterly strike, and the river gravels — consisted of laterite. Richthofen states that this is the most northerly occurrence of laterite in China, but I later saw some of the same geological formation near Yueyang on the Yangzi. Its exposures revealed a red-brown loamy mass, densely interspersed with irregular narrow wormlike bands of grey-white material, said to be pure clay. It formed a tableland some 50 m above the river, seamed by small hollows and innumerable gullies, narrow and broad, and its contours were everywhere smooth and rounded. The valley bottoms were planted with rice, and at their margins were the farmsteads, always solitary, surrounded by small patches of woodland of the kind previously described, these woods being delimited by earth banks. The slopes and ridge tops were planted with pines (*Pinus massoniana*). *Cunninghamia lanceolata* was also frequent; young plantations looked exactly as if they were intended to produce Christmas trees of perfectly regular shape. Among them grew *Ilex cornuta*, a shrubby holly with spiny ornamental leaves. In late autumn the tea oil shrubs (*Thea oleifera*) were studded with large white flowers. Early in the New Year *Loropetalum sinense*, a shrub related to the witch-hazel (*Hamamelis*), made a striking picture, its closely packed flowers covering its twigs and leaves like a veil of perforated paper. The large orange-yellow blossoms of *Rhododendron molle* seemed to gleam with their own light, and somewhat later came the flowers of *Gardenia augusta*. All these made the environs of Changsha — once one had passed through the zone of vegetable gardens with their stench of human ordure — a most attractive place in which to roam, more so perhaps than the surroundings of any other city in China. Well kept bridle paths led in every direction. Quite apart from the excellent opportunities for botanical collecting which the district afforded, it was exceedingly enjoyable to ride through the countryside on my splendid Sichuan pony, with my collecting bag and often my camera slung over my shoulder, sometimes even with the added bonus of agreeable companions. Even the steppe grasslands brought forth flowering plants in some profusion. The narrow-leaved *Viola betonicifolia* began to flower very early, accompanied by *Daphne genkwa*, which because of its clusters of violet blooms arranged along the whole length of its stems was taken for a lilac by most of the European residents, and also by *Spiraea prunifolia*, a small shrub with little white flowers arranged in a similar pattern. The grasses, uniformly distributed over the ground and for the most part growing close together but nowhere forming a closed or interlacing sward, did not flower until late summer, when they reached a height of around 70 cm. In open spots lichens (*Diploschistes scruposus, Cladonia bacillaris*) and mosses (*Rhaco-mitrium canescens, Thysanomitrium blumii*) carpeted the ground.

Several of our compatriots in Changsha owned motorboats and with their aid I was able to reach more distant objectives, among them Zhao Shan mentioned above. Europeans were perfectly safe in the vicinity of Changsha. The Hunanese, despite having built a dyke at Hezhou as recently as 1895 with the purpose of preventing "yangguizi" (foreign devils) from setting foot in their province, were now the friendliest of Chinese people in their attitude towards foreigners. On many occasions during my rides in the country I would halt at a farmstead for a few minutes, and the people would at once offer me tea or invite me to smoke one of their tin tobacco pipes. Nevertheless, violent crime was not unknown among the Chinese. Once when my friend Schnabel and I were on Yuelu Shan we came upon the body of a man who had just been strangled, lying beside a carved stone several thousand years old protected by a roof; the inscription which it bore was a copy from a still older stone on Heng Shan. The murderers had run off as we approached, but later, when we were some way off and dusk was falling, we saw a band of men carrying away the body. There was an Englishman who claimed to have found a head in the Yuelu Shan forest. Living in Changsha were more than twenty German nationals, for the most part businessmen, mining experts or missionaries. They made up the majority of the foreign community in Hunan. In addition to those already mentioned, the mission superintendent, Herr H. Witt, was of great assistance to me. Besides correcting the Chinese names on my plant labels he also made available his painstaking route surveys for joint publication with my cartographical studies. During the following summer Herr A. Brammer collected some plants for me on Mount Yuelu Shan.

Chapter 39. To Xikuang Shan

Surreptitious departure — troublesome soldiery — a madman — Daleping and Loudi — a large antimony mine — plant cover — tea processing — the Qilijiang cave

At the end of April 1918 the Beijing government once again decided to intern all enemy aliens, and this time matters looked really serious. According to private reports from Shanghai, contracts for the construction of barracks on the island of Tiantaishan had been awarded many months previously, and applications for permits to visit holiday resorts were now being flatly rejected by the authorities in Beijing, even in the most pressing cases of grave ill health. If I were to continue my botanical explorations in the coming season, I therefore had to vanish as swiftly as possible into the territory occupied by the southern forces. After the latter had occupied Changsha the German missionaries enquired whether they might now be allowed to travel. The southern authorities replied that permits granted by Beijing were no longer valid, but privately told them that although passes could not be issued they should simply travel as usual, but should make themselves inconspicuous and should try to avoid being seen by Allied nationals. The rest of us naturally assumed that this advice applied to ourselves as well as the missionaries, and in the event no one attempted to prevent businessmen from travelling to Xikuangshan. Since Fu Liangzuo's departure the supervisory commission for enemy aliens had ceased to exist and even the postal censorship had been suspended by the postal commissioner himself. The police, who were personally acquainted with most of us, had not yet been reinstated after the occupation of Changsha by the northern forces, and at the end of April 1918 the authorities had more urgent matters on their minds than the possibility that one of us might decide to transgress their uncouthly worded directives; their troops had been overwhelmingly defeated near Liling and the southerners had pushed forwards to within fifty kilometres of Changsha. As the private advice given by the southern authorities had not been rescinded, I saw that, although it was certainly not intended to cover journeys of several months' duration, it gave me a means of talking myself out of trouble if necessary, and even if this were unsuccessful, such a journey would be a *fait accompli*, and I was prepared to put up with the risk of subsequent unpleasantness for the sake of the results which it would assuredly bring.

This time I did not wish to travel far, but simply to stay in a few favourable localities where I could collect plenty of plant material and prepare satisfactory herbarium specimens, as I wanted a surplus of plants to sell and to cover the expected wastage. For the same reason I aimed to keep my travelling expenses as low as possible. To avoid having to take a cook I decided that I would rely on my fellow countrymen to provide my meals. I could carry provisions with me for a few days on the road, and my coolie had already learnt the basics of elementary cookery by watching the cook at work in the kitchen. Baggage transport was expensive; in Hunan a porter cost far more than a pack animal in Yunnan, but I succeeded in cutting down my party to five porters. A few days before my departure came the welcome news that the Academy of Sciences had granted me a fresh subsidy [184]. The money arrived at the Dutch legation, at a somewhat better rate of exchange than before. Messrs Schnabel, Gaumer & Co, transmitted it to me at Changsha without charge and were kind enough to make me an advance before the formalities had been completed. As traffic through the city gates was now watched with greater vigilance than ever, I split up my baggage into several lots and had them taken on different days and through different gates to Linguandu outside the city, accompanying each lot personally.

On the morning of 2nd May I swung myself into the saddle and rode out through the Liuyang Men gate as I had done so often before, but this time I skirted round behind the city wall, crossed the river and disappeared from public view. My porters belonged to a guild of coolies who conveyed business correspondence, money and baggage for the above-named firm to their antimony smelter at Xikuangshan. They were therefore well acquainted with the roads and the people, and knew how to slip through along minor routes. This was useful, for I had to avoid the main roads; they were guarded by sentries posted by the northern forces, who would certainly have been troublesome and might even have put a premature end to my whole undertaking. Some soldiers, notably those of the notorious Seventh Division under the command of the dujun Chang Qinyao himself, had already robbed and wounded Europeans.

My route from Changsha led westwards away from the river Xiang Jiang, along a small tributary via Daoling towards the tract of hills between Ningxiang and Xiangxiang. These hills were covered only by shrubs and, like all the uplands in that district, appeared to consist solely of sandstone. We skirted round their northern edge, through a pleasant landscape where the road crossed several brooks which fed a little stream flowing northwards. A new species of alder (*Alnus trabeculosa*) was growing beside them. My route ran along the southern edge of a chain of hills strewn with gigantic boulders, presumably of granite; it then came to a small river (the Shiluosan He) and turned due south. While I was snipping off some flowering twigs from a guelder rose I suddenly saw a small green tree-snake (*Lachesis gramineus*) lying half a metre away. Its bite is venomous, but luckily this one was sluggish, having recently fed. A blow from my cane stunned it, and in a few moments it was in my formalin jar. Riding was not a usual means of travel in those country districts and in the circumstances existing at that time my appearance on horseback roused suspicion. Most of the country people at first sight took me for a military officer and ran off or barred themselves noisily inside their houses. On one occasion a madman tried to attack me. He came towards me along a narrow track flanked by rice-fields, hopping on each leg alternately, seized my

---

[184] 6000 crowns on 31st January 1918.

horse by the bridle, knelt down and pointed with a
vacant look to the sky, chattering nonsense at me. I
grasped my cane and he turned away hurriedly.
Some peasants dragged him away, but soon afterwards, as my men came past with the mule, which
I had sold to a man in Xikuangshan and was now
delivering to him, he was there again. This time he
had a lump of earth as big as a man's head tied up
in a cloth, and he swung it repeatedly in the air,
striking the mule on the rump. In their alarm my
men ran forwards with the mule, but some of my kit
which had been packed at the sides of the saddle
came adrift and was left dangling below the mule's
belly. My camera had a narrow escape from falling
into the water.

Daleping, where we stopped for the third night,
lies at 190 m on the watershed between the Shiluosan He and the Lian Shui, to the west of the 600 m
mountain range just referred to. The people who
lived there were thoroughly offensive and insolent;
their attitude was totally different from that reported
by the missionaries who had recently travelled in the
country, namely that the people were now extremely
friendly towards foreigners in general and Germans
in particular. Soon after starting next morning we
surmounted the first westwards dipping limestone
beds. Continuing south-westwards, we reached the
Lian Shui river not far from Loudi, and crossed it.
There and onwards all the mountains were of limestone.

Loudi was one of the few towns of any size in
that district. The rest of the countryside was dotted
with peasants' farmhouses and rich men's country
residences, some of them quite imposing. Sangua-
qiao, where we spent the next night, was situated on
a lateral stream, reached after crossing a small
saddle. The route continued across two more such
saddles along the northern edge of a range of deeply
dissected hills on which were numerous little woods
of *Cunninghamia* and bamboo and here and there a
grove of oaks. We reached the river at Lianyuan, a
large town which was the only transhipment centre
for Xikuangshan. After crossing the river we continued northwards to our fifth night stop, Tangtiaoqiao,
150 m above sea level. A short distance further on
was the confluence of the three streams which
formed the Lian Shui: one from the southwest,
another from the Anjiapu district to the northeast and
the third from the hills around Xikuangshan. A
fourth stream flowed past Tangtiaoqiao to join the
river just below Lianyuan. Our route climbed along
the middle stream, in places quite steeply, into a
range of hills stretching from southwest to northeast.
Since the previous day I had been riding on paved
roads, in contrast to the gravel tracks, so much more
pleasant for horse and rider, on which I had travelled
for the first few days after leaving Changsha. We
crossed two passes, the first and higher of which
reached an altitude of 715 m. Beyond the second
pass the track led along the side of a U-shaped
valley, both sides of which were clothed with forest
and bamboo extending into the distance. Then,
sticking up in the middle of a deeply dissected tract
of hills, we saw the first chimney-stacks of the
mining town of Xikuangshan. As it rained all day I
was unable to collect much material, but I saw

enough to convince me that, despite the conflicting
advice given to me in Changsha, the district offered
worthwhile prospects for my work.

Xikuangshan was the largest antimony mine in
Hunan, and as Hunan produced more than half the
world output of the metal, it was probably the
largest in the world. However, it was only after the
outbreak of war that it reached such prominence;
before 1914 there had been only two chimney-stacks,
but now there were forty. As there were seams of
coal nearby the ore was smelted in Xikuangshan
itself, then carried by porters, some to Lianyuan and
some to Lengshuijiang, and conveyed by boats on
the Zi Jiang and Lian Shui to Changsha. The metal
was produced in two grades: crude (60 to 70%) and
regulus (96%). The ore was found between limestone
strata dipping not very steeply east-northeastwards,
the best deposits being associated with dolomite. It
outcropped on a ridge between two branches of a
valley, the entire length of the ridge being occupied
by opencast and drift workings. The town filled the
whole of the higher, eastern branch of the valley,
covering a stretch ranging from roughly 530 to 650
m in altitude, and also the lower half of the other
branch. At the height of the boom it was said to
have had 50,000 inhabitants. Apart from the works
buildings and a small number of superior dwellings,
it consisted solely of wretched huts. The European
mines and a few of the Chinese had modern equipment, but other Chinese owners ran their mines "tsa
budo" ("anyhow") [185] their ventilating machinery,
instead of being powered by a steam engine, was
driven by four coolies operating treadles. It was of
no consequence that this failed to produce a proper
draught and that much of the ore was blown away
and wasted; the business was cheap to run and
yielded a profit. I was accommodated in the residence provided for employees of the Kaili Gongsi,
Schnabel, Gaumer & Co., and am most grateful to
the company and to Herr A. Brauer in particular.
The sulphur fumes emitted from the smelting works
were carried by the prevailing north wind straight
into the houses occupied by the Germans, where
they spoilt the lacquer on the tables and made my
stay less agreeable than it might otherwise have
been.

The immediate neighbourhood of Xikuangshan
was completely deforested but a three day trip which
I made in the company of my friend Herr Wolf on
his way back to Changsha took me through the best
parts of the district, notably to Anjiapu, where
Pseudolarix kaempferi was a major element of the
forests, consisting otherwise of pines, *Cunninghamia,
Liquidambar, Aleurites* and other trees. I had seen
one specimen of *Pseudolarix* in Changsha, growing
as a bonsai in a pot, but I did not believe the owner's claim that it grew wild in the mountains to the
west, since it had never previously been reported
further west than Guling in Jiangxi [186] Near Anjiapu,
however, this tree, closely similar in colour and habit
to our larch, was one of the glories of the forests.

[185] Literally 'more or less' (SGH).

[186] In the Lu Shan mountains.

Sassafras tzumu, an equally symmetrical and slender tree with trilobed leaves, also grew in these woods; it has a relative in North America. There was an interesting understorey of numerous shrubs, the dominant species being the tall *Diervilla japonica* and the small *Malus sieboldii* with aromatic leaves. There were some large coalmines in Anjiapu. The coal was coked on the spot; for this purpose it was simply piled inside a brick chamber, covered with earth and ignited, the flames emerging through chimneys constructed from a few tiles.

On the second day we went on to Lianyuan. Except in one gorge filled with oak forest the terrain was treeless, but tea was widely planted and the product was now being packed. This was black tea, the sort made by pressing the leaves and drying them over a fire, whereas simple drying in the sun yields green tea, the sort drunk by the Chinese. The pressing was performed with bare feet, the leaves being spread on the paved highway, and the process was not exactly appetising. This tea was taken to Hunan for sale and was reputed to be one of the best of the products exported from there. Wolf departed from Lianyuan in one of the antimony boats. These boats had been waiting for weeks, fully laden, as their captains were unwilling to face the cordon set up by the northerners' army; indeed their soldiers' main activity was to obstruct all the traffic of the province. Brauer and I returned to Xikuangshan next day along the main road.

There were a few spots elsewhere which yielded rich pickings, among them a small wood on the steep side of the sandstone crest above the village of Tongjiapai, where I clambered down from top to bottom, continually halting to cut my way through the brambles; also a remnant of tall-trunked forest in the stream gorge below, and, some way further on, shrub vegetation on moist ground near coal-seams on the road to Xinhua. The whole district was adorned by wild roses of three different species (*Rosa microcarpa, R.cathayensis* and *R.laevigata)*; their brilliant flowers of white and pink perfumed the air. Another trip took me to a cave near Qilijiang, the southern extension of the antimony deposits, which totalled four kilometres in length. It formed a huge dome with an opening in the roof which let in a little light; there was a manmade shaft which gave access down slippery steps and a ladder. The rock clefts were studded with geodes lined with delicate translucent needles of crystalline calcite, mingled with white granular pillars resembling stalactites.

Several well organised bands of robbers, operating over wide areas, had their hideouts in the neighbouring mountains. One day four of the bandits, one of them on horseback, were captured in Xikuangshan with stolen property in their possession. The town councillors had already signed their death warrants when the wisest amongst them had second thoughts.

"If we execute them," he said, "the rest of the bandits will come down upon us, and in any case their thefts were not committed here. We had better send them to Xinhua." And that is what was done.

Chapter 40. Summer on Yun Shan Near Wugang

A journey in a carrying chair — checkpoints — useless coolies — flowering trees on the Yun Shan — profusion of species — climbers and shade plants — mosses and fungi — rainstorms and mist — animals — the Liebenzeller mission — civil war — bandits in uniform

After visiting Anjiapu a second time I set off from Xikuangshan on 28th May aiming to reach Wugang, my second night's stop, in good time to see the trees on the Yun Shan in flower. Brauer had to go to Xinhua and I therefore took the opportunity of travelling in his company as far as Lengshuijiang, on the river 20 km upstream from Xinhua and 180 m above sea level. On the journey I found that my pony was temporarily unfit to travel. Some time earlier, when I had been riding on paved roads near Loudi, it had lost both front shoes and as there was not a smith to be found and I could not wait to let the hoofs harden, both of them had worn down very badly and unevenly, as I had already noticed on my excursions around Xikuangshan. So I sent it back there, and my friend Tolkmitt, whom I knew to be a man who loved and understood horses, most kindly agreed to look after it in my absence. Brauer lent me his carrying chair, which was brought that very night. Much against my will I squeezed into the box, which to anyone except the lazy Chinese is an instrument of torture rather than a pleasant means of conveyance.

Some five kilometres upstream we crossed the Zi Jiang and soon afterwards turned into a valley leading south-westwards. Tall bamboos (*Phyllostachys puberula*) with pendent crowns of delicate bright green leaves, in many places without any admixture of trees, clothed the hills on both sides of the narrow valley, creating a pleasing picture. The journey by travelling chair soon proved anything but enjoyable. The bearers bumped the chair against every corner that we passed, and before long it looked sadly battered. At one spot they tipped it right over and finally, having reached a large village called Wenjiaqiao, three of them declared that they had never learnt how to carry a chair and if they were to go any further they required a fifth man. I of course refused, but a stout and helpful bystander quickly found me new bearers, and my old ones were so considerate as not to insist on payment for their valuable services. It was amusing to see how the populace, attracted by the unaccustomed sight of my European crates and boxes, at first crowded round and then, as my bearers halted and set down the chair with me in it, suddenly scattered and ran off, to the merriment of the few who remained.

Next day we surmounted the gently sloping watershed (420 m) at the head of the valley and descended into a hollow harbouring the village of Longqiaopu. It was situated on another minor tributary of the Zi Jiang, which emerged from a little ravine and flowed on to join the river through a second, much deeper gorge to the north of a mountain called Baiyunya. At this point the main road from Xinhua to Shaoyang was barred by guards posted by the southerners' forces. They had several hundred men there and in the next two villages. With their large coolie-style hats they looked less military than the northerners, and they did not have their coarse features and crude manners; on the contrary, many of them stood to attention when they saw that I was a European. At the picket on the next ridge, where there were some old fortifications, some officers were present and a checkpoint had been set up. With the utmost politeness, the soldiers asked to examine my baggage. Under ordinary circumstances I could have refused, as no one except the Maritime Customs was empowered to open Europeans' baggage. However, since the cessation of diplomatic relations the authorities had given orders that the baggage of any German or Austrian who had been granted a travel permit was to be inspected. A refusal would only have aroused suspicion, and might have prompted the soldiers to enquire how it was that I came to be travelling at all. I accordingly declared that I was not in possession of any forbidden articles — I had strapped on my revolver under my coat — and requested them to make haste, as I had no time to lose. After opening my tin trunk, always an object of intense suspicion, they said they were satisfied and at my request most obligingly issued a certificate which would exempt me from further molestation. With my nose in the air, I stated that I did not intend to travel via Shaoyang since the northerners' troops were occupying it. This probably helped to speed the baggage inspection, which was actually quite unobjectionable, and when one of the officers pretended to find cause for suspicion in a roll of cardboard the other officer did not back him up. My men had to answer searching questions about their places of origin, but as none of them came from Northern China they were allowed to pass without demur. One of my new chair porters, a man who had already made trouble after every short rest and who had to be shoved and tugged before he would take up his place once more, seized the opportunity to abscond.

A fairly long descent led to Qukoupu below the southwest side of Baiyunya, a bare sandstone mountain. Here a man was found to replace the missing chair porter. I continued southwards and on the fourth day reached Yakoupu, a place on the road from Shaoyang to Wugang, about thirty kilometres to the west of the former. There I found two of the Liebenzeller missionaries, who kindly invited me to stay in the mission building at Taohuaping. After leaving the mountain tract I entered the Shaoyang basin, which extends to the west of Wugang as far

as Xinning [187]. It was a uniformly undulating landscape of severely weathered limestone which outcropped here and there, occasionally forming projecting escarpments with spires and turrets. Many of the low hills were clothed with woods of *Pinus massoniana*, and further on were groves of *Cupressus funebris* on the rock scarps.

This was my first journey in a carrying chair, and it soon proved so unpleasant that I swore it would be my last. To sit there between four coolies stinking of garlic and other unmentionable things is certainly no pleasure. Moreover, any glimpses of the wayside are no more than momentary, and to show untrained collectors what plants to gather is practically impossible without stopping, getting out and walking back. Growing on the fieldbanks and near the houses was a not uncommon scarlet fungus, *Ithyphallus rubicundus*, but I was hurried past at such a speed that I failed to recognise the toadstools, thinking that they were animal entrails discarded by some passer-by, and in the end I had to be content with a very poor specimen. The daily cost was ten times that of horseback travel, and I began to think longingly of my brave little pony in Xikuangshan. I could have had him sent on to me after he had recovered, but he would certainly have fallen into the hands of soldiers or bandits. On reaching Taohuaping I therefore bought another pony, a handsome and well proportioned grey mare, after putting her through her paces that morning, and sent the carrying chair home. I knew that I could get back the price I had paid for her, but in my haste I unfortunately went wrong in my assessment of her teeth; not until some time later did I realise that she was barely four years old and hence not really strong enough to carry me. That afternoon I set off again and, travelling mostly along the river, reached Wugang at noon on the third day (4th June).

There had been heavy rain in the previous few days, and I spent a day there drying out my things, so as to be ready to set to work immediately on arriving at Yun Shan. A coolie from Xikuangshan, an unutterably stupid and apathetic fellow, although he knew very well how to extract "squeeze", managed to scorch my tropical helmet, saddle cover and one of my panniers, and even set fire to a bundle of paper. To light the lamp he used a strip of paper soaked in paraffin as a spill, and then amused himself by balancing it, still blazing merrily, on his hand. When given the job of buying fodder and conveying it to the mountain on the horse, he simply refused to do the work; so I finally chased him out and reported the matter to the Chinese who had supplied him. However, he crowned his stupidity by reappearing in Xikuangshan, where he was thrown out on his ear. Serviceable coolies are much more easily found in Yunnan than in Hunan, though the inhabitants of Hunan are supposed to be the most intelligent people in China [188].

Unfortunately I once again reached Yun Shan too late and missed the flowering of some of its

---

[187] But Xinning is SSE of Wugang (SGH).

[188] Mao Zedong was Hunanese (SGH).

trees. Nevertheless, repeated traverses of the forest revealed an undreamt of wealth of trees and shrubs which had escaped my notice in the previous year, and I was now able to study and collect them in various stages of development. *Aesculus wilsonii*, a horse chestnut with long dense panicles of small florets, had just come into flower at the sides of the woodland streams. Many of the ten different oaks (chiefly *Lithocarpus*) still carried their pollen catkins, as did the sweet chestnuts. *Lithocarpus henryi*, an evergreen tree of frequent occurrence in the beech zone on the upper part of the mountain, opened its male flowers, borne on angular, branching panicles, somewhat later, and there was a new species, *L. paniculata*, which did not flower until August. Maples were also well represented, among them the tall *Acer amplum* growing in sunken channels at the upper edge of the forest and the interesting *A. henryi* with leaves of three leaflets. Here and there the pink flowers of *Albizzia julibrissin* gleamed among the trees. The white-leaved crowns of *Sorbus nubium* (a new species) stood out conspicuously in the upper storey of the forest. Growing on the crest to the southwest of the temple was one solitary example of a remarkable new species of lime tree (*Tilia endochrysea*) which did not flower until August. Another stately tree, seldom seen in flower, was *Emmenopterys henryi* with large, opulently perfumed, pale yellow flowers and enlarged calyx lobes of the same colour as an added attraction to pollinators. *Bretschneidera sinensis*, the sole representative of its family, is a splendid tree discovered by Henry in southern Yunnan and not seen again since. I collected its previously unknown fruits, though their identification had to await the arrival of further material gathered by my collector during the following spring. *Manglietia fordiana*, a tree with a stout trunk and a broad crown, was still carrying its rather small red magnolia-style flowers with a scent of lemons. Cinnamon bark was gathered by the Chinese and used for medicinal purposes, but the tree from which they collected it (*Cinnamomum jensenianum*, a new species) is not common, and is seldom found with its tiny flowers and its fruits, the latter borne on stalks as thin as hairs. Although only five or six square kilometres in area, this seemingly inexhaustible forest harboured over one hundred species of trees and shrubs. There were numerous huge climbers (lianas) which had just come into flower, including *Schizophragma integrifolium*, *Ficus baileyi*, *Parthenocissus heterophylla*, *Kadsura chinensis*, several species of *Actinidia* (*A. chinensis*, *A. arguta* and *A. purpurea*) and a bramble (*Rubus malifolius*) with undivided leaves and stems 5 cm thick which scrambled up into the highest treetops. Out of the four species of bamboo which grow on that mountain I found three in flower. Not many of the herbaceous plants were yet flowering, but I found the yellow-brown *Impatiens siculifer*, a large flowered Solomon's seal (*Disporopsis fusco-picta*), a dainty violet meadow rue (*Thalictrum clavatum*) in large numbers, the low growing *Lysimachia trientaloides* with clusters of starry golden yellow flowers in the middle of whorls of narrow dark green leaves, a new orchid (*Liparis pauliana*) with a flat brown lip and thread-like tepals, growing in moss on top of rocks,

and a broad-leaved sedge, *Carex scaposa*, which displayed pretty white and pink coloration at its flowering time. Some of the shade-loving plants did not flower until late in the season, followed by *Fordiophyton gracile* (a new species) and *Sarcopyramis nepalensis* and hordes of inconspicuous species of *Lecanthus*, *Elatostema* and *Pilea*. Last of all came two Gesnerads, turgid with sap, *Hemiboea henryi* and *H. subcapitata*, which had large bell-shaped violet flowers with orange yellow markings and white hairs, though these flowers were almost completely enclosed by a mantle of water-filled bracts, and just peeped out through an opening at the apex. Growing in wet spots on the rocks were other, rosette-forming Gesnerads (*Oreocharis primulina* and the new *Chirita fimbrisepala*), while yet another (*Lysionotus pauciflorus*) dangled its flowers on hair-thin stalks among the ferns which clothed the tree trunks. One of these ferns was *Cyclophorus sheareri* with tongue-shaped fronds, golden brown on their undersides. There were several dozen species of ground-living ferns ranging from ordinary bracken and *Diplazium orientale* with broad triangular foliage 1.5 m tall to the dwarf *Trichomanes parvulum* which carpeted the rocks in sheets less than 1 cm thick. There were many species of mosses: *Aerobryum speciosum*, of which I found a specimen with capsules, *Floribundaria intermedia* and other species of *Neckeraceae* hung in profusion from the trees, while others grew on branches and leaves, and beside and in the water. However, plump cushions of moss were confined to the rocks, and were not to be found on the forest floor as in Europe. Lichens were abundant, and fungi were represented by parasitic forms and by toadstools, the latter emerging in large numbers in late summer. I also found what I took to be the fruiting bodies of the mycelium which causes rotting wood and bamboo to glow in the dark. The parasitic fungus *Cordyceps aurantiacus* (a new species) was putting up its club-shaped growths from the body of a grub which lives in rotting wood. *C. sinensis* is of course a well known species found in mountainous districts and used as a medicine. There were numerous species of slime fungi bulging out from beneath the bark of the trunks of certain trees. Algae, however, were poorly represented.

My accommodation was a room in a large temple called Guanyin Ge. As its window and door were on one side only it became extremely dank and musty in wet weather and it was no easy task to prevent moulds from spoiling the botanical material which I had collected. Although the room had a board floor and was not actually damp, even my good German saddle became mouldy, something that had never happened before, even in the Salween valley. Bad weather often hampered my field work; out of the seventy four days which I spent on that mountain only eighteen were without rain. From time to time there were violent rainstorms which brought the mountain-sides down in landslips and cut deep channels through the bean fields round the temple. On one occasion a stream came surging through the temple dining room and flooded the courtyard to such a depth that one could have floated a boat there. However, the rheumatism which had troubled me in the summer of 1916 vanished completely in the first few days of my stay on Yun

Shan. Possession of a permanent base made the work much easier than it was when I was constantly on the move, and as I was able to obtain charcoal and make a fire for drying the paper, the botanical specimens which I prepared were really excellent.

One piece of equipment which saved a great deal of tree climbing was a six metre pole with hooks at the top, but it was too awkward to take on my travels and not something for which a replacement could be found at every halt. I also collected zoological material; insects of the most varied kinds were abundant, and in the mountain streams there were salamanders of a species (*Pachytriton brevipes*) which had been found only twice before, and, strangely enough, crabs. In the forest there were many different snakes, the commonest being the harmless *Zaocys dhumnades*, usually black in colour and never less than two metres in length. Also present was a poisonous snake, *Ablabes maior*, with protective colouring of leaf green. A wild cat caught a hen quite near the temple, but was driven off before it could carry it away. Tracks of wild boar were often to be seen, and a muntjac deer was caught in a trap. Living in the trees were small squirrels with two pale stripes on the back and a thin tail without much hair.

Throughout August the rain persisted unrelentingly and I therefore had to abandon my plans for a trip to the mountain range to the southwest, the crests of which were some 200 m higher than Yun Shan, though I should have liked to make the journey at the same time of year as my previous visit to Yun Shan in 1917. From the summit of Yun Shan there were clear views of the valleys on the near side of the mountain range. All parts of it were green, being covered with shrub meadows; high forest was confined to a few deeply cut channels and was presumably composed of the same tree communities as the forest on Yun Shan. However, I particularly wished to see one forest which filled an extensively branching gorge, because it was at a lower altitude. In the mist, however, I might have failed to find the place, especially as the porters whom I would certainly have needed for the three or four day trip would have sought every possible excuse for shirking a journey into the mountains.

I took my meals with the German missionaries and I am deeply grateful to Herr L. Jensen for his hospitality; indeed, it was he who made it possible for me to spend the summer there. Herr R. Paul and Sister E. Gramenz also assisted me in all kinds of matters. The Liebenzeller missionaries belonged to an extreme sect whose members believe in the literal truth of the Bible. To his credit, however, Herr Jensen, once he realised that I did not share these convictions, made no attempt to win me over. Yet it remains a mystery to me how Dr E. Witt, the mission's medical officer, a man with a first-rate medical education — to whom I also owe a debt of gratitude — could believe that the laws of nature have a cause which is to be found outside the natural world itself. Yet evening after evening, when the distant clouds, piled up in the shapes of mountains and dragons — always different, yet always the same — had been replaced by a stain of sombre red spreading across the western sky, almost anyone might have felt inclined to see the sunset as a sign from heaven: a symbol of the decisive battle then being fought on the fields of France.

Otherwise there was not much news from the rest of the country. The general commanding the southern troops in Wugang had mustered the bandits from the west and southwest to fight against the northern army. In mid-June two thousand of them arrived with their women; they were given uniforms and after some delay sent off to attack Shaoyang. While in Wugang they behaved much better than the soldiers, especially the northerners. In the meantime the northern forces had occupied Xinhua and the road leading from it to Shaoyang. They even established a small garrison in Xikuangshan, but all remained quiet there, though their troops played havoc in Shaoyang and Xinhua. The only flag that they respected was the German — ostensibly their enemy's. The very morning after entering Shaoyang they posted a sentry outside the German mission, though their soldiers climbed over the walls of the British mission and shouted insults at the missionary, and the guard sent that afternoon to protect him — at the request of the Germans — absconded almost immediately. Herr Paul, sailing along the Zi Jiang river to fetch long awaited supplies for the mission, was advised by northerners and southerners alike to hoist the German flag on his boats — although it had long ago been officially forbidden — so that he would then be allowed to pass in safety. While on a journey Tolkmitt heard some soldiers grumbling about him: "Why doesn't he go back and join the Army?" they said, evidently thinking he was an Englishman. They went on complaining until his servant explained that he was actually a German. And the most telling fact of all was that Allied nationals were unable to travel at all; they required passports, but owing to the unsafe conditions existing in the province none were being issued.

One day a gang of twenty bandits appeared at Lanxinguan on the southern side of Yun Shan. Ten of them were slaughtered on the spot and the others scattered. Four of them fled on to the mountain, throwing away their rifles as they ran, and took the road down to Wugang. However, the people there were ready for them, and only one turned back and got away. On 14th August a further thousand bandits from the west arrived in Wugang, the general having lured them there. Once they were inside the town he ordered his soldiers to surround them and told them they were too unreliable to be of any use to him. After brief parleyings he had their rifles confiscated, gave them each a dollar and let them depart in peace.

On 20th August I left Yun Shan, travelling eastwards down a long, gently sloping valley and reaching Wugang that evening via the Xinning road. The whole valley was filled with tall bush meadowland; only along the stream were there any surviving shrubs, conspicuous among them being the large white panicles of *Hydrangea paniculata*. I found a bog moss (*Sphagnum palustre*) — the first I had seen for a long time. Near the lower end of the valley there were some little woods on the slopes, consisting of pure stands of *Cunninghamia* trees. Splashing down a rock face was a waterfall, and despite its deforested state the valley was not entirely without scenic attraction.

Chapter 41. Back to Changsha via Xikuangshan

Montane woods — cypress groves — granite mountains — Liuduzhai — ruin of my tropical helmet — subtropical flora near Lengshuijiang — Mount Dongtai Shan near Xiangxiang.

I spent a day in Wugang, where I had my pony shod, though I soon found that the farrier had driven the nails into the quick. The general commanding the southern forces having furnished me — in total contravention of the decrees issued by Beijing — with a large and imposing passport, I took the road to the north, partly because it led through country I had not seen before, but chiefly because northern soldiers were now stationed along the route to Wugang which I had used in the spring. On reaching Gaosha Si the road turned north-eastwards, continuing via Xixiajiangpu and Huangbaiqiao through hilly country similar to that surrounding Shaoyang. Here too the hills consisted mainly of limestone, the strata undulating but in the main sloping upwards towards the west, though along the first part of the route some of the beds were tilted vertically, parallel to the mountain range which ran along the left side of the broad valley leading northwards from Wugang; this range probably outcrops beneath it like Yun Shan.

Further to the north were several chains of mountains running in roughly the same direction as this range, and emerging from them were the three rivers which flowed past the villages or towns just mentioned. The hills were clothed with splendid forests of oaks, pines, *Cunninghamia*, sweet chestnuts, *Platycarya* and *Celtis*, among which were the crowns of *Koelreuteria integrifoliola* covered with countless yellow blossoms. From Huangbaiqiao, which lay at an altitude 60 m below Wugang, the road climbed northwards over a little saddle (395 m) and then down along a lateral valley. *Cupressus funebris*, often growing in pure stands, formed extensive woods along the crest bordering the eastern side of the valley. Grey-green as if powdered with dust, of pyramidal outline, its close-set twigs hanging down like veils from the spreading branches, even growing in woods as it did here, the funeral cypress creates an impression of gloom and mourning.

On our left the Shaoyang basin was bounded by Haidong Shan, a rounded, almost treeless mountain of igneous rock rising to an altitude of about 1100 m from beneath the limestone, which extended for some distance up its lower slopes. Below Zhangpuzi, at an altitude of some 300 m, we came to the river Longhui, which flows into the Zi Jiang at Taohuaping. Some way upstream we found lodging for the night in a fair sized town called Liuduzhai (Laodao in the local dialect). The mountains to the northeast sloped right down to the river, formed here by the confluence of two streams. One stream came down a narrow gorge from the northwest of Lunghui, beyond which we could see a range of high mountains, and the other, which I followed, also flowed through a ravine from the north-northeast, rising in the Wangyun Shan, a mountain dome apparently over 1300 m high. The rock at this point was slate; further on it was granite, and the funeral cypresses — confined to limestone — were once more replaced by *Cunninghamia*. In the broad basin of Niaoshuxia the southern forces had set up another checkpoint, but

thanks to my passport I was able to pass without hindrance. To the southeast of Wangyun Shan we crossed a saddle named Mawang'ao at 500 m and descended into territory drained by the river which runs through Qukoupu; the route continued east-southeastwards across its northern tributaries. At the first of the streams I sought lodgings for the night in Daqiao Si[189]. The ridges were again formed of sandstone with seams of coal. After descending through a ravine filled with bamboo I reached the road at a point not far from Longqiaopu. This was the road which I had used for my outward journey, and I now followed it as far as Xikuangshan. A violent storm followed by steady rain brought ruin to my splendid new tropical helmet, a local product made for me in Wugang just before I left. It was covered with white silk, to which it owed its smart appearance, but its paper shell disintegrated into a semiliquid mass stinking vilely of paste, and the colours from the lettering — black, red and blue — seeped through to the exterior.

I stayed in Xikuangshan from 28th August to 8th October, in accommodation provided by Tolkmitt. There was still plenty to be collected, most notably on a two day trip to Lengshuijiang. The flora there was of subtropical type, whereas Xikuangshan was just within the warm temperate zone. Its bush steppe, which had just reached the highest point of its development, represented an intermediate stage between the bush meadows of this zone and the subtropical grass steppe. It was much less green than the bush meadows, but contained far larger numbers of woody plants than the grass steppe and also had a great variety of herbaceous perennials not found there. The silver panicles of the tall grasses (*Miscanthus japonicus*) were extremely conspicuous; this grass was presumably a survivor from the time, barely more than ten years earlier, when Xikuangshan was still surrounded by forests and the soil was hence moister than it was now. On the return journey I resumed the route survey — a task which I had not ventured to undertake in the spring. I measured a baseline and triangulated the terrain with the aid of two plumb lines, as I had left the theodolite behind for safety. Meanwhile the flowering season was drawing to a close, and the plans hatched by the British to send us to Australia, though they leaked out in the summer, had now been finally abandoned. The authorities in Changsha remained in ignorance of my travels and did not bother to enquire into the activities of German nationals. As everything remained quiet, on 9th October I set out on the return journey.

As far as Loudi I followed the same route as on the outward journey, but there I branched off towards Xiangxiang, intending to visit a well known temple forest and to compare it with the similarly situated Yuelu Shan. Soon after the route forked the main road left the limestone ranges and continued henceforth through sandstone terrain, cutting off the

---

[189] "Si" is a Buddhist temple (SGH).

windings of the river Lian Shui though following its general direction. On the morning of 12th October, accompanied by the missionary R. Seeliger, I visited Dongtai Shan, a mountain 300 m in altitude. Its plant cover proved to be entirely as I had expected. From there I wanted to go straight on to Changsha, bypassing Xiangtan so as to avoid any encounter with Allied nationals. That afternoon I travelled twenty li as far as the village of Yama'ao with the object of shortening the next two days' journeys. I told the porters my plans and soon after they had departed I rode off, taking the road which I had instructed them to follow. I expected to overtake them before I had gone very far, but soon after the route branched off from the main road to Xiangtan I learnt that they had not passed along it. Had they perhaps taken a shortcut to the village? I therefore went on to Yama'ao, stopping from time to time to ask the way. I reached the village as dusk was coming on, but there was no sign of the porters. However, I heard from a man who had come from Xiangtan that he had met them on the road leading there. As I did not want to spend the night without my camp bed in some louse-ridden shack, I turned round and rode back to Xiangxiang, arriving at Herr Seeliger's house very late that night. Among the day's booty was a small poisonous snake with black and white rings (*Bungarus multicinctus*) which had been wandering about the ground beside my horse's hoofs. My plan was to send a man that night to catch up the porters, to tell them to wait for me and to report to me where he found them. However, as the missionary thought they had enough common-sense not to give the game away and in any case he could not find a messenger I had to give up that plan.

Next morning I set out at first light and after riding for nine hours with hardly a halt I at last caught up with them at 2 pm outside the walls of Xiangtan, just in time to prevent them from entering the town, which I was anxious to avoid for fear of trouble with the authorities. As was natural in the circumstances I had no kind words to spare for them, yet those disdainful Hunan coolies pretended to be deeply hurt by an insult which I hurled at them; the word was "goupi" [190], which means the rear end of a dog and also that which comes forth from it. It was 3 pm before I finally stopped for lunch, and by then the ponies were feeling the effects of the long ride, mainly on paved roads, though the surfaces were in good condition. Ten li further on I stopped for the night, and rode on to Changsha the following day. There I enjoyed pleasant accommodation with a view over the river and Yuelu Shan. It cost me nothing, and I am deeply grateful to Herr L. Alff for making it available and for allowing me to take my meals in his household. News of the capitulation of Bulgaria [191] had already reached me while I was at Xikuangshan. Soon after my arrival in Changsha came the collapse of Austria, swiftly followed by the surrender of Germany. What these events forebode for us in China was something which no one could foretell.

---

[190] Literally "dog-fart" — generally used in the way Americans use "bull-shit", to imply that words spoken are lies or waffle (SGH).

[191] The Bulgarians signed an armistice on 29th September 1918, the Austrians on 4th November and the Germans on 11th November.

Chapter 42. Repatriated

Surveillance by the Chinese authorities — safeguarding my collections — departure — unpleasantness in Hankou — river and sea voyages — the British escort — boils — first news of the peace terms — via Wesel and Munich to Tyrol and Vienna — my collections restored at last — further work by my collector and his disappearance

Christmas had come before the authorities began to bother their heads about us. In response to orders from Beijing, we were then required to register our names and have our photographs sent there. Although the newspapers reported that China now wished to ship all enemy aliens back to their own countries, none of us believed these stories, especially as the government had hitherto put up valiant resistance to any such proposal from the Allies. Unhappily, our trust soon proved to have been misplaced. The belief, previously shared by all the Chinese, that we were going to win the war, and the fear that they would then be called to account for their actions, were the main reasons why the Chinese government had refrained from imposing sterner restrictions on our lives. Now, however, they outdid all the shabby tricks which they had played on us during the war itself. Only a government as venal as the Chinese would — for a payment of half a million dollars — have acceded to such unreasonable demands on the part of the Allies, despite the objections raised by large sections of the Chinese population, notably the business community, and despite the fact that the armistice had been signed. Strict control of all business premises was imposed at the beginning of February 1919, and their owners were forbidden to take out or bring in goods of any description. On the very first evening after the new regulations had come into force, as I was going home after dinner, a policeman stopped me and wanted to search my jacket pockets. He actually took hold of my raincoat to detain me, and I had to exert some force to free myself, though I remained calm. However, our complaints proved effective and we were spared any personal molestation; we did not even have to report regularly to the authorities, though such a measure was enforced in other parts of China.

We received word that 26th February had been fixed as the day of our departure, but the dujun found ways of prolonging our stay, much to the annoyance of those like myself who wanted to get home without further delay. We were allowed only 350 lb of personal baggage, and I therefore gave up any idea of taking my collections with me, especially as they would have been subject to repeated searches at every frontier crossing, and made arrangements for them to be stored in safety until they could be forwarded to Europe. At first we were told that we would be permitted to sell all our movable property, but this concession was then altered to cover household goods only; everything else was to be requisitioned. As I felt that it would be impossible to instil into the official mind any understanding of the nature and importance of my collections I decided to deceive the authorities into thinking that I was selling them. This was not easy, as the dujun himself wished to purchase them, saying that he would present them to the provincial agricultural college. Then he said that he simply wanted to take them into a place of safety, and finally claimed that they were not really household goods at all. However, I outwitted him by pretending that the sale was a *fait accompli*, having been transacted in accordance with the ill-translated terms of the original decree. In fact I conveyed them to the Catholic mission and left them in the custody of the procurator, Pater Prandi, an Italian who had been the landlord of several of my compatriots and who was a helpful and trustworthy man. The officials of the aliens control commission, who were presumably well aware of my ruse but realised that my collections were really of no interest or value to them, remarked to our Chinese servants that I was a crafty fellow and that I was probably plotting, even now, to decamp and slip away to Yunnan once more. Despite this suspicion no one placed any restrictions on my freedom and I was allowed to continue my rides in the country right up to the end. Indeed, the officials behaved very decently, evidently on the instructions of the dujun Chang Qinyao, who was known to be a good friend of the German community. As none of us knew what we would be permitted to take in the way of written or printed matter, and as the shorthand extracts from my diaries did not fit into any of the categories listed in the regulations, I consigned all my papers to the care of the Dutch consul general, so that even if the worst came to the worst they would be safe. However, this had one serious disadvantage: without my botanical specimens and my notes the enforced delay was a sadly unproductive time, and my gloom was deepened by the miserably wet weather which persisted throughout the winter and made trips into the country almost impossible; nevertheless, the security of my collections had to be the paramount consideration.

As the end of the peace negotiations now seemed to be in sight I gave up any thought of further travels and sold my splendid stallion, which had carried me for three years, to a compatriot who had been exempted from repatriation. However, in response to violent objections from the British consul he was expelled one night at the very last moment, together with his wife and three young children. Too distressed to utter a word, he left the pony in the care of his mafu, who probably let it starve. Of all the partings which I endured in China hardly any was more sorrowful than this. I sold the mare to a Chinese, who gave me quite a good price for her. Because of the first slump in the exchange rate at home, all the extra dollars which I scraped together by selling my possessions — among which was my long forbidden Browning pistol — built up into a nice little capital sum. I also took back with me the unspent half of the last remittance from the Academy of Sciences in Vienna; when changed back into Austrian crowns it yielded roughly double the amount of the entire original payment.

Our personal liberty remained unrestricted up to the end; on the afternoon before our departure — for lack of other occupation and knowing that it would be my very last outing — I borrowed Wieczorek's pony and despite the bad weather went for a long ride into the country. As the Liebenzeller mission at Wugang had been exempted from repatriation, although they had at times suffered much annoyance from the authorities, I took the opportunity of sending my factotum Wang Dehui there, having arranged for him to travel in the company of Sister Gramenz, who had just recovered from a grave illness and was now returning to the mission. The purpose of his trip was to spend six weeks collecting the spring flora of Yun Shan. He carried out his task successfully, but was unable to continue to the very end; while he was in the temple robbers stole some of his clothing and soldiers took his blankets.

During the last few days the supervisory authorities became somewhat neglectful; they were reluctant to bother with any matters which might make work for them. We were then told that we had to be at the railway station after lunch on 25th March and that we should arrive at Wuchang [192] on the following afternoon.

"What are you going to provide for us on the journey?" we asked the officials.

"Tea!" was their answer.

"Yes, and what to eat?"

"Cakes!"

"Really? Do you think we're going to put up with that?"

Just at that moment a Chinese hotel keeper happened to come past and, pushing the officials aside, we arranged with him to have our evening meal served in a dining car specially coupled on to the train. No one who knows the German community in China will be surprised to hear that it was a wild and convivial evening, and that the official interpreter — a good natured fellow — imbibed his share of liquid refreshment. Throughout the entire journey we took good care that the whole of the daily allowance of $3 a head which the government provided for our board went into our stomachs, and that not a cent was diverted into the pockets of the officials. Dr Hume, the American physician, boldly came to the station to see us off and wished us all a hearty "Auf Wiedersehen, really!" In particular he came to bid farewell to Herr Wollheim and his family, for whose exemption he had pleaded energetically but in vain against the wiles of the British consul, who was in a position to blackmail the dujun by threatening to reveal his involvement in opium and smuggling rackets.

At 10 o'clock that night, in pouring rain, the train steamed out of the station, carrying a party of soldiers to guard our baggage. Among the officials who accompanied us there were some pleasant young men, in particular two of the officers, but their chief was an elderly bureaucrat, dull and sluggish, who installed himself in a first class compartment with his cronies and his provision hampers and stayed there. As day broke we were approaching Yueyang. The flood plain of the Dongting lake was now a rich green meadow, probably consisting for the most part of *Carex* species kept short by mowing. Further on there were extensive tea plantations, some of them between fields of *Vicia faba.* The vegetation appeared to be the same as that around Changsha. To the right of the railway were some chains of hills of moderate elevation, but then the country became flatter and flatter and at 4 o'clock that afternoon we reached a grimy little station on the outskirts of Wuchang. The baggage was unloaded and taken to the steamship landing place. The officials waited at the station for the billeting officers, who had gone ahead, and we waited patiently beside them until it began to grow dark. Then we began to worry about our baggage, imagining that it was lying out in the pouring rain, and realised that unless we did something to expedite matters it would be midnight before we moved into our accommodation. We told the official in charge that we wanted to go at once.

"Not yet!" was his reply.

Then one of us started getting ready to leave the railway station.

"You must not leave!" cried the elderly Chinese official, and a soldier seized our compatriot by the elbow. He tore himself loose and struck out with his cumbersome Chinese umbrella, open as it was, against the soldiers, who responded by drawing their sabres halfway from their scabbards with a clatter, and loosening their Mauser pistols in their holsters. It was clear that one man alone could do nothing effective and that we must all act together. We therefore got back into the railway carriage, dragged out the elderly bureaucrat and the rest of the officials — or at least persuaded them to get out — and all set off together from the station. In the meantime the billeting officers arrived, and before long the steamship took us to Hankou, where we were accommodated in a Chinese hotel. Though cold and draughty, it was comparatively clean. The old bureaucrat took his revenge by telling the authorities in Hankou and the officials from the German consulate that we were highly dangerous people and that we all wanted to abscond, with the result that we were not allowed to step outside the hotel during the two and a half days we stayed there. This led to certain minor incidents, for we were accustomed to rebuff any Chinese who attempted to touch us. One particular scuffle was provoked by a Chinese soldier who stopped a Chinese nursery-maid while she was taking the children in her charge to visit some acquaintances, and gave her a prod in the back. The officer presented himself and requested us most humbly and earnestly not in any circumstances to strike his soldiers.

"Certainly we shan't," was our reply, "but when someone lays hands on a German citizen he is not prepared to tolerate any assault, be it minor or major. Surely you understand that?"

"Yes", he replied, "quite right. None of the soldiers will touch any of you again."

---

[192] One of the cities of the conurbation of Wuhan on the Yangzi River in Hubei. The others are Hankou and Hanyang (SGH).

On 29th March, a fine sunny day, we boarded a splendid river steamer, the "*Jiangyong*". We were allotted the best cabins, for even the Germans from Hankou had refused to travel otherwise than first class European; for some of them it was probably their first and only experience of first class travel — and free into the bargain. In Shanghai we were housed in the Nantou camp, and we were allowed exit permits for the whole of the following day. Through the kindness of the Netherlands consul general I met the French consul general, H. Wilden; he had formerly been in Kunming and was acquainted with my scientific work. It was he who had recommended the American zoological expedition to call on me for advice, and in return for the help I had given them he now promised that the French authorities would do what they could to safeguard my collections.

On the morning of 3rd April we embarked on a British freighter, the "*Antilochus*". This was the last stroke of good fortune which I experienced during my travels in China, for the "*Antilochus*" was a far better ship than the steamers previously employed as transports, the "*Nora*", "*Novara*" and "*Atreus*". The conditions prevailing on the "*Atreus*" — used for bachelor accommodation —were scandalous: miserable rations without any bread, temperatures of up to 43°C in the berths, no baths, extreme shortage of water, no room for exercise on deck, and other indescribable hardships which resulted in the deaths of seven of the men who were shipped home on her. Since that time various newspapers — not only neutral but even American and Japanese — had voiced such strong criticism of Fraser, the British consul general — he had even forbidden German doctors to join the ship — that everything possible had been done to improve conditions on board the "*Antilochus*". Nevertheless, the accommodation was bad: deep down in the hold, devoid of any portholes and quite impossible to ventilate. However, the baths were good and the food was adequate, though the Chinese "comprador" tried to make money out of the provisions supplied to him — by baking cakes and similar dainties and selling them for his personal profit — until we brought him to heel by staging a "cake strike". The British escort party, who posted only four guards in all, behaved irreproachably, and the three hundred soldiers who joined the ship in Hong Kong to return to Plymouth did not make themselves objectionable, though their officers did occasionally utter offensive remarks. I had planned to fish for plankton during the voyage and through the kind intervention of Dr Blumenstock, a German doctor from Shanghai who sailed as the ship's medical officer, obtained permission from the captain to do so, but unfortunately my five-year-old net fell to pieces on the very first cast and I had to give up the attempt.

The voyage was the most agreeable which any of the ship's officers had experienced during the past thirteen years. The 9000 ton ship steamed smoothly at speeds of up to 14 knots, touching only at Hong Kong, Singapore, Colombo, Suez, Port Said, Gibraltar and Plymouth. In the Red Sea I had my last two attacks of malaria, one of them extremely severe, but

a course of quinine and a stay in the well ventilated sickbay which had been erected on the deck rid me of it for good. I was also troubled by recurrent boils, first occurring in November and numbering about forty in all. With his limited resources, the ship's doctor was unable to treat them effectively. When I got home it became apparent that they were due to scabies, and a course of autovaccination cured me completely. The voyage was not without scientific interest. Dr O. Israel and Dr H. Weigold, members of the Stötzner expedition to Sichuan [193], joined the ship in Hong Kong. Weigold, who had formerly been a teacher in the German-Chinese secondary school in Guangzhou, was able to tell us all about the marine creatures which we saw, including sea snakes (two species) off Singapore, flying fish, dolphins (both common and bottle-nosed), whales and in particular the birds, ornithology being his speciality. Some of the Germans who had been in Kunming, among them Stiebritz and his family, also joined us in Hong Kong. They had travelled there via Tonkin, where the French had treated them with unexpected kindness. We had all thought that once the armistice had been signed we should soon be home, and the worry caused by not knowing what we would find when we got there was made worse by the reports printed in the few scraps of newspaper which we got hold of in the ports where the ship touched. In Plymouth a socialist newspaper was smuggled on board for us; it assumed that the peace conditions were already known to its readers, but we were able to deduce them, though only incompletely, from the hostile comments which it made on them. So this was how "peace with law and justice" would look. Compared with such a contemptuous dismissal of the fair and reasonable aspirations of democratic Germans towards justice and freedom, our hated militarism seemed nothing more than a children's game. This, then, was how President Wilson, the world's worst swindler, had trapped us into accepting his fourteen points, and had then proceeded to twist them into something completely different. Filled with rage and foreboding, we steamed through the Channel; we had to wear life jackets and the helmsman steered clear of all floating objects including one which, so we were told, really was a mine. On 16th May, in the morning, we disembarked at Rotterdam, and found that everything was even worse than the impression given by that paper in Plymouth. Was it really necessary for our deluded neighbours to pander to the revengeful urges of a

---

[193] Walter Stötzner led an expedition to Western China and Tibet in 1914. He was accompanied by H. Weigold, founder of the bird observation station on Heligoland, Otto Israel, Professor of Geodesy in Dresden, E. Funcke, entomologist, and W. Limpricht, botanist. They explored the mountains north of Kangding [Tatsienlu] from 101° to 104° 30' and 30° to 31° 40', in an area about 300km by 200km. The outbreak of war brought the expedition to a premature end. Stötzner managed to get home to Germany via the USA in 1917, but the others were interned . Stötzner, Walter, *Ins Unerforschte Tibet, Tagebuch der Deutschen Expedition Stötzner 1914*, Leipzig, 1924, pp.316 with numerous photos and three maps. W. Limpricht reported his botanical work in his book *Botanische Reisen in den Hochbergen Chinas und Ost Tibets*, Feddes Repertorium, XII,1922.

hundred million people, instead of leading mankind towards peace?

The friendly welcome which we received from the Dutch and from the Germans resident in Rotterdam, and the enthusiastic reception which awaited us at the German frontier and at Wesel, our dispersal camp, where we arrived late in the evening of the same day, did little to relieve our bitter disappointment. We stayed there for three days waiting for our baggage; when it finally arrived we had to unload and reload it ourselves. Weigold and I spent the days most enjoyably in exploring the moorlands, which I had never seen, under the guidance of the local pharmacist E. Gansloser and his wife, who entertained us most sumptuously. Our native countryside, seen for the first time after five years' absence in China, left some vivid impressions, notably the keen air, the uniform pale green of the beech woods newly in leaf, and the sombre grey of our sparsely branched short-needled pines. Together with the other Austrians of our party and seven Turks, I travelled by local trains to Munich, where we separated. A further week passed before I found out where my mother was living and obtained an entry permit for Tyrol. Through the kindness of my colleagues in the Nymphenburg botanical gardens I was enabled to look through the five wartime volumes of the *Osterreichische Botanische Zeitschrift.* Devouring their contents like a starving man, I was to some extent consoled to find that life in the world of science was still going on.

On 30th May I at last left Munich. Next morning, as the train bore me along the Inn valley, its well remembered mountains now struck me as absurdly small: they looked as if their lower halves were missing. At 10.30 am I reached Maierhofen in the Zillertal, where I was reunited with my mother. She, dear soul, had endured five years of worry and anxiety, though of course, had I remained in Europe, she would probably have lost me for ever. Out of tender consideration for my feelings — perhaps too tender when dealing with a matter-of-fact scientist — she had withheld news of her failing health. Her heart, undermined by the happenings of those terrible years, had more than once been on the brink of fading into nothingness, but her constitution, steeled by her love of Nature — a love which she had passed on to me — had rallied again and again, though the mortal husk which remained was a wreck seemingly twenty years older than her actual age. Yet it was a great joy to see her once more; during my stay in Changsha there had been a gap of eight months without news from her, and I had begun to fear the worst. Then after a short stay in Linz I reached Vienna on 5th June.

On the stroke of midnight, just as Whit Sunday was ending, I opened the door of my apartment. On

emerging next morning, my steps turned first to the centre and focus of my scientific life, the Botanical Institute. Life in the city was not as bad as the foreign newspapers had made out, and it was a relief to find that the streets were free from spiked helmets, gaudy uniforms and rattling sabres. Though living conditions were still miserably cheerless, I soon adapted myself to the new ways of existence and was glad to find that the ordinary people of Vienna were just the same as they had always been. Likewise little changed were my colleagues and my chief, Professor Wettstein. He had fought my cause with unflagging tenacity during my absence, and his delight on seeing me safe and sound was expressed in a welcome of more than ordinary warmth and cordiality. I also owe it to him that I was able to make good use of that unhappy postwar time.

The Chinese, however, had now begun to realise who had tried to trick them and who had dealt honestly with them. In October 1919 the government in Beijing accordingly declared that personal property belonging to German and Austrian citizens was to be restored to its owners. The British promptly returned those of my crates which they had found and seized on an Austrian ship when war broke out, but General Tang Rirao, the governor of Yunnan, had other ideas. Besides smuggling opium and printing counterfeit banknotes, he hoped to make money out of my plants. Thus began a period of dreadful anxiety and uncertainty, a mental torment far worse than any of the minor troubles which I had endured during my years in China. Many of the plants which I had found had in the meantime been collected by Forrest, who had subsequently traversed some of the routes which I had travelled, and as his material was shipped to Britain without delay its publication gained priority over my discoveries. Despite the pleas of the Netherlands Legation and the vigorous efforts of the Norwegian missionary Amundsen [194], the Yunnan government hung on to my collections until May 1921, and refused to surrender them until the German consul in Hankou, Dr Bracklo, intervened. Herr R. Schnabel advanced the shipping charges and Dr J. Stonborough defrayed the costs of conveyance from Trieste to Vienna, but when they finally reached me on 5th April 1922 it was too late for my mother to share my rejoicing. The letter which I wrote to the governor was not one which he would have wished to frame and hang on the wall; indeed I doubt whether any of his staff would have dared to translate it to him in full.

[194] Amundsen had returned to Kunming in 1919 in the service of the Norwegian Mission Society and had been appointed German consul, a post which he held from 1919 to 1924.

Through the good offices of my friends in Changsha my plant collector Wang Dehui was able to spend the summer of 1920 in Pingxiang in the west of the province of Jiangxi ("Kiangsi"), from which he brought back an excellent though not very large collection. In 1921 he resumed his activities in the border zone between Jiangxi and Fujian, where he worked under the aegis of Pastor A.Seipel in Ningdu, and again achieved highly satisfactory results — until he met his death on Mount Xunfeng Shan near Nanfeng, presumably killed by a tiger. Enclosed with his last consignment of plants was the following poem:

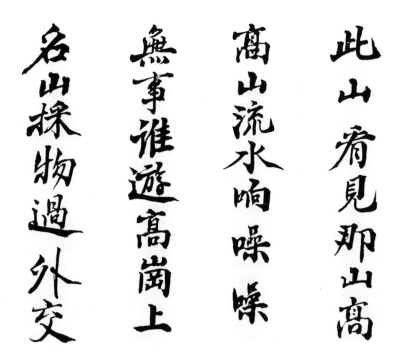

Dsi schan kan dien na schan gao
Gao schan liu schui hsi yang tsao
Wo schi wei yu gao gang schang
Ming schan tsai wu gwo wai djiao.

From the highest mountain peak
Rivulets run murmuring towards the valley
On the crest I gather for a distant country
The flowers that Nature brings forth

BIOGRAPHICAL NOTES

Camillo Karl Schneider 1876 - 1951

Camillo Schneider was born on 7th April 1876 on an estate at Gröppendorf in Saxony, where his father was a tenant farmer. After attending the village school at Glossen he received his secondary education at Zeitz in Thuringia. He wanted to study science at university, but because of his father's bankruptcy he had to leave school early. He worked as a gardener's boy at Zeitz from 1892-94, and was then employed for two years at a horticultural college in Dresden and later as a gardener in the botanical gardens in Berlin and Greifswald. After this, while working in the City Parks Department in Berlin, he became involved in editorial work for the well known periodical *Gartenwelt*. This led to engagements as assistant to several garden architects in Darmstadt and Berlin. In 1900 he moved to Vienna, now as a freelance garden architect and horticultural writer, and attended Wettstein's lectures at the University Botanical Institute. He travelled widely, visiting Italy, Switzerland, France and England in 1904, Bulgaria, Serbia and Bosnia in 1905 and the Caucasus in 1908. In 1904 he published his first books, including the commencement of his *Illustrated Handbook of Broad-leaved Trees*, a work of 2016 pages issued in parts from 1904 to 1912. The next year saw the appearance of his preliminary studies for a monograph on the genus *Berberis*. This was to have been his *magnum opus*, but in March 1943 the manuscript, together with hundreds of drawings and photographs, was lost when the Botanical Museum in Berlin was destroyed in an air raid.

During his years in Vienna Schneider joined the Austro-Hungarian Dendrological Society and became its general secretary. The society's president, Count Silva Tarouca, set aside three hundred hectares of his estate at Pruhonitz near Prague for the society's use and under the direction of Franz Zeman this became a famous park where rare trees, shrubs and herbaceous plants were grown and propagated. The experience gained at Pruhonitz was put to good use in his work as a landscape architect and garden planner. Between 1910 and 1913 he wrote a series of illustrated books on garden plants, the first entitled *Unsere Freiland-Stauden (Our Hardy Perennials)*; this was followed by similar works on broad-leaved trees and on conifers. In his capacity as secretary of the Dendrological Society he published six issues of *Die Gartenanlagen Österreich-Ungarns (The Parks and Gardens of Austria-Hungary)*, in which he made full use of his skills as a photographer.

In 1913, at the instigation of the Dendrological Society, he travelled to China to collect plants and seeds for the garden at Pruhonitz. He was accompanied by Heinrich Handel-Mazzetti, whose interests were directed towards botanical taxonomy and plant geography rather than horticulture. In the foreword to the third edition of his *Unsere Freilandstauden* (1922) Schneider says that part of the material that he collected in China in 1914 — several hundred seed samples and some three hundred photographs — was lost. Furthermore, the seeds which he sent from China, or later from the USA via Norway to Germany and Austria-Hungary, did not all receive proper care owing to the disruption of garden work caused by the war. However, the herbarium material arrived intact and duplicates were supplied to botanical institutes in Germany and Switzerland. In 1920 the Dendrological Society was dissolved and the garden at Pruhonitz was converted into a commercial nursery. This enabled much of the stock to be preserved, including the plants raised from seed of Chinese origin. Some survived in other commercial nurseries, such as Arends, Späth and Sundermann, and in 1925 there were still numerous species of *Berberis* and *Cotoneaster* raised from his seed in the garden at Pruhonitz.

In 1915 Schneider left Yunnan and travelled via Shanghai to Boston where he was offered a post in the Arnold Arboretum. He worked there with Sargent, Rehder and Wilson from April 1915 to September 1919, identifying the plants that Wilson had collected in China and writing parts of *Plantae Wilsonianae* together with papers on *Salix*. He also wrote articles on his stay in China. Though they do not add much to Handel-Mazzetti's account of their travels in 1914, Schneider's photograph gives a vivid impression of their camp below Yulong Shan (*Westermanns Monatshefte*, 1915, **119**, 861).

In October 1919 he returned to Vienna via Norway, though to raise money for the fare he had to sell most of the herbarium specimens he had collected in China. In 1921 he moved to Berlin, where he worked on the periodical *Gartenschönheit* which Oskar Kühl and Karl Förster had just started. It was the best publication of its kind in German, and continued until 1942. After its demise he worked on its successor *Gartenbau im Reich*. His work at Pruhonitz had gained him an international reputation and he continued to work as a landscape architect, laying out and remodelling gardens and parks in Austria, Hungary, Czechoslovakia and Germany until 1944. He also served as adviser on landscaping to the German autobahn authorities. He visited Pruhonitz every year until the death of Count Silva Tarouca, his last visit being in 1944. The end of the war left him in straitened circumstances and he had to go on working almost to the end of his life, his last book *Hecken im Garten (Hedges in the Garden)* appearing in 1950. He died of a stroke in Berlin on 5th January 1951.

Stearn,W.T. Gard. Chron. 1951, **129**, 32.

Kriechbaum. *Garten-Zeitschrift Illustrierte Flora* 1951, **74**, 27-29 (with portrait and partial bibliography).

Edward Amundsen   1873 - 1928

Edward Amundsen, a Norwegian missionary and explorer, was born on the island of Kirkholmen near the town of Kragerø on 27 January 1873. At the age of twenty, having graduated at the Norwegian Missionary Society's College in Oslo, he went to England for further training and in 1894 joined the Tibetan Pioneer Mission led by Annie Taylor, who planned to enter Tibet via Sikkim. He spent two years in Sikkim, occupying his time in the study of Tibetan. He became so fluent in Lhasa Tibetan that he was subsequently invited to translate booklets into that dialect. During his stay in Sikkim he made several journeys into Tibet, once coming within eight days' travel of Lhasa.

Because he found the British authorities obstructive, he and another Norwegian missionary moved to a new base in Western China from which to continue their work in Tibet. Travelling in Chinese dress, he reached Tatsienlu (now Kangding). In the winter of 1898-99 he made the journey for which he is best known, into the Tibetan province of Kham. He visited the independent "kingdoms" of Chagla and Mili, and was probably the first white man to see the latter. He also saw the great bend of the Yangtze north of Lijiang. He reported his journey in the Geographical Journal and became a Fellow of the Royal Geographical Society in 1909.

In 1899 he married Petrea Naess, but because of the Boxer rebellion he was obliged to leave China in 1900. He went back to Sikkim, continued his Tibetan studies, and wrote a Primer of Standard Tibetan. In 1903 he became a superintendent in the British and Foreign Bible Society and was sent to Western China. He was based in Yunnanfu (now Kunming), the capital of Yunnan, with responsibility for missionary work in Yunnan and Eastern Tibet. He travelled widely and served as correspondent for the North China Daily News and Herald.

He came home on leave in 1910, but soon after returning to China he was obliged to leave Yunnan because of the rebellion. After a long spell of sick leave he went back to Yunnanfu at the end of 1913.

In the summer of 1915 trouble arose between Amundsen and Herbert Goffe, the British consul in Yunnanfu. Goffe complained to the Bible Society that he made no attempt to conceal his anti-British and pro-German sympathies, that he frequently flew the Norwegian flag from the Society's premises, and that he had imported stores in his own name for the German consul. Goffe alleged that Amundsen's actions were most prejudicial to British interests and were detrimental to the Bible Society's prestige. After the Society's secretary had read an article from the Hankow Daily News under the headline "An English-Norwegian Flag Story. Bible Society's Representative Must Resign His Position", the committee decided to recall Amundsen and ordered him to return to London at once.

After an interview at which he accepted six months' salary in lieu of notice, he returned to Norway where he bought a substantial property named Orebukta on an island not far from Kirkholmen — clear evidence that he was not a poor man. However, he sold the property in 1917 and went back to Yunnanfu in 1919, this time in the service of the Norwegian Mission Society, and he held the post of German consul there until 1924. He then returned to Norway and settled in Larvik, where he died on 21 November 1928.

Køhler, Kai Arvid. *Edward Amundsen - en norsk misjonaer, sprakforsker og oppdagelsesreisende (1873 - 1928).*
Telemark Historie. Tidsskrift for Telemark Historielag, 1985, Nr. 6.
Amundsen, Edward. *A Journey Through South-West Sechuen.* Geographical Journal, 1900, **25**, 620-625 and **26**, 531-537.
Bible Society, London. *Extract from the minutes of the committee,* 4 November 1915.

Roy Chapman Andrews 1884 - 1960

Born at Beloit, Wisconsin, in 1884, Andrews owned his first gun at the age of nine and became a skilled taxidermist before he left school. He graduated in science at Beloit College in 1906 and got a job at the American Museum of Natural History,

New York, at first doing menial tasks such as washing floors and mixing clay. Despite this unpromising start, his progress as a naturalist was swift. He went on whaling voyages as the Museum's representative, rediscovered the Californian grey whale, then believed to be extinct, and in 1913 gained his master's degree from Columbia University for a thesis on the grey whale.

In 1916 he travelled to China to study mammals, accompanied by his wife Yvette as photographer and Edmund Heller as collector. In 1919 he went to northern China and in 1921 to Central Asia, where the expedition found the first dinosaur eggs ever discovered.

More of an explorer and publicist than a research worker or scholar, in 1942 he was "bumped" from his post as director of the museum and spent the rest of his life until his death in 1960 writing popular books and articles.

Current Biography 1953

Andrews, Roy Chapman and Yvette Borup Andrews. *Camps and Trails in China.* New York, Appleton, 1918.

Frontiers of a Forbidden Land. Silent film of the AMNH First Asiatic Zoological Expedition to Yunnan and Fukien, 1916 - 1917.

THE MAPS

The maps have been reproduced from Handel-Mazzetti's own surveys[1] and are intended to be used in conjunction with modern maps. Handel-Mazzetti's critical comments on Chinese map-making (page 34) are still largely valid today. The definitive maps are the Operational Navigation Charts (ONC H-10 and H-11) at a scale of 1:1,000,000, and the Tactical Pilotage Charts (TPC) at 1:500,000, published by the Defence Mapping Agency, Aerospace Center, St Louis Air Force Station, Missouri 63118, USA. Though strong on rivers, relief and altitudes, they are weak on roads and villages. More widely available are the maps published by Nelles Verlag at 1:1,500,000. Other useful maps include those given by Rock[2] and Gregory[3]. Handel-Mazzetti's method of transliterating Chinese names has been superseded by the Pinyin style, which is used in this edition. A glossary of place names in Handel-Mazzetti's style and Pinyin is given on the next page.

Map 1 Itinerary 6th March to 16th October 1914.
Map 2 Part of the route in 1914 — Xichang (Ningyuen) and Yanyuan (Yenyuen).
Map 3 Routes in the Mekong, Salween and Irrawaddy gorges in 1915 and 1916.
Map 4 Routes around Lijiang and elsewhere in Yunnan in 1914, 1915 and 1916.
Map 5 Routes from Muli to Lijiang and near the Jinsha Jiang loop in 1914, 1915 and 1916.
Map 6 Route from Kunming to Changsha in 1917 (western part).
Map 7 Route from Kunming to Changsha in 1917 (eastern part).

---

[1] For references see his foreword, page iii.

[2] Rock, Joseph F. *The Ancient Na-Khi Kingdom of Southwest China.* 2 vols. Harvard, 1947.

[3] Gregory, J.W. & C.J., *To the Alps of Chinese Tibet,* London, 1923.

Glossary of Chinese Place Names

The first column gives Handel-Mazzetti's names as used on his maps and in the original German edition (*Naturbilder aus Süd-West China*, 1927). In the second column are the corresponding modern names in the Pinyin version as used in the new edition. Besides names of places the list contains a few tribal and personal names.

H-M's Name	Pinyin Name
Aben	Aben
Ahsi	Axi
Ahung	Ahong
Akelo	Akelo
Alami	Alami
Alaodjing	Alaojing
Alo	Alo
Alülaka	Alülaka
Amidschou	Kaiyuan
Anangu	Anangu
Aoalo	Aoalo
Apa-la	Apa La
Asandschai	Asanzhai
Atendse	Deqen
Atsako	Atsako
Badschai	Danzhai
Bahan	Bahan
Balaschu	Balashu
Baling	Baling
Bandjiaying	Banjiaying
Bangdsera	Benzilan
Banschan	Banshan
Banschan-miao	Banshan Miao
Bantjiao	Banqiao
Baodu	Baodu
Baoma-liangdse	Baoma Liangzi
Baorong	Bawolong
Baotie-schan	Baotie Shan
Baotjing	Shaoyang
Bapadji	Bapaji
Basulo	Basulo
Batang	Batang
Bayiwa	Bayiwa
Bedjihsün	Beiqicun
Begung	Baigong
Bei-ho	Bai He
Beida-he	Nanpan Jiang
Beischaogo	Beishaoge
Beitjeho	Meiyu
Beling-schan	Bailing Shan
Bema-schan	Baima Shan
Bematschang	Baimachang
Bengaidse	Baiyazi
Beschui	Baishui
Beschui-badse	Baishuibazi
Beshui-ho	Baishui He
Betiaoho	Baitiaohe
Beyendjing	Yanfeng
Biendjio	Pianjiao
Bintschwan	Binchuan
Bitjigwan	Biqiguan
Bödö	Bedi
Bögowan	Baiguowan
Boloti	Boluoti
Bonga	Bonga

H-M's Name	Pinyin Name
Böscha	Baisha
Böyünngai	Baiyunya
Buschao	Bushao
Butji	Buqi
Butji	Puqi
Da-Niutschang	Da Niuchang
Dadjienlou	Kangding
Dadjin	Dajin
Dadjingtou	Dajingtou
Dadschwangkou	Dazhuangkou
Dagu	Dagu
Dahe-schan	Dahei Shan
Dahosa	Dahosa
Dahsinba	Daxinba
Dahsintschang	Daxinchang
Dahutu	Dahutu
Daidsedien	Daizidian
Dali	Dali
Daliang-schan	Daliang Shan
Dalidjing	Dalijing
Daloping	Daleping
Daoling	Daoling
Daörlbi	Daerbi
Dapingdse	Dapingzi
Dara	Dara
Daschao	Dashao
Daschi	Dashi
Daschiban	Dashiban
Datiaoku	Datiaogu
Datiengai	Dadianjie
Datjiao-se	Daqiao Si
Datung	Datong
Dawan	Dawan
Dayao	Dayao
Delipu	Delipu
Dienso	Diansuo
Dingyüen	Mouding
Diörl-schan	Dier Shan
Dischuitan	Dishui Tan
Dji-schan	Ji Shan
Djiangdi	Jiangdi
Djianghsi	Jiangxi
Djiangyi	Jiangyi
Djiangying	Jiangying
Djiatschrin	Qagcheng
Djiatschrin	Xiangcheng
Djidsung	Jizong
Djientschang	Jianchang
Djientschwan	Jianchuan
Djifangkou	Jifangkou
Djigungbei	Jigongbei
Djindien-se	Jindian Si
Djindschischan	Jinzhishan
Djingdschou	Jingxian
Djingutang	Jingutang

H-M's Name	Pinyin Name
Djinkou	Jinkou
Djinsolo	Jinsuoluo
Djiou-djiang	Drung Jiang
Djioudse	Drung
Djitin	Jitin
Djitschangping	Jichangping
Djiuyaping	Jiuyaping
Djüdien	Judian
Djüdjing	Qujing
Dodjie	Duojie
Döke	Deke
Doker-la	Doker-la
Doschiratscho	Doshiracho
Dötschang	Dechang
Dou-tschu	Shuiluo He
Doyon-lumba	Doyon-lumba
Dre-tschu	Dre Qu
Dsala-schan	Zala Shan
Dsaluping	Zaluping
Dsang-schan	Cang Shan
Dschadse	Zhazi
Dschang-Yi-Dschou	Zhang Yizhou
Dschangdjiatang	Zhangjiatang
Dschanggwandschung	- Zhangguanzhong
Dschangpudse	Zhangpuzi
Dschao-schan	Zhao Shan
Dschaotung	Zhaotong
Dschenmindö	Zhenminde
Dschennan	Nanhua
Dschenning	Zhenning
Dschenyuen	Zhenyuan
Dschere	Zhere
Dschöndschou	Chenzhou
Dschöngdu	Chengdu
Dschungdien	Zhongdian
Dschungdjiang-ho	Zhongjiang He
Dschungduilung	Zhongduilong
Dsengo	Dsengo
Dsiliba	Ziliba
Dsilidjiang	Zilijiang
Dsilu	Zilu
Dsiyang	Qiyang
Dsolin-ho	Longchuan Jiang
Dsuningkou	Zuningkou
Du-djiang	Du Jiang
Dugwantsun	Tuguancun
Duinaoko	Duinaoke
Dung-schan	Dong Shan
Dungdien	Dongdian
Dungdjia	Dong
Dungdschuling	Dongzhuling
Dungngan	Tongan
Dungngan	Dongan
Dungtai-schan	Dongtai Shan

H-M's Name	Pinyin Name
Dungtien	Dongtian
Dungting-hai	Dongting Lake
Dungtschwan	Dongchuan
Duörl-liangdse	Duer Liangzi
Duyün	Duyun
Dyinaloko	Dyinaloko
Dyipalo	Dyipalo
Falang	Falang
Fongkou	Fengke
Fuliangdso	Fu Liangzuo
Fumadi	Fumadi
Fumin	Fumin
Fungdjia	Fengjia
Gaba	Gaba
Gaitiu	Gaitiu
Gandeng	Gandeng
Gangpu	Gangpu
Ganhaidse	Ganhaizi
Gaoscha-se	Gaosha Si
Gaoschanpu	Gaoshanpu
Gaotscha	Gaocha
Gitüdü	Gitüdü
Gobankou	Gebankou
Gomba-la	Gomba La
Gondonrungu	Gondonrungu
Gonschiga	Gonshiga
Gu-schan	Gu Shan
Gudschou	Rongjiang
Guiding	Guiding
Guidschou	Guizhou
Guiyang-sen	Guiyang
Gumadi	Gumadi
Gümbalo	Gümbalo
Gungmuying	Gongmuying
Gwamaoschan	Guamao Shan
Gwandien	Guandian
Gwandong-hsien	Guangtong
Gwanfang	Guanfang
Gwangdung	Guangdong
Gwanghsi	Guangxi
Gwanling	Huanjiang
Gwanschan	Guanshan
Gwanyilang	Guanyilang
Gwanyin-go	Guanyin Ge
Gwanyingai	Guanyinjie
Gwubö	Gwube
Gwulowo	Gwulowo
Haba	Haba
Haidung-schan	Haidong Shan
Hailo	Hailuo
Halao-schan	Halao Shan
Handschou	Hanzhou
Hankou	Hankou
Hedjing	Heijing
Heilugö	Heiluge
Heischanmen	Heishanmen
Helungtang	Heilongtan
Heschui	Heishui
Ho	He
Hodjing	Heqing
Hodschou	Hezhou
Hohsi	Hexi
Hokou	Hekou

Holoscha	Houlong Shan
Höngdschou	Hengyang
Höngschan	Hengshan
Hoörl	He'er
Hosayigo	Hosayigo
Hoschang-schan	Heshang Shan
Hoschinga	Heshiya
Houdsengai	Houziya
Houyendjing	Houyanjing
Hsaiying	Xieying
Hsi-schan	Xi Shan
Hsiagwan	Xiaguan
Hsialapu	Xialapu
Hsiang-djiang	Xiang Jiang
Hsianghsiang	Xiangxiang
Hsiangschuiho	Xiangshuihe
Hsiangtan	Xiangtan
Hsiao-Djing-ho	Xiao Jin He
Hsiao-Dschungdien	Xiao Zhongdian
Hsiao-Magai	Xiao Majie
Hsiao-Niutschang	Xiao Niuchang
Hsiao-Weihsi	Xiao Weixi
Hsiaodien	Xiaodian
Hsiaodsang	Xiaozang
Hsiaokoudschou	Xiaokouzhou
Hsiaomadschang	Xiaomazhang
Hsienschendung	Xianshendong
Hsienschengyi	Xianshengyi
Hsifan	Pumi
Hsikwangschan	Xikuangshan
Hsingyi	Anlong
Hsinhwa	Xinhua
Hsiniutan	Xiniutan
Hsinlung	Xinlong
Hsinning	Xinning
Hsintscheng	Xingren
Hsintschwang	Xinzhuang
Hsinyingpan	Xinyingpan
Hsiolamenkou	Xuelamenkou
Hsitji	Xiqi
Hsiungbe-ling	Xiongbei Ling
Hsüeschantsun	Xueshancun
Hsüetschou-schan	Xuechou Shan
Hsünfeng-schan	Xunfeng Shan
Hsüning	Suining
Huili	Huili
Hunan	Hunan
Hung-djiang	Hongjiang
Hungga	Hungga
Hungguwo	Hongguwo
Hungngai	Hongya
Hungschischao	Hongshishao
Hungtsun	Hongcun
Hwadjiaoping	Huajiaoping
Hwangbetjiao	Huangbaiqiao
Hwangdjiaping	Huangjiaping
Hwangdschön	Huangzhen
Hwangdschutschang	Huangzhuchang
Hwangdupu	Huangdupu
Hwanggoso	Huangguoshu
Hwangliangdse	Huangliangzi
Hwangniu-ho	Huangni He
Hwangschuitang	Huangshuitang
Hwangtsaoba	Xingyi
Hwaping	Huaping
Hwapolu	Huapolu
Hwatjiao-ho	Beipan Jiang

Hwayanggo	Huanyangge
Jenhogai	Yongxing
Jöschui-ho	Reshui He
Jöschuitang	Reshuitang
Kakatang	Kakatang
Kakerbo	Kakerbo
Kalaba	Kalaba
Keluan	Keluan
Kinscha-djiang	Jinsha Jiang
Konkaling	Gongling
Kotu-he	Kedu He
Küdü	Küdü
Kuling	Guling
Kunka	Gongga
Kunyang-hai	Dian Chi
Kupesu	Gubaishu
Kwapi	Guabi
Laba	Laba
Laba-schan	Laba Shan
Labadse	Labazi
Labako	Labako
Labikou	Labikou
Ladjimin	Ladjimin
Ladsagu	Ladsagu
Lagatschang	Lagachang
Lakonra	Lakonra
Lalong	Anlong
Lama-schan	Lama Shan
Lamatso	Lamacuo
Lanba	Lanba
Landji-dschou	Ninglang
Langtai	Langdai
Lanhsingwan	Lanxinguan
Lantien	Lianyuan
Lantschouba	Lanchouba
Lao Li	Lao Li
Laodjing-schan	Laojing Shan
Laodschun-schan	Laojun Shan
Laogui-schan	Laogui Shan
Laoling-schan	Laoling Shan
Laomei-schan	Laomei Shan
Laoyagwan	Laoyaguan
Laschi-ba	Lashiba
Latsa	Latsa
Lemoka	Lemoka
Lenago	Lenago
Lendo	Lendo
Lengschuidjiang	Lengshuijiang
Li	Li
Li-tschu	Li Qu
Liangschanpu	Liangschanpu
Lidjiang	Lijiang
Lidsekou	Lizikou
Lien-djiang	Lian Shui
Linbinkou	Linbinkou
Lingwandu	Linguandu
Liping	Liping
Lissu	Lisu
Litang	Litang
Litere	Li Tere
Litiping	Lidiping
Liugu	Liugu
Liugu-liangdse	Liugu Liangzi
Lodse	Luozi

H-M's Name	Pinyin Name
Loheitang	Luoheitang
Loiao	Luoyao
Lojatso	Lozhatso
Lokü	Luoqu
Lolo	Yi
Lolokou	Luoluokou
Loloping	Geliping
Londa-ho	Londa He
Londjre	Londjre
Loping	Luoping
Lopipema	Lopipema
Loschuitang	Luoshuitang
Lose-schan	Luosi Shan
Losiwan	Luoxiwan
Lota	Luota
Lotue-schan	Luotui Shan
Loudi	Loudi
Loutschang	Louchang
Lowa	Luowa
Loyü	Luoyu
Lu-djiang	Nu Jiang
Lu-schan	Lu Shan
Luanfenba	Luanfenba
Lüdi	Lüdi
Ludse	Nu
Lududsai	Liuduzhai
Luföng	Lüfeng
Lühogai	Lühe
Luidaschu	Leidashu
Lukudsche	Lukuzhe
Lung-schan	Long Shan
Lungdschu-schan	Longzhu Shan
Lungdsu	Longzu
Lunggai	Longjie
Lunghui	Longhui
Lungli	Longli
Lungtangho	Longtanghe
Lungtjiaopu	Longqiaopu
Lungtou-schan	Longtou Shan
Lutien	Ludian
Lutschang	Luchang
Lutschwan	Luchuan
Mabaho	Mabahe
Madjiadwen	Majiadun
Madjiping	Majiping
Magai	Majie
Mahaidse	Mahaizi
Mahao	Mahao
Maliping	Maliping
Maliutang	Malutang
Maliutschai	Maluzhai
Mangan-schan	Ma'an Shan
Maokoyendjing	Maogeyanjing
Maotsaoping	Maocaoping
Matang	Matang
Matschang	Machang
Mawangngao	Mawang'ao
Maya	Maya
Meidsiping	Meiziping
Mekong River	Lancang Jiang
Meradon	Meradon
Meti	Meti
Miao	Miao
Mindjia	Bai
Minying	Mingyin

H-M's Name	Pinyin Name
Mitien	Midian
Möka	Meka
Molien	Molian
Möngdse	Mengzi
Moschi	Moshi
Moso, Nahsi	Naxi
Mudji-schan	Muji Shan
Mududjin	Mudijin
Mugwadso	Muguazuo
Muhsie	Muxie
Muki-liangdse	Muji Liangzi
Muli	Muli
Muyu	Guanling
Naiwanglong	Naiwanglong
Namdi	Nanxi
Nandjing-schan	Nanjing Shan
Nanfeng	Nanfeng
Nanmutschang	Nanmuchang
Nanyo, Nanyo-schan	Nanyue
Ndwolo	Ndwolo
Ngaikoupu	Yakoupu
Ngaitschekou	Yachekou
Ngaitsou	Yazuo
Ngandjiapu	Anjiapu
Ngannantschang	Ananchang
Nganning-dschou	Anning
Nganning-ho	Anning He
Nganping	Pingba
Nganschun	Anshun
Ngoi-ko-den	Ngoi-ko-den
Ngomei-schan	Emei Shan
Nguka-la	Nguka La
Nguluko	Nguluke
Niaoschuhsia	Niaoshuxia
Ningdu	Ningdu
Ninghsiang	Ningxiang
Ningyüen	Xichang
Nisselaka	Nisselaka
Nitscheluang	Nicheluang
Niualo	Niualo
Niugai	Niujie
Niutou-dschou	Niutou Zhou
Niutschang	Niuchang
Oia	Eya
Omintsoka	Omintsoka
Orl-hai	Er Hai
Orldaoho	Erdaohe
Orltsun	Ercun
Oti	Eti
Pältschua	Pelchua
Pangblanglong	Pangblanglong
Panglingkou	Panglingkou
Patong	Patong
Patü-la	Patü La
Pehalo	Beixialuo
Pen	Ben
Phomoi	Phomoi
Piepun	Piepen
Pingdjiang	Pingjiang
Pinghsiang	Pingxiang
Piyi	Piyi
Podjio	Pojue
Pongatong	Pongatong
Pudi	Puwei

H-M's Name	Pinyin Name
Pudu-ho	Pudu He
Puke	Puge
Ronscha	Ronsha
Rüschatong	Rüshatong
Saba	Zaba
Sabä	Sabe
Saganai	Saganai
Sandjiang	Dujiang
Sandjiatsun	Sanjiangkou
Sandjigu	Sanjigu
Sandjio	Sandu
Sandschwanba	Sanchuanba
Sangwatjiao	Sanguaqiao
Sanli-ngan	San Li An
Sanschischao	Sanshishao
Santang	Santang
Santante	Santante
Sanwangho	Sanwanghe
Sanyingpan	Sayingpan
Saoa-lumba	Saoa-lumba
Satseto	Satseto
Schadien	Shadian
Schadscho-he	Shazhuo He
Schagoma	Shaguoma
Schagu	Shagu
Schamenkou	Shanmenkou
Schanggwan	Shangguan
Schanghai	Shanghai
Schao-schan	Shao Shan
Schatsakon	Shatsakon
Schatyama	Shatyama
Schengli-se	Shengli Si
Schidjiaping	Shijiaping
Schidsaru	Shidsaru
Schidsi-schan	Shizi Shan
Schifung-se	Shifeng Si
Schigu	Shigu
Schilosan-ho	Shiluosan He
Schilungba	Shilongba
Schischi-se	Shishi Si
Schödse	Shezi
Schogo	Shogo
Schöndsu-la	Shenzu La
Schualo	Shualuo
Schuba	Shuba
Schuidien	Shuidian
Schuidjia	Shuijia
Schuigaodji	Shuigaoji
Schuising	Shuixing
Schulakadsa	Shulakaza
Schunning	Fengqing
Schusutsu	Shusuzu
Schutschamba	Shuchamba
Schutsche	Shuche
Schwanghsünba	Shuangxunba
Serä	Sere
Setschwan	Sichuan
Si-la	Xi La
Sidsung	Shizong
Sihsiadjiangpu	Xixiajiangpu
Sikwai	Xikuai
Sitjitong	Xiqitong
Siwanho	Shiwanhe
Soso-liangdse	Suosuo Liangzi
Sosokou	Suosuokou

H-M's Name	Pinyin Name
Sugö	Suge
Suifu	Yibin
Sunggwe	Songgui
Sungpingdse	Songpingzi
Taipinggai	Taipingjie
Tangjijao	Tang Rirao
Tangtiaotjiao	Tangtiaoqiao
Taohwa-schan	Taohua Shan
Taohwaping	Taohuaping
Tienhsin-tjiao	Tianxin Qiao
Tienschenggwan	Tianshengguan
Tientaischan	Tiantaishan
Tientang	Tiantang
Tima	Tima
Tjata-schan	Haba Shan
Tjato-ho	Haba He
Tjiaoding-schan	Qiaoding Shan
Tjiaodjio	Zhaojue
Tjiaoli	Qiaoli
Tjiaolou	Qiaolou
Tjiaotienschang	Qiaotianshang
Tjiaotou	Qiaotou
Tjidwen	Qidun
Tjigungpo	Qigongpo
Tjilidjiang	Qilijiang
Tjintschanggwan	Qinchangguan
Tjionatong	Qunatong
Tjionra	Tjionra
Tjiontson	Tjiontson
Tjiungdschu-se	Qiongzhu Si
Todschu	Toju
Totyü	Totyü
Tratje-tra	Tratje-tra
Tsadjio	Yongren
Tsai-Wo	Cai E
Tsarong	Tsarong
Tsasopie	Tsasopie
Tschahungnyotscha	Chahongnyocha
Tschaimou	Chaimou
Tschamutong	Gongshan
Tschangscha	Changsha
Tschangtschinyao	Chang Qinyao
Tschangtschung-schan	-
	Changchong Shan
Tschaörl	Cha'er
Tschebei	Chebei

Tschedjiang	Zhejiang
Tschescha	Chesha
Tschiangschel	Chiangshel
Tschingdschen	Qingzhen
Tschoso	Chuosuo
Tschoso Lake	Lugu Lake
Tschü-djiang	Qju Shui
Tschüdschou	Zhuzhou
Tschuhsiong	Chuxiong
Tschükoupu	Qukoupu
Tschumehe	Chumehe
Tschundjia	Buyi
Tschwadse	Chuazi
Tschwanghwa	Changhua
Tschwenning-schan	Qianling Shan
Tsedjrong	Cizhong
Tseku	Cigu
Tsi-djiang	Zi Jiang
Tsukue	Tsukue
Tugungpu	Dugongpu
Tungdjiapai	Tongjiapai
Tussu	Tusi
Tutschün	Dujun
Ünlüpe	Ünlüpe
Ururu	Ururu
Waha	Waha
Wali	Wali
Wang-Te-Hui	Wang Dehui
Wang-Wen-Djing	Wang Wenjing
Wangtang	Wantang
Wangyün-schan	Wangyun Shan
Waschua	Washua
Webi-schan	Weibi Shan
Weihsi	Weixi
Weischa	Weisha
Wendjiatjiao	Wenjiaqiao
Wendwen	Wendun
Woholetye	Woheletie
Wolo-ho	Woluo He
Wongtschengtjiao	Wangcheng Qiao
Wu-djiang	Wu Jiang
Wudadjing	Wudajing
Wudjio	Wujiao
Wukang	Wugang
Wuli-ngan	Wu Li An
Wuschi-liangdse	Wushi Liangzi

Wusoling	Wu Suoling
Wutschang	Wuchang
Yadschou	Ya'an
Yaftscha	Yafcha
Yakou	Yakou
Yalung	Yalong
Yamangao	Yama'ao
Yameti	Yameiti
Yangdschu-ho	Yangzhu He
Yangdse-djiang	Yangzi Jiang
Yanggai	Yangjie
Yanggu-miao	Yanggu Miao
Yangling	Yanglin
Yangpi-djiang	Yangbi Jiang
Yangtsung-hai	Yangzhong Hai
Yao-schan	Yao Shan
Yaotou	Yaotou
Yedsche	Yezhi
Yelu-schan	Yelu Shan
Yenaping	Yenaping
Yenyüen	Yanyuan
Yidjiadschan	Yijiazhen
Yidse-ho	Kuaizi He
Yigöru	Yigeru
Yiliang	Yiliang
Yimen	Yimen
Yingpangai	Yingpanjie
Yinimi	Yinimi
Yissutsa	Yisitsa
Yodschou	Yueyang
Yolu-schan	Yuelu Shan
Yüanschikai	Yuan Shikai
Yüen-djiang	Yuan Jiang
Yüenmou	Yuanmou
Yulo	Yuluo
Yülong-schan	Yulong Shan
Yün-schan	Yun Shan
Yungbei	Yongsheng
Yungdschou	Yongzhou
Yungdschou	Lingling
Yungning	Yongning
Yünnan	Yunnan
Yünnan-hsien	Xiangyun
Yünnanfu	Kunming
Yünnanyi	Yunnanyi
Yüno	Yunuo
	-END-

REFERENCES

Most of the necessary references have been given in the text, but this list is intended for readers who want pictures of the plants and landscapes.

Brickell, Chris and others. *Alpine Garden Society Expedition to China, 1994. The Plants A-Z.* Quart. Bull. Alp. Gard. Soc. 1996, **64**, 175-249.
Feng Guomei. *Rhododendrons of China, Vol. I, Yunnan.* Beijing, 1988.
Grey-Wilson, C. *Journey to the Jade Dragon Snow Mountains, Yunnan.* Quart. Bull. Alp. Gard. Soc. 1988, **56**, 16-34, 115-130, 221-242, 289-306.
Grey-Wilson, C. *Alpine Jewels from the Jade Dragon Mountains.* The Garden, RHS, 1993, **99**, 99-104.
Haw, Stephen. *Asian Bellflowers (Adenophora).* The Garden, RHS, 1987, **112**, 567-569.
Haw, Stephen. *The Lilies of China.* 1986.
Hutchinson, Peter. *Expedition to the Cang Shan Range,1981.* Quart. Bull. Alp. Gard. Soc. 1983, **51**, 140-149 (with map).
Hutchinson, Peter. *The Red Grasslands and the Scarlet Meconopsis (Sichuan).* Quart. Bull. Alp. Gard. Soc. 1987, **55**, 144-149.
Lancaster, Roy. *Travels in China.* Antique Collectors' Club, Woodbridge, Suffolk, 1989, pp. 516 with numerous illustrations in colour and monochrome, and bibliography.
Lancaster, Roy. *Five orchids of Yunnan.* The Garden, RHS, 1982, **107**, 425-430.
Lauener, L.A. *The Introduction of Chinese Plants into Europe.* SPB Academic Publishing, Amsterdam, 1996. Edited by David K. Ferguson. Numerous black and white drawings.
Polunin, Oleg, & Adam Stainton. *Flowers of the Himalaya.* Oxford, 1984, and *Supplement,* Adam Stainton, 1988.
Rock, Joseph F. *The Ancient Na-Khi Kingdom of Southwest China.* 2 vols. Harvard, 1947. Splendid black and white photographs of tribespeople and scenery.
Simmons, John. *A 7000 foot mountain with a five step snake* (Fan Jin Shan, 2608m, the highest in Guizhou) The Garden, RHS, 1986, **111**, 567-572. Some distance north of Handel-Mazzetti's route. Pictures of *Sapium sebiferum,* etc.
Wang Dajun & Shen Shao-Jin. *Bamboos of China.* London, 1987.
Wiltshire, Trevor. *Alpines of the Orient. The Alpine Garden Society plant hunting expedition to Yunnan and Sichuan.* The Garden, RHS, 1995, **120**, 219-221.
Zhang Jingwei (editor). *The Alpine Plants of China.* Beijing, 1982.
Zhao Ji and others. *The Natural History of China,* London, 1990.

Guidebooks
Booz, Patrick R. *Yunnan.* Chicago, 1987.
Corrigan, Gina. *Guizhou.* Hong Kong, 1995.
Holdsworth, May. *Sichuan.* Hong Kong, 1993.
Stevens, K. Mark, & George Wehrfritz. *Southwest China off the Beaten Track.* London, 1988.

INDEX